Low Temperature
Spectroscopy

Low Temperature

Optical Properties of Molecules
in Matrices, Mixed Crystals,
and Frozen Solutions

Spectroscopy

Beat Meyer

University of Washington
Seattle, Washington

American Elsevier Publishing Company, Inc.
NEW YORK • 1971

PHYSICS

AMERICAN ELSEVIER PUBLISHING COMPANY, INC.
52 Vanderbilt Avenue, New York, N.Y. 10017

ELSEVIER PUBLISHING COMPANY, LTD.
Barking, Essex, England

ELSEVIER PUBLISHING COMPANY
335 Jan Van Galenstraat, P.O. Box 211
Amsterdam, The Netherlands

International Standard Book Number 0-444-00083-6

Library of Congress Card Number 75-127771

Printed in the United States of America

Contents

CHAPTER 9: Spectra of Individual Systems

CHAPTER 10: Tables of Molecular Data

Preface

This book deals with physical and chemical properties of molecules in weakly interacting solids. Typical samples are matrix isolated atoms, diatomics and polyatomics, trapped free radicals, mixed organic crystals, and aromatic hydrocarbons in frozen organic glasses. Since low temperature spectroscopy of these systems constitutes a large field and has never been reviewed comprehensively before, severe and arbitrary restrictions had to be imposed on field and depth of coverage.

This volume is instrinsically exploratory. Pure solids and ionic solids are not discussed. To make the subject matter manageable, only electronic spectra of samples below 100°K are considered. Complementary infrared data are included to support identification of species. Electron spin resonance work exceeds the scope of this book and is not included despite the fact that electron nuclear double resonance and similar methods, in recent years, have proven most fruitful tools for studying triplet state processes. Polarization effects and discussion of quantum yields are also virtually omitted. Many of these important topics are covered adequately in the literature. Any advanced researcher could add to the list of material which is omitted in his field of specialization, but I hope that he will feel compensated by discovering new data in other areas of interest, and by the bibliography which contains about 2200 complete references with titles.

The ten chapters form five different parts. Chapters 1 and 2 contain a short introduction and a history of low temperature spectroscopy. Chapters 3 and 4 cover a review of spectral properties and perturbations in weakly interacting cold solvents and hosts, while chapters 5 and 6 deal with radiative and radiationless transitions, energy migration, chemical diffusion, and photochemistry. Chapters 1 through 6 are for students at the senior or graduate level in science, and for readers generally interested in the field.

Chapters 7 and 8 contain information on sample preparation and properties, and explain equipment used to make or study samples. Here is information for scientists who want to understand experiments, or plan to take up research in this field, and for those who actually perform experiments. In chapter 9, selected representative guest and solute species are discussed. This chapter and the tables of optical properties in chapter 10 are intended as a guide and subject index for literature search for individual species.

The bibliography with exact titles of all references, makes it, together with the tables of chapter 10, an independent guide to the literature.

This book resulted from the author's need to have a text for undergraduates, Ph.D. students, and visiting scientists, who want to experiment or to evaluate work on low temperature samples. Its goal is to provide an interdisciplinary guide to matrix work (traditionally performed by physical chemists), organic glasses and polymers (mainly investigated by theoretical chemists), and mixed crystals (originally the domain of solid state physicists). It is hoped that this book will contribute toward overcoming the historical and educational barriers between these various fields. Interdisciplinary contact is especially timely because commercial liquid helium can now be shipped throughout the U.S. and Europe, and low temperature spectroscopy, once the privilege of those who had access to left-over refrigerants at a low temperature physics laboratory, is now within reach of almost every scientist. Microrefrigerators provide easy access to low temperatures even for those who want to experiment only intermittently.

Many co-workers assisted in the preparation of this book. Dr. G. D. Brabson helped select material and arrange chapters 1 through 8. Dr. J. J. Smith wrote section 9C, and drafted tables 10C and 10D. Dr. Smith also assisted in drafting section 6B, in collecting and checking data for many figures and tables, and in compiling the first draft of the bibliography. Miss L. Williamson and Miss D. Young searched literature and collected material for chapter 10. Mrs. Daina Renard edited and typed the tables of chapter 10 and the bibliography, while Mrs. Marilee Kapsa typed the entire text, prepared the tables, helped with figures, and proofread all material.

This book was made possible by Professors P. Karrer and G. Schwarzenbach, who acquainted the author with the challenge of chemistry; by Professors W. Heitler and H. H. Staub, who introduced him to spectroscopy; by Professor C. Clusius, who taught him low temperature techniques; by Professor E. Schumacher, who challenged and guided him in his Ph.D. work, and by Professor L. Brewer, who untiringly encouraged his endeavors and showed him the joys and rewards of research.

The author is deeply indebted to all his students, postdoctoral fellows and staff, and many visiting scientists, and to the National

Science Foundation, the Atomic Energy Commission, the National Institute of Health, and the National Air Pollution Control Administration (Environmental Protection Agency), who supported much of the research reported here.

This book is dedicated to H. P. Broida, M. Kasha, G. C. Pimentel, G. W. Robinson, E. V. Shpolskii, and to all other pioneers who opened the path, originally charted by Dewar, Wiedemann, and Vegard, into one of the most promising and challenging fields, embracing chemistry, biology, and physics.

BEAT MEYER

Seattle, Washington
December 1970

CHAPTER 1

Introduction

I. DESCRIPTION OF SYSTEMS

This book deals with optical and other physical and chemical properties of molecules and atoms that reside as isolated guests in a weakly interacting, cold host. The guests may be any stable or unstable, large or small species, but only four types of host materials are considered:

1. Inert matrices
2. Organic glasses
3. Polymer glasses
4. Mixed and doped crystals

In all these solids the lattice energy is small. For argon, for example, it is 2 kcal/mole, and for organic molecules 10–20 kcal/mole, while a representative value for an ion crystal, such as NaCl, is 180 kcal/mole. Therefore, in the case of neutral matrices and simple molecular crystals, the interactions between host atoms or molecules are weak, as are the interactions between host lattice and the guest species isolated in the host. Similarly, in the case of organic glasses, both the solvent-solvent and the solvent-solute interactions are weak. As a consequence, the optical properties of the guest are generally characteristic of the free guest molecule, and host-guest interactions exert comparatively small distortions on the guest electron configuration. In some cases, however, these small changes can bring about large changes in the appearance of the spectrum. This is especially evident in emission. In all the systems discussed in this book, emission is strongly characterized by phosphorescence, which is absent if the guest is a free molecule or a pure solid. Phosphorescence is, in fact, the most characteristic emission feature of the low temperature samples covered here.

The systems covered in this book have many other characteristics in common. Generally, guest-guest interactions are small, the host and guest systems do not react together chemically, and the host energy levels lie higher than those of the guest. In matrices and glasses, the lowest host level is high above the guest levels studied; i.e., the host is transparent in the guest absorption region. In most cases, matrices, glasses, and polymers are also colorless. In mixed crystals, guest and host levels are closer. This results in temperature-dependent interactions. Before dealing with the different forms of energy exchanges, we briefly summarize the characteristics and differences of the four types of samples (listed in Table 1.1, pp. 4–5).

A. Matrices

The use of matrices has been introduced by Pimentel and his co-workers (Whittle, 1954). Matrix samples are prepared by vapor codeposition of a matrix gas and the vapor of the guest molecule on a low temperature target, usually at 20° or 4°K. The target temperature is chosen below 0.3 of the matrix melting point, so that diffusion of the cold host remains negligible. The matrix to guest (or radical) ratio, M/R, is between 10^2 and 10^5 so that guest-guest interactions are small. The sample thickness depends on the oscillator strength of the optical transition that is to be observed. For allowed electronic transitions, only micromole quantities of guests are necessary. For infrared (IR) or forbidden visible transitions, a millimole or more might be necessary. The composition of the nonequilibrium matrix is determined by the concentration of vapor constituents, statistical processes during condensation, and diffusion. Any material that vaporizes without decomposition can be embedded in a matrix. Other molecules can be synthesized *in situ* by diffusion, controlled chemical reaction, or photolysis of any vaporizable reagent. This makes matrices an immensely useful medium for the preparation and observation of small molecules, atoms, and free radicals. The weak interactions make matrices attractive also for the study of large inorganic and organic molecules, and aromatics, including natural products such as phthalocyanines and porphyrins. The guest environment depends on preparation conditions, but it seems that it is nearly always oriented in a random fashion. There is now evidence for orientation in some small molecules, particularly diatomics and nitrates (Kasai, 1966). There is little doubt that magnetic fields will be used to orient molecules with dipoles, and there are indications that certain large planar aromatics preferentially deposit parallel to the target.

The solute cage often is not unique, and different types of sites can be observed. Therefore, matrix spectra often contain fine structure due to absorptions from the different sites. Matrices are soft enough for small guest molecules to diffuse. Consequently, dimers and aggregates complicate the interpretation of spectra. The concentration of impurities depends on the origin and preparation method of the sample. In the case of chemically or photolytically prepared guests, the impurities might actually outnumber the desired product by a large factor. To compensate for impurity concentrations in these systems, the M/R ratio is often kept small. Thus, in matrices, impure and multicomponent systems are not uncommon, and guest-guest interactions between next-nearest neighbors, and even nearest neighbors, must be considered for a finer interpretation of spectral details.

Typical matrix materials are the rare gases, H_2, SF_6, lighter hydrocarbons, and nitrogen. SF_6 can be deposited at 77°K. N_2 yields beautifully transparent solids, making it especially suitable for thick films. For many purposes more reactive materials, for example, CO, O_2, and CO_2, are also used. The useful temperature range is from 1.5°K to about 0.6 of the matrix melting point. Above this temperature, the vapor pressure of the matrix leads to vacuum breakdown, diffusion becomes significant, and phase separation can occur. The rare gases are optically transparent from the far infrared up to their lowest singlet exciton bands, which lie in the vacuum ultraviolet. SF_6, CH_4, and other matrices have infrared absorptions which reduce their usefulness for IR work.

B. Organic Glasses

The use of organic glasses has been pioneered by Lewis and his co-workers in Berkeley (Lewis, 1941–1949; Kasha, 1947 to present), Porter (Norman, 1954) in Cambridge, and Ermolaev (1956 to present) and Shpol'skii (1951 to present) in Russia. The advantage of glasses is that the solute need not be vaporized, and that much thicker samples can be made. All molecules that form stable room temperature solutions can be studied. A wealth of information on electronic properties of organic molecules has been obtained from frozen solutions. Liquid hydrocarbons, alcohols, ethers, CCl_4, and mixtures of these are used to prepare dilute solutions of the desired molecule. The equilibrium solution is then chilled. During cool-down, the solvent viscosity increases rapidly. This prevents solute expulsion. As in matrices, the metastable solid contains malformations that lead to multiple sites and strains that relax slowly, often only over periods of weeks. Below 77°K, the strain may lead to fracture, but it is possible to obtain clear fragments at 20°K. The line width of optical transitions in organic glasses depends on solvent and solute. If both are matched, spectra can be very sharp (Shpol'skii, 1960a–c). For accurate work, the poor thermal conductivity at low temperature is a nuisance. The free spectral region of organic solvents starts at

Table 1.1

Comparison of Four Types of Weakly Interacting Hosts

	Matrices: rare gases, N_2, O_2, H_2, CO, CH_4, SF_6, hydrocarbons, fluorocarbons	Glasses: hydrocarbons, fluorocarbons, cyclohexane, EPA, ROH, CCl_4	Polymers: polymethyl methacrylate polyvinyl alcohol	Mixed Crystals
Useful temperature range (°K)	1.5-2/3 mp^a	77-mp	1.5-transition	1.5-phase transitions
Spectral range	Vacuum UV to far IR	UV and visible	Near UV and visible	Part of visible
Suitable guests	Vaporizable, or derived from vapor species	Stable, soluble at room temperature	Unreactive, soluble	Structural and spectral match
Normal solute concentration (mole %)	10 to 10^{-3}	10^{-3} to 10^{-6}	10^{-3} to 10^{-6}	10 to 10^{-5}
Normal impurity concentration (% of solute)	$<10^{-3}$ up to >100	$<10^{-5}$ (O_2)	$\sim 10^{-3}$	$\sim 10^5$ of solute
Sample Preparation	Vapor deposition, photolysis	Freezing of solution	Polymerization at 300°K	Melting
Orientation of guest	Usually random	Usually random	Usually random	Oriented

Table 1.1 (continued)

	Matrices:	Glasses:	Polymers:	Mixed Crystals
Diffusion	Small guests and during deposition	Weak	None	None
Energy migration	Host to guest, guest to guest	Guest to guest	Guest to guest	Host to guest, guest to host
Host-guest physical interaction	Weakest	Weak	Weak	Resonance coupling
Chemical interaction	Weak (except Xe with F)	Reactive	Reactive	—
Energy gap between lowest host and guest states	$S_h, T_h > S_g$	$S_h > S_g$	$S_h > S_g$ $T_h \approx S_g$	$S_h \approx S_g$ $T_h \approx T_g$
Drawback	Multiple sites, complex preparation equipment	Often broad spectra	Limited to inert organic molecules	Only matched systems are useful
Common use	Trapping of radicals, unstable species	Spectra of organic molecules	Spectra of organic molecules	Energy migration

a 1.5°K to two-thirds of the matrix melting point.

about 220 nm and extends to the near IR, where $C-C$ and $C-H$ stretches render the solvent intransparent.

Very large and transparent samples of organic glasses can be made. This makes possible the observation of weak and forbidden absorption of solute molecules, for example, $T_1 \leftarrow S_0$. For such studies very pure solvents must be used, and care must be taken to prevent excessive light exposure, because organic glasses may react with radicals inadvertently formed during UV excitation.

C. Polymers

In recent years, solid solutions have been prepared by dissolving the molecule of interest in a chemically compatible monomer which can be polymerized at or close to room temperature (Geacintov, 1968). Chapter 8 lists some polymer systems that have been successfully used for spectral studies, and discusses preparation methods.

The free spectral range of polymers is limited, starting only near 280 nm. It usually covers the visible and near IR, where phosphorescence phenomena occur. Polymers are often used for emission work and energy transfer studies. The theoretically useful temperature range extends from $1.5°K$ to just below the polymer softening temperature, but, practically, low temperatures are difficult to reach and impossible to control because of the low thermal conductivity of this type of host. Therefore, polymer samples should always be immersed in a cold bath. Like the organic glasses, polymers are susceptible to oxygen penetration, because their permeability is great. The time required for removal of dissolved oxygen is dependent on the sample thickness and may be several days for samples 1 cm thick.

D. Mixed Crystals

Mixed crystals are stable solutions of guests that occupy well defined substitutional sites in the lattice of a matching host. Mixed crystals differ from the other systems in that the guest occupies only one or a few simple, well defined sites and maintains a preferred orientation. This yields observations that can be used to compute accurate symmetries of states, crystal fields, and level splittings. McClure recognized in 1954 that resonance coupling is absent in spectra of impurities in mixed crystals. This advantage led to intensive research on mixed crystals, resulting in a wealth of useful data.

There is no generally useful host crystal. In each case, host and guest have to be matched. One of the best known examples is durene : naphthalene, where naphthalene occupies a substitutional site with two molecules per unit cell. For many studies, two different guests are introduced—for example, phenanthrene and naphthalene in a biphenyl host, or differently deuterated benzenes in benzene. In all mixed crystals, host and guest energy levels are so close that the emission and absorption often partly overlap. The useful temperature range of mixed crystals extends from 1.5°K to room temperature, except when phase transitions lead to crumbling of the sample. In such mixed crystals, energy migration between the host and guest and between different guests is strongly temperature dependent. At very low temperatures, excitated guests dissipate energy in a manner similar to that in matrices and glasses. However, even at moderately low temperatures, kT becomes comparable to the relatively small energy gap between host and guest states. In this range, excitation transfer becomes complex. At still higher temperatures, excitation can migrate freely, almost as in a pure crystal.

In order to prevent this book from becoming unwieldy, the scope had to be severely restricted. We discuss only the above four types of solid samples despite the fact that clathrates, frozen aqueous solutions, and adsorption on surfaces yield often sharp and characteristic solute or guest spectra. Doped ion crystals are excluded because of the effect of large coulombic forces, although ion crystal spectra have many similarities in line width, transition energy shifts, and temperature dependence. Pure solids are excluded because the spectral properties of the molecule are severely altered by resonance broadening and other effects.

It was also necessary to limit the spectral range to the vacuum UV, UV, visible, and infrared regions where electronic and vibrational transitions occur; and infrared techniques are not discussed. This restriction is regrettable because other methods, especially electron spin resonance (ESR) and electron nuclear double resonance (ENDOR) spectroscopy yield invaluable data on radicals and excited states of molecules.

Only properties of samples in the temperature range below 100°K are discussed. Thus, work in dry-ice cooled containers is normally not reported. Throughout this book, rare gas matrix work is favored.

II. GLOSSARY AND NOTATIONS

Before proceeding to a further discussion of observations and models, it is necessary to define some terms and values. The need for this is demonstrated by many examples. One is the term "impurity." On hearing it, a chemist thinks of a chemically different species, with the connotation that it might be chemically defined and that its presence might be inadvertent, or attributable to sloppy preparation or procedure. For a solid state physicist, an impurity in a doped crystal is a well chosen compound that is deliberately placed into the lattice at a well defined concentration. The word has a clearly defined meaning for both chemists and physicists. Confusion arises only if the two professional groups mix, as in the field of low temperature spectroscopy. We will use the word in the chemical sense and will replace it in the physicist's use with the term "guest."

A somewhat different problem is connected with use of the terms solvent and solute. For most low temperature spectroscopists the solvent signifies the material that forms the bulk of the sample. The solute is the molecule

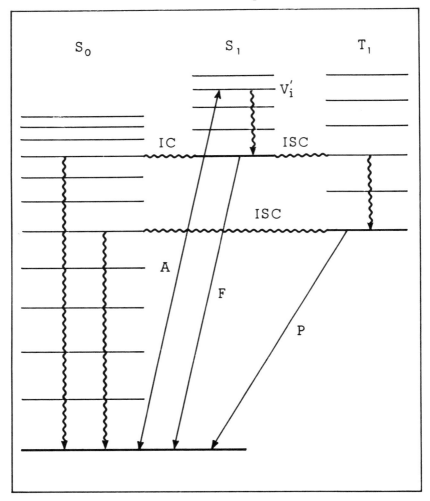

FIG. 1.1.   Jablonski diagram. A, absorption; F, fluorescence; P, phosphorescence. The other abbreviations are listed in the glossary.

of optical or chemical interest. This definition annoys the physical chemist because not all low temperature samples are solutions. The terms "solvent" and "solute" are normally reserved for substances that form thermodynamically stable solutions; worse yet, they are used to distinguish between stable solutions and mixtures, i.e., to differentiate between exactly those properties which the first definition disregards. We will use here three different terms. *Solvent* and *solute* will be used for glasses formed by cooling a stable solution; metastable, nonequilibrium solids will be called *matrices*, the undisordered impurities *guests*; if it is irrelevant or not known whether the sample is a solution or a matrix, we will use the terms *host* and *guest*.

A. Glossary

Some terms are explained in the following list. Terms not listed here may be found in the subject index. This section is intended to help in the identification of frequently used terms. A fuller definition may be found in the text, but definitions of basic terms and units are not always given in this book. Figure 1.1 is a Jablonski diagram and lists the basic radiative and radiationless processes that are important for understanding Chapter 5. Here, as throughout this book, solid lines indicate absorption or emission of light. Wiggly lines refer to radiationless excitation transfer or decay.

Activated fluorescence. Fluorescence of solute excited via energy transfer from a physically or chemically bonded activator complex. This process is observed in chlorophyll.

Annealing. Heating of sample to a temperature of about one-half of the solvent melting point to reduce solvent imperfections.

Chemiluminescence. Light emission due to chemical reaction.

Delayed fluorescence. Same as T—T annihilation. Due to conversion of two excited triplets into one excited singlet and one relaxed singlet.

Delayed thermal fluorescence. Fluorescence excited by thermal depletion of excited triplet state.

Doped crystals. Crystal containing a guest.

Excimer. Excited dimer.

Exciton. Mobile electronic excitation. Exists only in solid materials.

Exciton fission. Fission consisting of spontaneous conversion of excited singlet state into two excited triplet states. This process is the reverse of triplet annihilation.

External heavy atom effect. Same as solvent heavy atom effect, intermolecular heavy atom effect.

F. Fluorescence.

$\Delta G_{1/2}$.   First vibrational quantum. $\Delta G_{1/2} = \omega_e - 2\omega_e x_e = \omega_0 x_0$.

Guest.   Same as trap; impurity; solute in mixed crystal.

Half-width of spectral line.   Here used as (full) width of line at half intensity.

Host.   Same as solvent; matrix; used for mixed crystals and matrices.

IC.   Internal conversion. Radiationless transition between states with equal spin.   See Figure 1.1.

Impurities.   (a) Here used as chemical (inadvertent) impurity.   (b) In solid state physics: solute, guest, or supertrap.

Internal heavy atom effect.   Same as intramolecular heavy atom effect.

Infrared (IR).   Region above 600 nm.   The far IR lies below 200 cm^{-1}.

ISC.   Intersystem crossing.   Radiationless spinforbidden transition.   See Figure 1.1.

k_{IC}.   Internal conversion rate; $S_x - S_{x-1}$ or $T_y - T_{y-1}$.

k_{ISC}.   Intersystem crossing rate;   very often referring to $S_1 - T_1$.

k_{VR}.   Vibrational relaxation rate.

Luminescence (L).   (a) Emission of light due to fluorescence or phosphorescence of a solid excited via absorption or production of energy in any form.   (b) Sensitized fluorescence of phosphors.

Luminescence center.   Luminescent molecule and its immediate environment.

Matrix.   Serves to isolate the guest (solute) to prevent chemical and physical interaction between neighboring guests.   Nonequilibrium solvent; serves as host of solute.   Normally vapor deposited.

$\nu_1, \ldots$ (Greek nu).   Vibration mode. ν_1: symmetric vibration; ν_2: bending mode of triatomic; ν_3: antisymmetric stretching mode.

Φ.   Greek phi, normally used for quantum yields.

Φ_A.   Absorption quantum yield.

Φ_E.   Emission quantum yield.

Φ_F/Φ_P.   Fluorescence to phosphorescence ratio.

Phonon.   Acoustic energy quantum which allows temperature dependent energy transfer between host lattice and electronically excited guest.

Phosphorescence (P).   The production of radiation from the energy stored in the phosphorescent body.   Normally used for long-lived emission $T_1 \rightarrow S_0$.

Recombination luminescence.   Luminescence due to chemical or ion recombination.

S_0.   Singlet ground state.

S_n.   The nth excited singlet state.

Sensitized fluorescence.   Fluorescence of a solute excited via energy transfer from host or another guest.

Solute.   Molecule isolated in matrix, glass, or polymer.   Synonym for *guest* (in matrix or mixed crystal), and for *impurity* as used in solid state language.

Spin-lattice relaxation. Energy quenching of excited spin component due to energy transfer from the excited solute species to the host lattice.

Spin-orbit coupling. Coupling between spin vector and electronic vector enhances the probability of transitions between states with unequal spin.

T_e. Computed electronic transition energy; does not contain zero point energy.

$T_{0,0}$. Electronic transition energy, measured between 0,0 bands. Includes zero point energy. Some authors also use $\nu_{0,0}$.

T_1. Lowest excited triplet state; in most molecules it has the same electron configuration as S_1.

$T_1 \leftarrow S_0$. Absorption from ground state singlet to first excited triplet.

$T_1 \rightarrow S_0$. Emission from first excited triplet to ground state singlet.

τ. Greek tau; normally used for lifetimes and decay times.

τ_F; k_F. Fluorescence lifetime and fluorescence decay rate.

τ_P; k_P. Phosphorescence lifetime and phosphorescence decay rate.

τ_S; k_S. Radiationless singlet decay rate.

$\tau_{S,obs}$. Observed singlet decay; includes all radiative and radiationless processes.

τ_T; k_T. Radiationless triplet decay rate.

$\tau_{T,obs}$. Observed triplet decay rate; it includes radiative and radiationless processes τ_P and τ_T.

Thermal phosphorescence. Phosphorescence excited by thermal depopulation of trap.

Trap. Solute, impurity, or lattice distortion acting as a trap for electronic energy.

UV. Ultraviolet. Region between visible and vacuum ultraviolet part of the spectrum. Normally 180–400 nm.

v'. Vibrational quantum number of excited state.

v''. Vibrational quantum number of ground state.

$v_1, \ldots$. Vibrational quantum number.

ω. Vibrational frequency; $\omega_0 = \omega_e - \omega_e x_e$.

B. Units and Conversion Factors

We tried to use in each case the best accepted or most sensitive unit system. Whenever possible, the recommendations of the International Union of Pure and Applied Chemistry (IUPAC) and the International Union of Pure and

Applied Physics (IUPAP) are followed. If the above three criteria lead to different units, we have chosen the units used by experimentalists because they are tied to the units in which their equipment is calibrated.

Unfortunately, all good will fails in the choice of the best energy units for light quanta. There are at least seven different energy units in regular use. Each unit has its assets and its fervent advocates. It is impossible, at this time, to chose one generally acceptable unit. Instead, we adhere to the units in which the effect or observation would be reported in a leading research journal. Wavelength is reported in nm, vibrational modes in cm^{-1}, and electronic transition energies in μm^{-1}. We are aware that many readers will disagree with our choices; we share their feelings and frustrations, but decisions had to be made; where we could not obtain a consensus, we chose the unit which allows the simplest representation of data. In the case of electronic transition energies, this led us to prefer μm^{-1} to cm^{-1}, because 5.000 μm^{-1} is simpler than 50,000 cm^{-1}, when low temperature accuracy is less than $\pm$ 50 cm^{-1}.

Table 1.2 contains some of the most important conversion factors for frequently used units. It also lists some basic constants.

Table 1.2

Conversion Factors and Physical Constants

Units of Length		Units of Area	
Units	cm	Units	cm^2
1 cm	1	1 cm^2	1
1 in.	2.54	1 sq in.	6.45
1 μm	10^{-4}	1 sq ft	929.03
1 nm	10^{-7}		

Units of Volume		Units of Mass	
Units	ml	Units	g
1 cm^3	0.99997	1 g	1
1 cu in.	16.3867	1 kg	10^3
1 cu ft	28316.2	1 lb	453.592
1 ml	1		
1 liter	1000		
1 gal (U.S.)	3785		

Table 1.2 (continued)

Conversion Factors and Physical Constants

Units of Pressure

Units	dyne/cm²	atm	kg/cm²	torr
1 dyne/cm²	1	0.9869×10^{-6}	1.0197×10^{-6}	7.50×10^{-4}
1 atm	1013250	1	1.0332275	760
1 kg/cm²	980665	0.9678411	1	735.5592
1 mmHg = 1 torr	1333.2237	1.3157895×10^{-3}	1.3595098×10^{-3}	1
1 in. Hg	33863.95	0.03342112	0.03453162	25.40005
1 lb(wt)/sq. in.	68947.31	0.06804570	0.07030669	51.71473

Units of Energy

Units	eV	cm⁻¹	°K	cal	kcal/mole	J_{int}
1 J_{int}	0.6244×10^{19}	0.5038×10^{23}	0.7246×10^{23}	2.3897×10^{-1}	14.39×10^{19}	1
1 kW-hr	2.247×10^{25}	1.813×10^{29}	2.607×10^{29}	0.8601×10^{6}	51.80×10^{25}	3.59932×10^{6}
1 cal	2.612×10^{19}	2.108×10^{23}	3.031×10^{23}	1	6.00×10^{20}	4.1846
1 kcal$_{IT}$	2.613×10^{22}	2.108×10^{26}	3.033×10^{26}	1.0003×10^{3}	6.02×10^{20}	4.186047×10^{3}
1 eV	1	0.8068×10^{4}	1.1603×10^{4}	3.827×10^{-20}	22.96	1.601×10^{-19}
1 cm⁻¹	1.239×10^{-4}	1	1.438	4.744×10^{-24}	28.46×10^{-4}	1.985×10^{-23}
1 °K	0.8617×10^{-4}	0.6953	1	3.298×10^{-24}	19.79×10^{-4}	1.380×10^{-23}
1 cm³ atm	0.6325×10^{18}	0.5103×10^{22}	0.7340×10^{22}	2.4209×10^{-2}	14.53×10^{18}	1.01306×10^{-1}
1 ft-lb (wt)	0.8464×10^{19}	0.682×10^{23}	0.9822×10^{23}	3.2394×10^{-1}	19.44×10^{19}	1.35556
1 HP hr	1.675×10^{25}	1.352×10^{29}	1.944×10^{29}	0.6414×10^{6}	38.48×10^{25}	2.68401×10^{6}
1 BTU$_{IT}$	0.6586×10^{22}	0.5314×10^{26}	0.7643×10^{26}	2.5209×10^{2}	15.12×10^{22}	1.054866×10^{3}

Table 1.2 (continued)

Conversion Factors and Physical Constants

Thermal Energy kT

T (°K)	kT (cm^{-1})
4.2	2.92
10.0	6.95
20.0	13.90
77.0	53.52
300.0	208.5

Equivalents

$1 \, \text{nm} = 10 \, \text{Å} = 1 \, \text{m}\mu$

$1 \, \mu\text{m}^{-1} = 10{,}000 \, \text{cm}^{-1} = 10 \, \text{k Kayser}$

$1 \, \text{eV} = 0.8068 \, \mu\text{m}^{-1} = 22.96 \, \text{kcal/mole}$

$1 \, \text{kcal} = 4184.6 \, \text{joules} = 4.1846 \times 10^{10} \, \text{ergs}$

Values of Constants

Speed of light in vacuum	c	2.997925×10^8 m/sec
Avogadro constant	N	6.02252×10^{23} molecules/mole
Elementary charge	e	4.80298×10^{-10} esu (cm$^{3/2}$ g$^{1/2}$/sec)
Planck constant	h	6.6256×10^{-27} erg sec
Gas constant	R	8.3143×10^7 ergs/mole °K
		1.98726 cal/mole °K
		0.0820597 l.atm/mole °K
Boltzmann constant	k	1.38054×10^{-16} erg/°K
Rydberg constant	R_0	1.0973731×10^5 cm^{-1}

CHAPTER 2

History

I. OPTICAL STUDIES

The history of luminescence goes back to ancient times. Throughout the history of mankind, scientists have observed and reported emission of light from solids (Harvey, 1957). Modern scientific studies started in 1888 when E. Wiedemann reported in a detailed paper that quinine, esculin, and many dyestuffs, absorbed in gelatin, phosphoresce more strongly at $-80°C$ than at room temperature. Six years later, on April 19, 1894, J. Dewar made an oral communication to the Royal Society "stating that he had observed that many bodies cooled to between $-180°C$ and $-200°C$ after stimulation by light became remarkably phosphorescent, not only in increased intensity, but in duration." His observations were communicated in three long papers. The last one, in 1901, is the transcript of his famous lecture, "The Nadir of Temperature." In the early studies, Dewar immersed his samples in liquid nitrogen in an open beaker, illuminating the substance from above, through the liquid surface. The results of the work of Wiedemann and Dewar still hold, and they constitute the beginning of very productive research which led to the development of the field covered in this book.

All early research was on emission. E. Wiedemann and G. C. Schmidt published (1895a,b) a fifty-page report on x-ray stimulated luminescence in which the influence of individual parameters was discussed. The solvent effect on luminescence color was studied using Group II and IIa salts doped with manganese sulfate. The fluorescence of pure $MgSO_4$ is red, $MgSO_4$ in $CaSO_4$ green, and $MgSO_4$ in CaF_2, blue. Concentration effects were reported for the system $ZnSO_4$ with $MnSO_4$. The temperature effect on color change was unpredictable, but the observation was made that, on cooling to $-80°C$, the luminescence lifetime increased for all solutions and substances, including anthracene. Quinine hydrochloride was singled out for its clear and long-

15

lived afterglow.   Some solutions, such as $CaSO_4$ with $MnSO_4$, were found to glow for several months after irradiation.   The authors also discovered that traces of impurities could drastically shorten or totally suppress the luminescence.

The photoluminescence, under sunlight, was found to correspond in most cases to the x-ray-stimulated emission, lifetimes for most materials being of the order of one to a few seconds.   In addition to chemiluminescence data, Wiedemann and Schmidt supplied a list of the most beautifully luminescing materials, which included ionic crystals as well as organic substances.   This paper describes almost all spectral observations and effects on which modern low temperature spectroscopy is based.   It also lists most problems for which modern spectroscopists still seek detailed answers.   Thus, the phenomenological basis for the sciences covered in this book were secured before the theories of atomic physics, quantum theory, and electronic spectroscopy were developed.

The first review on low temperature spectroscopy appeared in 1904 in the *Jahrbuch für Radioaktivität und Elektrizität*; in this, Nicholls (1904) reviewed most of the earlier work in Continental Europe, England, and the United States.   Nicholls is also coauthor of an extensive research paper in which fluorescence and phosphorescence of sixty-three substances at 76°K with lifetimes between 1 second and several minutes are reported (Nicholls, 1911).   Except for some errors in a list of substances that were believed not to luminesce, most of the data are amazingly accurate.

Russian interest in low temperature spectra is reflected in a paper by Borisov (1905) in which the observations of Wiedemann are independently confirmed.   Borisov summarized ten points, of which the most important are that luminescence is common among organic solids and that it starts 50° to 150°C below the melting point of the material.   Of all molecules studied, albumin and alkaloids were found to luminesce most strongly.   The color most frequently observed was green.   The lifetimes and intensity were found to be temperature dependent, the intensity always increasing with decreasing temperature.   Borisov also confirmed that solid solutions luminesce more strongly than pure solids, and that in dilute solution concentration does not affect spectral properties.   In 1911 Kowalski and E. Goldstein (1911, 1912) started a series of reports on cold solutions of aromatic molecules in glycerin-ethanol solutions.   During this time several authors explored all types of solvents, including borax solutions, which were called "boric acid phosphors" by Tiede (1920 to 1922), and, also, hydrated aluminum sulfate, used extensively by Travnicek (1933).   Absorption of molecules on silica gel, aluminum hydroxide, and filter paper was successfully practiced by

Kautsky (1931, 1932) and later by Pringsheim (1926). Kowalski's elegant and accurate work on organic molecules, ion crystals, pure inorganic and organic solids, and solid solutions was seminal for the use of liquid air cooled samples.

The study of absorption spectra at low temperature started much later than that of emission because the experimental difficulties are greater. While early luminescence studies could be made with poor samples that scattered light, absorption measurement had to wait for carefully prepared transparent solids, mounted in transparent, insulated vessels. Kautsky's (1931) work on ethanol glasses foreshadowed the development of glasses by Lewis (1945 to 1949) and his students, who, after the second world war, perfected a viscous, highly transparent glass made from ether, isopentane, and ethanol in the ratio 5 : 5 : 1. Work similar to that of Lewis was started independently in Cambridge by Norrish's group, which originally used gelatin and paraffin as solvent, until Porter (Norman, 1954) switched to hydrocarbons. This prepared the ground for *in situ* photolysis and preparation of free radicals in glasses by Norman and Porter (1954), a method which became rapidly obsolete because of Pimentel's simultaneous development of chemically inert matrices for infrared study of reactive species. Terenin (1941) and other Russian workers prepared transparent organic glasses during the second world war. The Russian research led to the important discovery of sharp line spectra in absorption and emission of coronene and pyrene in *n*-hexane and benzo[*a*]pyrene in *n*-heptane (Shpol'skii, 1960a—c, 1962a—c, 1963a,b). Ermolaev (1963) reported energy transfer within and between solute molecules. The Russian school established organic glasses as a powerful tool for determining the optical properties of aromatic molecules. The use of organic glasses for the analytical study of organic molecules and biological substances has developed into a widely practiced, independent field.

Kowalski (1911), and later Pringsheim and Vavilow (1926a), established that the luminescence spectrum at low temperatures is different from that at room temperature. They distinguished between high temperature and low temperature luminescence, which they later called phosphorescence and slow fluorescence. Lewis and his co-workers used the terms α- and β-phosphorescence. Jablonski (1935a,b) analyzed the states participating in electronic transitions and helped simplify the situation by introducing term schemes in which transitions can be simply, graphically expressed. He established that almost all organic molecules have a strong absorption in the near UV to an excited upper state from which short-lived fluorescence can originate, and that they have a lower lying, long-lived state from which phosphorescence originates. Lewis, Magel, and Lipkin published in 1941 correlations on the temperature dependence of lifetime. Porter (Norman, 1954) in England and Lewis and co-workers in California discovered and established almost simultaneously that this lowest excited state has triplet character.

In 1934 Winterstein discovered that, in an anthracene crystal containing traces of tetracene, absorption by anthracene yields strongly enhanced fluorescence of tetracene. This effect is called sensitized fluorescence. Similar effects are observed in liquid solution. Therefore, early theory was inspired by room temperature work. Beginning in 1949, McClure measured phosphorescence decay times of a large number of pure organic substances. The usefulness of such spectra had already been demonstrated by Prikhotko, who observed, in 1933, very sharp line spectra in single crystals of benzene. McClure developed important theories on radiationless energy transfer in mixed molecular crystals. Such crystals constitute now an independent area of research. This field developed from the study of single crystals, which often contain impurities.

Most of the presently known energy transfer effects in crystals were discovered in the late 1940s by McClure, Schnepp, and others. Davydov (1948, 1951, 1962) developed theories for band splittings and excitation migration. Excitons in solution were first studied in the group of Förster (1948 to present) in Stuttgart.

Trapping of isolated free radicals in rare gas solids began after the first world war when Vegard (1924 to 1948) and later McLennan (1924, 1928) started a thorough and detailed study on x-ray and electron bombardment of rare gases and atmospheric gases condensed at 4° and 20°K. Their work concentrated on the stimulation of the auroral glow under laboratory conditions. Although errors occurred in the identification of isolated species, Vegard's work not only contributed to the knowledge of solid spectra, but also significantly enlarged the knowledge of the gas phase spectrum of nitrogen. Vegard also discovered the temperature dependence and the matrix heavy atom effect (Fig. 2.1).

There was a gap of almost thirty years between Vegard's pioneering work and the beginning of systematic physical and chemical research in this area. This was partly due to experimental and technological difficulties encountered in handling the rare gas solids, which must be prepared at 4° and 20°K. In 1954 Pimentel (Whittle et al., 1954) developed the matrix isolation method, and since then has demonstrated the full potential and power of this method for the study of chemical reactions. Today, matrix isolation is a flourishing science, and its results have influenced almost all fields of science (TRACES report, 1968).

Research on free radical stabilization accelerated in the United States in the mid-1950s, when it was hoped that stabilized free radicals might make good rocket fuels. An intensive program, under the guidance of H. P. Broida and A. M. Bass, at the U.S. National Bureau of Standards brought a rich harvest of data, even now not fully evaluated, on trapped radicals and dilute radical solutions. This work is partly summarized in an excellent book edited

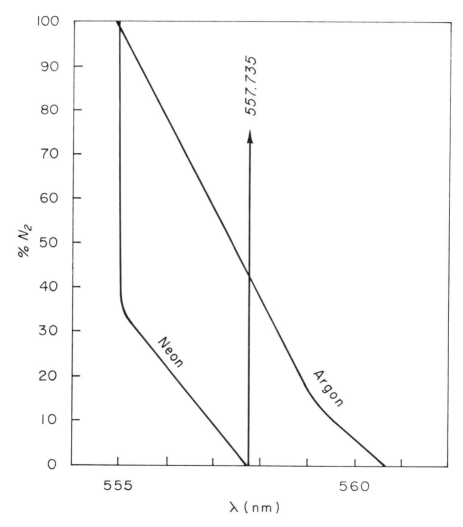

FIG. 2.1. Emission spectrum of oxygen atoms in solid nitrogen argon and nitrogen-neon mixtures as a function of concentration. After Vegard (1924b).

by Bass and Broida (1960), which contains contributions from almost all groups active in this field at that time. The above work was inspired by the exploratory work of F. O. Rice (1951, and later) on trapped vapors of sulfur and electrically discharged ammonia. Rice observed that such condensed products were deeply colored and contained metastable free radicals. G. W. Robinson (1958 to present) pioneered the study of electronic spectra of radicals and molecules in matrices. Figure 2.2 shows the spectrum of NH_2 and HNO taken by Robinson (1958b). The lines are unusually sharp, and there is indication of rotation. Early experiments often involved two molecules in the same matrix.

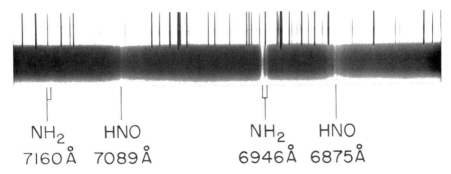

Fig. 2.2. NH_2 and HNO in argon at 4°K. Unpublished photograph of plate taken by G. W. Robinson.

II. CRYOCHEMISTRY

Vegard's work did not arouse interest in cryochemistry because he was too far ahead of his time, and he published in physical journals. The chemists had to find their own path into radical chemistry via Paneth's gas phase experiments on thermal decomposition of methyl compounds. Interest in cold trapped radicals stems from post-World War II experiments by Rice (1951 to 1959), who, with simple equipment, produced beautifully colored cold solids from discharges containing ammonia or sulfur. Analysis and study of these systems had to wait for Pimentel's development of the matrix isolation method. However, the experiments of Rice stirred immediate interest in trapping undiluted reactive species, and this interest continued among those who had no access to liquid helium or hydrogen, which are necessary for matrix work. Many unstable species can be trapped in low temperature solids by rapid quenching. There is an active group of chemists who continues to study reactions in the style of Rice. Timm (1969), for example, found interesting products in solids formed by condensing hot iron atoms with benzene or PF_3; silicon atoms with B_2F_4; and copper atoms with BCl_3. Margrave (1969) condensed hot SiF_2 with BF_3; Skell (1963), carbon vapors with alkanes, alcohols, epoxides and alkyl halides; and Libby (1969), carbon vapors with benzene. For small and highly reactive species, an inert matrix must be used.

Free radicals do not yield metastable pure solids for two reasons. First, the activation energy for free radical reactions is zero or so small that reaction occurs at 77°, 20°, or even 4°K. And second, chemical reactions are initiated because of heat dissipation during the deposition of the warm material on a cold surface. The species S_2 serves as a good illustration. When S_2 vapor is condensed from a molecular beam, condensing molecules form larger molecules, predominantly chains, of various sizes. The molecular composition of the resulting solid and the relative concentration of individual species formed depends on the deposition speed and target temperature. Chain growth yields inert molecules which can act as a neutral matrix for S_2 and the smaller reactive intermediates. The resultant multi-component systems form macroscopically homogeneous looking, deeply colored glasses, containing a large number of components, but at 76°K only $0.1-1\%$ S_2 is preserved (Meyer, 1960a,b). In contrast, rare gas matrices, codeposited with S_2, yield 90% or more S_2 (Meyer, 1962; Brewer, 1965b).

If cryochemical reaction between stable reagents is initiated by photolysis, a matrix or an inert solvent serves to isolate primary products, prevents secondary reactions and acts as a heat sink for exothermic reactions. The use of these effects was conceived by Pimentel (1954 to present), and elegantly exploited by himself, Milligan (1958 to present), and others. Without matrix, there is no temperature control, and no selective reaction. If, after reaction, matrices are not further needed, they can be pumped off by stepwise warming. If preparative reactions with bulk quantities of chemicals are desired, the matrix can be regenerated.

Whether with or without a solid solvent, the reactions described in this book are proof that cryochemistry has already had a great impact on basic chemistry that will surely lead to many applications (TRACES Report, 1968).

Recommended Reading

Bass, A. M., and H. P. Broida, eds., *The Formation and Trapping of Free Radicals*, Academic Press, New York, 1960a.

Bass, A. M., and H. P. Broida, Nat. Bur. Std. (U.S.) Monograph **12** (1960b). "Stabilization of Free Radicals at Low Temperatures."

Curie, M., *Fluorescence and Phosphorescence*, Hermann, Paris, 1946.

Förster, T., *Fluoreszenz organischer Verbindungen*, Vandenhoeck & Ruprecht, Göttingen, 1951.

Harvey, E. N., A. *History of Luminescence*, American Philosophical Society, Philadelphia, Pennsylvania, 1957.

Kasha, L., and M. Kasha, *Molecular Electronic Bibliography*, Vol. 1: Molecular Quantum Mechanics and Molecular Electronic Spectroscopy. Early Workers. Publishers Press, Tallahassee, Florida, 1958.

Shpol'skii, E. V., Opt. Spectrosc. (USSR) (English Trans.) **23**, 357 (1967). "The Development of Soviet Optics and Spectroscopy During the Past Fifty Years."

TRACES (Technology in Retrospect and Critical Events in Science). Report prepared for the National Science Foundation by Illinois Institute of Technology Research Institute, Contract No. NSF-C535; Dec. 15, 1968. Foreword by C. E. Falk.

CHAPTER 3

Basic Observations and Models of Behavior

If the optical properties of a guest molecule isolated in a cold host lattice are compared with the optical properties of the same guest species in the gas phase, it is discovered that the differences can be attributed to the influence of temperature and guest-host interactions. It is the objective of this chapter to investigate these phenomena and to explain, or at least rationalize, the consequences of lowering the temperature and of introducing intermolecular interactions.

The principal directly observed experimental quantities, from which all models, theories, and conclusions are deduced, are transition energies of electronic, vibrational, rotational, or combined transitions; line widths; intensity and polarization of absorption and emission during and after excitation; and decay times of emission. From these data, molecular properties, such as absorption strengths, emission quantum yields, lifetimes, oscillator strength, symmetry of transitions, can be deduced and normalized. These data are then further translated into idealized properties that fit the individual parameters of models and theories.

This chapter has been divided into three parts. In the first, the guest will be treated as a cold gas and it will be shown that, even in this rather crude approximation, many observations can be adequately described. The second part will discuss the ramifications of allowing host-guest interactions to perturb the guest species. Finally, the optical observations and patterns of behavior due to guest-guest interaction will be described and discussed.

I. THE COLD GAS MODEL

For many purposes it is adequate to consider the guest species as an infinitely dilute cold gas. In this model, the real temperature of the system is used,

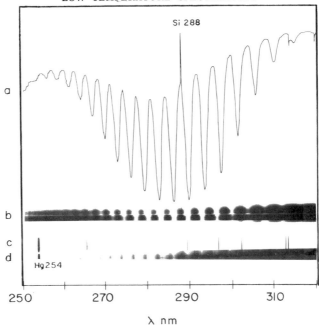

FIG. 3.1. Absorption spectrum of S_2: (a) tracing of matrix spectrum, (b) spectrum in Xe at 20°K, (c) mercury standard, (d) gas phase absorption at 1000°K. After L. Brewer (1965b) and from unpublished data.

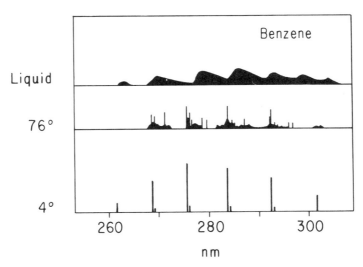

FIG. 3.2. The absorption spectrum of liquid benzene; of gas at room temperature; at 77°K, and at 4°K in a nitrogen matrix.

but the host species are assumed to be absent while the guest remains a perfect gas. Under these circumstances, all intramolecular processes occur without environmental influence; i.e., the observed molecule absorbs and dissipates energy before it collides with or enters the interaction radius of other molecules. For allowed resonance transitions, such conditions are realized at pressures below 10^{-3} torr, and gas phase spectra of such transitions can be treated as being due to free molecules. For spin forbidden transitions, the situation is different. A typical $T_1 \rightarrow S_0$ transition of an aromatic molecule has a lifetime of about 20 seconds. For such transitions to be collision free, the collision frequency would have to be less than 0.05 $\sec^{-1}$. This is not convenient in a laboratory. However, apparently collision free triplet emission is observed quite frequently. This is because collisions often have very low quenching cross sections, and because the photon emission process occurs during a very short time interval.

The cold gas model predicts that, because of the lack of intermolecular interaction, the spectrum of the guest in a cold host should be very similar to the characteristic spectrum of the free gas phase guest species. This is in fact what is observed, in visible ultraviolet and infrared absorption, and visible and UV emission spectroscopy.

Two examples will serve to illustrate this point. Figure 3.1 shows the absorption spectrum of S_2 in the gas phase and in a xenon matrix; the vibrational spacings and intensities closely parallel one another. Figure 3.2 compares the absorption spectrum of benzene at room temperature, 76°K, and 4°K; again, the similarities of the Franck-Condon curve and the vibrational spacing are striking. In infrared spectroscopy, it is likewise observed that the spectra of guest molecules isolated in cold hosts bear great resemblance to the spectra of the same molecules in the gas phase. However, Fig. 3.2 also illustrates the second consequence of the cold gas model. At low temperature, the absorption spectrum is vastly simplified because an absorption transition can originate only from a thermally populated state, and only the lowest levels are populated in a cold system.

The temperature dependence of population for vibrational levels follows the equation:

$$N_r = M \exp(-\omega/0.69 \cdot T)$$

where N is the population, ω the vibrational frequency, and T the absolute temperature. As an example, Table 3.1 lists the vibrational population of SnS at 4°K and at 1000°K. In the gas phase, absorption with up to $v'' = 8$ is observed. In matrices, only $v'' = 0$ occurs. The reduction of vibrational

Table 3.1

Vibrational Population of SnS

v''	Relative Vibrational Population[a]	
	$4°K$	$1000°K$
0	100	50
1	10^{-75}	25
2	—	12
3	—	6
4	—	3
5	—	2
6	—	0.7
7	—	0.4
8	—	0.2

[a] Expressed as percentage.

Table 3.2

Rotational Levels with Highest Thermal Population for SnS and C_2

Molecule	B (cm^{-1})	J with Highest Population					
		$2°K$	$4°K$	$20°K$	$77°K$	$300°K$	$2500°K$
C_2	1.82	(0.1)	(0.4)	$2-1$	3	7	22
SnS	0.136	2	12	7	13	27	55
							(at 1000°K)

Table 3.3

Relative Thermal Population of $X'\,^1\Sigma$ and $X\,^3\Pi$ of C_2 [a]

State	Energy (μm^{-1})	Relative Population[a]			
		$4°K$	$77°K$	$300°K$	$2500°K$
$^1\Sigma$	0	100	100	95	58
$^3\Pi$	0.06	10^{-90}	10^{-3}	5	42

[a] Expressed as percentage of total molecules.

population is also responsible for the color change sulfur and other molecular crystals undergo upon cooling.

For rotational levels, the state with highest population at a given temperature is given by:

$$J_{max} = 0.5896\sqrt{T/B} - \tfrac{1}{2}.$$

The fraction of molecules in this state is $N_{T_{max}} \simeq \sqrt{B/T}$.

Table 3.2 indicates that, at high temperature, the highest populated state is no longer the ground rotational state, but in SnS at 1000°K where the molecules are thermodynamically stable, $J = 55$, and for C_2 at 2500°K, $J_{max} = 22$. If $J = 55$ has the highest population, levels with up to $J = 160$ still contribute noticeably to absorption. If low-lying electronic energy levels are close to the ground state, kT can induce population of excited electronic states.

Table 3.3 gives the relative populations in $^1\Sigma$ and $^3\Pi$ for C_2 at 4°K and 2500°K. Under equilibrium conditions, C_2 is most stable around 2500°K. At this temperature about 40% of the molecules are in the $^3\Pi$ state.

If a state has a multiplicity other than one, the sublevel population is also temperature dependent. Table 3.4 gives data for different λ values of a triplet state assuming that the splitting between all three levels is equal.

Table 3.4

Relative Thermal Population of Triplet Sublevels

Temperature (°K)	Relative Thermal Population[a]			
	$\lambda = 0.1$	$\lambda = 1$	$\lambda = 10$	$\lambda = 100$
2	1/3	50/32/18	98/2/0.1	10^{13}/1/—
4	1/3	40/33/27	83/14/3	10^6/1/—
20	1/3	1/3	46/32/22	98/2/0.1
77	1/3	1/3	37/34/29	64/25/11
300	1/3	1/3	1/3	50/31/19

[a] Assuming even splitting of all three sublevels; λ in cm^{-1}.

For heavy high temperature molecules with small B and ω values, the combination of all vibrational, rotational, and spin sublevels belonging to one allowed electronic transition can yield 500,000 or more spectral lines in the gas phase. Below 77°K, for all practical purposes, only $v'' = 0$ is populated. Accordingly, absorption spectra in low temperature solutions consist of about thirty lines belonging to a single progression with $v'' = 0$.

J is normally so small, or rotation is suppressed because of steric effects, that it does not significantly contribute to the solid state line width. Figure 3.2 shows that for each vibrational quantum only one sharp line with a weak phonon side band remains. Since the number of absorbing molecules remains the same, i.e., the integrated absorption is unchanged, the intensity of each absorption line is increased by the same factor by which the number of lines is reduced. As a result, the intensity at the absorbing frequency is much higher in the solid, or one needs fewer molecules to obtain a given absorptivity. The same effect would be expected in S_2, but it is not apparent because the line width in the solid remains large, as a result of interaction with the solvent. This effect is discussed in Chapter 4.

As at higher temperatures, the relative intensity of the absorbing bands depends largely on the difference in internuclear distance between the excited and ground state. If the change in internuclear distance is small, as in the Swan bands of C_2, the 0,0 band is strongest and all others are weak. If the change in distance is large, as in the case of $^3\Sigma_u^- \leftarrow {}^3\Sigma_g^-$ of Se_2, the Franck-Condon maximum may shift so far from the origin that the 0,0 band becomes very weak. In the latter case, vibrational numbering becomes ambiguous. The ideal experimental molecule should have a strong origin and still have a sufficiently long progression to yield ω_0 and $\omega_0 x_0$ data. Vibrational numbering is then unambiguous, and $T_{0,0}$ can be deduced.

In emission, the Franck-Condon principle also holds, but the intensity of emitting states is not determined by the Boltzmann distribution (Chapter 5).

It is perhaps worthwhile to note at this point that, because of the spectral simplifications that result from working with cold systems, many investigators have turned to the matrix isolation technique for the study of high temperature molecules. For these workers, the technique has the additional advantage that significant concentrations of molecules can be easily accumulated and retained for leisurely study.

II. CONSEQUENCES OF INTRODUCING GUEST-HOST INTERACTIONS

A more careful examination of Figs. 3.1 and 3.2 reveals that, although the similarities between the gas and solid phase spectra are great, there are small but significant differences. Thus, for example, the origins of the electronic transitions are slightly different in each case, the lines observed in the solid phase are broad by comparison with their gas phase counterparts, and extra features, not present in the gas phase spectra, appear in the spectra of solid samples. Indeed, as will be discussed below, many phenomena are observed that cannot be understood unless one takes account of the fact that guest-host interactions play a significant role in the determination of the characteristics of the solid phase optical properties.

A. Qualitative Aspects

In the presence of host atoms or molecules, the guest species is perturbed; as a consequence, the physical parameters of the guest are altered and energy transfer between the host and guest becomes possible. For simplicity's sake, we assume here temporarily that guest and host are identical molecules. To understand the guest-host interactions, it is useful to begin with an infinitely dilute gas and observe how the interactions develop as the gas is compressed into a solid.

At moderate pressure, gas collisions cannot be treated as in the classic hard shell model, because of the interaction between neighboring molecules. Three forces are responsible for the interaction. The first, the London dispersion force, takes into account the perturbation of the ground state of the system by all excited states. The second, discovered by Debye and Falkenhagen, is an induced attractive force due to electrical polarization of nonspherically symmetrical molecules. The third, the Keesom orientation effect, results from dipole-dipole interaction. The average of all orientations of this force is attractive only for the lowest B levels. It is therefore very temperature sensitive. Table 3.5 gives values for five molecules of the individual components of the r^6 force component C which enters the potential

$$E_r = B \exp(-r/\rho) - C/r^6$$

where E is the potential energy, r is distance, B is the repulsion due to valence forces at small distances, C is a constant determined by dispersion, induction, and orientation.

Table 3.5

Relative Values of Dispersion, Induction, and Orientation Effects for HI, HBr, HCl, NH_3, and H_2O [a]

Effects	HI	HBr	HCl	NH_3	H_2O
Dipole moment (Debye)	0.38	0.78	1.03	1.47	1.84
Dispersion: induction	0.0035	0.018	0.037	0.085	0.158
Dispersion: orientation	0.0007	0.028	0.13	0.72	3.0

[a] After Herzberg (1967).

B. Gases at Intermediate Pressures

At very low pressures, the molecules of a gas are far apart, do not interact, and collide only infrequently; under these circumstances, excited molecules can give up their energy only through radiative processes. By contrast, at atmospheric pressure, the collision frequency is large and energy transfer between molecules becomes important. As a consequence, internal conversions, vibrational quenching, and intersystem crossings occur, and new emission processes are observed, including phosphorescence and sensitized fluorescence.

A well studied example of energy transfer is SO_2. At room temperature, at pressures below 10^{-3} torr, SO_2 fluoresces exclusively $S_i \rightarrow S_0$, where S_i is the terminal state of absorption. If SO_2 or an inert gas is added to increase the pressure, the fluorescence intensity decreases and phosphorescence, $T_1 \rightarrow S_0$, appears. At 1 torr, the phosphorescence comprises approximately one-fourth of the total emission intensity. Solid SO_2 also phosphoresces, although with reduced efficiency (Phillips, 1969). The energy transfer mechanisms will be discussed in Chapter 5. However, it is already apparent that collisions can activate molecular faucets which are less active or not used in the free molecule, and that the appearance of the spectrum can change.

C. Gases at High Pressures

When the gas pressure exceeds a few atmospheres, the gas becomes so dense that a significant fraction of the transitions occur while molecules are within interacting range of each other. As a result of the distortion and interactions of electron clouds, forbidden transitions can become allowed.

The best-studied cases of small molecules at high pressures are H_2 in H_2, D_2 and in rare gases, and O_2 (Blickensderfer, 1969). The infrared absorption of $H_2(v'' = 1) \leftarrow H_2(v'' = 0)$ is forbidden because the molecule is homonuclear, but at about 5 atm with an absorption path of 30 meters, the strong interactions cause the transition to become sufficiently allowed to be observed. As expected, the intensity of the transition is pressure dependent, as are the line width and transition energy.

If the colliding molecules are identical, transitions can involve simultaneous changes in both molecules, and the colliding particles can form a dimer which, upon absorption, results in an excimer. All combinations of the following forbidden simultaneous electronic transitions of two interacting molecules of oxygen are observed and occur by absorption of one light quantum:

$$(^1\varDelta)(^1\varDelta) \leftarrow (^3\varSigma)(^3\varSigma)$$

$$(^1\varSigma)(^1\varDelta) \leftarrow (^3\varSigma)(^3\varSigma)$$

$$(^3\varSigma^+)(^3\varSigma^+) \leftarrow (^3\varSigma_g{}^-)(^3\varSigma_g{}^-).$$

These simultaneous transitions cause the blue color of liquid and solid oxygen (Tsai, 1969; Blickensderfer, 1969).

Since interaction between colliding molecules in the ground state and an electronically excited state are different, emission and absorption of the same transition do not coincide.

D. Solids

An especially simple type of solid is a single crystal. The weak coupling of species in low temperature solids is in many respects similar to that of high pressure gases. However, in the low temperature solid, two changes occur. First, at high density, molecules are at no time free. Therefore, the random motion is restricted, and motion and excitation of molecules becomes coupled. Second, at low temperature, when thermal energy and motion are lost, time-dependent parameters are replaced by symmetry-determined constants. Since the distance between neighboring molecules ceases to be a function of time, lines sharpen and the gas-phase to crystal shift of the transition energy is determined by the crystal field.

The lattice coupling between like molecules causes two other distinct effects, which are observed in single crystals as well as mixed crystals. First, the energy levels broaden and split, depending on the symmetry of the molecule and site; and second, excitation energy can migrate through the delocalized molecular energy levels, in the form of excitons. The first effect will be discussed in Chapter 4, the second in Chapter 5.

In addition to the spectrum due to coupling of molecular energy levels, characteristic lattice spectra are observed. Figure 3.3 shows a schematic spectrum of an organic crystal. Lattice vibrations are typically in the range below 150 cm^{-1}. Gaslike vibration spectra are observed in the near IR with small line shifts. The electronic transitions are normally due to π-electrons and appear red-shifted from the gas phase. Forbidden transitions become enhanced unless totally symmetric vibrations are present, and the intensity of bands is strongest when the symmetry change is small. In the far UV, Rydberg-type series approaching the ionization limit are observed. Normally only one electronic transition, $S_1 \rightarrow S_0$, is observed in emission, and the wavelength of the emission spectrum is independent of excitation energy.

This results from lattice coupled quenching of all excitation to S_1, so-called internal conversion, before radiative decay can occur.

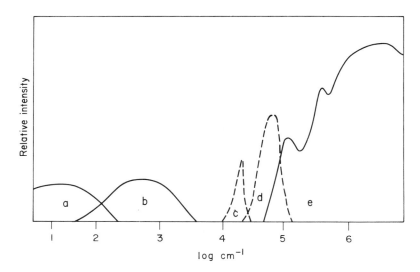

FIG. 3.3. Schematic absorption spectrum of an organic crystal: a, phonon bands; b, vibrations; c, phosphorescence; d, fluorescence; and e, electronic absorption. After Wolf (1967).

III. CONSEQUENCES OF GUEST-GUEST INTERACTIONS

If guests come into contact with each other, severe physical and chemical changes can result. This is, indeed, the reason why low temperature spectra of molecules are studied in weakly interacting matrices. Therefore, it is normally the experimenter's aim to reduce guest-guest interaction by dilution. Figure 3.4 shows the spectrum of acridine orange in ethanol at 90°K for various concentrations. It is observed that the spectrum does not further shift if the concentration is reduced to below 10^{-5} M. At this concentration, guest-guest interactions in glasses cease to be important. In matrices, the critical concentration for disappearance of guest-guest effects is not so well defined. It depends on condensation conditions and on the relative size of guest and host molecules. It also depends on diffusion, i.e., the sample temperature, because a matrix is not an equilibrium solution, thus, diffusing guests aggregate irreversibly.

The severity of the disturbance by guest-guest interactions depends on the purpose of the experiment. It is generally assumed that at an M/R

ratio of 1000 : 1 most of the guest is present as a monomer, but dimer and polymer spectra can be present up to an M/R ratio of 100,000 : 1. For synthesis and identification of a new free radical it might be tolerable to have an M/R of up to 50 : 1. Such a high concentration might be necessary for the study of reactions between reagents that are prepared by *in situ* photolysis, or that derive from vapor in which they constitute only a minor component.

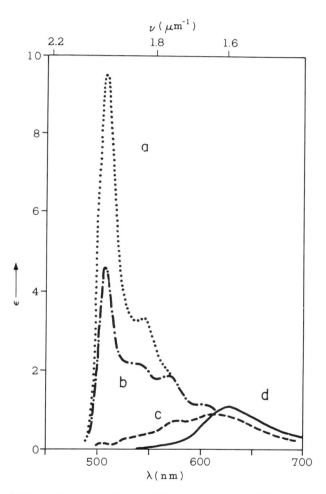

FIG. 3.4. Concentration dependence of fluorescence of acridine orange in ethanol at 90°K: *a*, $5 \times 10^{-5} M$; *b*, $2 \times 10^{-4} M$; *c*, $2 \times 10^{-3} M$; *d*, $4 \times 10^{-2} M$. Data from Zanker (1959).

In absorption, guest-guest interaction influences fine details of the spectrum at M/R ratios of 1000 : 1 or smaller. It results in line broadening, shoulders, and fine structure due to site distortion or dimer formation. In emission studies, guest-guest interaction can occur even at an M/R of 10,000 : 1. It can result in sensitized fluorescence, depolarization, and changes of decay times. For the study of guest-guest energy transfer, very pure matrices and glasses are required. Otherwise, the guest emission can become comparable to, or smaller than, that of impurities. This effect is also observed in the gas phase. Emission from discharges of compounds that contain traces of sulfur containing impurities is always deep blue because minute quantities of transient S_2 are found. S_2 is a stronger visible emitter than any other compound. The inadvertently present traces of impurities cause effects that are similar to, or worse than, those due to interactions between like guests. Oxygen, for example, suppresses emission of all excited molecules. Details on long-range guest-guest interactions, dimers, excimers, polymers, and aggregates are discussed in several of the following chapters.

Recommended Reading

Bondi, A., *Physical Properties of Molecular Crystals, Liquids and Glasses*, Wiley, New York, 1968.

Bowen, E. J., *The Chemical Aspects of Light*, Oxford Univ. Press (Clarendon), Oxford, 1946.

Herzberg, G., *Spectra of Diatomic Molecules*, 2nd ed., Van Nostrand, Princeton, New Jersey, 1961.

Herzberg, G., *Electronic Spectra and Electronic Structure of Polyatomic Molecules*, Van Nostrand, Princeton, New Jersey, 1967.

Kovac, I., *Rotational Structure in Spectra of Diatomic Molecules*, American Elsevier, New York and Amsterdam, 1969.

Nudelmann, R., Optical Properties of Solids, Plenum Press, New York, 1969 (Proceedings Nato Conference, 1966).

Parker, C. A., *Photoluminescence of Solutions with Applications to Photochemistry and Analytical Chemistry*, American Elsevier, New York and Amsterdam, 1968.

Robinson, G. W., in *Methods of Experimental Physics*, Vol. 3: *Molecular Physics* (D. Williams, ed.), p. 155, Academic Press, New York, 1961c. "Electronic Spectra."

Schnepp, O., Ann. Rev. Phys. Chem. **14**, 35 (1963). "Electronic Spectra of Molecular Crystals."

CHAPTER 4

Details of Observed Spectra

In this chapter and in Chapter 5 a variety of complications will be discussed which crop up when one investigates the optical properties of guest species violated in cold hosts. An example is the gas to solute shift of transition energy in absorption and fluorescence. As indicated in Chapter 3, the absorption spectrum of a guest is slightly shifted but similar to the gas phase spectrum of the cold guest molecules; however, in emission the shift can be quite large. For SnS, for example, the gas to xenon matrix shift is -270 cm^{-1}; in emission it is -9970 cm^{-1}. The shift in absorption is typical for matrix shifts of radiative transitions. The large shift in emission is due to excitation quenching. SnS shows resonance fluorescence in the gas phase, but in a matrix only T_1 $(v' = 0) \rightarrow S_0$ phosphorescence is observed (Fig. 4.1). Therefore, the emission of matrix isolated SnS is green and long-lived, not blue and short-lived as in the vapor. This is due to matrix-induced vibrational quenching and intersystem crossing. Both effects are nonradiative; they are described in Chapter 5.

In this chapter we discuss environmental effects on line shift, line shape, fine structure, and oscillator strength.

I. LINE SHIFTS

On closer inspection it is found that the spectrum in the solid is shifted from the gas phase. Here four types of shifts will be considered. First, the gas-solid shifts; second, the dependence of shifts on the host properties; third, the shift between absorption and emission; and, finally, the dependence of shifts on temperature.

A. Gas Phase to Matrix Shift

Table 4.1 presents typical data that show that, as a rule, the wavelength
of electronic and vibrational transitions of a guest isolated in a cold host
is observed to shift by less than 1% of the transition energy from the wavelength of the same transition when the guest species is in the gas phase.
The shift arises because the excited state of the guest interacts with the
host to a different extent than does the ground state of the guest. The shift
is a measure of the relative difference in interaction energy, but, unfortunately,
it does not give a measure of the absolute interaction energy of the host with
either state of the guest. Depending on the relative magnitude of the interactions involved, the wavelength of the transition may be shifted either
to longer or to shorter wavelength.

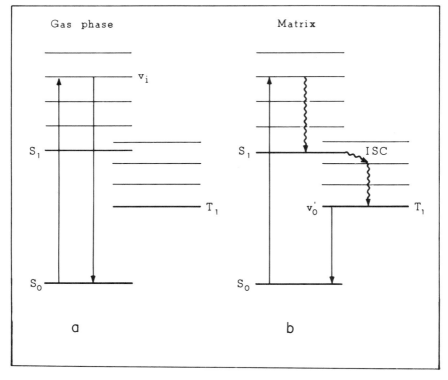

FIG. 4.1. Emission process of SnS: (a) gas phase, (b) in matrix at 20°K.

Table 4.1

Gas Phase-to-Matrix Shifts of Origins of Electronic Transitions

Species	Transition		Matrix						Temperature (°K)	References
	Character	Energy (μm^{-1})	Ne	Ar	Kr	Xe	N_2	SF_6		
Cd	$^1P - {}^1S$	4.3693	—	1557	357	-1138	—	—	4	Duley (1967a)
						-822			20	Merrithew (1969)
Zn	$^1P - {}^1S$	4.6745	—	1355	105	-1345	—	—	4	Duley (1967)
Ag	$^2P_{1/2} - {}^2S$	2.9552	—	1378	1329	158	—	—	20	Brewer (1968)
				2180	2305	871				
				3377	2708	1043				
						326			4	Shirk (1968)
						983				
						1123				
	$^2P_{3/2} - {}^2S$	3.0473	—	3049	2813	452	—	—	20	Brewer (1968)
				2556	1861	122				
				1259	1384	-58				
						497			4	Shirk (1968)
						202				
Kr	$^3P - {}^1S$	8.0918	4760	6130	420	62	—	—	4	Schnepp (1960)
										Baldini (1962)
Xe	$^3P - {}^1S$	6.6310	5210	6330	4650	—	—	—	4	Schnepp (1960)
										Baldini (1962)
Hg	$^3P - {}^1S$	3.9412	940	1255	760	10	—	—	20	Brewer (1965a)
				1270	775	10			4	McCarty (1959)
				1280	795	30			4	Duley (1965, 1967)
				1168	678	24			20	Roncin (1967)
				908						

Table 4.1 (continued)

Species	Transition: Character	Transition: Energy (μm^{-1})	Matrix: Ne	Matrix: Ar	Matrix: Kr	Matrix: Xe	Matrix: N_2	Matrix: SF_6	Temperature (°K)	References
	$^{1}P_{1} - {}^{1}S_{0}$	—	2081	1996	551	-1374	—	—	4	Brabson (1969)
Li	$^{2}P - {}^{2}S$	1.4904		1921	431	1239	—	—	4	Duley (1967)
				366	226	46			4	Andrews (1967)
				324	248	254				Belyaeva (1968)
Na	$^{2}P - {}^{2}S$	—		135	400	200			2	Weyhmann (1965)
				200	600	900			4	Meyer (1965)
K	$^{2}P - {}^{2}S$	—		150	-71	-331			2	Weyhmann (1965)
				100	0	-400			4	Meyer (1965)
				1400	900	300			4	Weyhmann (1965)
Cs	$^{2}P - {}^{2}S$	—		323	95	-179	-46		4	Weyhmann (1965)
N	$^{2}D - {}^{4}S$	1.9	-10	-42	-91	-263			4	Tinti, unpubl.
O	$^{1}S - {}^{1}D$	—	1	-92	-162	—	21	-90	4	Tinti, unpubl.
										Schoen (1960)
										Peyron (1959)
Mg	$^{1}P - {}^{1}S$	3.5051		342	217	-1000			4	Schnepp (1961)
In	$^{2}S - {}^{2}P$	—		-100	-1350	-3580			4	Duley (1967)
	$^{2}S - {}^{2}P$	—		—	1406				20	Currie (1969)
					3646					
Cu	$^{2}P - {}^{2}S$	3.0784		—	1667	451			20	Currie (1969)
						138				
					1317	443			4	Shirk (1968)
						137				
S_2	(B – X)	3.0535		—	1218	112			20	Currie (1969)
		3.1690	-10	-340	-790	-910	-210		20	Brewer (1965, 1966)

Table 4.1 (continued)

Species	Transition Character	Transition Energy (μm^{-1})	Ne	Ar	Kr	Xe	N_2	SF_6	Temperature (°K)	References
NH	($^3\Pi - {}^3\Sigma$)	2.9773	-192	—	-264	-370	—	—	4	McCarty (1959)
O_2	(C → X)	3.5000	-940	—	-910	-740	-930	—	4	Schoen (1960)
C_2	(A — X)	—								
Assuming C_2		1.9380	—	-155	-245	-410	-255	-105	4	Barger (1964)
Assuming C_2^-		1.8459	400	766	676	511	666	316	15	Milligan (1969)
CO	(A — X)	6.4747	-65	-590	-1000	-1660			4	Roncin (1967)
N_2	(A — X)	4.9755	-103	-131	-238	-342			4	Tinti (1968)
SnS	(D — X)	2.8260	—	100	80	-270			20	J. J. Smith (1968)
NO	(B — X)	—	-70	-205	-350				1.5	Roncin (1967)
				-185					4	
	(B' — X)	—	-50	-305	-690				1.5	
				-900					4	
	(G — X)	—	-70	-400	-970				1.5	
				-605					4	
SiO	(A — X)	4.2657	—	109	-232	-802			—	Shirk (1968)
C_3	($^1\Pi \leftarrow {}^1\Sigma$)	2.4675	-33	-235	-325	-1065	-40	410	4	Barger (1964)
									4	Weltner (1964)
NH_2	—	—	—	25	-7	-40	-500		4	Robinson (1958a,b)
										Milligan (1965)
SO_2	($^3B \to {}^1A$)	2.5727	—	-352	-385	-583	-418		20	Phillips (1969)
CS_2	—	5.5555	360	-105	-305				20	Roncin (1969)
N_2O	(B — X)	6.5360	2960	2550	2000				4	Sibleyras (1968)
	C	—	4450	3950	2950					
Benzene	($^1B - {}^1A$)	3.8086	—	-133	-251	-396			4	Robinson (1961)

Energy shifts in glasses are typically small. Atomic spectra are normally blue-shifted from the gas phase, as in the case of Hg (Brewer, 1965a), while molecular spectra are red-shifted. Thus, the most gaslike spectrum of mercury is obtained in xenon, of S_2 in argon (Brewer, 1965b), and of C_3 in neon (Weltner, 1964a,b). It is not uncommon, however, for the spectrum in some solvents to appear blue-shifted while in other solvents it appears red-shifted. In these cases, the most gaslike may be an intermediate solvent. For example, SF_6 gives more gaslike spectra for gold atoms (Brewer, 1970) than any rare gas matrix. As yet, despite the theories that are discussed below, it is not possible to make reliable predictions regarding optical gas phase to solid shifts.

Table 4.1 offers a representative sample of observed gas phase-to-matrix shifts of origins of electronic absorptions. A quick glance is sufficient to note that contradictory values are reported for silver in xenon, copper in xenon, and mercury in all matrices. A closer analysis shows that there is only very little agreement on any species studied by more than one author. There are various reasons for this. One is that many lines are broad and cannot be measured accurately. In such a case, it is tempting for a worker to push his luck, and claim a higher accuracy than can be obtained. In fact, many authors make a practice of reporting lines to within the accuracy with which their equipment could record an infinitely sharp line. Another reason is that matrix absorption depends on temperature concentration and sites. If temperature and concentration are considered, data for mercury, silver, the alkali atoms and many other species fall into line (Brewer, 1965b). Site effects are harder to establish because the formation of sites depends in such a complicated way upon the preparation, age, and history of the samples that it is hardly ever fully studied, and cannot be described in a normal literature report. Therefore, results of other groups are often difficult to reproduce. A further reason is the presence of impurities which, embedded in neighboring sites, distort the lattice and cause almost random shifts.

Study of site effects is only now coming of age, but it is already known that transition energy, lifetime and all other optical properties are strongly affected (Martin, 1969; Harrigan, 1968). Moisya (1968) studied anthracene in glasses, and found that shifts due to different sites in isopentane can be up to 1110 cm^{-1}. The number of sites observed in one sample, and consequently the number of fine structure components, can be very high. In the case of anthracene, it is at least nine. A simpler case, observed for alkali atoms, is described in Chapter 9 (Meyer, 1965).

A relatively simple theory for solvent shifts was proposed by Longuet-Higgins and Pople (1957). It considers only attractive forces due to induced-dipole–induced-dipole interactions. This leads, for moderately weak interactions, to the prediction of a red shift of the order of

$$\Delta E = - 3/8 E r^{-6} n \alpha_v \alpha_u$$

where α_v and α_u are the ground state polarizabilities, E is the transition energy, and each solute is surrounded by n solvent molecules at an internuclear distance r.

The neglect of repulsive interactions, which normally leads to a corrective blue shift, is a serious shortcoming because the latter might be sufficiently large to reduce significantly or even to cancel the shift. Repulsive interactions undoubtedly occur when a large molecule is trapped in a lattice of smaller molecules. Attractive forces alone obviously give an insufficient description of gas phase-to-solid shifts.

B. Solvent Dependence of Shift

While the predictions for gas phase-to-solid shifts of the above model are useless, the theory predicts a significant trend for relative solvent shifts, depending on the polarizability of the solvent. It is indeed seen that observed shifts, with a few notable exceptions, change in a regular manner as polarizability of the host species is changed; an increase causes the observed spectrum to appear at a longer wavelength.

This red shift due to increased polarizability can be followed easily by considering a homologous series of solvents, for example, rare gases. Since in this case polarizability is directly correlated to atomic weight, the observation of shifts is called external heavy atom effect (McGlynn, 1962a). Identical terms are intermolecular and solvent heavy atom effect. Examples of the heavy atom effect are given in Table 4.2. It is almost universally observed. The shift between individual solvents varies from 50 to 300 cm^{-1}. Solutes in heavy atom solvents have almost always lower transition energies than in methane or neon. This trend in Table 4.2 is striking. An exception is charge transfer complexes that display an inversed heavy atom effect. This is because the strength of binding in charge transfer complexes is lower in the ground state than in the more ionic excited state; this is the reverse of bonding in stable normal molecules.

The solvent can affect different electronic transitions to a different degree. Figure 4.2 shows the absorption of azulene in the 280 nm region (Robinson, 1969). The $^1A_1$ and the $^1B_1$ states are farthest apart in argon, and closest in xenon. Different solvents also perturb vibrational modes differently.

Table 4.2

Heavy Atom Effect on Relative Position of Electronic Transition Energy in Rare Gas Matrices[a]

Species	Matrix			Temperature (°K)
	Ne	Kr	Xe	
Cd	—	1200	2695	4
Zn	—	1250	2700	4
Ag $(^2P_{1/2})$	—	50	1170	20
		670	2330	20
$(^2P_{3/2})$	—	235	3500	20
Kr	—	5710	6070	4
Hg	310	495	1265	20
Li	—	140	410	4
Na	—	200	400	4
K	—	220	480	4
Cs	—	230	500	4
Mg	—	130	1340	4
S_2	330	450	570	20
CO	525	410	1070	4
N_2	28	107	210	4
C_3	200	90	830	4
NH_2	—	32	65	4
SO_2	—	30	230	20
Benzene	—	120	260	4
Porphyrin	—	75	200	20
Benzene-I_2	—	150	300	20

	Matrix			
	N_2	SF_6	CH_4	
ZnPc	150	110	30	20
Benzene-I_2	650	−880	—	20
C_3	190	120	—	4
SO_2	65	160	205	20
C_2	100	−270	—	4

[a] For references see Chapter 9.

This is evident in Fig. 4.3, which shows the spectrum of SO_2 emission $T_1 \rightarrow S_0$ in four matrices. Table 4.3 gives data for gas phase-to-matrix shifts of the first quantum of vibrational modes of a few select molecules. As in the case of electronic shifts, the vibrations never shift more than a few percent of the transition energy.

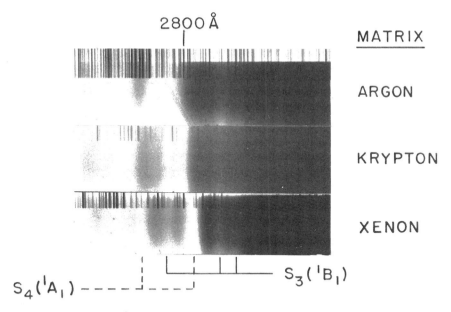

FIG. 4.2. The absorption spectrum of azulene in argon, krypton, and xenon at 4°K. Separation of two nearly coincident states of azulene by solvent perturbation technique. Unpublished data from G. W. Robinson.

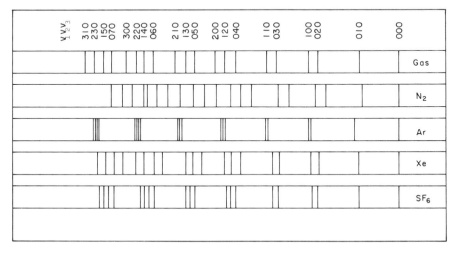

FIG. 4.3. Effects of four matrices on different vibrational modes of SO_2 ground state. After Phillips (1969).

Table 4.3

Gas Phase-to-Matrix Shifts of First Vibrational Mode

Species	Transition	v or ν (cm^{-1})	Matrix				References
			Ar	Kr	Xe	N$_2$	
CO	UV	(2143.3)	+5.3/−5.3	+1.9/−8.0	−1.9/−9.9	—	Charles (1965) Lewis (1964)
LiF	IR	(900)	−65/−60	−70	−77	−122	Linevsky (1961)
S$_2$	UV	(430)	−5	+18	+4	−23	Brewer (1965)
SO$_2$	UV	ν_1 (1125)	−15	−13	−13	−57	Phillips (1969)
		ν_2 (513)	+31	−2	−29	−42	
HN$_3$	IR	ν_1 (3335.6)	−12	−15	−37	−13	Pimentel (1963)
		ν_2 (2140.4)	−2	0	−8	+8	
		ν_3 (1269.0)	−5	+18	−6	+3	
		ν_4 (1152.5)	−6	−4	−7	+15	
HF	IR	P(1) (3920)	−44	−53	−69	—	Bowers (1966)
		R(0) (4001)	−38	−43	−47	—	
		R(1) (4039)	−42	−48	−55	—	
		Q ([3962])	−8	−28	−51	—	
HCl	IR	R(0) 2906.3	−18.2	−33.6	−48.1	—	Keyser (1966)
		R(1) 2926	−30	−39	−54	—	Mann (1966)
		P(1) 2865.1	−11.5	−27.7	−39.6	—	

McCarty and Robinson (1959a) developed an empirical theory for rare gases using estimated intermolecular interaction constants to compute spectral shifts of both polar and nonpolar molecules in substitutional sites in nonpolar lattices. They chose a Lennard-Jones potential of the type

$$V_{(u,v)} = A_{uv}r^{-12} - B_{uv}r^{-6}$$

for pair interactions, and assumed additivity of potentials because the dispersion energies arise largely from second-order perturbations. Since the solvent constants are known from the literature, the spectral shift is then

$$\Delta E = \sum_v [\sqrt{A_v}(\sqrt{A'_u} - \sqrt{A''_u}) \cdot r^{-12} - \sqrt{B_v}(\sqrt{B'_u} - \sqrt{B''_u}) \cdot r^{-6}].$$

The sum is carried out over solvent neighbors for upper state, designated with prime, and lower state (double prime). The second term represents the attractive contribution and corresponds to the Longuet-Higgins and Pople equation given above. One can demonstrate that, therefore, the shift can be approximated by

$$\Delta E = \sum_v (2\sqrt{A_v}\,\Delta_{12}r^{-12} - 3/8\alpha_u\alpha_v E_u r^{-6})$$

where $2\Delta_{12} = \sqrt{A'_u}\sqrt{A''_u}$. Since higher energy valence orbitals are larger than lower energy levels, Δ_{12} is positive. Thus, the first term contributes a blue shift. For face-centered cubic rare gas crystals, the sum over all solute molecules yields

$$\Delta E = 12.13(\sqrt{A_v}\,2\Delta_{12}r^{-12}) - 14.45(3/8\alpha_u\alpha_v E_u r^{-6}).$$

Solvent shifts are not linear with respect to α_v and r^{-6} because of the repulsive interaction. A dipole-induced dipole interaction term has to be added if, on excitation, the permanent dipole of the solute changes. The choice of r is critical, but the lattice parameter for a substitutional site proves experimentally quite satisfactory.

Roncin (1969b) used observed shifts of Xe, Kr, and Hg atoms and the light molecules CO, NO, and N_2O to compute the excited state Lennard-Jones parameters δ' and ε' from

$$V_{uv} = 4\varepsilon[12.13(\sigma/2)^{12} - 14.45(\sigma/2)^6]$$

He used the results from three different matrices to deduce the best-fitting values, assuming that δ' and ε' are independent of the matrix. The computed values fit very nicely the expectation that $\delta' \sim \delta''$ for valence transitions in diatomics, but that δ' is significantly larger for atoms (Table 4.4).

Table 4.4

Excited State of Lennard-Jones Parameters of Xe, Kr, Hg, CO, NO, and N_2O^a

Guest	Ground State	σ_A (nm)	ε_A/k (°K)	Excited State	$\sigma_A{}^*$ (nm)	$\varepsilon_A{}^*/k$ (°K)
CO	$X\,{}^1\Sigma^+$	0.359	110	$A\,{}^1\Pi$	0.375	275
Hg	${}^1S$	0.290	851	${}^1P$	0.425	825
Kr	${}^1S$	0.361	190	${}^3P$	0.465	225
NO	$X\,{}^2\Pi$	0.347	119	$B\,{}^2\Pi$	0.370	175
				$B'\,{}^2\Delta$	0.370	230
				$G\,{}^2\Sigma^-$	0.370	275
N_2O	$\tilde{X}\,{}^1\Sigma^+$	0.388	220	$\tilde{B}$	0.475	115
Xe	${}^1S$	0.406	229	${}^3P$	0.48	210
				${}^1P$	0.50	185

^{a} Data from Roncin (1969b).

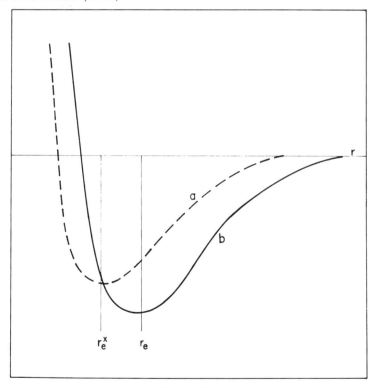

FIG. 4.4. Potential energy curve of ${}^3\Sigma_u^- \leftarrow {}^3\Sigma_g^-$ of S_2; curve a, gas phase; curve b, in xenon at 20°K. From Brabson (1965a).

Since repulsion and attraction in a matrix cage depend on internuclear distance, the guest-host forces on a given state change with vibrational excitation. Figure 4.4 shows the potential curve for S_2 (Brabson, 1965a). As expected, interaction is highest for small internuclear distance. At large vibrational values, repulsion squeezes the potential curve. Figure 4.5 (Brewer, 1965a) shows $\Delta G_{1/2}$ of the same transition as a function of v'. It is noteworthy that a nitrogen matrix distorts the free S_2 potential curve substantially, seemingly reducing anharmonicity.

The above holds only for van der Waals interactions. When stronger interactions occur, solvent shifts can be totally different. For example, large blue shifts are observed for charge transfer complexes of iodine (Voigt, 1968a). Such complexes are formed with hydrogen sulfide, benzene, pyridine, and other solvents. In these cases, the solute is a better electron donor in the ground state than in the excited state. The vibrational spectrum in these systems still exhibits red shifts, i.e., attractive interaction, because of a reduction in the iodine electron density.

C. Noncoincidence of the (0,0) Transition

It is neither necessary, nor expected that the origin of the $v' = 0$ progression in fluorescence of a solid coincides with the origin of the $v'' = 0$ progression

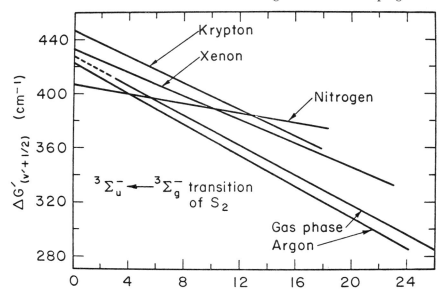

FIG. 4.5. $\omega_e x_e$ of $^3\Sigma_u^- \leftarrow \,^3\Sigma_g^-$ of S_2 as a function of vibrational excitation and solvent. After Brewer (1965b).

in absorption. Figure 4.6 assists in understanding this phenomenon. The guest molecule, unlike the case in the gas phase, is rigidly surrounded by the host cage. Immediately after the absorption process, the guest finds itself in an unstable excited state configuration relative to the surrounding solvent molecules. Under normal circumstances, the guest molecule will have sufficient time to approach its stable equilibrium configuration prior to emission. This configuration and, hence, the level from which emission occurs will be lower in energy. After emission, the molecule is in an unstable ground state configuration with respect to the solvent and again must undergo relaxation to the most stable arrangement. Thus, the (0,0) band in absorption involves slightly more energy than the equivalent transition in emission, and the latter will appear to be red-shifted.

Onsager (1936) developed a relationship for the relative displacement of absorption and emission origin, which correlates ε, the static dielectric constant, the refractive index n, and the dipole moment of the ground state μ'' and the excited state μ', and the Onsager radius a

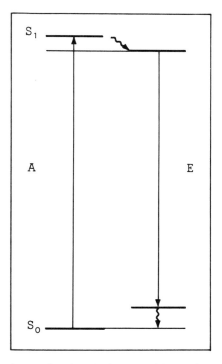

FIG. 4.6. Interaction of ground and excited states with matrices results in shift of (0, 0) of absorption (A) vs. emission (E).

$$\Delta \nu_{0.0} = \nu_{Ab} - \nu_{Em} = \frac{(\mu' - \mu'')^2}{a^3 hc} \left(\frac{2\varepsilon - 2}{2\varepsilon + 1} - \frac{2n^2 - 2}{2n^2 + 1} \right).$$

As a rule, the displacement is small; the N_2 molecule is a case in point: for Ne, Ar, Kr, and Xe matrices, the discrepancies are $- 103$, $- 131$, $- 238$, and $- 342$ cm^{-1}, respectively (Tinti, 1968). Several factors influence the magnitude of the discrepancy; these include the polarizability of the host species, the polarizability of the guest species in both the ground and the excited states, the rigidity of the host, and the relative sizes of the guest and host species.

D. Temperature Dependence of Shifts

Because of the high powers of r, dependence line shifts should be very sensitive to solvent density changes. Decreasing density should result in increasing attractive forces and a red shift. Such shifts have indeed been observed during reversible warm-up experiments with matrices containing Xe, Cu, Au, Na, K, and other atoms (Brewer, 1965b, 1968; B. Meyer, 1965, 1968). Shifts range in value from slightly less than 1 to 6 cm^{-1} per degree Kelvin depending on the atom and the fine structure component involved. Shifts are smaller for larger molecules, but they are not always negligible. Figure 4.7 shows the reversible temperature dependence of three different systems; (a) is a photograph of the spectrum of gold in krypton; (b) is silver in xenon; (c) is a plot of copper absorption peaks in solid krypton; and (d) is a photograph of mercury in nitrogen. In all cases, the line shift is reversible in the temperature range below 40% of the matrix melting point.

Schawlow (1961b, 1964) has explained similar temperature effects in doped ionic crystals, for example, Cr^{3+} in MgO, in terms of density changes. The density, or stress factor, has been qualitatively confirmed also by isothermal compression, which gives similar density effects (Offen, 1964 to present).

Duley (1967b) used observations on cadmium and zinc and known density changes of the rare gas lattices to compute temperature-dependent shifts from a differentiated form of McCarty and Robinson's formulas, yielding

$$d(\Delta E) = (- 12N\Delta_{12} + 6\Delta_6) \, dR/MR$$

where the parameters are the same as above. The values of Δ_{12} and Δ_6 were determined from plots of $M(\Delta E)$ versus N. Computations yield shifts of the order of $- 300 \pm 150$ cm^{-1}, which correspond qualitatively to the observed values of $- 100$ cm^{-1} for the temperature range of 4–40°K in krypton.

FIG. 4.7. Reversible temperature dependence of atomic absorption.

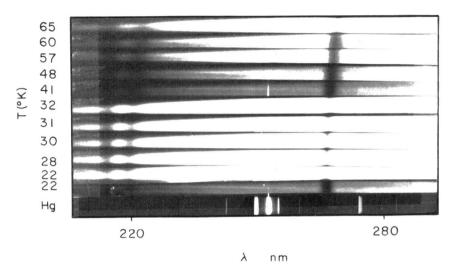

(a) Gold in krypton (Morelle, 1970).

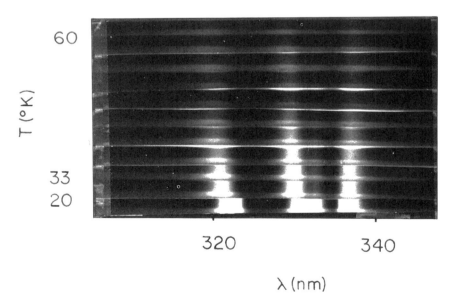

(b) Silver in Xe (after Brewer, 1968).

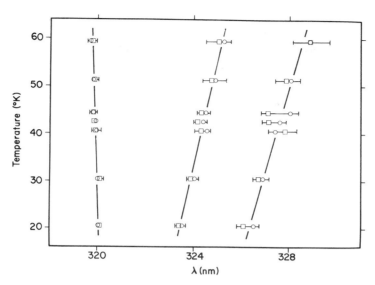

(c) Copper in krypton (Currie, 1970). ○ warm-up; ☐ cool-down.

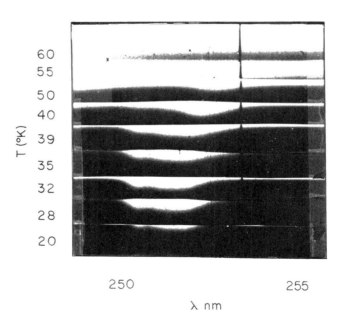

(d) Mercury in nitrogen (Brabson, 1965a).
All photographs were made from unpublished spectra.

Although Duley's treatment of zinc line shifts in krypton and xenon between 4°K and 40°K gives reasonable agreement in this one case, the behavior of spectra is much more complicated than one can deduce from a simple model. Individual fine structure components of some atoms have temperature coefficients for shifts which vary not only in size but also in sign. Furthermore, temperature coefficients are not constant or simple functions of temperature, and sometimes they exhibit changes in regions where the solvent has no phase transitions.

The observation of complicated temperature dependence is less astonishing when one considers that density changes are not the only effect of temperature. An equally important guest-host effect surely must arise from changes in lattice vibration and other thermal motions. No theory has yet dealt with this effect, probably partly because time-dependent effects in mixed solids are not yet well known.

II. LINE WIDTH

The natural line width of a transition of a free molecule is determined by the lifetime; for a typical allowed transition with a lifetime of 10^{-8} sec, the natural line width is about 10^{-4} nm. However, numerous factors contribute to broadening of the observed lines; for example, thermal motion, which causes Doppler broadening, and predissociation. The line width is further affected by environmental fields. Collision, resonance, Stark, and molecular broadening have all been observed and are discussed in detail by Breene (1961).

The observed line width is often larger than the theoretically predicted line width. This can be due to intrinsically unresolved fine structure, such as caused by nuclear spin, isotopes and electron spin, or overlap of rotational fine structure; or it may be due to low resolution of the spectrometer.

In solids, the natural line width is affected by interaction between nonpolar molecules. It results principally from the coupling of the oscillating polarization of the electron shells in the neighborhood of the excited molecule with the transition moment m of the excited molecule. In the dipole approximation, the line width is proportional to the square of the transition moment. In pure solids, lines are further broadened by resonance. In rare gas solids, Brith (1963) observed line widths of several hundred wave numbers. This indicates that coupling of the excited state with the lattice is strong in these crystals. The line width in anthracene is typically 10 cm^{-1}. In contrast, spectra of mixed crystals can be sharper, with line widths of the order of 5 cm^{-1}, because, as McClure recognized in 1954, resonance broadening does not occur in these crystals.

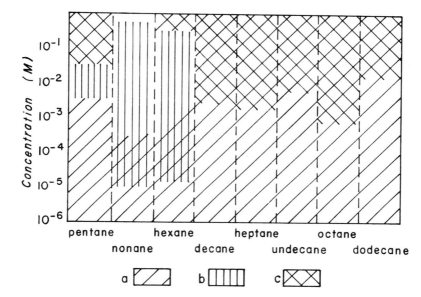

Fɪɢ. 4.8. Conditions for the appearance of a Shpol'skii effect: concentration dependence of line width for various solvent chain lengths. After Nakhimovskaya (1968). a, Broad lines; b, quasi-line spectra; c, aggregate spectra.

In organic glasses aromatic molecules have line widths that depend on solvent structure and temperature. Typical line widths of quasi-line spectra and Shpol'skii spectra are 10 cm^{-1} or wider (Shpol'skii, 1960a–c). The line width in glasses and matrices is not predictable and varies greatly for a given solute, even in a homologous series of solvents. Figure 4.8 shows the range of solvents and concentrations which lead to sharpest lines (Nakhimovskaya, 1968). The author concludes that matching solvent-solute interactions reduce the line width.

Figure 4.9 shows the SO_2 $\tilde{a} \rightarrow X$ emission in SF_6 and krypton. There is no obvious rationale behind the line width, but the spectrum in SF_6 contains more information and is easier to analyze than that in N_2. The spectra in most of the matrices are so broad and blended that, if the SF_6 spectrum were not known, one might be misled to believe that only one active mode is present. In the case of SO_2, the line width is obviously partly due to overlap of vibrational modes, which are differently shifted in different solvents.

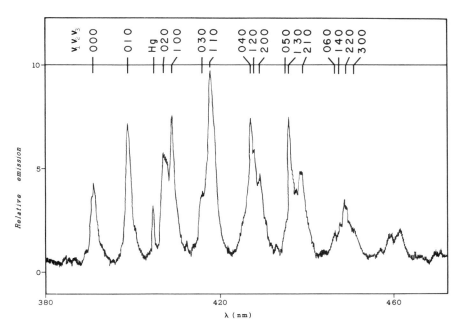

FIG. 4.9 (a) Line width of SO_2 emission in SF_6.

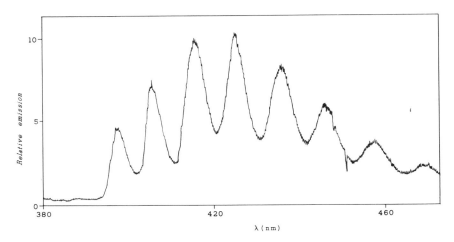

FIG. 4.9 (b) Line width of SO_2 emission in krypton. The krypton bands are so broad that the spectrum appears to consist of a progression of one single mode.

Line widths show a strong dependence on the electronic structure of the solute and on the change in electronic configuration during transition. Large organic molecules, particularly porphyrins and aromatics exhibit the Shpol'skii effect and give sharp line spectra in hydrocarbon glasses with chain lengths comparable to the solute skeleton length.

Many also exhibit sharp line spectra in the light matrices, such as argon, as shown in Fig. 4.10 for zinc-phthalocyanine in argon at 20°K. Heavier solvents yield broader lines. Benzene in rare gases and inert matrices has line widths below a wave number at low temperatures (Voigt, 1969). The line width increases for smaller molecules. Diatomics generally have line widths of 100 cm^{-1} and more. They are often sharpest in xenon and broadest in neon in absorption, but sometimes they exhibit inverse line width trends in emission. Atoms have very large line widths, up to 1000 cm^{-1}. They are commonly sharpest in xenon and broad in argon and neon. The trend of line width between small and large guests indicates that unshielded electrons of atoms and small molecules interact strongly with the host, whereas electrons in large molecules are so well shielded that the transitions are little affected by the environment and give almost pure cold gas spectra.

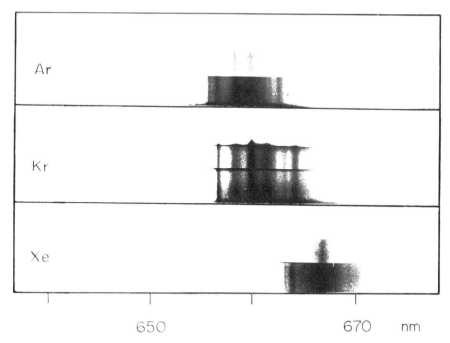

FIG. 4.10. Porphyrin in argon at 20°K (Bajema, 1970).

The strong interaction of atoms and host is confirmed by the fact that the ionization energy is reduced. Also, atomic spectra in matrices show many similarities with collision-induced gas-phase rare gas–alkali diatomics.

In weakly polarizable and weakly interacting solids, such as neon, the observed line width of atoms also is increased, because the small host-guest forces allow relatively large random lattice distortions. Brith and Schnepp (1963) have calculated that atoms are extremely sensitive to lattice shape. Random distortions of the order of 0.001 nm are sufficient to cause a line width of 100 cm^{-1} in the P state of magnesium (Table 4.5). In larger molecules, neon might give the sharpest lines because, in a shielded molecule, guest-host interactions depend on polarizability.

III. FINE STRUCTURE

The optical spectra of low temperature solids almost always show fine structure. For example, in the spectrum of C_3 in argon at 20°K, each transition yields four lines (Weltner, 1964a,b). Similarly, the absorption spectra of metals in rare gas matrices often show three distinct components. Figure 4.11 shows a typical example, mercury in rare gas matrices.

Fine structure can be caused by rotation, crystal field splitting, phonon multiple sites, and impurities.

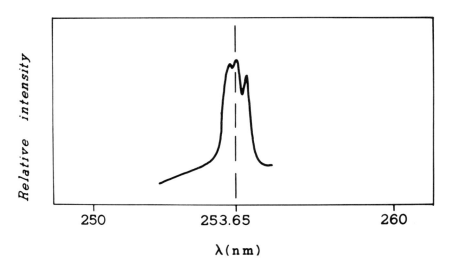

FIG. 4.11. Fine structure of mercury absorption in xenon at 20°K.

Table 4.5

Triplet Splitting of the ^3P State of Magnesium in a Distorted Rare Gas Lattice Site[a]

Distortion	R_1 (nm)	R_2 (nm)	ε Valence (cm^{-1})	ε Dispersion (cm^{-1})
	0.70	0.75	700	-300
	0.75	0.80	400	-190
	0.80	0.85	230	-120
Vacancy	R (nm)		ε Valence (cm^{-1})	ε Dispersion (cm^{-1})
	0.70	—	800	-440
	0.75	—	450	-290
	0.80	—	240	-200

[a] Adapted from Brith and Schnepp (1963).

A. Rotational Fine Structure

The motion of large molecules is severely restricted in solid media. Therefore, rotation is observed only for very light molecules, and when it occurs, the motion is severely changed by coupling with the lattice. There is infrared evidence for rotation of hydrogen halides in rare gas matrices, but the interpretation is complicated by the ever present dimers and aggregates. Better proof exists for rotation of OH and OD in solid neon (Tinti, 1968a). The latter two molecules seem not to rotate in argon (Acquista, 1968a). Evidence for rotation exists also in NH_2 (Robinson, 1959).

B. Environmental Effects

In ion crystals the geometry of the lattice site is often so well defined that spectral fine structure can be used to deduce the character of the electronic states involved in electronic transitions of the guest molecule. In weakly interacting solids this situation is approached only in the case of molecular crystals where the guest occupies well defined and matching substitutional sites.

In matrices and glasses the site character is normally not established. Experimentally observed splitting has been used to deduce the site geometry and character for atoms (Brith, 1963). It is observed that states which are degenerate in the free atom lose their degeneracy in the solid rare gas matrix. From this it can be established that the site symmetry is low. Since the pure

rare gases have fine structure, the low symmetry must be due to the fact
that the solute only rarely fits smoothly into a substitutional site. Thus,
lattice distortion will result in its environment. This is easily possible because
the rare gas lattice energy is very small, 2 kcal/mole for argon. Rare gas
lattice structure and lattice energies are further discussed in Chapter 8. It
is expected that guest-host interactions are stronger and that the rare gas
arranges itself around the guest, thereby distorting the lattice beyond the
immediate guest environment. In case of severe distortions, neighboring
lattice sites may remain unoccupied.

Brith and Schnepp (1963) considered covalent and dispersion forces
and developed a model to explain the spectra of Mn and Mg based on the
presence of unoccupied neighboring sites in the rare gas lattice. The lattice
distortions create asymmetric fields in the environment of the solute atom.
Consequently, atom orbital degeneracies are removed in a "pseudo"-Stark
type splitting. Using this model, Brith and Schnepp calculated the individual
values and dispersion shifts for the P state of magnesium, where a splitting
of 300 cm^{-1} is observed, on the basis of lattice distortion and vacancy, with
the result shown in Table 4.5. The results are of order of magnitude accuracy
and sufficient to establish that distortions of 0.01 to 0.02 nm are sufficient
to account for the observed effect. The same model also indicates that
random lattice distortions of 0.001 nm are sufficient to account for the observed
line width of 40–70 cm^{-1}. All subsequent atoms studied show spectral
behavior in agreement with this model. Kupferman and Pipkin (1968) used
optical and ESR techniques and computed site splittings for rubidium in
argon.

In mixed crystals, the symmetry of the site is usually known, and the
energy levels of the crystal can be computed. When the lattice unit cell
contains translationally nonequivalent molecules, Davydov splitting results
for all excited states, including nondegenerate states. The transition energy
of the crystal can then be expressed as the sum

$$\Delta E_{\text{cryst}} = \Delta E_{\text{free mol.}} + D + \Sigma I$$

where I is the exchange interaction (Wolf, 1959). In the dipole approximation,
the exchange interaction can be expressed through the transition moment
(m) of excited and ground state, m_m and m_n:

$$I_{mn} = m_m \cdot m_n / d^3$$

where d is the distance between neighboring nuclei. D_{mn} is the exciton
coulomb sum, computed from upper and lower state. The lower state interac-

tion is taken to be van der Waals forces, while the upper state interaction is proportionate to m^{12} (Wolf, 1959).

The number and symmetry of crystalline states can be determined for any given molecular crystal with known structure, by combining all vectors representing the direction and size of the transition moment for each molecule in the unit cell. Both the Davydov splitting and the spectral shift are proportional to the square of the transition moment. Splitting occurs when a unit cell contains more than one molecule, and when the projection of their transition moments does not vanish.

C. Phonon Side Bands

In highly ordered lattices, phonon interaction can lead to fine structure. The strong lines are paralleled by weaker temperature-dependent phonon side bands. The latter are often very broad. An example for this is shown in Fig. 3.2, which shows the spectrum of benzene in argon at 4°K, and in Fig. 6.3, which shows benzene in argon at 20°K and in nitrogen at 4°K.

D. Multiple Sites

Multiple sites arise when different molecules of a given host assume different environmental arrangements in a sample. This can be due to different positions or orientations in the solvent cage, or variations in the host structure in the guest environment, such as site symmetry, vacancies, or surface boundaries. An example is naphthalene in durene. Naphthalene can occupy either of two nonequivalent positions in the unit cell of the durene crystal (Jen, 1967). The sites differ in energy and orientation and yield different polarization, transition energies, and triplet decay time. An example for multiple sites due to solvent structure occurs in cyclohexane, where under certain conditions cubic and tetragonal sites can coexist (Spangler, 1968; Martin, 1969; see also Table 5.7).

A large number of ill-defined multiple sites occurs in almost all vapor-deposited matrices. At very slow deposition rates on 4°K surfaces, the number of different sites is so large that very broad spectra result (Meyer, 1965). In addition, matrices often contain vacancies and gross lattice defects with host molecules occupying distorted sites on the surface of the bulk crystal, bordering dislocations, and other faults. Such defects will be described in Chapter 6.

Normal matrix deposition procedure constitutes a complex compromise, established by trial and error and handed down from teacher to student. It optimizes the intrinsically contradictory demands for uniformly annealed solids with minimum diffusion. Amazingly enough, most guests settle in a few select matrix sites which lead to characteristic spectra. If the guest is an atom or free radical, multiple site effects cannot easily be annealed, for many because, as discussed in Chapter 6, small guest molecules diffuse easily.

E. Impurities

If a sample is chemically impure, fine structure can be complex because of guest-impurity interactions and impurity-induced lattice distortions. In the case of broad lines, or distorted line shape, and if the spectra are not reproducible, impurities must be suspected.

Inadvertently present impurities and impurities due to guest-guest interaction are common in rare gas matrices. Bands due to dimers and higher aggregates can be recognized by their concentration dependence. Their intensity diminishes quickly with dilution, and at guest-to-host mole ratios below 10^{-7} impurity bands disappear unless guest diffusion is extremely efficient.

However, identification of impurities by increasing M/R ratios can yield surprises. In the case of lithium atoms in krypton, for example, high M/R was observed to yield relatively less pure lithium spectrum, and more impurity. As it turned out, this was caused by 0.05% water in krypton. At an M/R of 200 : 1, much unreacted lithium remained. At an M/R of 10^5 : 1, each lithium had 50 water molecules to react with (Meyer, 1965).

In mixed crystals fine structure can be caused by impurities with similar physical properties and homologous chromophores. An example for this is thionaphthalene in naphthalene. The impurity has an $S_1 \leftarrow S_0$ transition which is only 27 cm^{-1} below that of naphthalene.

The five different site effects mentioned above can occur simultaneously. It is not always possible nor easy to establish which effect is present in a given system. Annealing, change of solvent, and measurement of optical characteristics are useful testing methods. Another technique involves observation of excitation spectra. If a different wavelength excites different emissions, impurities may be present.

Shpol'skii, in a series of studies beginning in 1951, observed the fine structure in the spectra of aromatics in linear hydrocarbon glasses. He developed detailed theories for his data based on the observation that the lines were sharpest when solute and solvent skeletons match in length. Since similar line structure has been shown to result in rare gas and small inert matrices, Shpol'skii's explanations seem doubtful. It is not even clear whether in some cases the effect is due to an intramolecular effect of the guest or due to the host.

IV. INTENSITY OF TRANSITIONS

The environment disturbs the electron configuration of the free molecule in several ways. We have seen that this leads to shifts of transitions, increased line width, and splitting of energy levels. The perturbation becomes apparent also in intensity change. We discuss here only two special cases, where the effect is observed in absorption and is large.

A. Rydberg Transitions

Rydberg series of small molecules are not observed. A typical case is NO. The reason for the suppression of the Rydberg transition is probably that the orbital size of the upper state is larger by a factor of about three. The host lattice is expected to resist such changes in guest size, as it resists changes in internuclear distance; and interaction during the transition causes very large broadening of the lines. This makes it appear very weak, and difficult to observe. The absence of Rydberg state in NO has a useful application. In the gas phase, the spectrum of this molecule is very complicated, because low lying Rydberg states overlap and perturb valence states. Since, in a matrix transitions to Rydberg states are absent, only unperturbed vibrational progressions of transitions between valence states remain (Roncin, 1967a, 1968).

It has been reported that the Rydberg states of aromatic molecules can be observed (Katz, 1969), but more work is needed to confirm the identity of the observed states.

B. Spin Forbidden Transitions; the Heavy Atom Effect

In the case of Russell-Saunders coupling, transitions between states with different spin are forbidden. In reality, pure Russell-Saunders coupling is rare, because spin angular momentum and orbital angular momentum interact noticeably, even in first row atoms. Therefore, pure spin states are rare. Transitions between mixed spin states are no longer strictly forbidden. The transition probability depends on spin-orbit coupling, which can become appreciable. It increases with the weight of nuclei. While triplet-singlet transitions are weak in elements of the first periodic row, in mercury, with an atomic weight of 196, the line $^3P_1 \rightarrow {}^1S_0$ at 253.652 nm is so strong that it serves as a common photolysis source.

Spin forbidden transitions occur also in diatomics, for example in $^3\Pi_{0,1} \leftarrow {}^1\Sigma_0$ of gallium and indium halides (Wehrli, 1949). $\Delta S \neq 0$ has also been observed in light gaseous diatomics; for example, in the atmospheric oxygen bands $^1\Sigma_g - X\,{}^3\Sigma_g^-$, which were analyzed by Mecke and Schlapp

(Kovac, 1969), $^3\Pi - X\,^1\Sigma$ transitions in CO observed by Hopfield and Bireg (1927) and Gerö, Herzberg, and Schmidt (Herzberg, 1961). Theories for these transitions are discussed by Kovac (1969, page 179). However, theories are still incomplete, and calculated and observed intensities do not match.

An example for spin forbidden transitions in large molecules is provided by the lifetimes of phosphorescence $T_1 \rightarrow S_0$ of substituted naphthalenes in EPA at 77°K, as reported by McClure (1949) and Ermolaev (1959a,b). The decay time decreases as the oscillator strength increases, in the following manner: naphthalene, 2.6 sec; α-F-naphthalene, 1.5 sec; α-Cl-naphthalene, 0.3 sec; α-Br-naphthalene, 0.02 sec; and α-I-naphthalene, 0.003 sec.

Spin-orbit coupling enhanced by a heavy nucleus within the species is called the *intramolecular* or *internal heavy atom effect.*

Kasha (1952) and McGlynn (1962a,b, 1963, 1964b) discovered that solvent-heavy atom substitution can have the same effect. They observed the induced $T_1 \leftarrow S_0$ absorption of α-Cl-naphthalene in ethyl iodide and found that a mixture of the two colorless liquids is yellow. This effect is also called *external* or *intermolecular heavy atom effect.* It is probably due to weak charge-transfer between solvent and solute, or to $T_X \leftarrow S_0$ intensity borrowed from the heavy-atom perturber. Figure 4.12 shows the enhancement of the spin forbidden transition for the same molecule in four solvents from CCl_4 to C_2H_5I. The effect is equally strong for molecules in rare gas matrices (Wright, 1960). It can be used to observe, in thin solid film solutions, forbidden transitions that cannot be easily studied in the gas phase. The $T_1 \leftarrow S_0$ of SO_2 serves as an example in point (Meyer, 1968). In the gas phase, 60 atmosphere-meters are needed to detect this system, while in $Xe-SO_2$ mixtures a fraction of a millimole yields sufficient absorption for photographic recording and for direct excitation of the $T_1 \rightarrow S_0$ emission.

Oxygen and some paramagnetic ions also affect the oscillator strength, but they also induce nonradiative quenching (Parmenter, 1969). Both are discussed in Chapter 5.

The effect of heavy atoms on emission in solids is quite complicated because it is always accompanied by various competing deactivation processes. Heavy atoms always result in a shortened $T_1 \rightarrow S_0$ lifetime, and, if present, weakened fluorescence; but the phosphorescence intensity is not reliably stronger. Also, the triplet lifetime is not always a reliable monitor for heavy atoms. This is also the subject of Chapter 5.

It is interesting to compare internal and external heavy atom effects and to determine whether both are of the same character. A comparison of the relative importance of internal and external heavy atom effects is available for the 1-halonaphthalenes (McGlynn, 1962a,b). In ethyl iodide, optical density of the absorption $T_1 \leftarrow S_0$ increases much more for 1-iodonaphthalene than 1-bromonaphthalene. The relative increase for a given *external* heavy atom perturber increases with increasing *internal* heavy atom content. That is, the external heavy atom effect is greatest for those molecules that already possess significant spin-orbit coupling (McGlynn, 1969).

The detailed nature of the interaction of heavy atom host is not yet known. No theoretical treatment is available. It has been treated as an exchange enhancement (Hoijtink, 1960; Robinson, 1967a), as a charge transfer (McGlynn, 1958), and in some cases it might be related to hydrogen

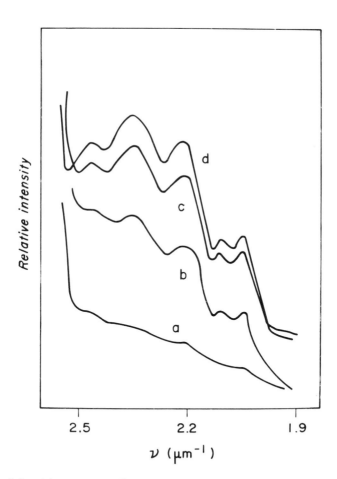

FIG. 4.12. Solvent heavy atom effect on chloronaphthalene in four solvents: *a*, CCl_4; *b*, $C_2H_4Br_2$; *c*, C_2H_5I (1 : 2); *d*, C_2H_5I (1 : 4). After McGlynn (1969).

bonding. For aromatic molecules in solution, the presence of charge transfer character has been established for several systems by McGlynn (1969). The experimental evidence is based on four facts: First, the highest relative absorptivity of a solution is obtained when the components have $1:1$ stoichiometry; second, the absorption strength decreases with increasing temperature, with a temperature coefficient representative of charge-transfer bond strength; third, increasing electron donor properties of the aromatic and electron acceptor ability of the solvent enhance the $T_1 \leftarrow S_0$ absorption; and fourth, infrared spectra are consistent with charge-transfer.

Recommended Reading

Breene, R. G., Jr., *The Shift and Shape of Spectral Lines*, Pergamon, New York, 1961.
Robinson, G. W., Advan. Chem. Ser. **36**, 10 (1962b). "Production of Free Radicals and Their Physical Properties in the Liquid and Solid State."
Schnepp, O., *4th International Symposium on Free Radical Stabilization*, Washington, D.C. (1969e). "Interactions Between Trapped Species and the Matrix."

CHAPTER 5

Excitation Transfer and Decay

This chapter deals with processes that lead to the depopulation of electronically and vibrationally excited molecules. In small, free molecules excitation can be dissipated only by spontaneous radiative emission. Therefore, the observed spectrum is due to resonance fluorescence; i.e., the emitting state is identical with the terminal state of absorption. In solids additional processes occur because a large number of different radiative and radiationless deactivation channels come into action and compete with each other at rates that depend on many parameters. We begin this chapter by reviewing the various transfer and decay mechanisms observed in weakly interacting solids. Throughout this chapter, only physical processes are considered; photochemical reactions are covered in Chapter 6, Section II.

I. PATHS OF EXCITATION TRANSFER AND DECAY

Figure 5.1 shows a schematic representation of some important paths. The absorption shown on the left side of the figure represents any process of absorption of energy from visible, UV, or vacuum UV light; or x-ray, electron, or ion bombardment; or through the recombination of ions or chemical fragments, which leads to a molecule in an excited state. If the excited molecule is a host, the first deactivation process is vibrational relaxation $v'_i = n$ to $v'_i = 0$ of the corresponding electronic state. Then electronic quenching to lower excited states with equal spin, *internal conversion*, (IC), takes place. Conversion from S_1 to S_0, is slower. Therefore, excitation quenching yields predominantly S_1. If S_1 belongs to the host, the excitation can migrate through the host exciton bands, which are formed through coupling between like host molecules. From there, the energy will then be dissipated by host fluorescence, internal conversion, or transfer to any energetically equal or lower lying state of a guest, where vibrational relaxation will trap and localize the excitation. When the transfer is followed by emission between spin allowed states, the process is called *sensitized fluorescence*. In mixed crystals, where the solute and solvent energy levels are close, the energy trap can thermally repopulate the solvent exciton band, provided kT is comparable to the energy gap. If the energy gap is large, the singlet state can depopulate via internal conversion to S_0. The efficiency of this process is normally low and temperature dependent because the Franck-Condon overlap is comparatively small since the $S_1 - S_0$ gap is a high multiple of the vibrational mode of the solute molecule.

The radiative process, *fluorescence*, and the nonradiative *internal conversion* compete with *intersystem crossing* (ISC), $S_1 \leadsto T_1$, to depopulate the S_1 level. The ratio of fluorescence to ISC depends on environment, temperature, and solute intramolecular characteristics. Heavy atoms in and around the solute and small $S_1 - T_1$ gaps enhance ISC. ISC leads to population of vibrationally excited T_1 which is vibrationally quenched to $v' = 0$. Emission from T_1 to S_0 is spin forbidden. It is called *phosphorescence*. Phosphorescence has to compete with radiationless quenching, $T_1 \leadsto S_0$, which again involves ISC and vibrational quenching. If T_1 is close to S_1, thermal repopulation of S_1 from T_1 can become noticeable above 77°K. This results in *delayed thermal fluorescence*. At high solute concentrations and upon direct excitation of T_1 with intense light sources, an additional form of *delayed fluorescence*, due to *triplet-triplet annihilation*, is observed. The latter is caused by combination of two excited triplet states forming an excited singlet

$$T_1 + T_1 \rightarrow S_1 + S_0$$

The excited singlet then decays as above. This effect is concentration dependent. If the $S_1 - T_1$ gap is comparable to $T_1 - S_0$, the reverse process can occur. Evidence for *singlet exciton fission* has been observed in tetracene by Merrifield (1969). This process may occur also in chlorophyll and other biologically important molecules. However, not enough is yet known about the detailed mechanism which proceeds on the overall path

$$S_1 + S_0 \rightarrow T_1 + T_1$$

Each triplet consists of three sublevels that can be distinguished by spin polarization. The sublevel splitting, in organic molecules in the absence of an external field, is typically a few wave numbers. This splitting is smaller than kT at normal observation temperatures. Energy conversion between these sublevels takes place as a result of enhancement by *spin-lattice coupling* (SLC). Therefore, all sublevels are in equilibrium, and emission occurs from all levels. Accordingly, the triplet decay rate consists of several components. At very low temperatures SLC and kT imbalance can change the emission mechanism substantially. At temperatures where the splitting is greater than kT, the population of each sublevel will no longer be in equilibrium, but will depend on the T_1 population mechanism and the rate of sublevel relaxation. This effect was discovered by van der Waals (M. S. De Groot, 1967b) and has recently been observed for a variety of systems. The effect is complicated by the fact that the T_1 population mechanism is different for individual sublevels because each may mix with different S-states.

In the following part of this chapter we will discuss intramolecular radiationless processes, then intermolecular transfer of energy, and, finally, radiative processes.

II. INTRAMOLECULAR RADIATIONLESS PROCESSES

A. Observations

This section deals with nonradiative transfer and decay of excitation within a molecule. The existence of such transfer and decay is based on the fact that the known radiative processes are insufficient to account for dissipation of all absorbed energy. Phosphorescence, shown in Fig. 4.1, is an example of apparent energy loss because it is red-shifted, i.e., lower in energy than the excited state. Other examples of energy imbalance are the inequivalence of absorbing and emitting oscillator strength of fluorescence and phosphorescence in solids, and the fact that observed lifetimes are shorter than predicted from radiative decay. In all these cases it must be assumed that, along the way, the lacking energy is converted into some other form, presumably heat or perhaps far infrared radiation.

The mechanism of intramolecular excitation dissipation can be represented by a combination of two processes, vibrational quenching and energy "crossing." In the first, vibrational excitation of an electronic state is converted into lattice heat; in the second, excitation is retained but transfers from one electronic state, usually a vibrationally relaxed state, to a vibrationally excited, lower-lying electronic state. In combination, the two processes can form a cascade through which energy can drain, until the excited molecule is relaxed to the ground state.

1. Vibrational Quenching

The emission of molecules in a solid originates normally from the lowest vibrational state, $v'_i = 0$, of the emitting states. This proves that vibrational quenching is efficient. As a result, the spectral distribution of emission is normally independent of excitation frequency, throughout the absorbing

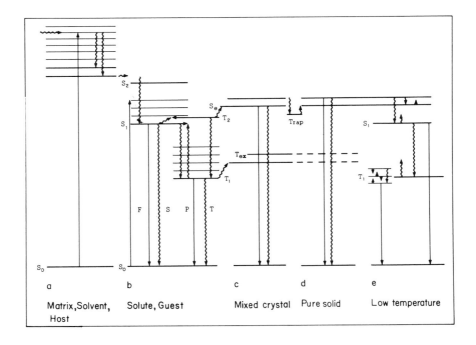

FIG. 5.1. Paths of excitation transfer

(a) In a matrix, vibrational quenching and internal conversion to the solvent state S_1 is quick. Energy from a center excited with x-rays, with α or β irradiation, or through light absorption is transferred to the S_1 exciton band in which it migrates through the crystal until spontaneous fluorescence occurs, until it is quenched, or withdrawn into a trap. Since matrices and glasses are chosen so that their S_1 state lies well above the solute S_1, i.e., so that the solvent is transparent in the solute absorption region, at least a fraction of the solvent excitation is trapped by the solute.

(b) When excitation reaches the solute, various intramolecular processes can set in: again, internal conversion and vibrational quenching are quick. From S_1 ($v_i' = 0$)

excitation can decay by fluorescence F, or by radiationless internal conversion S to S_0. It is customary to indicate the excitation source of fluorescence: prompt fluorescence results from absorption of light by the solute; sensitized fluorescence is caused by energy trapped from the solvent. Fluorescence corresponds to fully allowed emission $S_1 - S_0$ with a radiative lifetime of the order of 10^{-8} sec. The observed decay times are shorter because of radiationless internal conversion $S_1 - S_0$ and intersystem crossing $S_1 - T_1$. Long-lasting fluorescence is caused by slow population of S_1, as in the case of recombination fluorescence which results from chemical reactions or recombination of ions, or thermal delayed fluorescence or delayed fluorescence which result from processes acting on T_1.

In solution, a substantial fraction of S_1 excitation crosses into T_1, which is quickly vibrationally quenched. S_1 can also transfer energy to another solute by Förster type excitons, or thermal repopulation of the solvent exciton band. It is conceivable that thermally excited S_1 can also cross into T_2, which in turn would convert to T_1. T_1 can emit spontaneous phosphorescence P, or decay without radiation to S_0. Alternatively, T_1 can produce Förster excitons, or thermally return into S_1. At higher concentration, two T_1 can annihilate, forming an S_1 and an S_0.

(c) In mixed crystals, host and guest energy levels are close. At moderately low temperatures thermal excitation is sufficient to suppress irreversible trapping by the guest. Therefore, guest and host emission compete. If kT is smaller than the guest-host energy gap, excitation transfer in mixed crystals is analogous to that in matrices.

(d) In pure solids, vibrational quenching and internal conversion are quick, as in all other cases, but since no solute is present, the lowest exciton band decays directly, via fluorescence or radiationless quenching. Lattice distortions can act as traps. In pure solids, intersystem crossing to T_1 is not proved to occur, because phosphorescence is extremely rare and is reported only for one or two materials.

(e) Solute-solute interactions can cause various optical effects: Such effects are strongest in liquid solutions where solute diffusion enhances the effect, or in solid solutions at very low temperature when radiationless processes are too slow to compete. High concentrations of T_1, produced by direct excitation of T_1, can yield delayed fluorescence via triplet-triplet annihilation. If the T_1 energy is at or below one-half that of S_1, the reverse process, i.e., fission of S_1 yielding phosphorescence from two T_1, can occur. Since this book deals with systems in which solute diffusion is negligible, energy cannot migrate with molecules, and processes involving solute-solute collisions cannot occur. However, if solute concentrations are high, solute dimers and aggregates are present. Emission from such excimers and excited aggregates is similar to that of the monomeric solute molecules. It complicates the interpretation of optical properties in the same way as impurities with homologous chromophores, by leading to overlapping fine structure and seemingly nonexponential lifetime values due to simultaneous decay from different species.

At very low temperature, lattice distortions and different lattice sites of solutes cause discontinuities in the temperature dependence of properties. At the same time, population between triplet sublevels can become unbalanced. This latter effect can be directly observed by ESR observations. It is partly caused by a slowdown of spin-lattice relaxation, and it results in changes in the triplet decay time, which becomes strongly dependent on magnetic fields.

region. The intensity of emission depends on the Franck-Condon curve, and the absorption coefficient of the absorbing state. Figure 5.2 shows this for the case of SnS. Each tracing represents excitation via a different vibrational state of the absorbing molecule.

Vibrational relaxation is assumed to occur within 10^{-14} sec. This is quick, compared to a radiative transition, which, if allowed, takes about 10^{-8} sec. However, several cases have been observed where vibrations relax much more slowly. In light molecules it can be so slow that electronic emission from excited vibrational states becomes possible. Table 5.1 lists eight diatomics for which data in low temperature matrices are available. All are relatively light molecules with large vibrational spacing and low energy state density. Vibrationally excited emission occurs for both allowed and forbidden transitions. A strong solvent effect is apparent: of all solvents neon seems to be the best vibrational quencher. In contrast, xenon exhibits

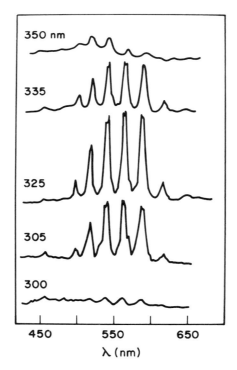

FIG. 5.2. Phosphorescence spectrum of SnS in the rare gas matrix as a function of excitation frequency.

more vibrationally excited emission, and from higher levels, than the lighter solvents. At first glance, this might indicate an inverse heavy atom effect on vibrational quenching, but when one considers the electronic decay times which decrease from neon to xenon, it is obvious that the different emission from excited vibrational levels is due to the heavy atom effect on electronic oscillator strength.

2. Internal Conversion (IC)

Electronic relaxation between states with equal spin is called internal conversion. Internal conversion between excited states is efficient. With the exception of N_2 in neon, azulene, and SeO_2, all known molecules, regardless of excitation, emit only from the lowest excited states of a given multiplicity, namely, the first singlet and triplet, or the first doublet and quartet state. The IC process can be written:

$$S_i \rightsquigarrow S_{i-1} \rightsquigarrow S_1$$

It is always followed by very quick vibrational quenching of S_1. The crossing is facilitated by the Franck-Condon overlap between the states. Since higher excited states are close lying, their overlap is large. $S_1 \rightsquigarrow S_0$ is comparatively slow because the two states are far apart. The comparative rates of IC and fluorescence are

$$K(S_i \rightsquigarrow S_1) > K(\text{fluorescence}) \sim K(S_1 \rightsquigarrow S_0)$$

No one has observed whether for excited triplet states direct IC $T_i \rightsquigarrow T_1$ is important or whether $T_i \rightsquigarrow S_1$ intersystem crossing prevails. We will show in the section on intersystem crossing that, at least between the lower-lying states S_1, T_1, and S_0 the energy separation is a more important factor than the spin allowedness. This means that symmetry rules and the Franck-Condon factor give the appropriate deactivation path, and that Kronig's $\Delta S = 0$ is less important. There is no reason to assume that the same does not hold for excited states. Therefore, it is doubtful that $T_i \rightsquigarrow T_1$ is important, and $S_i \rightsquigarrow S_1$ is probably not a pure IC process but results from ISC with a contribution from IC:

$$S_i \rightsquigarrow T_x \rightsquigarrow S_{i-1} \rightsquigarrow T_{x-1} \rightsquigarrow S_{i-2} \rightsquigarrow T_{x-2} \rightsquigarrow S_1$$

For theoretical reasons, one would believe that internal conversion should be quicker than intersystem crossing. There is so far no proof for this. However, it is generally observed that

$$K(S_iT_i \rightsquigarrow S_1) \gg K(S_1 \rightsquigarrow T_1) > K(S_1 \rightsquigarrow S_0) \sim K(T_1 \rightsquigarrow S_0)$$

i.e., the state T_1 is preferentially populated.

Table 5.1

Trapped Diatomics for Which Emission from an Excited Vibrational State Has Been Observed[a]

Diatomic	Transition	Matrix	Approximate Radiative Lifetime (sec)	v' observed	References
C_2	$A\,^3\Pi_g \rightarrow X'\,^3\Pi_u$	Ar, Kr, Xe	10^{-6}	0,1	McCarty (1959a), Barger (1964)
CH	$C\,^2\Sigma^+ \rightarrow X\,^2\Pi$	Ar		0	Keyser (1965)
	$B\,^2\Sigma^- \rightarrow X\,^2\Pi$	Ar	10^{-6}	0,1	Keyser (1965), Bennet (1964)
	$A\,^2\Delta \rightarrow X\,^2\Pi$	Ar	5×10^{-7}	0	Keyser (1965), Bennet (1964)
N_2	$A\,^3\Sigma_u^+ \rightarrow X\,^1\Sigma_g^+$	Ne	5.4	0	Tinti (1968b)
		Ar, Kr, Xe	0.5	0–6	
	$C\,^3\Pi_u \rightarrow B\,^3\Pi_g$	Ne	10^{-8}	0,1,2	Tinti (1968b)
NO	$a\,^4\Pi \rightarrow X\,^2\Pi$	Ar, Kr	0.1	0	Frosch (1964)
	$B\,^2\Pi \rightarrow X\,^2\Pi$	Ar, Kr	10^{-6}	0	Frosch (1964)
O_2	$A\,^3\Sigma_g^+ \rightarrow X\,^3\Sigma_g^-$	Ar, Kr	10^{-3}	0,1	Schoen (1960b)
		Xe	10		
	$b\,^1\Sigma_u^+ \rightarrow X\,^3\Sigma_g^-$	Ne	10^{-6}	0,1	Schoen (1960b)
OH	$A\,^2\Sigma^+ \rightarrow X\,^2\Pi$	Ne		0,1,2	Tinti (1968a)
OD	$A\,^2\Sigma^+ \rightarrow X\,^2\Pi$	Ne		0–4	Tinti (1968a)
S_2	$B\,^3\Sigma_u^- \rightarrow X\,^3\Sigma_g^-$	Ne, Ar, Kr		0	Brewer (1965b)
		Xe	10^{-6}	0,1	

[a] Data from Meyer (1968).

3. Intersystem Crossing (ISC)

Intersystem crossing is defined as a radiationless transition between spin forbidden states. ISC induces phosphorescence by stealing energy from higher excited states, and it weakens phosphorescence through draining of the triplet to S_0.

If the lifetime of phosphorescence $T_1 \rightarrow S_0$ is used to compute the oscillator strength of the transition, a value obtains which is larger than that computed from absorption coefficient; i.e., emission is apparently more allowed than absorption. This discrepancy is due to radiationless decay $T_1 \leadsto S_0$. This decay weakens and shortens phosphorescence. The observed decay rate is the sum of radiation decay K_P and radiationless ISC, K_{T_1}:
K observed $= K_P + K_{T_1}$.

Radiationless intersystem crossing is, however, not restricted to $T_1 \leadsto S_0$. As a matter of fact, the transition $S_1 \leadsto T_1$ influences the spectral properties of molecules in low temperature solids much more. It causes drainage of energy from the singlet faucet into T_1 and leads to the appearance of phosphorescence in molecules which normally fluoresce. This is shown in Fig. 5.3. The size of the effect, the relative strength of phosphorescence to fluorescence, depends on many factors which are described in Section IV.

The fact that phosphorescence is observed when a singlet state is excited proves that $S_1 \leadsto T_1$ is efficient enough to compete with fluorescence and internal conversion $S_1 \leadsto S_0$. This is remarkable because ISC is a spin forbidden process. The observation of phosphorescence also proves the inequality $S_1 \leadsto T_1$ and $T_1 \leadsto S_0$, for if $T_1 \leadsto T_0$ had a rate of 10^8 sec^{-1}, similar to $S_1 \leadsto T_1$, $T_1 \rightarrow S_0$ emission would not be observed.

Normally, the $T_1 \leadsto S_0$ nonradiative process is assumed to be 10^6 to 10^9 times slower than the $S_1 \leadsto T_1$ process. This means a rate constant for the overall process of 10^3 to 10^{-2} sec^{-1}. The fact that $S_1 \leadsto T_1$ is larger than $T_1 \leadsto S_0$, and competitive with $S_1 \leadsto S_0$, is at least in part due to the Franck-Condon factor for the three transitions. It is far larger for $S_1 \leadsto T_1$ than for the others, because the energy gap between S_1 and T_1 is small. A detailed discussion of these processes is given by McGlynn (1969) and Becker (1969). Theories for ISC are discussed in Section II, B.

It is now known that ISC is affected by density changes (Offen, 1964 to present) and temperature (Meyer, 1968). The heavy atom effect on ISC

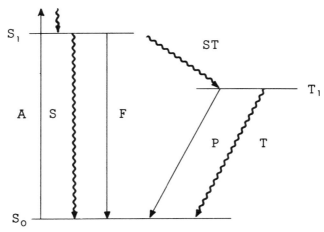

FIG. 5.3. Radiative and radiationless processes between low-lying states. A, Absorption; S, internal conversion $S_1 \rightsquigarrow S_0$; F, fluorescence; ST, $S_1 \rightsquigarrow T_1$ intersystem crossing; P, phosphorescence; T, $T_1 \rightsquigarrow S_0$ intersystem crossing; $v_i' \rightsquigarrow v_0'$, vibrational relaxation.

Table 5.2

Phosphorescence Decay Times and Intensities for SO_2 in Various Matrices[a]

Solvent	Lifetime (msec $\pm$ 1)	Intensity (% relative to Xe)
Xe	5.2	100
Kr	8.4	60
Ar	9.0	40
Ne	17.5[b]	15
CH_4	10.0	30
CD_4	9.6[b]	30
SF_6	11.0	100
O_2	0.5	0.5
Pure SO_2	8.5	1

[a] Data from Meyer (1968).

[b] Measured at 4.2°K.

is not yet fully understood, but it is generally believed to be comparable to that of radiative transitions. Oxygen and paramagnetic impurities enhance ISC drastically. This is due to enhancement of spin flipping by exchange of spin, or magnetic perturbation. This effect is discussed in the next section.

4. Oxygen Effect, Paramagnetic Effects on Spin-Orbit Coupling

A special type of external perturbation on $T-S$ transitions is caused by oxygen, nitric oxide, and paramagnetic metal ions. Evans (1956) was the first to report that $T_1 \leftarrow S_0$ absorption strength increases when oxygen is dissolved in a solvent. The oxygen effect is stronger than the heavy atom effect. It is now believed that most phosphorescent lifetimes and quantum yields in frozen solutions are in error (Lower, 1966) because of the presence of traces of oxygen. The efficiency of $T_1 - S_0$ enhancement by O_2 is evident in Table 5.2, in which the decay time of SO_2 phosphorescence is given for a variety of matrices. The striking difference between the heavy atom effect and the paramagnetic solvent effect is that oxygen and other paramagnetic species simultaneously enhance radiationless transitions. Emission of oxygen-induced transitions is, therefore, much weaker than expected from absorption. In the case of SO_2, mentioned above, oxygen matrices exhibit much weaker emission than xenon; in fact, oxygen matrices emit weaker than neon or even pure solid SO_2. The same is observed for naphthalene and other molecules. The weakening of phosphorescence in the presence of oxygen is so strong that in phosphorescent polymers oxygen diffusion can be followed by eye (Czarnecki, 1963).

The nature of oxygen-induced transitions is not clear, but several peculiarities of oxygen are now known. The low-lying energy levels $^1\Delta_g$ and $^1\Sigma_g$ participate in many cases in transitions of neighbor molecules. In the case of naphthalene, Hoijtink (1960) assigned a band at 2.90 μm^{-1} to the simultaneous transition

$$(^3B_{2u})(^1\Delta_g) \leftarrow (^1A_g)(^3\Sigma_g{}^-)$$

In pure oxygen, simultaneous transitions of oxygen pairs are well established. Table 5.3 lists observed oxygen transitions and the transition energies. The blue color of liquid oxygen and solid oxygen is due to these transitions, which are absent in atmospheric air (Tsai, 1969).

The emission quenching by oxygen has been studied already by Kautsky (1931, 1932), who suggested the process

$$S_1 + O_2(^3\Sigma_g{}^-) \rightarrow T_1 + O_2(^1\Sigma) \rightarrow S_1 + O_2(^3\Sigma_g{}^-)$$

Kasha (1952) and Reid (1958) have expanded this model, which seems more likely than the ionic complex proposed by Weiss (1946) and Baur (1932), which assumes

$$S_1 + O_2 \rightarrow S_0^+ + O_2^- \rightarrow S_0 + O_2$$

We believe that, for many cases, quenching occurs primarily from T_1, perhaps via the triplet annihilation process

$$T_1 + O_2(^3\Sigma) \rightarrow S_0 + O_2(^1\Sigma) \quad (\text{or } ^1\Delta)$$

The quenching of excited singlet molecular oxygen would follow the path:

$$S_1 + X\,^3\Sigma_g(O_2) \rightarrow T_1 + a\,^1\Delta(O_2)$$

$$T_1 + O\,^1\Delta(O_2) \rightarrow S_0 + B\,^3\Sigma_u^- , \quad \text{or}$$

$$T_1 + X\,^3\Sigma(O_2) \rightarrow S_0 + b\,^1\Delta(O_2)$$

$^1\Delta$ oxygen can decay via radiationless processes.

Table 5.3

Low-Lying Energy
Levels of Oxygen[a]

State	T_1 (μm^{-1})
$B\,^3\Sigma_u^-$	4.980
$A\,^3\Sigma_u^+$	3.609
$b\,^1\Sigma_g^+$	1.320
$a\,^1\Delta_g$	0.792
$X\,^3\Sigma_g^-$	0

[a] Data from Herzberg (1961).

The quenching mechanisms are, however, not yet understood, and the actual importance of the above processes is highly doubtful, because Parmenter (1969) and others have observed that quenching is often just as efficient when the energy gap of the excited molecule is too small to excite oxygen into the first excited state.

Nitric oxide is a similarly efficient quencher. Observations with NO are fully reversible and analogous to those of O_2 (Evans, 1957; Grabowska, 1967b). The quenching rates are comparable to those of oxygen, but the quenching mechanism must be different than for oxygen, because the ground state of NO is $^2\Pi$ and the spin exchange would have to be $S_1 + (^2\Pi)$ NO $T_1 + (^4\Pi)$ NO. However, this is energetically not feasible, because the lowest excited state of NO is at 3.794 μm^{-1}, or 262 nm, which is high above the energy gap for the quenched molecules. The situation is equally unclear for paramagnetic ions. Metal acetyl acetonates appear to enhance $T_1 - S_0$ transitions in anthracene, naphthalene, pyrene, and naphthacene (Nag-Chaudhuri, 1963). The appearance of phosphorescence has been taken as evidence that Cu^{2+} has a similar effect. McGlynn (1969) discussed the external spin-orbit coupling by paramagnetic perturbers, considering various sources for the effect of oxygen on aromatics. Assuming complex formation, he concluded that the zero-order transition moment of the complex is unchanged. The inhomogeneous magnetic field of the paramagnetic oxygen is equally ineffective. However, configuration interaction with the state S_1 can lead to an exchange mechanism, as developed by Dijkgraaf and Hoijtink (1963), in which the induced $T_1 - S_0$ transition borrows intensity from $S_1 - S_0$ of the same molecule. The borrowed intensity is proportional to the square of the transition moment; and, because the exchange integral, representing the two overlap densities, is proportional to S^2, it is roughly proportional to the fourth power of the intermolecular overlap integral. A further source of intensity borrowing is the configuration interaction with the charge-transfer state. This effect is also proportional to the fourth power of the intramolecular overlap integral.

Tsubomura and Mulliken (1960) assume that oxygen quenching is caused by transient contact charge-transfer complexes with negligible stability. Intensity borrowing in this unstable complex is from $S_1 - S_0$ transitions of the acid or the base, or from the dipole moment of the contact dimer.

It is difficult to decide at this time which model best describes oxygen quenching, largely because the process is not accurately studied. Robinson (1967a) favors exchange interaction for benzene-O_2. McGlynn (1969) takes the increased band width of oxygen-perturbed molecules as an indication that various geometric isomers of a charge-transfer complex are present. In any case, oxygen participates in the process. Therefore, the quenching is not, in the strict sense, a solvent-induced process but exhibits a dimer or excimer character.

B. Theories of Radiationless Transitions

1. Free Molecules

In small molecules in low pressure gases, radiationless transitions are rare. The first such case was discovered in 1924 by Henri and Teves, who observed predissociation in the gas-phase system, $^3\Sigma_u^- \leftarrow {}^3\Sigma_g^-$, of S_2. Above a certain value, lines appear broadened because of the Auger process, i.e., interaction between the levels of the stable state with those of a continuum. Energy levels for the Auger process are shown in Fig. 5.4. Similar predissociation occurs in Se_2 (Barrow, 1966) and HNO (Dalby, 1958). In emission, predissociation results in a break-off of the spectrum, but this effect is often weak. The broadening of absorption lines is caused by the high transition probability between the stable and the continuous state. In the above examples, the transition probabilities are larger than 10^{12} sec^{-1}. This yields a line half-width of almost a wave number, which is far larger than that due to the Doppler effect and radiative decay.

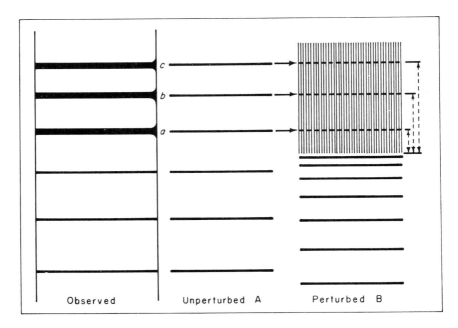

FIG. 5.4. Auger process; broadening of lines due to predissociation. A: Energy levels of unperturbed state A; B: State with dissociation continuum; in the observed spectrum the levels a, b, and c of state A are broadened. After Herzberg (1967).

Predissociation is not always so strong. If predissociation is less allowed, it cannot be recognized by line broadening, even if it is still comparable to the radiative decay. In such cases, predissociation must be detected by photochemical decomposition products which are often hard to detect.

Predissociations are governed by Kronig's selection rules for perturbations, i.e., $\Delta J = 0$; $+ \leftrightarrow -$; $s \leftrightarrow a$. In the case of spin-lattice coupling, Hund's case c holds: $\Delta\Omega = 0, \pm 1$. In the presence of spin-orbit coupling, the selection rule, $\Delta S = 0$, is not strictly observed. Coupling is usually small, but even if an S—T transition is a thousand times less probable than an allowed predissociation, it can alter the appearance of the spectrum. If, for example, the predissociation probability is $D = 10^{11}$ sec^{-1}, the spin forbidden transition could be $J = 10^8$ sec^{-1}. This is sufficiently strong to compete with a fully allowed radiative transition which also has a probability of $\tau = 10^8$ sec^{-1}. Examples for such processes are the breaking-off in the UV bands of P_2, in the Ångström bands of CO, and in the $^1\Sigma^+ - {}^1\Sigma^+$ bands of CuH at 428 nm (Herzberg, 1961; Kovac, 1969).

An interesting case of energy crossing into a radiative state via a perturbation between the two states was studied by Broida for CN (Iwai, 1967). In large organic molecules, transfer of excitation from one state to another occurs frequently and easily because of strong electronic mixing due to the high density of states. Robinson (1967b) has discussed the effect for small and large molecules and intermediate cases. Jortner and co-workers (Freed, 1969; Bixon, 1969) have proposed a model for large molecules in the gas phase at low pressure.

Predissociation can be induced by collisions or by a magnetic field, as observed for I_2 in the gas phase. A theory for induced predissociation has been developed by Zener (1932, 1933).

2. Environmental Effects

Radiationless transitions are enhanced by collision and environmental effects in solids. When a transition occurs between states of like multiplicity, the term *internal conversion* (IC) is used. In the case of spin conversion, the technical term is *intersystem crossing* (ISC). Various theories for IC and ISC have been proposed (Henry, 1968a).

All theories discussing radiationless transitions are based on either of two causes for coupling between states in a molecule. The first cause, and the most extensively investigated one, is failure of the Born-Oppenheimer approximation. The second cause is intermolecular perturbations.

The first theory on failure of the Born-Oppenheimer approximation for free molecules was advanced by Zener (1932). He treated the crossing of potential curves of zero-order ionic and covalent states by linear combination. Teller (1937) discussed the case of polyatomic molecules where potential curves of the same symmetry can cross. Crossing is determined by the shape and position of the state surface, not by interactions. In 1962, Coulson and Zalewskii used the time-dependent Schrödinger equation to compute a more general model based on Zener's approach. Ross and co-workers, starting in 1962, dealt with radiationless transitions between an excited state and a vibrationally excited lower state. The latter model was worked out quantitatively for aromatic hydrocarbons using the C—C stretching frequency, 1400 cm^{-1}, as the only active vibration. From this, they deduced diagrams of preferred decay paths. All the above approaches are based solely on intramolecular effects.

In contrast, Gouterman, in 1962, proposed a theory based on the approximation that intermolecular interactions alone cause coupling. He developed a model for the interaction of a phonon field with a solute in a solid matrix. In this model, radiationless transitions are treated in analogy with radiative transitions, except that the Planck formula for energy density of the radiative field is replaced by the Debye formula for a phonon field. The theory considers only one-phonon processes. Therefore, transitions are restricted to levels closer than $\hbar\omega_{max}$, i.e., energies smaller than that of the largest phonon oscillator. This theory predicts a temperature dependence for radiationless transitions. To date, this remains the only theory for radiationless transitions solely due to intermolecular effects.

In all following theories the reason for transitions lies in intramolecular effects, with the environment serving only as an energy sink or as a source for additional vibrational modes which enhance the degeneracy of intramolecular states. In the model of Robinson and Frosch (1963b), the solvent interaction arises from coulombic interactions between electrons and nuclei of solvent and solute. Coupling between excited and lower states is indirect via intermediate directly coupled states. The electronic matrix elements are chosen to give satisfactory agreement with experiment. Slow radiative transitions between $S_1 - T_1$ and $T_1 - S_0$ and the deuterium effect are explained by the small Franck-Condon factor.

Since 1965, Ross and co-workers have adapted Robinson's model and used CH-stretching frequencies and skeletal stretching and bending modes to compute Franck-Condon factors. In 1966, Siebrand published an analysis of Franck-Condon factors and deduced an empirical relationship between radiationless transition rates and the energy separation between T_1 and S_0.

All the above theories use time-dependent perturbation theory to predict radiationless transition rates. Harris (1963) questioned the validity of a time-dependent model, pointing out that excitation transfers a system as an entity to a stationary state. Kasha (Taylor, 1969) and Jortner (1968; Bixon, 1968) have recently proposed stationary state models in which the absorption takes place into a manifold of states. This approach is most meaningful for absorption of broad band widths. It is too early to review these models, which are still evolving. However, it is certain that much more experimental and theoretical work will be needed before completely reliable models can be formulated.

At the present time, no comprehensive theory is available. One major reason for this is that experimental data are incomplete and too qualitative to yield critical parameters. Also, observations are never due to one isolated effect. Untangling complex processes will require observations of many different systems and molecules. Therefore, it is unfortunate that most researchers have so far studied only benzene, naphthalene, and anthracene. Present theoretical calculations are either unwieldy or depend on arbitrary choice of variables. At best, they correlate, in a semiquantitative way, generally established trends. Present models agree, for example, that the Franck-Condon factor is important; however, theory has not yet predicted which vibrational modes are important. Siebrand (1967a,b) assumes that CH is active and demonstrates that the observed $C-D$ deuterium effect is predictable. His model fails, however, to explain Ermolaev's (1966) data for perfluorinated and perchlorinated aromatics. Similarly, none of the present theories is able to predict radiationless rates or paths of decay for any unobserved molecule.

3. Excitation Decay in Pure Organic Crystals

In pure solids, energy levels are coupled and, therefore, delocalized. Energy can migrate through the solid in the form of excitons, vibrons, and phonons. Schneider and Labhart (1965) developed a theory on optical excitation transfer in pure organic crystals which deals with the crystal as a volume occupied by an exciton, phonon, and vibron gas. Excitation transfer from optically excited nonequilibrium states to thermal equilibrium is considered as a sequence of individual two-particle collisions, neglecting anisotropy. Quadratic dispersion is assumed for the exciton energy, and the crystal lattice is treated as a Debye continuum. Quantitative evaluation, summarized in Table 5.4, indicates that transition probabilities for phonon absorption and emission without molecular readjustment is the quickest of all processes, with a probability of about 10^{11} sec^{-1}. Vibrational relaxation to S_1 (0,0) is expected to occur within 10^{-9} to 10^{-10} sec. From this intermediate state, there occur radiationless transitions to high vibrational levels of S_0 or to excited vibrational levels of T_1, or fluorescence. The respective rate constants of these three processes depend strongly on the Franck-Condon factors. $S_1 \leadsto T_1$ may occur equally well via vibron or phonon emission; it is enhanced by spin orbit coupling and a high density of T_1 energy levels in the region of S_1. In this model triplet excitons, formed via intersystem crossing, vibrationally relax within 10^{-11} sec. In nonpolar molecules, radiationless phonon deactivation is forbidden. $T_1 \leadsto S_0$ vibron emission is much greater and more efficient and significant than the analogous $S_1 \leadsto S_0$ because the Franck-Condon factor for the lower lying T_1 is much greater. In single crystals, therefore, phosphorescence is normally suppressed.

In summary, we see that under normal conditions emission from a crystal excited above S_1 will always be from S_1. It is indeed well established that x-ray bombardment, electron bombardment, and UV irradiation, which induce very different primary reactions, all lead to emission of the same spectral wavelength. The free path of excitons in neon, computed from a corresponding coupling model, is 1 nm. Such short ranges are apparently due to large distortions around the excitation center.

Table 5.4

Relative Rates of Exciton (E), Vibron (V), and Phonon (P) Decay in a Pure Organic Crystal[a]

Transition		k (sec^{-1})	Collision Process
Phonon emission, no molecular change	S_x	7×10^{11}	EP
	T_x	7×10^{10}	
Phonon absorption, no molecular change	S_x	$10^{11} \sim 10^{12}$	EP
	T_x	10^{12}	
Phonon absorption with molecular change	S	10^{11}	EP
	T	10^{6}	
	$S_i \rightarrow T_i$	10^{5}	
Vibron emission with molecular change	S	10^{10}	EV
	T	10^{11}	
	$S_i \rightarrow T_i$	10^{6}	
Vibron, no molecular change		10^{7}	EV
Vibron, with molecular change	$S_i \rightarrow S_0$	10^{5}	EV
	$T_i \rightarrow S_0$	10	
Photon emission	S	10^{8}	None
	T	10	
Phonon + photon emission	S	10^{6}	None
	T	10^{3}	

[a] Data from Schneider (1965).

III. ENERGY MIGRATION

Collisions are known to induce excitation transfer. Details of mechanisms in the gas phase are still the subject of complicated, intensive investigation which has led to a new and independent field of study using sophisticated experiments, such as collisions of molecular beams and chemical lasers. This topic exceeds the scope of this book. However, the basic fact, the existence of electronic energy transfer, has long been familiar to spectroscopists because in emission, unlike in absorption, the strongest emitter is often not the initially excited or the most abundant species. It is not uncommon that the strongest emission is due to traces of inadvertently present impurities. Thus, a gas phase microwave discharge through any gas containing sulfur impurities yields predominantly blue emission due to the S_2 system $^3\Sigma_u^- \to$ $^3\Sigma_g^-$. Similarly, in solids, low-lying electronic states of impurities act as energy traps. Thus, all spectra of crystals containing naphthalene were characterized by the sensitized emission of thionaphthalene until, in 1961, it was discovered that the latter has a triplet state 27 cm^{-1} below that of naphthalene (Wolf, 1961).

Winterstein discovered in 1934 that energy migration in anthracene containing traces of tetracene resulted in *sensitized fluorescence*, whereby absorption of anthracene yielded strongly enhanced tetracene fluorescence. This latter system has now been extensively studied. Work before 1965 has been reviewed by Windsor (1965). A more recent review is given by Parker (1968).

Energy can migrate from a donor to a suitable acceptor on various paths. We discuss here host-guest transfer, guest-guest transfer, and intramolecular energy transfer.

A. Host-Guest Transfer

In matrices and mixed crystals, guest fluorescence can be stimulated by excitation of the host. X-ray excitation of molecules in rare gas matrices provides a good example. As indicated in Fig. 5.1, the host excitation center relaxes to the host S_1 exciton band. The yield of sensitized fluorescence depends on the diffusion length of the exciton, the radiative and radiationless decay rates for host S_1, and the guest concentration. Migration in the host, i.e., the pure material, has been extensively studied. Frenkel (1931) was the first to treat the excitation as traveling through the crystal as a wave with a vector in quanta, called "excitons." Wannier (1937) introduced an electron-hole pair migration model in which the excitation energy is equal to the valence band-conduction band gap minus the binding energy of the

Table 5.5

Transfer Constants for Singlet Excitons[a]

Host	Guest	Transfer Constant[b]	References
Anthracene	Tetracene	$k = (6 \pm 3) \times 10^4$, $(p = 0.8 \pm 0.2)$	Benz and Wolf (1964)
	Tetracene	1×10^5	Korsunskii and Faidysh (1966)
	Phenazine	7.5×10^4	Zima and Faidysh (1966)
	Anthanthrene	2.5×10^4	
	Acridine	1.5×10^3	
	Anthraquinone	7.5×10^3	
Naphthalene	Anthracene	2.5×10^4	Zima (1966)
	β-Methylnaphthalene	3.5×10^2	
	Acridine	2.4×10^4	
	Anthranilic acid	4.35×10^4	Bonch-Bruevich (1966)
	1,4-Diphenylbutadiene	1×10^5	
	1,6-Diphenylhexatriene-1,3,5	3.22×10^4	Schmillen (1965)
2,3-Dimethyl-naphthalene	Anthracene	1×10^5	
Naphthalene	Perylene	8.7×10^4	Schmillen and Kohlmannsperger (1963)
Fluorene	Perylene	8.5×10^3	
Phenanthrene	Anthracene	$k = (3 \pm 2) \times 10^4$, $(p = 0.85 \pm 0.1)$	Benz and Wolf (1964)
	Tetracene	$k = (3 \pm 2) \times 10^4$, $(p = 0.9 \pm 0.1)$	

[a] Data after Wolf (1967).

[b] k = energy transfer constant, p = exponent of concentration dependence, $I_G/I_H = kC_G^{p}$.

electron-hole pair. Agranovich (1960a, 1966) and Knox (1959, 1963) have recently developed and summarized exciton and phonon theories for molecular crystals. Knox computed energy levels for rare gas crystals, especially argon, which, although not accurate, are in acceptable agreement with observations. Schnepp (1960b) measured exciton energy levels in rare gas solids and determined their free paths. In mixed crystals and in matrices, host-guest transfer can be followed by observation of sensitized fluorescence.

The effect can be followed by measuring any of three sets of quantities:

1. The host lifetime as a function of guest concentration, $\tau_H = f(C_g)$, or the guest lifetime as a function of guest concentration, $\tau_G = f(C_g)$.

2. The ratio of the relative quantum yield of guest and host fluorescence Φ_G/Φ_H.

3. The concentration dependence of the ratio of host quantum yield of the pure host to that of host plus guest, $\Phi_{H_{(0)}}/\Phi_{H_{(C_g)}}$.

From these observed quantities using appropriate assumptions and models, one can deduce values for an exciton diffusion coefficient D, the average displacement radius $\bar{r}$, diffusion length L, which is defined as $L = \bar{r}/\sqrt{3}$, the exciton velocity v, the hopping time t_H, and the number of hops per lifetime, n.

A very important difficulty in determining these constants is that delayed fluorescence is so efficient that inadvertent chemical impurity traces can act as traps and steal excitation. Thus, "self-trapped" anthracene states have been shown to be impurities (Wolf, 1967), and most of the naphthalene data published before 1961 were based on crystals containing β-methylnaphthalene and thionaphthalene.

The energy transfer probability is proportional to the guest concentration and is represented by k, the transfer constant. For its determination the guest concentration must be known:

$$I_g/I_n = k(C_G)$$

The concentration is never measured as accurately as intensities, and the measurements contain intrinsic uncertainties, due to inhomogeneous crystallization. Some typical transfer constants are given in Table 5.5.

Delayed fluorescence is affected by host defects, which act as shallow traps, and by the presence of impurities. Lattice defects emit characteristic host fluorescence, red-shifted by an amount equivalent to the trap depth. Plastically deformed naphthalene contains such traps with a depth of 165 cm^{-1}. Thionaphthalene in naphthalene acts as a trap with 29 cm^{-1} depth. In such multitrap systems, emission can become very complicated. The emission is also temperature dependent. Whenever kT becomes larger than the depth of a given trap, the trap loses its efficiency. At lower temperatures, the trap competes with all other deactivation processes. Below 10°K, for example, thionaphthalene steals energy from naphthalene.

In pure mixed crystals with only one type of trap, exciton diffusion becomes more efficient with decreasing temperature, as predicted by Agranovich and Konobeev in 1963 (Agranovich, 1966). The transfer constant changes proportional to $1/\sqrt{T}$ because the exciton migration is limited by phonon scattering. The activation energy for hopping of excitation energy is apparently zero.

At very low temperature, processes become complex. Delayed fluorescence competes with several other processes, including host fluorescence, partial thermal detrapping, and exciton transfer. All these processes have to be considered when quantum yields are evaluated. Figure 5.5 shows the

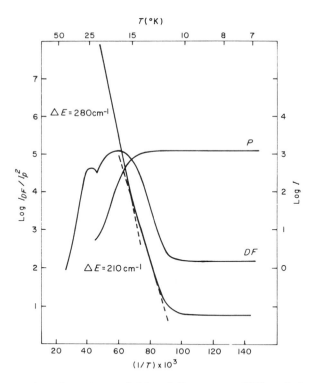

FIG. 5.5. Temperature dependence of delayed fluorescence (DF) and phosphorescence (P) of chloronaphthalene in a naphthalene host between 7 and 150°K. After Schwoerer (1968a,b).

logarithm of the phosphorescence (P) intensity and the intensity of delayed fluorescence (DF), and also the ratio I_{DF}/I^2_P for the system β-methyl-naphthalene in naphthalene (Port, 1967). Shallow traps and guest-host energy differences affect the temperature dependence in a complicated way. The wavelength dependence of the spectrum yields information on the emitters, but analysis of details of the behavior of the solid is not always present. In their films, the situation is yet worse because surface migration is substantial. Figure 5.6 shows the emission of anthracene in a naphthalene film deposited at 77°K, at four different temperatures. The spectra of films are broad, but the relative yields of fluorescence change so much that it can be easily followed.

B. Guest-Guest Transfer

In glasses and matrices, the guest-host energy gap is usually 1 to 5 μm^{-1}. Therefore, kT is much smaller than the energy gap between guest S_1 and the host S_1-exciton band. Consequently, excitation can move only from host to guest, but not from guest to host. For all practical purposes, trapping is irreversible, and excitation of the guest must decay through intramolecular

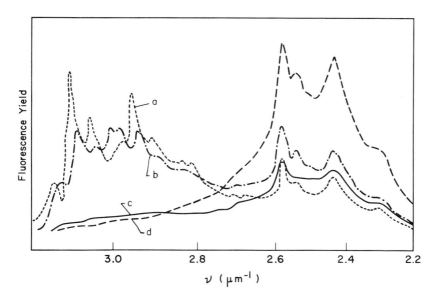

FIG. 5.6. Emission spectrum of a thin film of naphthalene containing 10^{-5} mole of anthracene at four different temperatures: a 8°K, b 25°K, c 54°K, d 77°K. After Gallus (1968b).

channels unless it migrates from one guest to another. Since guests do not diffuse in low temperature solids, energy migration between guests is restricted to long range interactions. Guest-guest interaction can lead to quenching of excited states, or, in the case of excited triplets, to delayed fluorescence via the mechanism $T_1 + T_1 \rightarrow S_1 + S_0$. This process is called triplet annihilation. If unlike guests are present, sensitized fluorescence and sensitized phosphorescence can result.

1. Guest-Guest Quenching

This quenching is concentration dependent. Förster (1948, 1949a,b) treated guest-guest energy quenching with the help of dipole-dipole models. The quenching rate of q/q_0 depends on concentration in the following way:

$$q/q_0 = 1 - \sqrt{\overline{\Pi}}(c/c)_0 \exp(c/c_0)^2 |1 - \phi(c/c_0)|$$

where

$$\phi(c/c_0) = 2/\sqrt{2} \int_0^{c/c_0} \exp(-x^2) \cdot dx$$

c_0 is the critical concentration and is correlated to the effective radius R_0 by

$$c_0 = (2/\sqrt{\overline{\Pi}})(3/4\Pi)(1/R_0^3)$$

The effective quenching radius can be correlated to macroscopic properties of a solid sample, for example, the absorption coefficient or the refractive index (Förster, 1951). Jablonski (1954) developed a model based on the volume of an active sphere. Jablonski's active quenching radius is the third root of Förster's definition. Experimentally, quenching yields are determined by comparison of an unknown quencher against an efficient "indicator" of known effective radius.

2. Guest-Guest Annihilation; Delayed Fluorescence

Delayed fluorescence due to $T_1 + T_1$ annihilation was originally observed in liquid solution and believed to be due to diffusion of the solute. This is not necessary, as has been shown with the help of mixed crystals. For a given system, the annihilation rates depend on guest concentration, temperature, and the intensity of the light source. All three parameters have complicated effects. The study requires strong light sources, preferably lasers (Lipsett, 1967). This can cause confusing side effects, for example, two-photon absorption which yields prompt fluorescence. The latter has a much shorter lifetime than the long-lived $T_1 - T_1$ annihilation. At higher temperature the lifetime of delayed fluorescence is also affected by thermal delayed fluorescence, which is caused by thermal excitation of T_1 into S_1. In low temperature glasses and matrices, thermal delayed fluorescence is normally absent. Instead, traps, due to distorted sites, contribute to the effect in a complicated manner (Siebrand, 1967b). This is shown in Fig. 5.7 for the case of pure anthracene. Work in this field is very active, and a better understanding of the effect can be expected.

3. Guest-Guest Migration; Delayed Sensitized Fluorescence, Delayed Phosphorescence

Figure 5.8 shows the energy levels of phenanthrene, naphthalene, and biphenyl. If phenanthrene is excited to S_1, not only fluorescence and phosphorescence from phenanthrene are observed, but also phosphorescence from naphthalene. This effect is due to sensitized phosphorescence. The interaction between the two guests is exactly the same as in the preceding two cases and can be explained qualitatively with Förster's models, but the difference is that only one excited molecule is present. The energy exchange can be described (Terenin, 1956) as

$$\text{Phen } (T_1) + \text{Napht } (S_0) \rightarrow \text{Phen } (S_0) + \text{Napht } (T_1)$$

Although we know from above that singlet excitons have larger ranges than triplet excitons (because they have much larger dipole interactions, while the triplet interaction is due only to overlap of charge distribution), the reaction

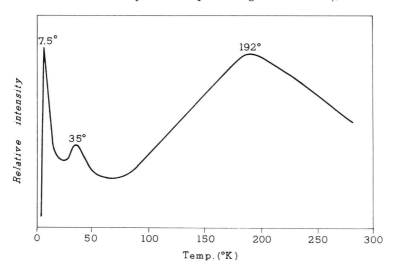

FIG. 5.7. Temperature dependence of delayed fluorescence of an anthracene crystal. After Lipsett (1967).

occurs as written because the lifetime of the triplet state is so much longer than that of the S_1 that it is responsible for all observed transport. The exchange rate is strongly dependent on the host lattice. A coherent exciton in a crystal at 77°K is hundred times more efficient than an exciton in a glass (Hochstrasser, 1968a).

Sensitized fluorescence and delayed phosphorescence occur between guests for which the donor state emission coincides with the acceptor absorption. Typical critical radii are of the order of 1 nm. Table 5.6 lists some old established values. Interaction between guests in a host leads to partial depolarization of emission.

C. Intramolecular Energy Migration

In large molecules with two or more chromophoric groups separated by inactive molecular fragments, energy migration can occur within the molecule.

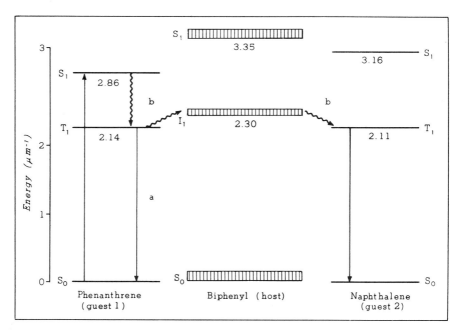

FIG. 5.8. Energy levels of phenanthrene, naphthalene, and biphenyl. After absorption $S_1 \leftarrow S_0$ by phenanthrene, intersystem crossing to T_1 of phenanthrene occurs. At low temperature, phenanthrene fluorescence (a) prevails. If kT is sufficiently large, thermal population of the biphenyl host state T_1 occurs, followed by exciton migration. Then T_1 of the secondary guest, naphthalene, can act as a trap, followed by naphthalene emission.

Table 5.6

Critical Radius R_0 and Reciprocal Half-Time Concentration K for Select Triplet-Triplet Donor-Acceptor Pairs[a][b]

Donor	Acceptor	Solvent	Temperature (°K)	K	R_0 (nm)	λ_{ex} (nm)
Acetophenone	Naphthalene	Ether/ethanol	77	—	1.1	365
Anthraquinone	1-Bromonaphthalene	Ether/ethanol	77	—	1.2	334
Anthraquinone	Naphthalene	Ether/ethanol	77	—	1.1	334
Benzaldehyde	1-Bromonaphthalene	Ether/ethanol	77	9.4	1.2	365
	1-Chloronaphthalene	Ether/ethanol	77	—	1.2	365
	1-Chloroanthracene	Ether/ethanol	77	8.9	—	365
	Naphthalene	Ether/ethanol	77	8.5	1.2	
Benzene	Diacetyl	EPA	77	3.12	1.1	265
Benzophenone	1-Bromonaphthalene	Ether/ethanol	77	13.3	1.3	365
	Quinoline	Ether/ethanol	77	—	1.2	—
	1-Chloroanthracene	Ether/ethanol	77	16.4	—	—
	1-Chloronaphthalene	Ether/ethanol	77	—	—	—

[a] Data from Ermolaev (1963) and Landolt-Börnstein (1967).
[b] Concentration: 2×10^{-2} mole/liter.

This effect is so well established that energy migration in the molecule can be used as an optical ruler to measure distances within and between proteins and other biologically important substances. This effect is very well reviewed by Parker (1968) and Stryer (1968). Energy transfer occurs as though the chromophoric groups were separated.

IV. RADIATIVE DECAY, LUMINESCENCE, FLUORESCENCE, AND PHOSPHORESCENCE

Radiative decay of excitation is called luminescence. Photoluminescence is due to excitation with light, radio luminescence is caused by x-rays or impact of α or β particles, and chemiluminescence is the result of chemical reactions. Recombination luminescence can be due to chemical reaction, or it can be caused by recombination of ions.

The excitation mechanism of luminescence can be complex. Often, six or more processes are participating, and some are slower than the lifetime of the emitting electronic state. $MgSO_2$ in CaF_2, for example, fluoresces over several months (Wiedeman, 1888). Such a slow decay is typical for luminescence in ion crystals with large lattice energies or diffusion-controlled processes in solutions. In weakly interacting solids, recombination excitation is rare. It has been observed in the case of nitrogen atoms in rare gas lattices, which, under appropriate conditions, can emit the active nitrogen afterglow due to diffusion-controlled atom recombination (Vegard, 1924b; Tinti, 1968). In the same case, other luminescence phenomena are observed: On warming at $33°K$, for example, a sudden flash of light is emitted due to untrapping of energy from shallow traps. References to such observations are in Chapter 9, Section II. This and many other luminescence marvels of trapped nitrogen discharges are not yet entirely unraveled, but they constitute an exception among weakly interacting solids. Here we do not further focus our attention on the original cause of the excitation; instead, we discuss now decay of energy by excited centers.

A. Fluorescence

Radiative emission due to an allowed electronic transition is called fluorescence. Fluorescence is normally short-lived, because the lifetime of excited states is of the order of 10^{-8} sec. It has been pointed out that, in the gas phase, small molecules emit resonance fluorescence, i.e., emission from the terminal state of absorption. If the guest molecule is large, intramolecular quenching to S_1 can occur even in the gas phase. Since, in addition, in large molecules the vibrational mode ν'_n is similar to ν''_m, and the equilibrium shape of both states is similar, absorption and emission form mirror images. Since Levshin (1931), this mirror image relationship has been stressed in the organic literature. Kasha (1968) calls it vibrational envelope inversion. It has also been pointed out that in dilute solids, fluorescence originates from vibrationally relaxed S_1. Therefore, wavelength distribution of the spectrum is independent of the exciting frequency. If a change is observed, it is due to the presence of an impurity emission, or to one of a very few exceptions.

In azulene (Robinson, 1969) and in SeO_2 (Voigt, 1970), the emitting state is not S_1 but S_2. In both cases, this is due to intramolecular peculiarities. Another case of exceptional behavior is nitrogen emission in neon, where the second positive group $C\,{}^3\Pi_u - B\,{}^3\Pi_g$ is observed (Tinti, 1968b). This system consists of emission from a highly excited state. Even the lower state in this system is an excited state. The evidence for the second positive system is well established and is corroborated by a vibrational analysis of sixteen bands. The second positive emission is well known from gas phase work (Herzberg, 1961) and is an allowed transition. Emission from the upper state C to the ground state involves a spin forbidden transition and has not been observed. It is not surprising that the C $\rightarrow$ X emission does not favorably compete with the more allowed C $\rightarrow$ B second positive system. Therefore, the most interesting aspect of the observation is the fact that the C level emits at all. It is likely that other light molecules, when studied, will reveal similar effects. It is already known that excitation with high powered lasers can lead to two-photon absorption and emission of S_2.

Fluorescent lifetimes are of the order of 10^{-8} sec. No data on fluorescent lifetimes in solids are yet available because experimental work is complicated by scattering. The only measurement of lifetimes at 4°K deals with the two S_1 exciton bands of pure naphthalene, which are 30 and 70 nsec (Wolf, 1968). Tunable lasers will make work much easier. This is desirable because fluorescent lifetimes constitute an important link missing in the data on S_1 depopulation.

B. Phosphorescence

In this book we use the term phosphorescence for spin-forbidden transitions. The lifetime of such transitions depends on spin-orbit coupling. It is of the order of 10^{-6} to 10^{+2} sec. For simplicity of further discussion, we use the example of a stable molecule for which the ground state electronic configuration yields only one singlet state, S_0. The first excited electron configuration is assumed to yield a singlet, S_1, and a triplet, T_1. The lowest lying spin-forbidden transition in this system is $T_1 \leftrightarrows S_0$. The triplet character of the

T_1 state has been experimentally demonstrated by Lewis (1944b) and Porter (1954a). Table 5.7 lists representative values of triplet decay times of matrix isolated molecules.

The absorption $T_1 \leftarrow S_0$ is weak. In the gas phase, 50-meter atmospheres of SO_2 are necessary to photograph this transition. This corresponds to an unwieldy matrix experiment with 0.2 mole of argon and 0.2 mole of SO_2. However, in a heavy atom host, or in oxygen, which enhance spin-orbit coupling, only 1 mmole of SO_2 in 50 mmoles of matrix is necessary, but this is still much more guest and matrix than in a normal experiment and the transition is still weak. Thus, direct excitation of phosphorescence in matrices is difficult. Thick organic glasses and single crystals are better—preferably excited with a strong light source, for example, flashlamps or a laser. Recently, direct excitation of the triplet has been increasingly used, especially for the study of triplet exciton migration and delayed thermal fluorescence (Robinson, 1969).

In low temperature solutions and in solids, phosphorescence occurs always from T_1, never from a higher triplet state. It is stimulated, in a unique way, by radiationless transition from S_1, which can be excited by the allowed absorption $S_1 \leftarrow S_0$, or in any higher state. The mechanism for this type of T_1 population is discussed in the section on radiationless transitions. Quenching of S_1 is so commonly used to excite phosphorescence that, for low temperature spectroscopists, the term phosphorescence often implies indirect population of T_1 via S_1.

This type of phosphorescence is rarely encountered in the gas phase. One of the few known cases is SO_2, excited in S_1, which phosphoresces at a pressure above 10^{-3} torr (Meyer, 1968). Another case is in biacetyl vapor. In large molecules, phosphorescence is more common, but there is still controversy whether free molecules fluoresce, and to what extent $S_1 \rightsquigarrow T_1$ crossing is due to external perturbations (Freed, 1969; Bixon, 1968, 1969b). Theories based on both assumptions have been summarized above, in Section II, D.

In solids the intensity of phosphorescence from molecules excited in S_1 is commonly higher. In aromatic molecules with well shielded transitions the enhancement depends on the host characteristics. In small molecules almost any host is efficient, and fluorescence is often totally suppressed. Examples of such matrix-induced phosphorescence due to intersystem crossing are NO (Frosch, 1964), SnS, SnO (J. J. Smith, 1968a; Meyer, 1970c), and GeS.

A look at Fig. 5.3, which shows the deactivation paths of S, leads to two conclusions. First, the stimulation of phosphorescence by draining higher-lying states implies that $S_1 \rightsquigarrow T_1$ must be competitive with the other S_1

Table 5.7
Triplet Decay Times of Matrix Isolated Molecules, In Seconds

Molecule	Lifetime[a]			References
	Ar	Kr	Xe	
GeO	1.6×10^{-3}	9.6×10^{-4}	4.2×10^{-4}	Spitzer, 1970
GeS	2.4×10^{-3}	1.5×10^{-3}	6.2×10^{-4}	Spitzer, 1970
SnO	2.4×10^{-4}	1.7×10^{-4}	1.1×10^{-4}	Spitzer, 1970
SnS	5.2×10^{-4}	4.4×10^{-4}	2.3×10^{-4}	Spitzer, 1970
NO	0.093^{b}	0.035^{b}	—	Frosch, 1964
N_2	0.39^{b}	0.015^{b}	5×10^{-3} [b]	Tinti, 1968
SO_2	0.9×10^{-2}	8.4×10^{-3}	5.2×10^{-3}	Meyer, 1968
SeO_2	—	—	2×10^{-4}	Voigt, 1970
C_6H_6	16.0	1.0	0.07	Wright, 1960
$C_{10}H_8$	1.7	0.31	0.12	Metzger, 1969
$C_{14}H_{10}$	2.9	0.41	0.14	Metzger, 1969

[a] at 20°K, except as indicated.
[b] at 4°K.

depopulation processes, $S_1 \to S_0$ and $S_1 \rightsquigarrow S_0$. This fact is remarkable, because $S_1 \rightsquigarrow T_1$ is spin forbidden, while the competing processes are allowed. In the section on radiationless transitions we have explained that spin-orbit coupling, and the difference between the Franck-Condon factors are responsible for this. Second, the occurrence of phosphorescence by excitation of S_1 indicates that $T_1 \rightsquigarrow S_0$ is slower than $S_1 \rightsquigarrow T_1$, and comparable to $T_1 \to S_0$.

T_1 population is a complicated and competitive process. Since phosphorescence also competes against other T_1 depopulation processes, the intensity of phosphorescence is not easy to predict. Besides the strength of the excitation source and the absorption coefficient of the molecule at the absorbed frequency, the intensity can be expressed as the result of three processes: the intersystem crossing rate $S_1 \rightsquigarrow T_1 = k_{ISC}$; the radiative rate $T_1 \to S_0 = k_p$; and the intersystem crossing rate $T_1 \rightsquigarrow S_0 = k_T$.

$S_1 \rightsquigarrow T_1$ depends on all S_1 population and depopulation processes; $T_1 \to S_0$ depends on the natural lifetime and matrix-induced spin-orbit coupling; and $T_1 \rightsquigarrow S_0$ stands for all nonradiative T_1 processes, such as intersystem crossing, quenching by impurities, and excitons. Depending on the experimental system of particular interest, the above three primary processes might be written as a sum of individually important mechanisms. Above 77°K, for example, $S_1 \rightsquigarrow T_1$ can be the sum of the actual intersystem rate and the delayed thermal reverse reaction $S_1 \leftsquigarrow T_1$. If T_1 is directly excited, the latter process, delayed thermal fluorescence, contributes a negative sum, i.e., it helps drain T_1.

Any parameter that affects any of the above processes will also affect phosphorescence. This makes phosphorescence very sensitive to environmental changes and creates strange peculiarities because an intensity change can be due to several simultaneously occurring effects. Accordingly, analysis of observations is difficult. A case in point is the temperature dependence of phosphorescent intensity. All of the three primary processes above can contribute, and, for each, three or four contributions contain temperature dependent parameters. It seems logical to analyze such effects experimentally by stepwise systematic change of all parameters, but this is intrinsically difficult. We proceed now to discuss individual effects.

The contribution of environmentally induced spin-orbit coupling on T_1 can be tested by consecutive study of internal and external heavy atom substitutions. Figure 5.9 shows the effect of external heavy atom effect on relative phosphorescence yield of naphthalene and phenanthrene in methane, krypton, and argon. Since the same solvent series induces similar intensity changes in both guests, it is likely that the host heavy atom, rather than guest peculiarities, cause the change. A similar trend is observed in the lifetimes of benzene (see Table 5.8a) and naphthalene (Table 5.8b). We know now that spin-orbit coupling affects $T_1 \rightarrow S_0$ lifetime and intensity, but the contribution of individual processes still remains to be determined. The lifetime is caused by $T_1 \rightarrow S_0$ and $T_1 \rightsquigarrow S_0$, the intensity by the same, but also by $S_1 \rightsquigarrow T_1$. In order to unravel individual steps, we must know the lifetime of fluorescence, and the oscillator strength of $S_1 \rightarrow S_0$ and $T_1 - S_0$. These can be calculated from the absorption strength; this, however, is experimentally difficult to determine in a solid.

The effect of temperature on phosphorescence decay time is shown in Table 5.9. In rigid solids, the change is typically 5–10% of the decay time. This must be due to changes in $T_1 \rightsquigarrow S_0$ rates because the oscillator strength does not vary with temperature, and diffusion does not occur in rigid solids. The temperature dependence of T_1 quenching could be induced by phonons (Gouterman, 1962). A different temperature effect must be present in the case of reversible intensity changes shown in Fig. 5.10 for thiazole and SO_2. Twelve matrices give similar curves. Thiazole and SO_2 have different $S_1 - T_1$ energy gaps and different density of states, but show very similar intensity versus temperature curves. Since direct triplet excitation does not give any temperature dependence of phosphorescence under the above conditions, an artifact and guest-guest excitation migration can be excluded (Meyer, 1970b). The effect is real and due to changes in $S_1 \rightsquigarrow T_1$ processes. It has yet to be established whether the effect is general, for example, due to density changes, or whether it is due to peculiarities of the sample selection or sample properties (Phillips, 1969; Meyer, 1968; Metzger, 1969).

Table 5.8 (a)

Triplet Decay Time of Benzene in Various Matrices and Solvents

Matrix	Decay Time, τ_P (sec)[a]	Temperature (°K)	References
EPA	7 (13)	77	McClure (1949), Martin (1968a)
Dioxane	5	77	Kanda (1961b)
CCl_4	0.66	77	Kanda (1961b)
Methane	15.8 (22)	4	Robinson (1961b, 1963b)
Argon	16 (26)	4	Robinson (1961b, 1963b)
Krypton	1	4	Robinson (1961b, 1963b)
Xenon	0.07	4	Robinson (1961b, 1963b)
Cyclohexane			
cubic	1.2 (9.2)	77	Spangler (1968), Martin (1969)
monoclinic	4.75 (13.9)	77	Spangler (1968), Martin (1969)
mixed	11.8 (15.6)	4	Spangler (1968), Martin (1969)
C_6D_6	9.5	4	Hatch (1968b)
Borazine $(B_3N_3H_6)$	10.2 (12.5)	4	Hatch (1968b)
Ethanol	3.3	77	Kanda (1961b)

[a] Value in parentheses indicates lifetime of perdeuterated benzene.

Table 5.8 (b)

Triplet Decay Time of Naphthalene in Various Matrices and Solvents[a]

Solvent	Decay Time (sec)[b]	Temperature (°K)	References
Ethanol	3.6	300	Parker (1968)
Isopentane	2.4 ± 0.1	300	Hilpern (1964)
EPA, $3 \times 10^{-2} M$	2.6 (20) 2.2 (18)	77	McClure (1949)
Polymer	2.4 (22)	77	Kellogg (1964)
Durene	3.0 (16)	77	Hadley (1963)
Ethanol/ether	2.3	77	Ermolaev (1963)
Argon	1.7 (18)	4	Frosch (1965)
Krypton	1.4	4	Frosch (1965)
Xenon	0.09	4	Frosch (1965)
CH_4	3.2	4	Metzger (1969)
H_2	2.8	4	Frosch (1965)

[a] Data after McGlynn (1969).
[b] Values in parentheses indicate lifetime of perdeuterated naphthalene.
Singlet lifetime is 20; 100 nsec at 4°K (Gallus, 1968).

Table 5.9

Decay Time of SO_2 Phosphorescence as a Function of Temperature[a,b]

Temperature (°K)	Xe	Kr	SF_6	Pure SO_2
4	—	—	13.5	9.6
20	5.2	8.4	11	8.5
45	3.5	6.6	9.0	—
55	4.4	7.1	9.4	5.0
60	5.0	7.2	—	3.8
77	—	—	11	0.5
300	—	—	—	7

[a] Data from Meyer (1968).

[b] Values are in milliseconds; values obtained in the present work are believed to be accurate to $\pm$ 1 msec; lifetimes are not affected by annealing.

FIG. 5.9 Relative intensity of phosphorescence to fluorescence in three matrices for (a) naphthalene and (b) phenanthrene. After Metzger (1969) from unpublished tracings.

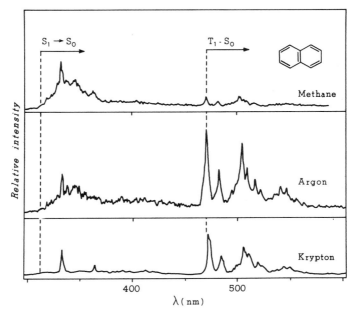

(a) naphthalene

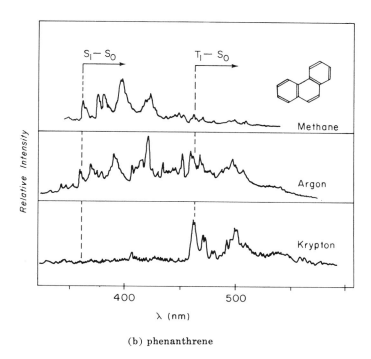

(b) phenanthrene

At higher temperatures, other effects on the intensity of phosphorescence occur. In numerous compounds, the intensity of phosphorescence decreases with increasing temperature in the region above 77°K. There are two phenomena that may cause this intensity decrease. One is thermal activation of the molecule into the S_1 level, as discussed in detail by Parker (1968); the other is nonradiative quenching of the triplet. Recently, increases in phosphorescence intensity have been reported for certain organic molecules in a small temperature range, above 77°K (Siegel, 1969). This has been interpreted as due to thermally enhanced crossing $S_1 \leadsto T_2$. An alternate possibility could be an increased $S_1 \leadsto T_1$ through an excited vibrational level of S_1. Both these mechanisms would give a different luminescence excitation spectrum.

Another process associated with phosphorescence is triplet-triplet energy transfer between guests, which, between two excited triplets of the same molecule, can yield *triplet-triplet annihilation* leading to delayed fluorescence. Transfer between unlike but similar guest molecules yields *sensitized phosphorescence* (Terenin, 1956).

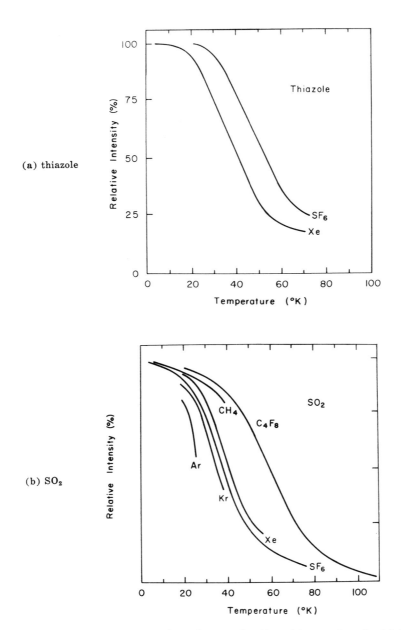

(a) thiazole

(b) SO₂

FIG. 5.10. Phosphorescence intensity as a function of temperature for (a) thiazole and (b) SO_2. After Meyer (1968) and Williamson (1970).

1. Phosphorescence at Very Low Temperature, and Zeeman Effect

The phosphorescence of molecules is polarized. This indicates that emission is predominantly from one spin level. It is not known whether $S_1 \rightsquigarrow T_1$ populates all spin levels. If it is selective, the receiving T_1 level would not be identical with the emitting. In either case, changes in the rate of energy conversion between triplet sublevels will affect the emission. Spin reorientation in solids is caused by spin lattice relaxation (SLR). Typical SLR rates at 80°K are 10^{-5} sec; this is quicker than emission. However, at 1.6°K, the rate is only 0.1 sec. This causes imbalance between triplet levels which shows in the decay curve, because the different sublevels, with different decay times, depopulate independently. This effect has been carefully studied for quinoxaline in durene (De Groot and van der Waals, 1967 to present; Schwoerer, 1967 to present; Azumi, 1969a) and in pyrazine by El-Sayed and Azumi, 1969b), by observation of phosphorescence, and by ESR measurements on the triplet sublevel saturation. A typical decay curve is shown in Fig. 5.11. At

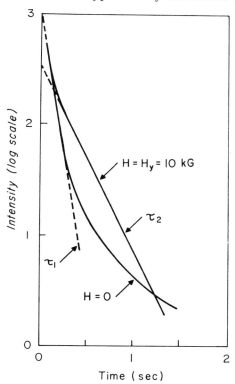

FIG. 5.11. Decay time curve for quinoxaline in durene at 1.56°K for zero field and 10 kGauss. $\tau_1 = 0.086$ sec; $\tau_2 = 0.26$ sec. After van der Waals (1967b).

high magnetic field, sublevels equilibrate, despite the low temperature, perhaps because the phonon spectrum has a higher density at the transition energy between split sublevels.

Another type of Zeeman effect is observed when a high field is applied to SO_2 in Xe at 20°K (Fig. 5.12). In all cases studied, decay curves show that more than one decay process is present (Williamson, 1970; Conway, 1969). Table 5.10 gives data from experiments on triplet emission of SO_2 in xenon at 20°K between 0 and 86 kGauss. The long-lived component gains intensity with increasing magnetic field strength up to 70 kGauss. Above, a Paschen-Back effect sets in. Simultaneously with lifetime changes, the line width increases.

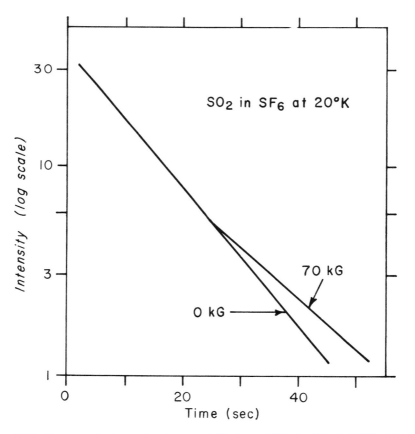

FIG. 5.12. Zeeman effect on phosphorescent lifetime of SO_2 in SF_6 at 20°K; (a) zero field, (b) 70 kGauss. After Conway (1969).

Table 5.10

Decay Time of SO_2 in SF_6 at 20°K as a Function of Magnetic Field from 0 to 90 kGauss[a]

Field (kGauss)	Decay Time (msec $\pm$ 5%)		Percent Contribution of τ_2 to Total Intensity
	τ_1	τ_2	
0	11.3	—	0
10	12.0	—	0
20	11.5	13.0	20
30	11.2	13.5	20
40	11.4	13.5	30–35
50	11.0	13.6	20–33
60	11.5	14.5	30
70	12.5	17.0	30
80	10.0	15.0	30
90	10.2	15.0	30

[a] Data from J. G. Conway (unpublished, 1969).

In the last few years a number of non-optical techniques have been applied to the study of intramolecular and intermolecular energy transfer. Electron Spin Resonance (ESR) and Electron Nuclear Double Resonance (ENDOR) yield valuable data on population and relative location of triplet sublevels. Other methods combine optical with microwave techniques. One example is Optical Detection of Magnetic Resonance (ODMR). As this book goes to press, these techniques are very successfully exploited, and accurate data is produced. However, it seems too early to review theories in this field, because interpretation of findings is so quickly improved and expanded that many of the present models will be obsolete within a few months. However, there is little doubt that during the next few years we will be able to understand quantitatively most processes and properties of excited triplet states of molecules in mixed crystals. In the meantime we refer the reader to progress reports in the research literature and at international meetings.

Recommended Reading

Becker, R. S., Theory and Interpretation of Fluorescence and Phosphorescence, Interscience-Wiley, New York, 1969.

Craig, D. P., and S. H. Walmsley, *Excitons in Molecular Crystals*, Benjamin, New York, 1968a.

Davydov, A. S., *Theory of Molecular Excitons* (translated from the Russian text by M. Oppenheimer, Jr., and M. Kasha), McGraw-Hill, New York, 1962.

Dexter, D. L., and R. S. Knox, *Excitons*, Interscience (Wiley), New York, 1965.

Lower, S. K., and M. A. El-Sayed, Chem. Rev. **66**, 199 (1966). "The Triplet State and Molecular Electronic Processes in Organic Molecules."

McClure, D. S., in *Phonons in Perfect Lattices and in Lattices with Perfect Imperfections* (R. Stevenson, ed.), Oliver & Boyd, Edinburgh and London, 1966. "The Electronic States and Spectra of Ions and Imperfections in Solids."

McGlynn, S. P., Radiat. Res., Suppl. **2**, 300 (1960a). "Donor-Acceptor Interaction."

McGlynn, S. P., T. Azumi, and M. Kinoshita, *Molecular Spectroscopy of the Triplet State*, Prentice-Hall, Englewood Cliffs, New Jersey, 1969.

Schwoerer, M., and H. C. Wolf, in *The Triplet State* (A. B. Zahlan, ed.), p. 133, Cambridge University Press, London and New York, 1967a. "ESR Investigations of Naphthalene-d_8: Naphthalene-h_8 Mixed Crystals."

Thomson, C., Quart. Rev. (London) **22**, 45 (1968). "Electron Spin Resonance Studies of the Triplet State."

Turro, N. J., *Molecular Photochemistry*, Benjamin, New York, 1965.

Windsor, M. W., in *Physics and Chemistry of the Solid State* (D. Fox., et al., eds.), Vol. II, 343, 1965. "Luminescence and Energy Transfer."

Wolf, H. C., Solid State Phys. **9**, 1 (1959). "The Electronic Spectra of Aromatic Molecular Crystals."

Zahlan, A. B., ed., *The Triplet State (Proc. Int. Symp., Amer. Univ., Beirut)*, Cambridge University Press, London and New York, 1967.

CHAPTER 6

Diffusion and Photochemistry

I. DIFFUSION

It is sometimes observed that the optical and physical properties of a low temperature system change with time. This can be due to diffusion of atoms or molecules that are in thermal equilibrium or move from less favored to more favorable thermodynamic configurations. Diffusion is extremely important during the initial preparation of a matrix sample, particularly as the atoms or molecules settle into place as the equilibrium temperature is reached.

Diffusion occurs continually in all systems at all temperatures. However, in many cases, the rate of diffusion is experimentally insignificant. For low temperature samples this is true when the temperature of the sample is less than about 0.3 of the host melting point and when the mobilities of the guest are small.

Under some circumstances, diffusion is undesirable or even disastrous. Thus, for example, when one is attempting matrix isolation of small free radicals, such as C_2, one must minimize diffusions that would allow the C_2 radicals to recombine into C_4 and larger polymers. On the other hand, controlled diffusion can often be turned to advantage. Thus, careful annealing can result in an increase in the perfections of a crystalline substance and to a corresponding narrowing of the spectral features of the guest species. Controlled short-range diffusion is necessary to produce radicals by *in situ* photolysis or chemical reactions.

A. Diffusion Mechanisms

Basically, there are four types of diffusion processes of interest. These are discussed briefly below. For a more complete review of diffusion processes,

105

the reader is referred to the review articles listed at the end of this chapter.

1. Vacancy Diffusion

Vacancy migration occurs when a particle migrates from its site through the "neck" of neighboring atoms to a neighboring vacant site. The probability for this type of diffusion depends on the relative size and chemical interaction between host and guest, and on the "strain" deformation necessary to allow hopping through the lattice "neck." It depends, therefore, on the elastic constant of the host and the temperature. Guest and host have different vacancy diffusion rates.

2. Interstitial Diffusion

Interstitial diffusion results from ejection of a particle from a lattice site into an interstitial site, thus creating a vacancy plus an interstitial guest. This is a relatively high energy process, but can occur when the sample is bombarded with x-rays or electrons. During annealing, the ejected particle returns to the vacancy. In rare gas solids, this is a relatively unimportant process by comparison with vacancy diffusion.

3. Interchange Diffusion

This is a yet higher energy process in which neighbors simultaneously interchange lattice sites. This type of diffusion is negligible at low temperature.

4. Diffusion along Imperfections and Surfaces

Diffusion along grain boundaries, slips, and imperfections is by far the most important process in weakly interacting low temperature systems. Theory differentiates between different types of mechanisms for the different imperfections. However, theory is available only for metals. For our purpose, it is reasonable to assume that in rare gases, with crystal energies of only one or a few kilocalories per mole, one major process prevails. In essence, the migrating species leaves its original site and emerges at a surface along which it moves one or two-dimensionally until it relocates at a new site. This process is particularly significant in the case of matrices, as indicated below.

B. Temperature Dependence of Diffusion

The temperature dependence of diffusion follows the exponential law

$$D = D_0 \exp(\Delta H / RT)$$

where $D_0 = \nu e^2 f$. D is the diffusion coefficient, ν the average jumping frequency, e the distance between sites, and f the correlation factor. For hcp and cfc symmetry the correlation factor is 0.78. For interstitial diffusion the jump frequency is

$$\nu = \nu_0 g \exp(\Delta S/R - \Delta H/RT)$$

where ΔS and ΔH are the quantities required for motion through a barrier separating neighboring sites, g is a geometrical factor,

$$\nu_0 = 1/2\Pi \sqrt{K/M}$$

K is the force constant for displacement in the potential well between sites, M is the mass of the diffusing particle. The jump frequency is different for guest and host, and it changes around impurity sites. For vacancy diffusion the jump frequency is

$$\nu = \nu_0 g \exp(\Delta S/R + \Delta S_v/R) - \exp(\Delta H + \Delta H_v/RT)$$

where ΔH_v and ΔS_v are the enthalpy and entropy for thermally formed vacancies. ν_0 is proportionate to the number of vacancies.

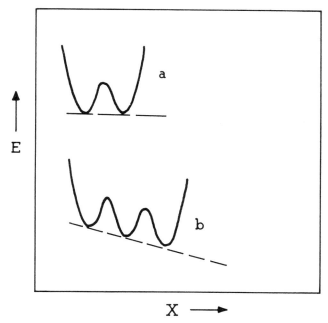

FIG. 6.1. Vacancy diffusion: *a*, self-diffusion; *b*, diffusion in a thermal gradient.

It is difficult to observe diffusion in rare gas crystals. Therefore, only few data are available, despite the fact that rare gases constitute ideally simple models of solids. Mukherjee (1967), Cotterill (1967), and others have computed the vacancy concentration (C_v) in argon at 80°K, just below the triple point, and arrived at values of about 10^{-3} to 10^{-4}, corresponding to

$$C_v = n/N = 100\exp(-2000/RT)$$

which corresponds to a diffusion coefficient of $D = 10^{-10}$ cm²/sec for argon at 80°K, but calculations of different workers disagree in entropy by as much as 50%. A schematic potential energy diagram for diffusion is shown in Fig. 6.1. If a thermal gradient exists, as when a sample is illuminated with light, or in a matrix during condensation between the window and the surface, diffusion becomes directional, as indicated in Fig. 6.1, *b*.

At *low temperature*, the equilibrium concentration of thermal vacancies becomes small. Diffusion processes are dominated by motions at imperfections. The resulting temperature dependence is shown in Fig. 6.2. Below the kink in curve *a*, imperfections regulate diffusion rates; above it, thermally produced vacancies are increasingly dominating. Curve *b* describes behavior

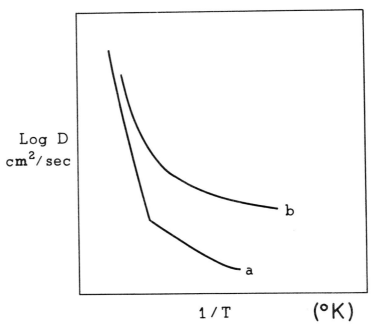

FIG. 6.2. Temperature dependence of diffusion; *a*, normal curve; *b*, in the presence of radiation.

under irradiation. Irradiation causes a steady state of vacancy concentration which enhances diffusion at all temperatures. Such vacancies are produced by dissociative displacement of atoms into interstitials, which normally remain correlated, and not random; thus, annihilation of these vacancies is efficient during annealing when radiation is interrupted.

We know of no direct studies of diffusion in thin rare gas films at matrix temperature. However, Michel (1958) demonstrated for thin Ag-Zn, Ag-Sn, and Ag-Cd films that extrapolation of diffusion coefficients to very low fractions of the melting point temperature gives good results. If the above can be applied to matrices, diffusion should be more significant in doped low temperature solids because the lattice energies are very small.

C. Diffusion in Rare Gas Matrices

When matrices are formed by quenching of gas beams on a cold target, a very imperfect solid is formed. The density and structure of the solid depends on temperature gradient, deposition speed, heat of sublimation of the matrix, and many other factors. Matrix experiments are normally performed at 4° or 20°K. Table 6.1 shows the rigidity of common matrices at the above and four other temperatures. It is obvious that matrices differ strangely in their diffusion behavior. However, in all cases, the target temperature is chosen so that the accommodation coefficient is close to 1. Therefore, the impinging molecules or atoms stick to the target and diffuse two-dimen-

Table 6.1

Rigidity of Matrices

Matrix	Matrix Temperature[a]					
	4.2°K	12°K	20°K	40°K	60°K	77°K
Ne	17	49	82	—	—	—
Ar	5	14	24	48	72	92
Kr	4	10	17	34	52	66
Xe	3	7	12	25	37	48
H_2	30	93	—	—	—	—
N_2	7	19	32	63	95	—
O_2	8	22	37	74	—	—
CO	6	18	29	59	88	—
SF_6	2	5	9	18	27	35
CH_4	5	13	22	44	66	85

[a] Expressed as percentage of matrix melting point.

sionally, along the target surface, while dissipating energy. At very high deposition speed, the surface film will be continuous and smooth, crystallizing as a well oriented, dense solid. At very low deposition speed, a snowlike solid with irregular structure will form. Ideal conditions, discussed in the chapter on sample preparation, lie in between. Practically, the deposition speed, about one molecular layer every second, is chosen so that short-range diffusion is encouraged, to ensure forming of reproducible and well defined stable solute sites. However, long-range diffusion is undesirable because it leads to solute-solute reactions and phase separation.

Detailed structure and processes are difficult to predict quantitatively because matrices are nonequilibrium solids and are not uniform. Experimental evidence—for example, fine structure of electronic transitions—indicates that, in most matrices and frozen solvent crystals, nuclei exist. It is less clear whether the nuclei are incoherent, in a quasi-liquid or snowy environment, or whether they are coherent, with large dislocations. In all cases, crystal growth is a relatively slow, low order process. The speed of crystal growth, for a given temperature, depends on crystal size. It goes through a minimum when the crystals touch, but growth along dislocations can suppress the minimum.

Matrices are often annealed or tempered. For this purpose, the sample is heated up to 0.5 of the melting point, where local site rearrangement becomes efficient, but long-range diffusion is still slow. During this process a temperature gradient develops through the sample. This gradient induces preferentially directional diffusion that can be very effective. At high temperature this process is very similar to zone refining. Therefore, care must be taken to keep the temperature sufficiently low to prevent solute expulsion.

In nonequilibrium solutions, annealing fulfills its purpose only if the guest is heavier than the host. Otherwise guest diffusion occurs, resulting in dimer formation and aggregates until such products are heavier than the host and remain trapped in their cage.

1. Effect of Relative Size of Guest and Host

Guest and host are usually of different size. Therefore, diffusion can take two totally different forms. If the chemical and physical nature of the components causes host diffusion to precede guest translation, the host will self-diffuse and anneal before guest-guest recombination becomes significant. One takes frequent advantage of this effect in vapor-deposited matrix spectroscopy, where the sample preparation leads to an initially highly unoriented solid with multiple solute trapping sites. Through annealing, the number of sites can be reduced to one or a few most stable arrangements. The resulting spectrum is sharper and has less fine structure than the original absorption. Figure 6.3 demonstrates spectral effects for the case of benzene in nitrogen. Line *a* shows a spectrum of 1 mmole of N_2 with 10^{-5} mole of benzene deposited at 4°K at a rate of 1 mmole per hour. Trace *b* is taken at 20°K, after 10 minutes' annealing at 35°K. In rare gas solids, typical annealing conditions are 30 minutes at 0.4 of matrix melting point. Only at much higher temperatures does guest diffusion become significant. This situation is typical for all guests that occupy multiple sites, for example, aromatic hydrocarbons or porphyrins in rare gas matrices.

If the guest is significantly lighter than the host, diffusion commences before annealing. A typical example for this situation arises in the cases of Li atoms in Xe, C_2 in Xe, or formaldehyde in SF_6. Since neutral matrices are not equilibrium solutions, guest diffusion yields dimers, aggregates, and eventually, phase separation. Thus, the spectrum of formaldehyde, trapped in argon at 4°K and heated to 30°K, shows after a few minutes the emission characteristics of pure solid formaldehyde consisting of monomeric aggregates,

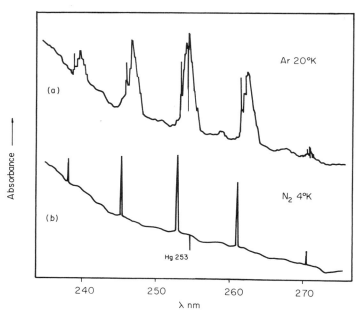

FIG. 6.3. Fine structure in the spectrum of benzene (*a*) in argon at 20°K, (*b*) in N_2 at 4°K the line width is less than 0.3 cm^{-1}. Unpublished data of E. M. Voigt and B. Meyer.

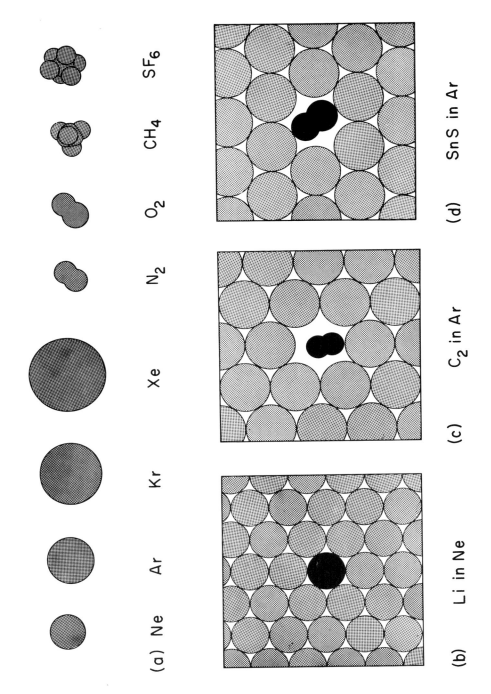

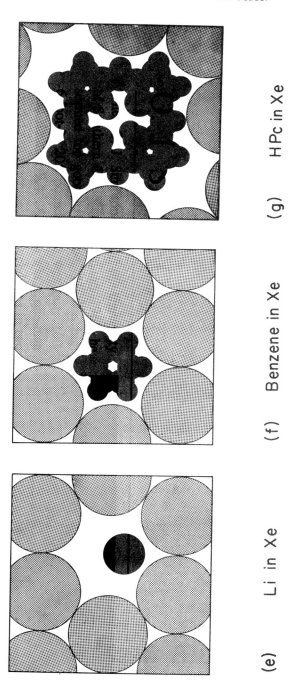

(e)   Li in Xe   (f)   Benzene in Xe   (g)   HPc in Xe

FIG. 6.4. Relative size of various matrix molecules. (a) Neon, argon, krypton, xenon, N_2, O_2, CH_4, and SF_6; (b) Li in Ne; (c) C_2 in Ar; (d) SnS in Ar; (e) Li in Xe; (f) C_6H_6 in Xe; (g) porphyrin in Xe.

while the emission of matrix-isolated formaldehyde decreases (Smith, 1969). The chemical recombination of monomeric formaldehyde to para formaldehyde is slow at temperatures below $-20°C$. In contrast, activation energy for reaction and recombination of C_2, Li, and other radicals is so low that diffusion results in new chemical species with different spectra. Li and C_2 are so mobile that recombination is severe during production or deposition of matrices. Such solids contain large amounts of side products, with the desired radical constituting often only 10% of the concentration of its impurities.

It is not always easy to differentiate between the above two types of diffusion processes. Since diffusion rates are unknown for most hosts and guests, the easiest way to distinguish between annealing and solute diffusion is to vary experimentally the size ratio of host to guest by substitution through analogous compounds.

An example for this was used for analyzing the spectrum of alkali atoms in rare gas matrices (Meyer, 1965). The appearance of lithium dimers at $20°K$ indicates that lithium diffuses in xenon long before xenon anneals, while in the absence of aggregate spectra, the sharpening of rubidium lines in argon after annealing at $30°K$, without loss of absorbance, proves that annealing is the predominant process in the latter system.

Figure 6.4 shows the relative size of various matrix materials, and the size relation between a carbon atom in xenon and a porphyrin molecule in xenon. Astonishingly, the sharpness of spectra is not directly correlated to an accurate fitting of the solute into a substitutional site: porphyrin lines in argon are less than one wave number wide, while lithium, which substitutes perfectly in neon has a half line width of several hundred wave numbers.

2. Diffusion during Photolysis

In situ preparation of free radicals is normally based on photolysis of a reagent trapped in a matrix. It is essential that the reaction products diffuse out of their original lattice cage so that recombination does not occur, because radicals have essentially no activation energy for recombination. On the other hand, diffusion beyond a next-nearest-neighbor site is undesirable because it could lead to reaction with radicals originating from another matrix cage. Therefore, the matrix temperature must be carefully chosen and controlled. Pimentel has given a detailed discussion of this dilemma (Bass, 1960).

D. Diffusion in Organic Glasses and Mixed Crystals

Mixed crystals are solid at room temperature. Therefore, diffusion at cryogenic temperature is negligible or slow. In organic glasses, diffusion is hindered by steric effects. The very fact that glasses form, rather than crystals, proves that solvent diffusion is slow. In quickly frozen organic glasses short-range diffusion processes also lead to transitions from quenched metastable phases to the thermodynamically stable solvent configurations. An example in point is cyclohexane, which is monoclinic at 77°K, but freezes in a cubic structure. Different preparation methods and aging yield different mixtures of the two forms. Under fortuitous conditions, it is possible to obtain an almost pure phase of either form. The kinetics are such that at 76°K substantial transformations from cubic to monoclinic cyclohexane can be observed within a day. Similar effects can be observed in other solvents. In matrices, phase transitions might be slower. If the temperature of a target is lowered from 40° to 4°K, annealed methane and CD_4 do not seem to assume stable phases. The transitions of oxygen and nitrogen are very slow.

II. PHOTOCHEMISTRY

In 1942, Lewis and Lipkin reported observation of three primary photochemical processes in rigid low temperature solids; photodissociation, photo-oxidation, and photoionization. Photodissociation results in the formation of radicals and provides the basis for trapping of numerous radical species. Porter and co-workers (Porter, 1958b; Norman, 1954, 1955; Brocklehurst, 1966a) have studied the photochemistry and resultant products of a large number of molecules in organic glasses.

The mechanism, the products, and the measured quantum yield of photochemical decomposition are influenced by the host rigidity. Rigidity constrains the product in its host cage. The magnitude of constraint depends on the relative guest and host size, host viscosity, temperature, residual energy after reaction, and the trapping site. Constraint can aid or restrict product formation. It aids when it prevents long-range diffusion, leading to radical–radical reactions. It adversely affects the production of desired photolytic fragments if the radical remains in its cage and recombines with other products. In the latter case, the observed quantum yield is lower than the primary photolysis yield. Radical formation is also reduced if energy absorbed by the molecule is transferred directly to the surrounding environment and relaxation of the precursor prevents fragmentation. Another important factor reducing observed quantum yields is light scattering. It is especially severe in cracked organic glasses and in heavy matrices such as Xe, SF_6, C_4F_8. The scattering is difficult to eliminate. Since it depends on so many parameters, including aging of the sample, it limits severely the accuracy of data. Reductions of quantum yields at low temperatures are not predictable, nor can they be estimated from gas phase studies. Despite this, doped low temperature solids are a convenient tool for the study of photochemical reactions because of their ability to stabilize normally reactive intermediates. In fact, the matrix isolation method was expressly developed for radical trapping (Whittle, 1954).

Lewis and Kasha in 1944 proposed (Lewis, 1944b) that photochemical reactions can occur by two excitation mechanisms, by reaction following directly after absorption of a photon

$$(AB) + h\nu \rightarrow A + B$$

or following transfer of the excitation to the molecular triplet state

$$(AB) + h\nu \rightarrow (AB)^* \rightsquigarrow {}^3 (AB)$$

$$^3(AB) + h\nu' \rightarrow A + B$$

The latter mechanism is biphotonic. Brocklehurst (1966a) developed a more detailed mechanism in terms of the molecular states.

The biphotonic mechanism owes its importance to the efficient triplet population process via intersystem crossing and the long triplet lifetimes characteristic in rigid low temperature solutions. With few exceptions (Lim, 1965), most molecules follow the biphotonic mechanism when undergoing photochemical change in rigid media (Cadogan, 1965; Gibbons, 1965; Brocklehurst, 1966a). It appears that solute triplet state population is necessary for many reactions, because excited singlets have sufficient energy, but are not long lived enough for the absorption of the second photon (Brocklehurst, 1966a). Irradiation with high energy sources such as γ-rays or electrons (Kondo, 1964; Charlesby, 1965a,b; Ranayne, 1962; Guarino, 1964; Sharma, 1956) yields similar processes.

Product formation proceeds via either of three mechanisms. In one mechanism, the free radical and a nonreactive fragment form. An example of this type is the decomposition of azides

$$XN_3 + h\nu \rightarrow NX + N_2$$

which yields the diatomic halide and molecular nitrogen. This method is especially elegant when the neutral side product is identical with the matrix. Other species prepared by this method include NH, NF, NCl, NCN, NBr, and CF_2 (Milligan, 1964b, 1968b). In all these cases the reactions are irreversible or slow. Therefore, recombination does not occur. Photolysis of CF_2N_2, CH_2N_2 does not yield CH_2 because CH_2 and N_2 react at 20°K to form CH_2N_2 (Moore, 1964a,b; 1965).

In the second type of mechanism, the undesired photolysis fragment is a light atom, which escapes from the trapping site. Milligan and Jacox (1969a) have demonstrated that the yield of the CN radical from photolysis of XCN precursors depends on diffusion which decreases with increasing atomic size in the order X = H > F > Cl > Br. The chlorine and bromine compound form little CN; instead, only ClNC and BrNC isomers form.

The third type of photolysis mechanism, characteristic of photochemical reactions of organic aromatic molecules, involves a resonance stabilized product. Quantum yields are invariably highest when one of the fragments has resonance stabilization available. Thus, triphenylmethane gives triphenylmethyl with nearly the same quantum yield as in the gas phase.

An additional difficulty occasionally encountered in low temperature photochemical reactions is the reaction of photolysis fragments with the host. Photolysis in organic glasses is particularly susceptible. Matrices such as N_2, CO, and CO_2 are also reactive under some conditions. The synthetic application of this effect is discussed in Chapter 9, Section II, C.

Recommended Reading

Calvert, J. G., and J. N. Pitts, Jr., *Photochemistry*, Wiley, New York, 1966.

Craig, D. P., and S. H. Walmsley, *Physics and Chemistry of the Solid State*, Vol. 2, Interscience-Wiley, New York, 1968b.

Debye, P., and J. O. Edwards, J. Chem. Phys. **20**, 236 (1952b). "Long-Lifetime Phosphorescence and the Diffusion Process."

Hannay, N. B., *Solid State Chemistry*, Prentice-Hall, Englewood Cliffs, New Jersey, 1967.

Noyes, W. A., Jr., G. S. Hammond, and J. N. Pitts, Jr., eds., *Advances in Photochemistry*, Interscience-Wiley, New York, Volume 1, 1963, ff.

Terenin, A., *Recent Progress in Photobiology* (E. J. Bowen, ed.), p. 3, Academic Press, New York, 1965. "Basic Photochemistry in Relation to Photobiology."

Turro, N. J., *Molecular Photochemistry*, W. A. Benjamin, New York, 1965.

Whelan, D. J., Chem. Rev. **69**, 179 (1969). "Intermediates in Radiation Chemistry at Low Temperatures."

CHAPTER 7

Experimental Apparatus

This chapter contains a general description of apparatus and experimental procedures. It intends to aid those who want to plan, perform, and understand experiments. It contains data for selecting, designing, and, on occasion, constructing equipment; it also supplies figures and facts for use during experiments.

The selection of material reflects to some extent interests in our own laboratory. More detailed data and descriptions of individual fields can be found in specialized books and articles and in manufacturers' products sheets.

Figure 7.1 is a schematic diagram of a low temperature spectroscopic experiment. The solid sample is mounted on a holder whose temperature can be lowered and controlled. The sample holder is attached to a refrigerant vessel or a refrigerator. The entire cold part must be isolated to exclude air and moisture. For this purpose a vacuum is applied in the entire assembly, which forms the cryostat. It is convenient to be able to monitor the vacuum and temperatures. For optical observation, the sample holder and the cryostat have windows or observation ports. For spectral studies, a light source, optical guides, and photon analyzers are used to record the observed parameters so that later they can be evaluated. In matrix experiments, the sample preparation and sample alterations are integral parts of the experiment. In frozen solutions, in mixed crystal experiments, and in the case of polymeric solutions, the sample may often be prepared separately, using independent auxiliary equipment and facilities.

In the following sections, the components are discussed in the sequence: Selection of equipment, the cryostat, properties of materials, heat transfer, refrigerants and refrigerators, vacuum systems, and spectroscopic train.

119

I. SELECTION AND AVAILABILITY OF EQUIPMENT

The development of space technology since 1956 has led to a breakthrough in cryogenic know-how, commercially available equipment, and refrigerants which has altered both the work and appearance of low temperature spectroscopy laboratories. The time of dependence on specialized low temperature groups and completely laboratory-built equipment is past. In 1924 Vegard had to travel from Oslo to Leiden to have access to liquid helium. In 1960 we were still dependent on local refrigerant supplies, and graduate students in low temperature spectroscopy spent significant amounts of time building or modifying equipment and liquefying refrigerants. Today, helium is air shipped or liquefied *in situ*, as needed, with microliquefiers, and ready-made equipment can be quickly purchased and assembled. Most of the laboratory time is now spent measuring and manipulating samples. This has changed the character of experiments and the problems connected with them because as experiments become routine, or very sophisticated, the main difficulty is no longer access to equipment, but proper use and understanding of equipment and of the data obtained.

It is possible to purchase many of the components used in low temperature spectroscopy at a reasonable price; often the components are of equivalent or better quality than can be achieved through laboratory construction. Much equipment is now so well developed, that it can be expected to be of

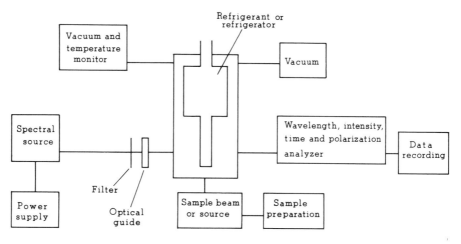

FIG. 7.1. Block diagram of equipment for low temperature experiments.

long-range value. However, no matter how well developed equipment may be, there is no one single simple set or piece of equipment that fits all needs of low temperature spectroscopy. This can be illustrated by pondering the eternally discussed choice between photographic and photoelectric recording. Both have experimental advantages and drawbacks, and both are used for recording light intensities, but photographs are specially suitable for simultaneously integrating intensity at different frequencies over extended periods of time, while photoelectric recording can easily yield highly time-resolved information. Therefore, the choice does not depend so much on which method is more perfected, but rather on how the inherent individual advantages and drawbacks of the operating principle affect the observation of the sample one plans to study.

In making decisions about the assembly of experimental equipment, it is well to note that cryogenic experiments are complex and long, and that a well planned experiment can save many hours of frustration and much money. It is well worthwhile to make a small cost efficiency study to optimize the selection of parts. The problem is usually to select the correct level of sophistication and the size. For this the choice of a vacuum system is a good example: a small vacuum pump is cheapest and takes the least amount of space, but the crucial fact is that if a small pump takes more than 20 minutes to achieve the ultimately desired pressure, the experimenter will waste his time, not once, but every day during each experiment. On the other hand, it is not always true that large equipment is better or more flexible. A high dispersion spectrograph is useless for recording vibrational structure of diatomics in matrices because the free spectral range is insufficient.

Before making decisions, it is valuable to check on new developments. The field of light sources affords many examples for this. Lasers get better and cheaper by the month, and the development of commercial, tunable UV lasers is imminent. The question in this field is whether one needs equipment now, or whether one can wait for a better or cheaper tool.

Another question regards the choice between commercial and laboratory-built equipment. On the one hand, commercial equipment made by a reputable manufacturer has the advantage that one knows what he will obtain, what the equipment can do, when it will be delivered, what it will cost, and, most important, that it will work. Presently, commercial sophistication is such that, for a specified task, a commercial component will almost always outperform a laboratory-built tool. On the other hand, most scientific equipment is usually not primarily designed for low temperature spectroscopy. Moreover, since the operator has not experienced the educational frustrations and joys of construction, he is much less familiar with his equipment and might remain unaware of intrinsic problems because he is not trained and accustomed to test performance. This is true even for a theoretically simple component, like a vacuum system.

II. CRYOSTAT

The basic function of the cryostat (see Fig. 7.2) is to provide a sample holder, refrigeration to cool the sample, a vacuum shroud to thermally insulate the sample, and an optical path for observation and excitation. Required for the operation of all but the most simple cryostats are a vacuum pump with cold traps and vacuum gauges to monitor pressure. For automatic or continuous use, level controls or feed controls for refrigerants are desirable. On occasion, additional accessories, such as a radiation shield as a thermal barrier for heat transfer, a deposition inlet for condensing gaseous samples,

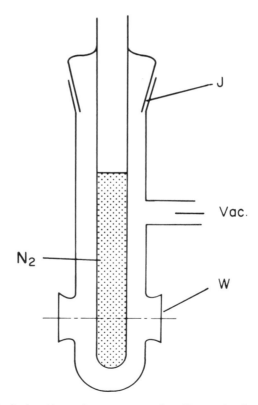

FIG. 7.2. Basic functions of a cryostat; glass Dewar for liquid nitrogen.

and a temperature probe for measuring the sample temperature, may be necessary.

A very large number of different designs have been proposed, and a newcomer will find a startling choice of commercial Dewars. There is no general purpose design available. The choice of the right equipment is more crucial than one originally might think because the cryostat determines the mode of refrigeration, which, in turn, determines convenience and cost of daily operation. The choice also depends on the stability or reactivity of the sample and whether it can be prepared at room temperature. The sample temperature, the precision of temperature control, and the length of cooling constitute further considerations. If all experiments are of the same type, routine procedures can be developed, and the equipment can be much more specialized and better optimized than when each experiment is different.

A. Commercial Cryostats *vs.* Laboratory-Constructed Cryostats

Some of the advantages of purchasing a commercial cryostat have been mentioned above. In addition, commercial cryostats are almost always smaller, lighter, and cheaper than laboratory-constructed ones.

By contrast, presently available commercial Dewars commonly have the following shortcomings: (1) Since they are usually constructed of welded stainless steel, they cannot easily be modified. (2) The pumping cross section is designed for static vacuum; it is too small for matrix isolation experiments. (3) Often, the connection to the vacuum system is located at the top of the cryostat. Because of this, uncondensable gases are pumped over the entire length of the evacuated chamber, thereby thermally shortening the refrigerant reservoir. (4) The window flanges are too small and designed so that only specially machined windows can be used; frequently these do not exist in the material desired.

Laboratory designed and constructed Dewars can be built to avoid such flaws, but they invariably constitute a sump for time and, therefore, for money. The engineering skills of the designer are not the only limit. Normal laboratory workshops do not have the necessary machinery to bend and press stainless steel sheet, or to weld copper to stainless steel. Furthermore, unless one operates an apprentice program, it is usually not worthwhile or possible to build the different jigs and dies required to construct the ideally visualized product. Therefore, the constructed cryostat is almost always larger and heavier than necessary, with the result that for each experiment it takes longer to reach vacuum and the equipment needs more coolant to reach a given temperature. Experienced researchers invariably admit that they constructed several different designs before they found a really useful cryostat, because only practical experience shows what aspects of the design limit the usefulness and efficiency of equipment.

B. Glass Cryostats

Figure 7.2 shows a cross section of a simple cryostat for work at and below 77°K. The vacuum space is fitted with a stopcock so that the Dewar can be periodically pumped out. The top part should be silver plated to reduce radiation losses. The bottom can be made of cylindrical tubing, but shaped glass or quartz will give a better light path. For optimal observation, outside and inside walls can be sealed to optical windows. However, complicated shapes are more susceptible to thermal stress and failure. At temperatures below 30°K, heat losses in a single Dewar become very substantial. Therefore, a double Dewar with heat shields is advisable for work at 20°K and imperative for use at 4°K. Glass double Dewars are very useful but are difficult to build and contain short bends that make them vulnerable. If optical flats or liquid cells are planned, as in Fig. 7.3, special provision must be made to relieve thermal stress due to the uneven thermal expansion of differently shaped parts. Glass tubes must be bent or coiled, or the flask will fracture on first use, regardless of the care in annealing the finished vessel. It is good practice to wrap outside walls with adhesive tape to prevent the free implosion of parts in the event of a fracture. This simple precaution can make the difference between an annoying but harmless interruption of the experiment, and a catastrophic failure. The safety section in Chapter 8, Section III, C describes other techniques to reduce explosion hazards.

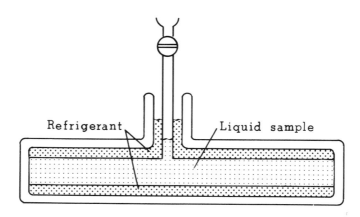

Refrigerant   Liquid sample

FIG. 7.3. Liquid cell with horizontal light path.

Glass Dewars are cheap and light, the samples can be easily inspected visually, and the building material is of itself an excellent insulator. This latter property has one disadvantage, namely, that samples mounted on glass walls are in good thermal contact only when they are immersed in the refrigerant or under a conductive gas atmosphere. A cryostat based on immersion is shown in Fig. 7.4. Otherwise, solids and matrices mounted or deposited on glass in the vacuum space are rarely at the temperature of the coolant. In addition, such solids easily flake off because of differences in thermal expansion.

C. Glass-Metal Cryostats

The thermal problems and optical losses in multiple-wall Dewars can be overcome with the modifications such as those shown in Fig. 7.5. The

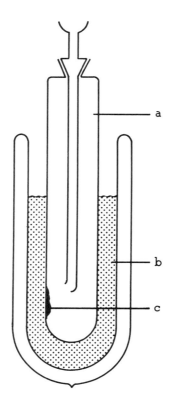

FIG. 7.4. Immersion cell for trapping in a cold bath. *a*, sample cell; *b*, refrigerant; *c*, sample.

Housekeeper seals, used to attach the copper cold finger, are commercially available and withstand many hundred temperature cycles between 20°K and 300°K if they are kept dry. Moisture and condensation on the seal will invariably lead to instant failure. It is our experience that Housekeeper seals are not suitable for liquid helium work. They often fracture after one to three temperature cycles and must be inspected before and after each use.

Broida (Schoen, 1958) has described a glass Dewar with a metal radiation shield. Figure 7.5 gives a cross section of a modified design of his Dewar, which proved to be flexible and cheap. In the metal–glass combination the design takes advantage of the thermal conductivity and reflectivity of copper. A complicated double-walled silvered glass shield can be replaced with a thin-walled, easily constructed copper shield. The parts A and B can be assembled and aligned before the bottom part C is connected. The top of the copper shield is slotted lengthwise and fits snugly around the Pyrex liquid nitrogen reservoir. In an early design, glass beads on the Dewar and bayonet-type slots on the copper were provided to lock the shield into position. This later proved to be unnecessary because copper contracts far more than Pyrex and clamps tightly to the glass. Without slots, the copper or glass would break.

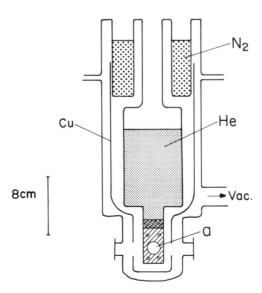

FIG. 7.5. Pyrex glass cryostat according to Meyer (1965); a, sapphire window; He, liquid helium; N_2, liquid nitrogen; Vac, vacuum pump port; Cu, copper shield.

D. Metal Cryostats

A metal cryostat can be machined very accurately and is sturdy. Parts built with flanges can be easily assembled and changed. O-ring seals make it possible to rotate or otherwise move parts relative to one another. The disadvantage is that the liquid refrigerant level is not visible and must be monitored by indirect means.

Figure 7.6 shows a typical matrix cryostat. Brass is especially suitable for exploratory design, because parts can be changed by machining or

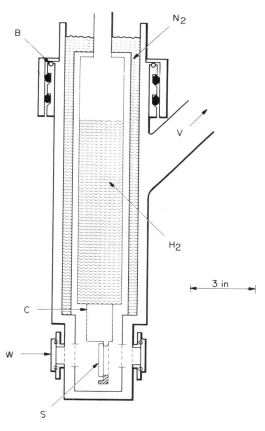

FIG. 7.6. Metal Dewar. (a) Cross section: B, ball bearing and O-ring joint for turning target; C, copper target holder; H_2, liquid hydrogen; N_2, liquid nitrogen; S, sapphire window target; V, vacuum connection; W, window observation port.

FIG. 7.6 (b) Picture of matrix Dewar.

soldering. Since brass easily adsorbs gases, it is recommended that finished surfaces be polished. Nickel or chrome plating give even better surface properties, but parts can no longer be soldered after plating. Stainless steel is so strong that a very thin wall, 0.02 inch or less, gives sufficient strength and stability for most applications. Stainless steel Dewars can therefore be made light and compact. The cryostat in Fig. 7.7 was made from a 0.016-inch stainless steel sheet. All parts were arc welded under helium or argon. The outside diameter at the window flange is 1 inch. The target holder is copper, plated with nickel. The copper target holder was directly welded to the stainless steel can under an argon atmosphere. Used in the design shown in Fig. 7.8, this weld has already withstood more than 200 cycles between 300° and 4°K.

III. PHYSICAL PROPERTIES OF CRYOSTAT COMPONENTS

Thermal, mechanical, and electrical requirements for different parts of the cryostat vary substantially. The sample holder, for example, has two functions. It must maintain thermal contact with the refrigerant and insulate the cold parts from the rest of the Dewar, which is at room temperature. Both functions require matching thermal expansion and resistance to thermal stress.

The following sections contain data that are useful for choosing the best construction material. More complete summaries of properties can be found in books on cryogenic engineering, in handbooks, in journals such as *Cryogenic Engineering* and *Cryogenics*, and in manufacturers' data sheets.

A. Thermal Expansion

Expansion coefficients change with temperature. The values for different materials vary widely. Typical values are 0.011% per degree for quartz, 0.33% per degree for copper, and 1.11% per degree for epoxy resin. If possible, these three materials should not be jointly heated or cooled. It is best to use only one material, and to join parts by welding without additional binding materials. Unfortunately, this is the most time-consuming method of construction. It is often possible to select different materials with closely matching expansion coefficients. Silver soldered brass constitutes a good compromise. Table 7.1 and Fig. 7.9 give linear thermal expansion of various materials at three temperatures. The values depend on the history of the sample and machining techniques. Organic plastics can have widely different values because of change in composition. Figure 7.9 shows that, for quartz,

FIG. 7.7. Stainless steel cryostat for use in a 1-inch magnet.

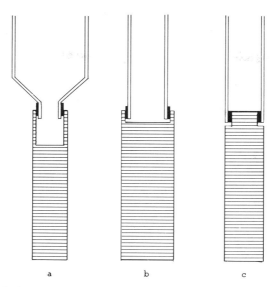

FIG. 7.8. Metal design eliminating thermal stress in copper-to-stainless steel junctions: (a) welded junction, (b) silver soldered junction, (c) incorrect design. In all drawings, Cu: Copper; st.st.: Stainless steel tubing.

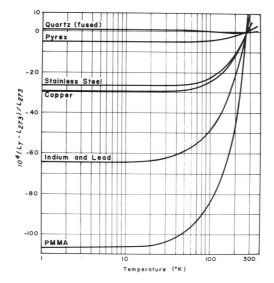

FIG. 7.9. Thermal expansion of copper, quartz, Pyrex, stainless steel, copper, indium, lead, and polymethyl methacrylate (PMMA).

Table 7.1

Linear Thermal Expansion for Various Materials

Material	Linear Thermal Expansion[a]		
	20°K	80°K	300°K
Quartz	+7.4	+1.2	+1.1
Pyrex	−50	−48	+8.5
304 Stainless steel	−265	−248	+42
Copper	−293	−269	+44
Brass	−346	−313	+50
Aluminum	−370	−346	+61
Epoxy	−929	−813	+168
Nylon	−1218	−1086	+222
Polymethyl methacrylate	−1060	−900	+205
Indium	−638	−532	+85
Soft Solder		$\sim$ −436	+69

[a] Values are 10^5 $[(L_T - L_{273})/L_{273}]$. Data from Scott (1959).

expansion coefficients are not linear functions of temperature. Often expansion coefficients cannot be matched, for example, between an optical window and a copper frame, or two parts of the same part may have to be maintained at different temperatures: for example, the top and bottom of the inside container of a liquid storage Dewar. In such a case, two precautions can be taken. The first is to design and machine parts in such a way that stress can be best absorbed. As an example, consider Fig. 7.8, which illustrates three ways in which stainless steel and copper can be joined. Figure 7.7 shows a common way of fitting a bottom plate to a piece of tubing. When the container is cooled, copper contracts more than stainless, and the silver solder joint absorbs large tensile stresses. If cycled between room temperature and the boiling point of liquid nitrogen, such joints quickly develop hairline cracks and, therefore, vacuum leaks. The arrangement in Fig. 7.8b takes somewhat longer to machine, but thermal stress results in compression of the solder, and less damage. This design can be cycled to 4°K many dozens of times without failure. Figure 7.8a shows a Dewar bottom that was welded under an argon atmosphere. Such pieces can be cycled between 300° and 4°K without failure. It is important that all joined parts be machined to the thinnest allowable wall strength because elasticity is a basic requirement for survival of such joints.

On a commercial scale, ingenious design can overcome incompatibilities between materials. Thus, several types of seals are available to permit joining of glass and metal surfaces and to allow electrical leads to be passed into a vacuum system. Housekeeper copper-to-Pyrex seals can be cycled between 20°K and 300°K. Kovar stainless steel-to-stainless steel seals fracture at very low temperatures but can be used at elevated temperatures.

As a last resort, plastic binders and intermediate materials may have to be used as buffers when materials cannot be joined by design geometry. At low temperatures few materials are elastic. Thus, it may be necessary to use plastic joints that are replaced after each temperature cycle.

Good low temperature gasket materials are indium and lead. When all else fails, parts can be joined by pressing with springs. This is suitable at temperatures as low as 77°K. Below 20°K, this method is undesirable.

B. Mechanical Properties

Parts must be strong enough to support themselves, to withstand handling, to withstand atmospheric pressure against vacuum, and to absorb thermal stress. Table 7.2 lists tensile strength and compressive yields of various

Table 7.2

Mechanical Properties of Plastic Materials[a]

Plastic	Temperature (°K)	Ultimate Tensile Strength at $\times 10^{-2}$	Compressive Yield Strength at $\times 10^{-3}$	Young's Modulus at $\times 10^{-4}$
Teflon	295	1.3	—	4
(Polytetrafluoroethylene)	77	100	12.0	50
	20	—	17.0	—
	4	—	18.0	68
Kel-F (polytrifluoromono-	293	4.3	—	17
chloroethylene)	77	110	—	57
	4	—	30	—
Polyethylene	300	9	—	1
	4	—	17	—
Polyvinyl chloride	293	53	—	35
	77	135	—	68
Nylon	293	65	—	29
	77	189	—	75
Mylar	300	140	—	69
(polyethylene terephthalate)	77	210	—	125

[a] Data from Scott (1959).

construction materials. These values hold only for homogeneous solid bodies. Parts that have suffered through machining and assembly may be weaker. Almost invariably, parts contain local stress concentrations due to design features; typical areas are the interfaces of joints. It cannot be pointed out sufficiently how important is the preparation and assembly of joints. Well prepared and executed solder joints can last indefinitely, while an insufficiently cleaned or heated joint will surely fail at low temperature because of corrosion and fracture due to moisture penetration.

C. Thermal Conductivity

Table 7.3 lists the thermal conductivity of various materials versus temperature. The behavior of copper and silver is outstanding in that their conductivity increases substantially as the temperature is lowered. Of the optical materials (Fig. 7.10) sapphire shows a similar low temperature advantage. Copper targets with sapphire windows make an ideal combination as heat

Table 7.3

Thermal Conductivity Data for Various Materials at Low Temperatures

Material	Thermal Conductivity[a]				
	4.2°K	20°K	30°K	80°K	300°K
Aluminum (2024-T4)	0.030	0.167	0.240	0.560	1.20
(6063-T5)	0.360	1.69	2.30	2.30	2.06
Brass (P6)	0.020	0.120	0.180	0.402	1.00
Copper (Elec T. T. P.)	3.4	13.1	14.0	5.3	4.1
(Phos. Deox.)	0.075	0.422	0.619	1.28	2.20
Glass (average)	0.00098	0.0015	0.0019	0.0043	0.0098
Gold: Annealed	17	15	7.3	3.4	3.1
Drawn	1.3	4.3	4.1	3.0	2.9
Nylon	0.00013	0.00098	—	—	—
Silver: Annealed	146	52	18	4.1	4.0
Drawn	0.43	2.3	2.8	3.0	3.9
Stainless steel	0.002	0.020	0.033	0.082	0.150
Teflon	0.00047	0.0014	0.0017	0.0023	0.0026
Polymethyl methacrylate	0.00058	0.00074	—	—	—
Sapphire	1.21	35.6	63.7	8.6	0.4
Quartz (fused)	0.0011	0.0016	0.0019	0.0045	—
Indium	8.5	17	12	—	—
Lead	21	0.58	0.46	0.37	0.35
Soft solder	0.16	0.56	0.54	0.52	0.5

[a] Values are expressed as centimeters per degree.

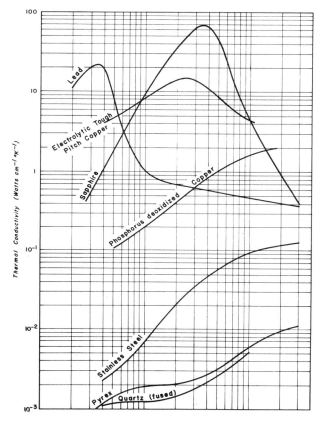

FIG. 7.10. Thermal conductivity of quartz, sapphire, Pyrex, stainless steel, copper, and lead.

exchangers. The thermal conductivity of metals and alloys is strongly dependent on impurities. Electrolytic copper is far superior to phosphorus deoxidized copper of which commercial tubing and sheet are commonly fabricated.

D. Absorptivity and Emissivity

Absorptivity and emissivity measure the efficiency of radiative transfer to or from a given surface as compared to that of a black body. Surface treatment, impurities, and temperature greatly affect these values. Table 7.4 demonstrates this for some commonly used cryostat materials. Polished copper, at 4°K, has an emissivity $\varepsilon = 0.006$. For oxidized copper at room

Table 7.4

Absorptivity and Emissivity of Various Materials at Room Temperature[a]

Material	Emissivity, Total Normal (ε_n)
Aluminum, electropolished	0.03
	0.018 (76°K)
	0.011 (4°K)
With 7.0 μ oxide layer	0.75
Vaporized on both sides of 0.5-mil Mylar plastic	0.04 (76°K)
Brass: Polished	0.03
Oxidized	0.60
Cadmium, electroplate	0.03 (76°K)
Chromium-plated copper	0.08
Copper: Black oxidized	0.78
Commercial polish	0.03
Electrolytic, careful polish	0.015 (76°K)
Electrolytic polish	0.0062 (4°K)
Gold, 0.0015″ foil on glass	0.01 (76°K)
Iron, electrolytic	0.05–0.065
Lead, 0.004″ foil	0.011 (4°K)
Nickel, electrolytic	0.04
Platinum	0.016 (85°K)
Rhodium, plated on stainless steel	0.078 (76°K)
Silver	0.022
	0.01 (76°K)
Tin, 0.001″ foil	0.013 (76°K)
Stellite	0.11
Monel, smooth but not polished	0.16
Ice, smooth	0.96
Pyrex	0.94
Lacquer: White	0.925
Black matte	0.97
Oil paints, all colors	0.92–0.96
Carbon, black	0.952
Paper	0.932
Quartz, fused	0.932

[a] Data from Scott (1959).

temperature the corresponding value is 0.78. Thus, careful surface preparation can reduce heat losses by a factor of over one hundred. This can be translated into large savings of liquid helium and other refrigerants. The values for polished metals are generally only a few percent of a black body, while ice, quartz, and Pyrex act like carbon black, giving more than 93% efficiency. Copper surfaces are very good heat reflectors as long as no moisture or chemicals cover the surface.

A very convenient heat shield is aluminized Mylar foil. It combines the high reflectivity of a metal surface with the insulating properties of plastic materials and is extremely tough.

IV. HEAT TRANSFER

In a cryostat three types of heat transfer are important: (1) thermal conduction through solid materials and liquids; (2) thermal transport through gases; and (3) radiative heat transfer.

Table 7.5 contains a comparison of the relative contributions of the different forms of heat transfer in a cryostat under conditions typical for cryogenic experiments. Heat transport through supporting elements can easily be kept small. A good vacuum is vital; and without shielding, liquid helium cannot be stored in a container.

Table 7.5

Contribution of Different Forms of Heat Transfer to Loss of Refrigerant in a 1-Liter Liquid Helium Can with a 5 cm² Window

Form of Transfer	Heat Transfer (milliwatts)	Boil-off of Liquid Helium (ml/hour)
Thermal Conduction		
Two support and vent tubes (Fig. 7.11),[a] 1.5 d × 0.010 cm × 10 cm	0.5	0.7
Heat transport by residual vacuum		
1 torr	2000	2800
11 micron	50	70
10^{-6} torr	4	5
Radiative heat transport		
No shield: Silvered Dewar	270	370
Unsilvered Dewar	8100	10000
Shield at 76°K, with 5 cm² window opening	3	4
Aluminum Mylar shield, 6 turns[b]	2	3

[a] Larger than reality, because cooling by escaping helium is neglected.
[b] Window absorptivity $\varepsilon = 0.1$.

A. Thermal Conduction

Conduction between refrigerant and optical sample should be large; exchange between the cold chamber and the atmosphere and outer wall should be minimal. Techniques for improving heat transfer consist in establishing intimate contact between parts built from conductors or using liquids or gases to fill spaces at interfaces.

Insulation is achieved by reducing the surface cross section and using poor thermal conductors. Figure 7.11 shows a cross section of a support for a calorimeter. The liquid refrigerant container is suspended by thin-walled inlet and vent tubing made of German silver, or stainless steel. Heat conduction through three tubes, 1.5 cm in diameter, 0.03 mm thick, and 6 cm long, is 0.5 mW per degree per second, corresponding to a helium loss of 0.7 ml per hour. This is negligible compared to heat transport through radiation or incompletely evacuated volumes.

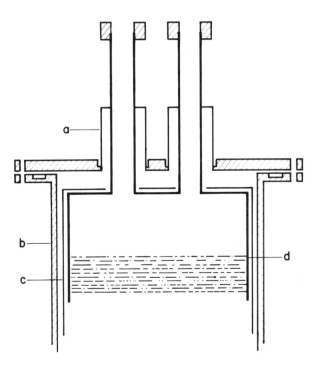

FIG. 7.11. Calorimeter support: *a*, insulating bells; *b*, vacuum shroud; *c*, heat shield; *d*, refrigerant can.

B. Heat Transport through Gases at Reduced Pressure

At reduced pressure heat convection decreases and the behavior of gases changes. In the so-called Knudsen range, from 1 to 10^{-3} torr, ideal gas laws are no longer strictly observed, and below 10^{-3} torr the mean free path becomes comparable to the cryostat dimensions. This means that gas molecules in a residual vacuum undergo mainly collisions with walls and rarely with each other. Pressures of this order are necessary to maintain low temperatures in cryostats because of heat transfer, and because of gas evolution during sample deposition of matrices. Residual gas also leads to impurity deposition, for example O_2, which can cause phosphorescence quenching.

Typical mean free paths of gaseous molecules are: for air at room temperature 5 cm, 1 cm at 76°K; for hydrogen 0.3 cm at 20°K and 10 cm at 300°K; and for helium 0.6 cm at 20°K and 15 cm at room temperature. Energy transfer depends also on the accommodation coefficient of gases, which is typically between 0.5 and 1, except for helium, where it is 0.3 and 0.6 at room temperature and 20°K, respectively. Figure 7.12 shows the effect of pressure on thermal conductivity between different surface materials.

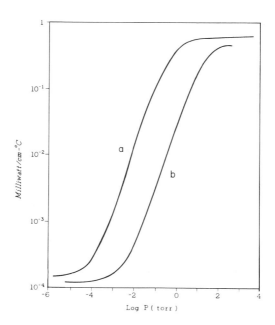

FIG. 7.12. Heat transfer between two surfaces as a function of pressure; *a*, gap = 0.7 mm (0.03 inch), *b*, gap = 0.025 mm (0.0001 inch). After Scott (1959).

C. Radiative Heat Transfer

Radiative transfer from a surface follows the Stefan-Boltzmann law

$$W = \sigma e A T^4$$

where W is the heat transfer, A the surface area, e the emissivity, T the temperature, and σ a constant with the value $\sigma = 5.67 \times 10^{-12}$ in watts per square centimeter, per the fourth power of temperature in degrees Kelvin. The wavelength of the radiation and the temperature are related by Wien's law: $\lambda_{max} \times T = 2898\,\mu \times$ degrees. The temperature dependence of the energy versus wavelength is further discussed in Section VII. Heat exchange between two surfaces is given by

$$W = \sigma e_t A (T_0^4 - T_1^4)$$

where all symbols are as above. σe_t represents the total effect of emissivities and absorptivities of both surfaces, T_0 is the higher temperature, T_1 the lower. σe_t depends on the shape, material, and surface structure. It is always less than 1. Table 7.6 shows values of radiated energy per surface unit versus the ratio of the surface areas of hot and cold surfaces for three experimentally important cases. The first represents room temperature radiation onto a surface at 77°K or below, the second contains radiation

Table 7.6

Heat Transfer through Vacuum, Insulating Materials, and Air[a]

Material Filling 15-cm Gap	Heat Transfer through Insulation (mW/cm²) at Indicated Temperature Gradient		
	300°–77°K	300°–20°K	77°–20°K
High vacuum, $p = 10^{-6}$ torr (0.02 emissivity)	0.45	0.46	0.002
Gases at atmospheric pressure			
H_2	19.3	19.6	0.8
He	17.1	17.7	1.7
Air or N_2	2.68	—	—
Evacuated perlite density of 5–6 lb/ft³	0.16	0.13	0.007
Gas-filled perlite			
He	18.7	18.7	2.2
N_2	4.8	—	—
Polystyrene foam	4.9	5.1	0.57

[a] Data from Scott (1959).

between a liquid nitrogen shield and a surface at 20°K or below. The curves have similar shapes, but the scale of the thermal units differs by a factor of a thousand. Radiative heat losses are also indicated in liquid helium loss, in milliliters per square centimeter surface per hour. It obviously pays to shield targets carefully.

If several shields are inserted between the storage vessel and the room temperature wall, the heat loss is approximately

$$W = A(T_0{}^4 - T_1{}^4) \frac{e_t}{n+1}$$

where all symbols are as above, and n indicates the number of shields. The above equation assumes that all surfaces have identical emissivities. In the absence of other heat transfer, the shields assume intermediate temperatures, establish an equilibrium temperature gradient, and reduce the net heat transfer proportionately to the number of shields present. In practice it is difficult and cumbersome to mount shields independently. It is more convenient to make multiple shields by wrapping several layers of an insulating material around the cold part. In order to reduce heat conduction, very thin metal foil is used, and individual layers are spaced by using corrugated foil or by punching warts into the foil. A good shielding can be achieved by simultaneously wrapping thin copper foil and thin polyethylene sheet. Even better is aluminum-coated Mylar foil, which in itself contains both a highly reflecting metal film and an insulating spacer. Mylar multiple shields are ideal for insulating liquid hydrogen vessels. Six layers of 0.1 mil Mylar foil are sufficient to insulate a liquid hydrogen matrix cryostat efficiently, and make a liquid nitrogen shield unnecessary. As a result, a cryostat containing a given refrigerant volume can be built lighter and much smaller. Normal metal shields slowly become covered with dirt and reaction products and are difficult to clean in matrix cryostats. Dirty old shields act as black bodies and are inefficient.

D. Insulation

The storage time of refrigerants depends critically on insulation. For short experiments in small containers, vacuum is almost always the easiest as well as best choice. However, for some applications vacuum insulation is not convenient. Table 7.6 affords a comparison of different insulation methods: air is the poorest of all listed insulators; vacuum with perlite acts as a heat shield. Unshielded vacuum gaps have large radiative transfer losses if the temperature gradient is substantial. Styrofoam is intermediate and, under some conditions, useful. Freshly foamed polystyrene still contains CO_2,

the expanding gas. When very low temperatures are applied, this gas condenses and styrofoam acts as a vacuum insulator, much better than indicated.
With time nitrogen, air, hydrogen, or helium diffuses into the plastic and
reduces insulation to the indicated values. For short time applications, foams
are suitable for liquid nitrogen, and even liquid hydrogen. Figure 7.13 shows
thermal conductivity for different types of insulating materials.

The choice between liquid nitrogen shielded Dewars and powder insulated
Dewars depends on the refrigerant and the size of the vessel. In the laboratory
it might be easier to use liquid nitrogen shields. Powder insulation is better
for large permanently sealed containers. In recent years, liquid helium has been
almost exclusively shipped and stored in powder insulated Dewars. In this
way, the evaporation rate is typically around 0.7–2% per day versus 5–7%
for more conventional containers.   Liquid hydrogen can be adequately
stored in an evacuated perlite container because conductive losses will be
larger than radiative, even if no liquid nitrogen is used. For helium a combination of high vacuum with vapor-cooled perlite is recommended. More details
on this subject can be found in Scott (1959) and other books.

Silvered glass thermos flasks are commonly used for handling liquid
nitrogen, oxygen, and occasionally for short-term storage and transfer of
hydrogen. Figure 7.14 shows a cross section of other storage Dewar flasks

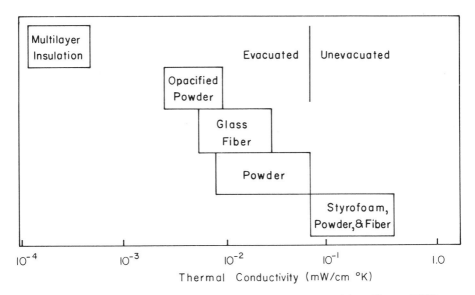

FIG. 7.13. Heat transport through insulating material. After Glaser (1969).

presently in use.   Diagram A shows a commercially available aluminum
flask with plastic foam lining.   Such 4-liter containers are very sturdy and
light. A round shape of similar construction is widely used for 25-liter Dewars.
Diagram B is a cross section of the well established helium-hydrogen Dewar.
It is heavy and, despite the metal construction, vulnerable to shock and
tilting because the concentric inner vessels are suspended by their necks.
Furthermore, the narrow open neck construction intrinsically causes danger
of forming an air plug.   Such Dewar flasks should always be capped with
0.25 or 0.5 psi relief valves to maintain a small positive pressure.   This
prevents air from coming in contact with the cold $\frac{1}{2}$-inch diameter refrigerant
tube. This type of container should be used only for storage of 10- and 25-
liter volumes for which no better commercial Dewars are available.

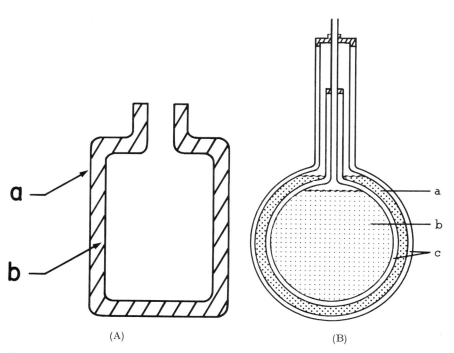

Fig. 7.14.   (A) Four-liter nitrogen Dewar (Linde); a, foam insulation, b, aluminum
shroud.   (B) Old-fashioned 25-liter Dewar for storage of liquid helium or hydrogen:
a, liquid nitrogen; b, liquid helium; c, evacuated gap.

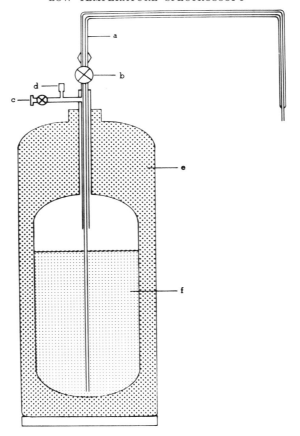

FIG. 7.14. (C). Ceramic insulated storage Dewar, 100-liter capacity: *a*, evacuated removable transfer line; *b*, valve; *c*, vacuum or helium; *d*, 0.25 psi relief valve; *e*, ceramic insulation; *f*, liquid helium.

For 100 liters and larger quantities up to 5000 liters, and more, perlite-insulated vapor-cooled vacuum flasks are now available. Figure 7.14C is a schematic cross section of such a vessel. Such containers are sturdy, light, and compact. They are ideal for air shipment of liquid helium. Since air pressure changes with altitude, the boiling point of helium changes during flight. This is very undesirable because it causes large losses. Therefore, liquid helium containers are equipped with absolute pressure relief valves that maintain a small constant overpressure. This self-pressurization also aids in the transfer of liquid into other containers.

Helium has a low viscosity and low heat of vaporization. Vibration can lead to large evaporation losses, and Dewars should be shock mounted.

Most commercial Dewars now have shock absorbers built into their bases.

V. REFRIGERANTS, REFRIGERATORS, TEMPERA-TURE CONTROL, AND MEASUREMENT

A. Refrigerants

This section deals with the properties of refrigerants used in open-ended cycles, where the liquid is available in bulk quantities and where the gas is discarded or collected in low pressure containers. This method is wasteful, crude, and probably obsolete for matrix work as compared with closed-cycle systems where the gas is liquefied directly into the sample cell as needed and immediately recirculated and recompressed into storage cylinders. However, open cooling cycles are still widely used for cooling samples during short and exploratory experiments.

Only five refrigerants are widely available: liquid air, liquid oxygen, liquid nitrogen, liquid hydrogen, and liquid helium. Liquid argon is also available but is still expensive. We do not discuss here liquid natural gas, which is of great industrial importance as a fuel.

1. Liquid Air

Liquid air contains all the components of atmospheric air, which consists principally of nitrogen and oxygen, with traces of other gases in concentrations shown in Table 7.7, except water and carbon dioxide, because both are solid

Table 7.7

Composition of Atmospheric Air
near the Ground[a]

Gas	Volume Percent
Nitrogen	78.09
Oxygen	20.95
Argon	0.93
Carbon dioxide	0.03
Neon	0.0018
Helium	0.00053
Krypton	0.00011
Hydrogen	0.00005
Xenon	0.000008
Ozone	0.000002
Radon	10^{-18}

[a] Data from Scott (1959).

at the air boiling point of 85°K. The boiling point and composition of liquid
air depend on the history of the liquid and change with time. Figure 7.15
shows the phase diagram for boiling nitrogen–oxygen mixtures. The curves
show that for a given temperature the composition of gaseous and liquid
air are different. If liquid air is obtained by total condensation of air, it
originally consists of 79% nitrogen and 21% oxygen. During boil-off, the
vapor contains only 10% oxygen and 90% nitrogen because of the higher
vapor pressure of nitrogen. Thus, the boiling point of liquid air increases,
and the liquid is increasingly enriched in oxygen. This process is greatly
enhanced when the liquid is in contact with atmospheric air, because gaseous
oxygen liquefies in exchange for nitrogen boil-off. As a result, liquid air
becomes visibly blue, more and more resembling liquid oxygen.

The oxygen enrichment in liquid air can be very substantial. Large
and well insulated open-neck Dewars often contain 60% or more O_2. This
leads to very serious increase in hazards. Combustible gases can condense
in liquid air and lead to a highly explosive mixture. Especially dangerous

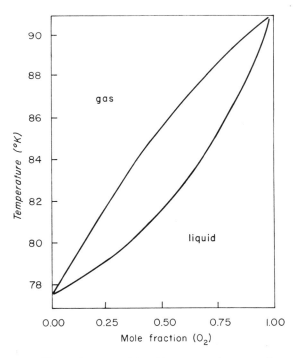

FIG. 7.15. Phase diagram of liquid oxygen–nitrogen mixture.

are mixtures of acetone and liquid air that can form when dry ice–acetone baths and liquid air are used in the same Dewars. Such "bombs" can result in severe explosions. In modern laboratories liquid air is no longer in use. It has been replaced by liquid nitrogen, which can be purchased in bulk quantities from industrial plants where oxygen is separated.

2. Liquid Oxygen

Some physical properties of oxygen are listed in Tables 7.8 and 7.9. Liquid oxygen is strongly paramagnetic and very reactive. Lubricants, solvents,

Table 7.8

Properties of Common Refrigerants

Substance	Temperature (°K) at a Vapor Pressure of:				Melting Point (°K)	Pressure at Melting Point (torr)
	10 torr	100 torr	1 atm	20 atm		
He	—[a]	2.64	4.2	—	—	—
H_2	11.7	15.1	20.4	—	13.95[b]	54[b]
N_2	54.0	63.4	77.3	115	63.1	96.4
O_2	62.7	74.5	90.2	133	54.4	1.1[b]
Ne	18.4	22.1	27.1	42.3	24.6[b]	324[b]
Ar	62.5	73.4	87.3	130	83.8[b]	517[b]
Kr	85.9	101.0	119.8	177	115.8[b]	549[b]
Xe	118.5	139.5	165.0	243	161.4[b]	612[b]
CH_4	77.7	91.7	111.7	165	90.6	—
CF_4	103.6	122	89.5	—	89.4	—

[a] Superfluid.
[b] Triple point.

Table 7.9

Comparison of Common Refrigerants

Refrigerant	Boiling Point	Density (g/ml)	Heat of Vaporization		Liters of Gas, STP	Typical Retail Price (dollars)[a]	
			cal/mole	Kcal/l		Per liter	Per kcal
He	4.215	0.1252	19	0.65	700	3.50	5.00
H_2	20.39	0.0708	216	7.64	780	1.50	0.20
N_2	77.3	0.808	1330	38.60	650	0.40	0.01
O_2	90.2	1.140	1630	58.10	799	1.00	0.02

[a] Price (1970) at a typical large university in the United States.

and vacuum pump oil form explosive mixtures with liquid oxygen. The density is 1.1415 g/ml at the boiling point and decreases to 0.43 g/ml at the critical point. Oxygen converts at 23.886°K from solid α into β oxygen, and at 43.800°K into oxygen(I). The heat capacity increases linearly with temperatures between 12°K and 42°K. The heat capacity of solid oxygen(I) changes very little with temperature, very much like that of liquid oxygen. The paramagnetic susceptibility of liquid oxygen is about 3×10^{-4} electromagnetic units (CGS). Because of the hazards involved, liquid oxygen is normally not used as a refrigerant except in those instances in which the temperature of "pumped" liquid oxygen, about 55°K, is desired. By contrast, the temperature of pumped liquid nitrogen is only about 63°K, because nitrogen solidifies.

3. Liquid Nitrogen

The element has two stable isotopes, ^{14}N and ^{15}N, with a relative abundance of 1 to 0.0038. It is chemically inert and constitutes 80% of the earth's atmosphere. Liquid nitrogen provides the cheapest and safest refrigerant. It is prepared on a large industrial scale by fractionation of liquid air because its commercial uses extend from space travel to the food processing industry. It is shipped in tank cars and presently sells for about $ 0.04 to $ 0.40 per liter. The heat of vaporization is 35 cal/g, the largest of any cryogenic liquid. Thus, the boiling point of 76°K and the low price make nitrogen an ideal coolant. It is used to precool containers for hydrogen and helium, and all gases with lower boiling points.

Several properties of nitrogen are indicated in Table 7.9. The heat capacity and heat of transition of solid nitrogen at 14°K are 3 cal/mole degree and 11 cal/mole degree at 61°K. At 35–61°K nitrogen has a transition with a heat of transition of 54.7 cal/mole. The thermal conductivity of liquid nitrogen between 65°K and 90°K decreases from 3.7 to 2.9×10^{-4} cal cm^{-1} sec^{-1} per degree. The heat of vaporization decreases from 6000 joule per mole at 63°K to 5570 joule per mole at 78°K.

4. Liquid Hydrogen

Hydrogen was first liquefied by James Dewar on May 10, 1898. Dewar was born on September 20, 1842 and died on March 27, 1923. He was very secretive about his equipment, but published all his optical observations, which he started with liquid nitrogen (Dewar, 1888).

The boiling point of hydrogen is 20.4°K. Hydrogen gas is abundant and easy to manufacture by electrolysis of water. This makes it an ideal low temperature refrigerant, but the hazards of using hydrogen are so high that it can be used only in specially equipped laboratories.

Hydrogen has three isotopes: $^1H_2$, $^2H_2$, and $^3H_2$. The latter are more commonly called D_2 (deuterium) and T_2 (tritium). The different relative orientation of the nuclear spins in hydrogen molecules causes different properties for *ortho* and *para* hydrogen. The two forms are in equilibrium at room temperature; 75% of the molecules have parallel spins (ortho) and 25% are para hydrogen, with opposite nuclear spins. At the boiling point, 20.4°K, the equilibrium composition is 0.21% ortho and 99.8% para. The conversion between the two forms occurs slowly. Therefore, the composition of liquid hydrogen is often far from equilibrium. The heat of conversion at 20.39°K is 338.648 cal/mole. Thus, nonequilibrium liquid hydrogen will boil, even in a perfectly insulated Dewar, because of the heat of conversion. Figure 7.16 shows the theoretical volume loss, and the fraction of para hydrogen formed as a function of time. This drawing explains why large savings can be achieved if hydrogen is catalytically converted before or during liquefaction. Charcoal is a very effective catalyst for ortho-para conversion.

The use of liquid hydrogen requires special precautions. First, radiation shielding is necessary in addition to other insulation to maintain liquid

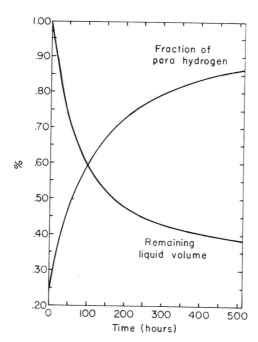

Fɪɢ. 7.16. Liquid hydrogen loss due to ortho-para conversion. Data from Scott (1959).

because radiative heat transfer becomes appreciable at 20°K; second, contact between air and liquid hydrogen must be prevented because air condenses, forming a solid. Solid air in contact with liquid hydrogen constitutes an explosive mixture. Furthermore, solid air may plug Dewar vents and necks; this would prevent venting of boil-off gas, leading to a pressure increase, and ultimately cause an explosion. Consequently, liquid hydrogen must be stored under a noncondensable atmosphere of hydrogen, or better, helium. Finally, hydrogen is a highly flammable material and requires special handling precautions on this account. Section III, B of Chapter 8 describes procedures for safe handling of hydrogen gas and liquid. Because of the dangers, most researchers prefer to use liquid helium despite its lower heat of vaporization and higher price (Scott, 1969).

5. Liquid Helium

Helium was first liquefied by Kammerlingh Onnes in 1908 at the University of Leiden. He precooled helium in the "Leiden cycle," which was based on chloroform (− 90°C), liquid ethane (− 145°C), and liquid air (− 183°C).

Liquid helium has the lowest boiling point of all elements and compounds. Helium is a rare gas and difficult to liquefy, but despite this, it is now widely used as a refrigerant, partly because the price has been drastically lowered during the last five years. At present, liquid helium is available for $ 2.80 to $ 5.00 per liter in the United States and for $ 3.50 and above in Europe. This has made home liquefaction unprofitable, even in Europe. The price reduction since 1964 is due to reduced federal control over helium production.

Helium is a by-product in certain natural gas sources, mainly in the United States and Russia. Since helium is lighter than air, it diffuses to the upper atmosphere when released and is permanently lost. Therefore, open cycle refrigeration, using helium, leads to an irreversible loss and attrition of the element. With increased production and use, this situation becomes increasingly untenable.

Liquid helium has many interesting properties, but for us it serves merely as a refrigerant, and only a few properties are relevant. Below 2.19°K helium is a superfluid. This shows in the low viscosity and creeping. Vessels for work at this temperature and below must be specially constructed because even minute faults in materials and leaks become porous to superfluid helium. Thus, below 2.19°K an otherwise perfectly useful Dewar flask might leak and lose its vacuum.

Even at room temperature, gaseous helium diffuses slowly through Pyrex and quartz. This results in thermal shortage of a Dewar. Therefore, permanently sealed flasks are not useful for handling liquid helium. On the other hand, traces of condensable gases are less disturbing at 4°K than above because the vapor pressure of all materials, except neon, is negligible at the boiling point of helium. Therefore, liquid helium produces adequate vacuum in any closed volume, and Dewar flasks need not be highly evacuated before use. Instead, it is better to purge containers periodically with a condensable gas, say nitrogen or carbon dioxide, to remove traces of non-condensable helium.

The heat of vaporization of helium is 650 calories per liter of the liquid. Because of the small heat of vaporization and the low boiling point, liquid helium must be carefully shielded against heat radiation.

6. Comparison of Refrigerants

Table 7.9 lists some significant properties of helium, hydrogen, nitrogen, and oxygen. For reaching the lowest possible temperature, helium has no competitor. In cooling, efficiency, and safety, nitrogen ranks first; it is also by far the cheapest. If safety considerations allow it, hydrogen constitutes an ideal compromise.

If the pressure above the refrigerant is controlled, the useful temperature range covered by helium, hydrogen, and nitrogen can be extended. Because nitrogen solidifies at 63°K, oxygen covers a larger useful range. Table 7.9 also includes data for other gases that find occasional use. Data on compounds that can be used as refrigerants is contained in Chapter 8, Section I, which lists properties of matrix solvents and low-boiling chemicals. Figure 7.17 shows the range of temperatures that can be covered with liquid refrigerants.

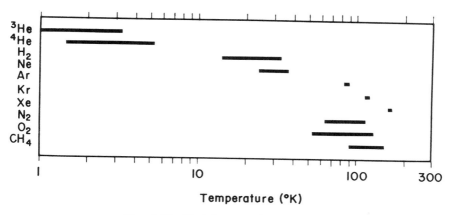

FIG. 7.17. Useful range of refrigerants.

B. Microrefrigerators

In optical experiments, little heat is generated. Maintaining a shielded optical sample at 4°K requires less than 1 mW, and even initial cooling of the sample from 300°K to 4°K uses little refrigerant. The major portion of the refrigerant loss occurs when cooling the sample holder, the refrigerant reservoir, and the transfer line between storage Dewar and sample cell. In a typical experiment, up to 2 liters of liquid helium are needed to cool the transfer line, 1 liter to cool the reservoir and sample, and 1 liter to fill the container and keep the sample cold for 4 hours. With each refill all external heat losses are repeated and less than 20% of the liquid from the storage Dewar ever reaches the sample cell. An inexperienced operator can waste even more helium. To overcome this waste, White and Mann (White, 1963a) developed a small liquefier which is now very popular in a modified commercial form. It consists of a Joule-Thomson (J-T) liquefier with a capacity of 0.3–8 W, depending on model, operating temperature, and gas used. Instead of collecting the liquefied gas first in a storage vessel, the J-T nozzle is mounted directly on the sample cell. Only a few drops of liquid are condensed—just enough to maintain a liquid–gas equilibrium. In this way, low temperatures are produced, *in situ*, where and when they are needed. No transfer of liquid is necessary, and no shrinkage of unused, stored liquid refrigerant occurs. The target temperature is controlled as part of the refrigeration cycle by adjusting flow rates, supply, and back pressure at the nozzle. The refrigerators work with normal grade commercial cylinder gases.

Microliquefiers constitute a major technical improvement. They are smaller, easier to operate, quicker, more accurate in temperature control, and simpler than any other means of refrigeration we presently know. They make low temperature spectroscopy economically feasible for small research groups where purchase of small coolant batches would be impossible and for groups outside of the area of large supply centers. For large groups, all the advantages are amplified. For extended use, spent gases can be recompressed or recycled.

C. Control of Sample Temperature

The best and easiest temperature control is obtained when samples are immersed in a boiling liquid. Table 7.10 lists the boiling point of various gases at 1 atm. The boiling point of gases can be changed by changing the pressure. This can be done by suction or by pressurization. In this way a large range of temperatures can be realized.

However, temperature control by sample immersion has a drawback. Many of the above liquids have small heats of vaporization. This means that large quantities of refrigerants are needed, and that the liquid constantly bubbles. The latter can be very annoying when one wishes to observe optical properties with photoelectric devices. The best way to avoid bubbles without sacrificing intimate contact with the coolant is to circulate cold gas over the sample. This can be accomplished by passing the boil-off through the sample chamber, or by mounting the sample chamber on the refrigerant reservoir and using a separate heat exchange gas, such as helium. If the heat exchange is kept incomplete by applying a deliberate temperature gradient, the sample temperature can be controlled at temperatures well above the liquid boiling point. Commercial equipment is now available which uses the flow rate of gas drawn from a liquid helium storage Dewar to cool samples to a wide range of temperatures. The gas flow rate is regulated until radiative and conductive heat flow to the sample holder are compensated, or until the desired temperature is reached. Electronic reading of a thermocouple can be used to automatically adjust and maintain the temperature within a desired range.

Temperature control can also be exercised if the pressure in the gas chamber between sample and refrigerant is used to control the heat transfer.

Table 7.10

Standard Temperature Reference Points

Point	Temperature ($^\circ$K)
Helium λ point	2.172
Helium boiling point	4.215
Parahydrogen triple point	13.813
Normal hydrogen triple point	13.95
Parahydrogen boiling point	20.27
Normal hydrogen boiling point	20.39
Neon triple point	24.54
Neon boiling point	27.09
Oxygen transition point	43.77
Oxygen triple point	54.36
Nitrogen triple point	63.15
Nitrogen boiling point	77.35
Oxygen boiling point	90.18

Such an arrangement can be combined with an electric heater and used as a calorimeter to measure absorbed energies, nonradiative excitation loss, heat of reactions, and recombinations and many other thermal transfer processes.

It is very popular to mount a sample on a window frame outside the refrigerant vessel, because in this way one or two optical windows can be avoided, which would be necessary if the sample were immersed in gas or liquid. However, frames provide only poor thermal contact and loss of temperature control, but low temperature spectroscopists are frequently forced to accept this in order to improve optical access to the sample.

In order to mount crystals and optical windows on refrigeration reservoirs, intermediate materials are usually inserted to reduce thermal stress, and, it is hoped, to improve thermal contacts. Lead, indium, aluminum gaskets, and "thermal grease," a vacuum grease containing powderized metal, are used for this purpose. When it is feasible to vacuum plate one surface of the sample with metal, it can be directly soldered onto the holder. It should be pointed out that the stress induced by cooling on the interface can change the optical properties of the sample. This is particularly true when single or mixed crystals are used as samples and stress is introduced directly into the crystal.

The thermal contact of matrices or liquid solutions, sprayed on cold windows is poor. Thus, a temperature gradient can develop between sample and target when light is absorbed, and the sample may remain several degrees warmer than the refrigerant.

If the matrix material is an intrinsically poor thermal conductor, as in the case of plexiglass-molded organic molecules, the sample temperature can be much higher than is suspected. In one case, a thermocouple planted in the center of a 1-inch diameter, 0.25-inch thick polymer disk mounted between two window copper frames with 0.75-inch diameter was at $76°K$ 6 hours after the frame had reached $4°K$.

When a crystal is formed by freezing liquid at a low temperature, the accompanying volume change often leads to loss of physical contact, and therefore loss of thermal contact. This consideration is very important when one is working with organic glasses, especially in cells constructed of quartz or other materials with low expansion coefficients.

D. Temperature Measurement

We are here concerned with measurement of sample temperatures in the range $1.5–100°K$. In this range, carbon resistors, gas thermometers, semiconductors, and thermocouples can be used. The usefulness of observed information depends on three items: the accuracy of absolute temperature measurement, the accuracy of relative temperature, and the correlation between measurement and actual sample temperature.

There is no point in determining a temperature unless it is correlated to the sample. This fact excludes gas thermometers and other large devices that cannot be placed into the sample, regardless of how useful or accurate they otherwise might seem. Carbon resistors and single crystals of semi-conductor materials may sometimes be more accurate, but we find that only thermocouples can be conveniently mounted in a sample. In glasses and polymers, thermocouples soldered to a large heat capacity metal piece can be inserted into the liquid before the solid forms. In mixed crystals, mounting is best achieved by partial vacuum silver plating of a surface on which the thermocouple can be tacked. However, this must be performed very carefully, because it is known that heating and mechanical stress can change the structure sufficiently to affect the optical properties. In matrices, close thermal contact is hardest. We mount our thermocouples on the optical window, either by pinching the junction under an indium washer which is connected to a screw leading through a hole in the target, or by soldering it to a metal which is vacuum-plated onto the target. We have no trust in correlating sample holder or metal frame temperature to sample temperature because we have observed gradients of up to 70°K in plastic samples and 5–10°K in matrices.

The easiest way to measure temperatures is to use a thermocouple calibrated against a standard. Table 7.10 lists such absolute reference points. The accuracy of the temperature reading depends then on the sensitivity of the couple in the measured range. Table 7.11 lists useful ranges and sensitivities for various thermometer materials at different temperatures. It is obvious that copper–constantan is practically useless below 77°K. It is presently common to use Au–Fe versus chromel P or Au–Co versus copper thermocouple. Three-mil wires and 10-mil wires are commercially available and constitute a good compromise of reasonable mechanical strength with tolerable thermal conductivity and heat capacity. Table 7.12 lists the junction voltage for temperatures between 0 and 100°K, and voltages measured against an ice (0°C) standard. The thermocouple voltage depends on individual samples, aging, and tempering. This is especially severe in the case of Au–Co, which is an oversaturated solution. Therefore, all junctions must be calibrated before use.

If temperature changes are to be measured accurately and if the absolute temperature is not critical, the reference junction can be mounted on the refrigerant wall. However, it must be remembered that the boiling points of refrigerants are very sensitive to pressure. Also, the boiling point might change with time because of changes in composition of the liquid refrigerant:

Table 7.11

Sensitivity and Useful Range of Selected Temperature Sensors

Material	Useful Range (°K)	Sensitivity (μV per °K)			
		At 4°K	At 20°K	At 77°K	At 300°K
Copper–gold (4% Co) AC	0.3–300	4.0	16.4	35.0	42.9
Chromel–gold (0.07% Fe) P-AF	0.3–300	12.2	16.3	17.6	22.3
Constantan–Copper, T	30–700	1.3	5.5	16.1	39.3
Constantan–iron, E	20–1000	2.1	8.5	25.8	59.3
Alumel–chromel, K	30–1700	0.8	4.1	15.7	39.8
Pt–Rh (13–40%) vs. Pt–Rh (1–20%)	200–2000	—	—	—	5.6–6.4
IR vs. IR–Rh	—	—	—	—	1.26
Pt–IR vs. Pd	—	—	—	—	7.02
Ga–As	0.3–400	5000	2000	25000	—
Ge	0.1–300	240 Ω	5 Ω	0.24 Ω	—

hydrogen converts from para to ortho, and nitrogen accumulates oxygen from the atmosphere. As shown in Fig. 7.15, this increases the boiling point from 76°K to 92°K. Even ice standard baths are not always safe, because impurities in the reference junction container and the ice reduce the temperature. This can be fatal for absolute measurements of low temperature, because the thermocouple sensitivity is often larger at 0°C than below. An extreme example is offered by copper versus constantan. A bath at − 1°C causes an error of 38 μV. For a target at 20°K, this leads to a reading of 12°, an error of 8°K. Thus, this thermocouple is obviously not ideal for low temperature measurement. However, in the case of gold (4% iron) versus chromel P, the error would still be 1.5°K.

VI. VACUUM

Experimenters in low temperature spectroscopy must be acquainted with basic vacuum techniques. A better knowledge of operation and design of vacuum systems is necessary for matrix spectroscopists who work with molecular beams and use the vacuum shroud for sample preparation, but it is also helpful for those who purify materials through vacuum sublimation or degassing. We will here review only the most important problems and questions arising during low temperature work. A large number of excellent books explain the design, operation, and theory of vacuum containers.

Table 7.12

Voltage of Thermocouple Junction (in μV) Measured against Reference at Melting Point of Ice (0°C)

Temperature (°K)	Chromel– Gold (0.7% Fe)	Constantan– Iron	Constantan– Copper	Alumel– Chromel	Gold (4.0% Co)– Copper
1	5258.43	9837.84	6258.95	6458.98	9871.22
2	5250.08	9836.94	6258.58	6458.51	9869.66
3	5238.43	9835.55	6257.79	6457.89	9867.09
4	5226.70	9833.69	6256.62	6457.10	9862.73
5	5214.03	9831.38	6255.10	6456.13	9859.01
6	5200.60	9828.63	6253.25	6454.98	9853.55
7	5186.51	9822.44	6251.09	6453.65	9847.18
8	5171.89	9821.82	6248.65	6452.13	9839.92
9	5156.84	9817.78	6245.92	6450.42	9831.79
10	5141.43	9813.33	6242.93	6448.50	9823.72
11	5125.75	9808.48	6239.68	6446.39	9813.03
12	5109.85	9803.22	6236.18	6444.87	9802.45
13	5093.79	9797.57	6232.43	6441.54	9791.10
14	5077.61	9791.53	6228.43	6438.80	9779.00
15	5061.35	9785.10	6224.19	6435.86	9766.15
16	5045.06	9778.28	6219.70	6432.69	9752.65
17	5028.69	9771.09	6214.97	6429.31	9738.55
18	5012.34	9763.51	6210.01	6425.71	9723.65
19	4996.00	9753.56	6204.79	6421.90	9708.25
20	4979.69	9747.16	6199.34	6417.86	9692.15
22	4947.14	9729.49	6187.70	6409.11	9658.05
24	4914.75	9710.28	6175.09	6399.48	9621.65
26	4882.52	9689.61	6161.51	6388.94	9582.95
28	4850.44	9667.52	6146.96	6377.51	9542.15
30	4818.48	9644.00	6131.46	6365.18	9499.23
32	4786.60	9619.08	6115.00	6351.95	9454.45
34	4754.77	9592.78	6097.62	6337.83	9407.75
36	4722.94	9565.10	6079.33	6322.82	9359.35
38	4691.09	9536.06	6060.14	6306.93	9309.25
40	4659.17	9505.69	6040.10	6290.16	9257.55
45	4578.89	9424.03	5986.38	6244.43	9121.85
50	4497.67	9334.42	5927.82	6193.39	8977.85
55	4415.30	9237.17	5864.81	6137.15	8856.55
60	4331.68	9132.58	5797.67	6075.85	8668.85
65	4246.78	9020.96	5726.65	6009.63	8505.55
70	4160.63	8902.59	5651.93	5938.59	8337.25
75	4073.26	8777.71	5573.65	5862.69	8164.65
80	3984.70	8646.57	5491.89	5782.57	7988.25
90	3804.15	8366.28	5318.14	5608.62	7724.95
100	3619.28	8063.06	5131.04	5417.47	7649.15
273	0.00	0.00	0.00	0.00	0.00

Vacuum has a wide range of meanings. For the preparative chemist using sequences of traps, 10^{-2} torr is adequate; for a semiconductor physicist, 10^{-9} torr is normal vacuum. For low temperature spectroscopists, three ranges of pressures are useful. Range a in Fig. 7.18 is for sublimation and purification of substances, range b for thermal insulation of refrigerants, and range c for the preparation of materials and oxygen-free samples.

A vacuum system is characterized by residual pressure and pumping speed. The residual pressure is the lowest pressure which in a tight given system can be ultimately reached. The pumping speed indicates how long it takes to reach a desired pressure, and the lowest pressure that can be maintained in the presence of a leak. We have mentioned before that a small pumping speed can daily cause a serious waste of time. In our laboratory we consider a system too slow when under normal working conditions it does not reach the desired pressure in 15 minutes.

Slow speed can be due to faulty design or to the choice of an inadequate vacuum pump. Almost all commercial cryostats we have seen are built adequately for cooling solid samples, but for matrix work all have an insufficient pumping cross section and other design features which make modification necessary. A typical optical cryostat needs at least a 75-liter to 150-liter per minute two-stage mechanical pump, and a matched 2-inch diameter diffusion pump. Diffusion pump and rotation pump should be matched to the volume and cross section of tubing, because the pumping speed of the entire system depends on the slowest component. Figure 7.19 shows a typical performance curve for a two-stage mechanical vacuum pump. The

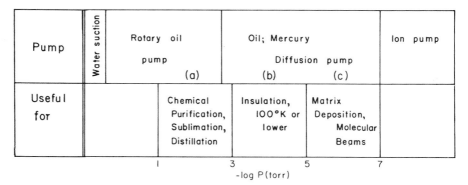

FIG. 7.18. Pressure ranges necessary for (a) preparation and purification of chemicals, (b) insulation of cryogenic vessels, and (c) production of molecular beams.

displaced gas mass decreases rapidly with decreasing pressure, and at a given pressure the displaced volume goes through a minimum at about 10^{-3} torr. At this pressure, the displaced volume is less than half of that at atmospheric pressure.

Diffusion pumps operate only at a back pressure below 20×10^{-3} torr; above this pressure they malfunction and contaminate the system with oil. Operation at too high a pressure, or exposure to bursts of gases leads to oil loss through spilling or combustion. The consequences of spilling are so severe that the vacuum system should be disassembled and cleaned after any mishap.

The residual pressure in a system depends on several factors. In a closed vacuum system it is always limited by the design of the pumping apparatus. Two-stage mechanical pumps can reach 0.2×10^{-3} torr. This is sufficient for "roughing" a helium Dewar, or reducing chemical reactions of pure substances. It is, however, insufficient to prevent frosting of a liquid nitrogen cooled vessel. For this, pressures below 10^{-5} torr are needed. Diffusion pumps reach such a pressure easily. A liquid nitrogen cooled trap in series with a diffusion pump makes pressures of 10^{-7} torr feasible. Such pressures are desirable for matrix work, although a pressure of 5×10^{-6} torr is adequate for exploratory work. For reaching pressures of 10^{-8} torr and below, charcoal traps, ion pumps, or getters are usually necessary. Actually, measured residual pressures may be far higher than is indicated by the

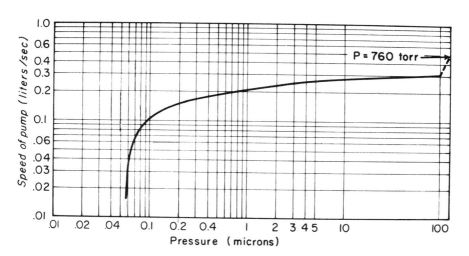

FIG. 7.19. Performance of mechanical pump.

pump limitation. This can be due to leaks, the vapor pressure of optical samples and cryostat material, or outgassing of the system.

Outgassing is caused by desorption of materials originally adsorbed on the wall of the vacuum container. Water, air, and solvents form surface films that adhere subbornly to walls. They vaporize slowly and simulate apparent leaks. An experienced operator recognizes outgassing quickly, because the pumping speed shows an apparent discontinuity at a pressure that depends on the characteristics of the vacuum system and the vapor pressure of the impurity. In our system, for example, water desorbs at 150×10^{-3} torr. Outgassing is also encountered in Knudsen furnaces. After a given amount of time, desorption at a fixed temperature becomes very slow and never completes. The desorption speed increases, however, with temperature. Therefore, it is better to prepare a system by pumping for 1 hour at $10°K$ above the operating temperature than overnight at working or ambient temperature. The best procedure is to prevent adsorption of gases that cause degassing. This can be done by maintaining vacuum systems at low pressure. If the vacuum must be broken, the system should be filled with dry gas. This is particularly important when a cryostat part is still cold. Moisture condensed on a cold part desorbs very slowly.

In matrix spectroscopy, vacuum is needed for thermal insulation, for formation of molecular beams, and to prevent contamination of cold samples. These applications have different requirements.

A. Insulation

Cryogenic liquids are efficient heat exchangers, and boil off quickly unless stored in an insulated vessel. The best insulator is normally vacuum. Insulating materials, such as oxides, fibers, etc., have thermal conductivities of 0.1 mW per centimeter and $°K$. A 1-liter styrofoam flask with a 1 cm thick wall looses about 20% liquid nitrogen per hour. Freshly formed foams are very efficient insulators at low temperature because they still contain CO_2 from the manufacturing process. The gas in the foam bubbles condenses yielding an evacuated structure. However, after a few cooling cycles, air diffuses through the foam and the thermal conductivity is no longer temperature dependent.

Vacuum acts as a reliable insulator because heat transport through collisions becomes negligible, when residual gas pressure is below 10^{-5} torr. Heat loss is then due only to radiative transfer. Below 10^{-5} torr, the mean free path of molecules in the residual gas is then less than 0.5 cm and comparable to container dimensions.

For low temperature experiments, radiative heat transfer can become critical. Radiation must be mechanically excluded by shielding, or absorption by cold parts must be prevented by polishing or coating surfaces to reduce absorpticity. For storage of liquid nitrogen, silver lining of walls at ambient temperature is sufficient. For liquid hydrogen and helium, a cooled shield is imperative. It can consist of a separate upper lining which is cooled with liquid nitrogen, or an aluminum-coated Mylar foil, which, if wrapped around a target, establishes its own temperature gradient between different layers.

B. Sample Contamination

Impurities alter the properties of the sample. O_2, for example, is a very efficient quencher for triplet energy, and its presence changes the lifetime of phosphorescent decay. In matrix spectroscopy, samples are produced and stored on cold surfaces in a vacuum vessel. Such samples are unprotected and constitute ideal absorbers for residual gases. At 77°K a vacuum of 10^{-6} torr is generally adequate to make contamination insignificant. At 20°K and at 4°K all gases in contact with the target condense, and the vacuum must be of the order of 10^{-8} torr, because at low temperature, cold surfaces themselves act as pumps and compete with other pumps. At 4°K, a target is more efficient than a liquid nitrogen trap, or a diffusion pump. Therefore, at 4°K the target pumps diffusion oil, and the diffusion pump acts as a slow controlled leak. At this temperature, it is best to close all valves and operate a static vacuum system.

C. Molecular Beams

When samples are formed by deposition of reactive materials from a Knudsen cell, the residual gas pressure must allow free mean paths equivalent or larger than the oven-to-target distance. If this distance is 5 cm, this condition is fulfilled at a pressure of 5×10^{-5} torr.

During deposition, the residual pressure depends on the sticking coefficient of molecules in the molecular beam. The sticking coefficient depends on the target geometry, beam geometry, the properties of the beam material, and the target temperature. At 20°K, large molecules have sticking coefficients close to one. Matrix gases such as argon, however, have smaller sticking coefficients. It is therefore necessary to remove the uncondensed part of the beam, and in molecular beam experiments pumping speed becomes an important consideration.

We want to list here one other factor which is important for matrix work. In a matrix Dewar, target and refrigerant at hydrogen and helium temperature are shielded against thermal radiation by nitrogen shields. If matrix gases are noncondensable at 77°K, as they almost always are, it is desirable to pump on the cryostat through a port at target level or close by. This reduces local pressure due to reflected matrix gas. Kinks, bends, and long tubing introduce unnecessary resistance and result in slower pumping speed.

D. Pressure Measurement

Figure 7.20 shows the range of commonly used vacuum gauges. As in the case of temperature, the pressure can vary greatly within a system. Therefore, it should be measured close to the point of interest. This is not always possible, because many vacuum gauges suffer from chemical attack by vapors. However, if a gauge is protected with a trap, it records only the pressure of uncondensable gases and is unreliable and does not indicate outgassing of hot furnaces. Another disadvantage of ion gauges is that different gases yield different readings because of their different ionization potential.

E. Vacuum Testing

For those who build their own vacuum systems, vacuum testing is a matter of daily routine, but for less experienced buyers of commercial equipment

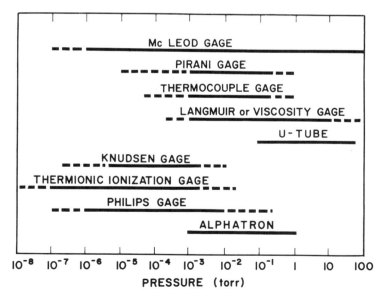

Fig. 7.20. Sensitivity range of pressure gauges.

vacuum failure can consume incommensurate amounts of time. When an already existing vacuum system is used, the development of leaks can be recognized by changes in the time versus pressure curves. Therefore, we routinely record in all our experiments detailed histories of pressures, temperatures, and visual observations.

When a pump-down takes longer than usual, or when the pressure levels off at a higher than accustomed value, degassing or a leak must be suspected. Figure 7.21 shows adsorbed water as a function of surface and material. As mentioned above, degassing also yields slower pump-down, but gives different pressure versus time curves than leaks. Degassing can be recognized by stepwise pressure reduction and by pressure bursts that come from vaporizing droplets. A leak and its location can be established by many different methods. The first step is always to close off the system part by part until the leaking component is recognized by pressure change. Large leaks are quickly recognized. Smaller holes on joints can be located by turning, gently and slowly, all movable parts. On flanges, leaks show when screws are tightened or loosened, when valve stems are turned or O-ring seals are squeezed or turned. If no commercial leak-detector is available, the ion gauge of the system can be used as an indicator of leak location. When a small leak is sprayed with helium, the high ionization potential of helium entering the system simulates a sudden improvement of vacuum. If the

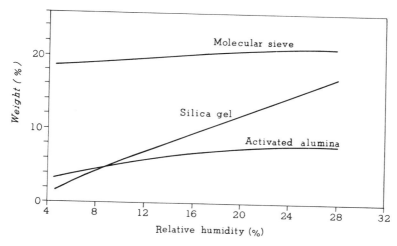

FIG. 7.21. Adsorption of moisture by various materials as a function of temperature and humidity.

leak is large, the reverse occurs. For helium testing, parts of the system must be isolated. This is best done with surgical rubber sheet or equivalent material. It is often helpful to close the rotation pump, or even the diffusion pump connection to enhance pressure surge. Since helium is lighter than air, one always starts testing at the highest point of the equipment. If a leak has been located, it can be temporarily blocked with a sealing compound, such as Dux-seal so that testing can continue. When temporary sealers have been used, care must be taken to clean the parts carefully before permanent repair is made.

VII. SPECTROSCOPY

This section deals only with those principles that are especially relevant for optical low temperature work. The spectral range considered is 100–1000 nm. Information on infrared techniques is added only when it is relevant for optical work. Auxiliary and electronic equipment is not discussed because it is well covered in many books. For convenience of discussion, we distinguish seven different components in an optical train, as shown in Fig. 7.22: (1) optical properties of samples, targets, and windows; (2) light sources; (3) light guides; (4) monochromators and filters; (5) light detectors; (6) decay time analyzers; (7) polarizers.

All parts for the above components are commercially available, but, except for analytical quality fluorimeters and phosphorimeters, the parts are not matched and the user must assemble his own components.

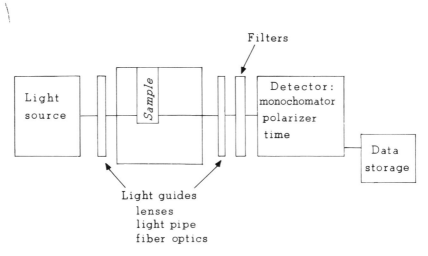

Fig. 7.22. Optical train.

A. Optical Properties of Samples, Targets, and Windows

Details on properties of samples and sample holders are also discussed in Sections II and III and in Chapter 8. We summarize here spectral ranges of matrices, mixed crystals and glasses and of targets and sample holders.

The free spectral range of some frequently used matrices, polymers, and glasses is shown in Fig. 7.23. Mixed crystals are not shown because they must be individually matched to the guests. Figure 7.23 shows the superior free spectral range of rare gas solids. Their disadvantage is the relatively large light scattering, which becomes prohibitive in thick samples. Polyatomic matrices and organic glasses are not transparent in the vacuum UV and have very limited usefulness in the IR. Polymers have yet a narrower range; however, they are less scattering.

Targets and windows must be as transparent as the samples. In addition, matrix targets must offer good thermal contact and thermal conductivity. Figure 7.24 shows the free spectral range of various commonly used materials. Pyrex has poor transmission and a poor spectral range. For quartz, the transmission depends on treatment and purity. Fire-polished fused quartz absorbs below 220 nm, but Suprasil is transparent to 160 nm. Similar differences are found in the red cutoff at 3000 nm. Sapphire has a larger free spectral range than glass and quartz. It has a far superior thermal conductivity. In fact, sapphire is the only one of the above materials that is suitable as a matrix target. In luminescence work, a feeble blue emission with a lifetime of several milliseconds at 4°K is observed. It is strongest and perturbs most when x-ray excitation is used.

For vacuum UV work below 100 nm, ion crystal windows are used. Calcium fluoride and lithium fluoride are transparent to 120 nm. For excitation below this, matrices and windows are not suitable, except for a few spectral regions. In the x-ray region beryllium windows and thin aluminum windows can be used. Thin films of aluminum also transmit the He line at 50 nm.

In the infrared, CsI and CsBr take a preferred position because their spectral range extends to 200 cm^{-1} and they are transparent through the visible up to 200 nm. This makes it possible to photolyze the guest and to observe optical and IR spectra in one experiment through the same optical window. Ion crystals are also good thermal conductors. They are the most popular matrix target materials. IR windows can be purchased in any size and shape, but for good transmission they must be occasionally polished.

For special applications, polycristalline glasses of alkaline earth salts, commercially called IRTRAN, and arsenic glasses may be useful. They

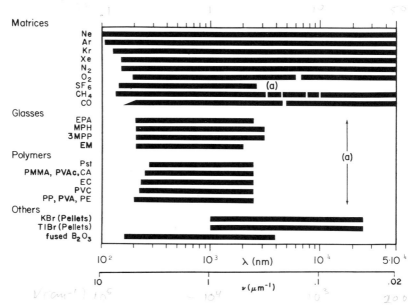

FIG. 7.23. Spectral range of matrices, solvents, and polymers. Abbreviations are given in Tables 8.8, 8.9, and 8.10.

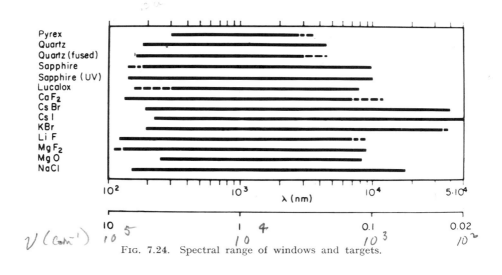

FIG. 7.24. Spectral range of windows and targets.

have good thermal conductivity and are resistant to temperatures up to 300°C, and above.

B. Light or Excitation Sources

1. Continuous Absorption Sources

For absorption work a continuous light source is needed. In choosing a lamp, one must distinguish power output in the form of light and the brightness temperature. These two properties are not always found together. A high powered lamp is usually larger and has a larger emitting surface or volume; but the brightness temperature, the light intensity in the brightest region of a lamp, need not be greater, because the power is spread over a larger surface. Therefore, "compact" arc lamps operating at 250 W are brighter than 1 kW and 2 kW lamps.

An ideal light source for absorption experiments should emit the same number of quanta at all wavelengths. It should have sufficient strength to penetrate the solid sample and all surfaces of the optical train and yield a conveniently detectable signal in parts of the spectrum where the sample absorptivity is 95% and more. A source of this type does not exist, but in many parts of the spectrum continuous light sources with a reasonable flat spectrum are available.

Carbon arcs and metallic sparks produce good continua, and incandescent bulbs yield reasonably white light, but they are inefficient emitters. In order to emit white light they have to be operated at high temperature, which shortens the lifetime of the source. Tungsten lamps can be used at higher than normal temperatures in the presence of iodine. In the tungsten-iodine quartz lamp, iodine reacts with tungsten vapor, forming volatile tungsten iodide, which is stable at lower temperatures, but decomposes on the hot filament surface. Thus, the filament regenerates itself and can be operated up to 3200°K instead of 2600°K, yielding more and bluer light than normal incandescent filament lamps. The emission from an incandescent black body can be calculated accurately. It is

$$E = \sigma T^4 F$$

where $\sigma = 5 \times 10^{-12}$ W $\times$ cm^{-2}. A Knudsen cell of 1 cm² front surface, for example, emits at 2000°K 80 W of radiation. Figure 7.25 shows the energy distribution of a black body source as a function of emitted wavelength for various temperatures. For calibration of optical trains for quantitative work, it is very convenient to use a tungsten lamp of known temperature

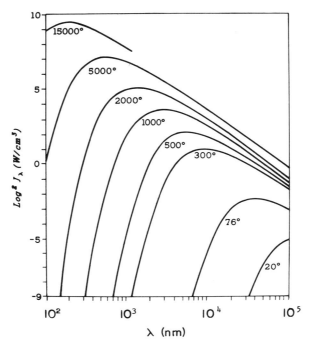

FIG. 7.25. Wavelength dependence of black body radiation at various temperatures.

Table 7.13

Black Body Radiation at Various Frequencies[a]

λ	Black Body Radiation						
	1250°K	1500°K	1750°K	2000°K	2500°K	3000°K	3200°K
0.23	—	—	2.15–2	1.83 0	9.05 2	5.61 4	2.03 5
0.25	—	1.22–3	2.87–1	1.72 1	5.21 3	2.34 5	7.64 5
0.30	—	3.15–1	2.99 1	9.07 2	1.07 5	2.55 6	6.86 6
0.40	1.83 0	2.19 2	6.66 3	8.61 4	3.08 6	3.33 7	7.00 7
0.50	1.84 2	8.45 3	1.29 5	1.00 6	1.74 7	1.16 8	2.11 8
0.60	3.33 3	8.05 4	7.81 5	4.29 6	4.61 7	2.24 8	3.67 8
0.70	2.34 4	3.57 5	2.49 6	1.07 7	8.13 7	3.13 8	4.76 8
0.80	9.14 4	9.85 5	5.37 6	1.91 7	1.12 8	3.61 8	5.20 8
0.90	2.41 5	1.98 6	8.92 6	2.74 7	1.31 8	3.74 8	5.16 8
1.00	4.79 5	3.21 6	1.24 7	3.41 7	1.41 8	3.62 8	4.86 8
2.00	2.29 6	6.37 6	1.34 7	2.39 7	5.49 7	9.91 7	1.20 8

[a] Energy is in erg cm^{-2} ster^{-1} μ^{-1} sec^{-1} (2.15 2 = 2.15 × 10^2; 3.15–1 = 3.15 × 10^{-1}).

and known surface. Such calibrated lamps are commercially available. Table 7.13 lists selected values for the visible and the near IR (de Voss, 1956).

The light output of tungsten lamps is always low compared to other types of light sources, such as gas discharge lamps. While a 1 kW tungsten lamp emits less than 200 W of light, a mercury arc of the same power emits 300 W of light.

In the ultraviolet part of the spectrum, gas discharges and sparks are normally used. The rare gases and hydrogen give good continua between 100 and 300 nm. Figure 7.26 shows three types of lamp containers. Diagram a is a high voltage lamp with metal electrodes which are water cooled. Such a lamp can be built by any skilled glass blower. The capillary in the discharge region is platinum plated. The lamp can be operated at a pressure between 5 torr and 100 torr and at 3000–4000 V. It draws typically 4–15 amp current. If it is filled with deuterium instead of hydrogen, the light gain is up to one hundred times greater. Since impurities reduce the light yield drastically, lamp containers should be carefully outgassed for 6 hours or longer at high temperature and high vacuum before filling. If this cannot be done, filler gas should be circulated continuously through a charcoal trap at 76°K.

Even carefully built lamps have a limited lifetime because after 24–100 hours of use sputtered electrode material dulls the windows and outgassing from the depleting electrode surface reduces light yields. To reduce deposition of impurities, the window should be far away from the electrodes. This also prevents heating and outgassing of the window seal. Seals for salt windows can be made with epoxy. Sapphire windows can be directly fused to Pyrex.

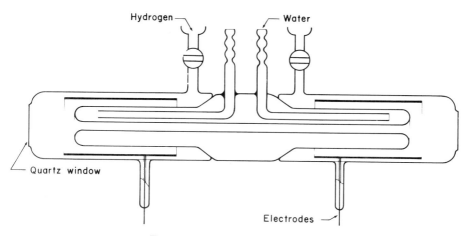

FIG. 7.26(a). H_2 continuum lamp.

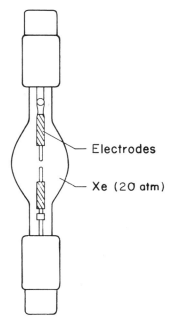

Electrodes

Xe (20 atm)

FIG. 7.26(b). Xenon high pressure arc.

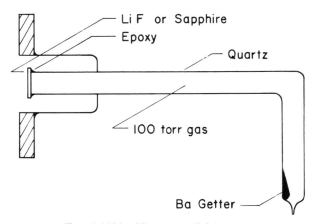

LiF or Sapphire

Epoxy

Quartz

100 torr gas

Ba Getter

FIG. 7.26(c). Microwave light source.

Figure 7.26b shows a cross section of a high pressure arc. Gas pressures are 20 atm and higher in such lamps. Therefore, care should be taken to protect the operator against explosion. Laboratory construction of this lamp is not practical.

Figure 7.26c depicts a microwave-stimulated electrodeless discharge tube. Any type of chemically stable gas can be used as light emitter to give the desired spectrum. The tube operates best if the quartz tube diameter does not exceed 12 mm. The quartz should be carefully outgassed at 1200°C for 12 hours before the emitter is admitted. If a solid or liquid is used, a starter gas pressure—for example, 1 torr argon—should be added. If rare gases, hydrogen, or deuterium are used, a getter metal such as a barium wire substantially prolongs the lamp's life. Medical microwave "diathermy" 150-W units are suitable power sources. A specially efficient tunable antenna for this source was designed by Broida (1964b). If the generator is fitted with a reflected power meter, tuning can be used to adjust the power yield by a factor of five or more. Power supplies with up to 1 kW and more can be purchased, but discharge tubes must then be water cooled. Electrodeless discharges have the advantage that they do not suffer from electrode sputtering and poisoning. However, discharges have a habit of "wandering," and focusing can be difficult.

An expensive continuous light source is the plasma jet, from which up to 10% of the power is emitted as UV light.

In the infrared, the most common light sources are black body filaments. So-called Nernst glowers consist of rare earth oxides that can be operated at 7800°C for extended periods of time. They are stable in air but suffer in pure nitrogen, which is commonly used to purge atmospheric absorbers from infrared instruments. In the far infrared more exotic light sources are used.

2. Pulsed Sources

Short light pulses serve studies of the lifetime of reaction products and emitting states of excited molecules and atoms. Solid state lasers and high voltage sparks are both intensive and short, but for all other present light sources, high time resolution must be paid for with intensity loss. Equipment can be divided into four categories according to time resolution:

a. PULSES LONGER THAN 10^{-4} SEC. These pulses can be made from continuously operated sources by mechanical chopping and triggering with rotating blades. However, only light sources operating on direct current are suitable, because alternating current sources produce radiation modulated by the line frequency, i.e., 60 Hz in the United States and 50 Hz in Europe. It is convenient to employ periodic pulsing for signal integration. This is discussed in the section on signal analysis. Alternative pulsing methods are listed below.

b. PULSES BETWEEN 10^{-6} AND 10^{-4} SEC. Three types of sources are suitable for work in the 10^{-6} sec to 10^{-4} sec range. Continuous light sources can be modulated by special mechanical devices, for example, a rotating "mirror" or grating wheel. The second method involves pulsed light sources, for example, commercial stroboscope lamps. The available spectral range, and the intensity of such lamps is limited. O_2, H_2, N_2, and xenon lamps in the visible and UV with 0.2 W of light are presently available. Both these methods allow high repetition rates and therefore periodic pulsing and integration of pulses. The third type of lamp emits very bright flashes at a slow repetition rate from a discharge of a capacitor through an air gap. Figure 7.27 shows a very strong source of this type (Holzrichter, 1970), which emits in the visible and UV. Ten farads at 1 kV yield a 2–5 μsec flash through air, argon, or other gases. The pulse width and shape depend on the gas. The pulse repetition rate is only 0.05 sec^{-1} or slower, but the pulse intensity is often sufficient for observation during a single discharge.

c. PULSES SHORTER THAN 10^{-6}. These shorter pulses are more difficult to produce. Light modulation of continuous light sources with a Kerr cell yield up to 20–40% modulated light. Ruby laser pulses are typically 10^{-8} sec, but the wavelength choice is small. UV light can be produced by frequency doubling with a Q-switch. Until dye lasers reach a commercial stage, short-lived visible and UV pulses will still have to be produced by 1 W or even weaker flash lamps filled with rare gas, deuterium, or nitrogen.

Flash repetition rates can often be kept high enough so that signal integration with waveform eductors and nuclear counting equipment become

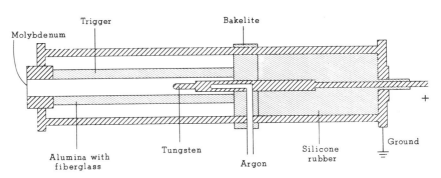

FIG. 7.27. Microsecond pulsed source; capacitor discharge. After Holzrichter (1970).

feasible. A schematic arrangement of a lifetime apparatus based on signal integration is discussed later.

The time region below 10^{-8} sec is only now beginning to be explored, because the presently available light sources are not bright enough.

3. Emission Sources

a. LINE SOURCES. The ideal spectral characteristics of a light source used to excite emission are different from those of an absorption source, because the output of the lamp should be concentrated in the absorption region of the sample. In practice, atomic sources approach this goal best, even if they do not coincide as exactly with an absorbing region as in the lucky case described by Bass and Shirk (1968), who found that 2ν of an argon laser coincides with the wing of CuO absorption in a mixture of argon and xenon at 20°K. In this example two tricks were combined ingeniously to accomplish near coincidence. First, the laser output was modified by passing it through an X-switch, a frequency doubler which yields 80% of the original energy at 2ν; second, the absorption was "tuned" by mixing matrix gases to shift the transition energy of the absorber to the desired wavelength. The development of commercial tunable lasers and other improved light sources will make excitation of weakly emitting species easier. For use until such date, Table 7.14 lists presently available laser lines and emission lines of easy-to-build atomic sources. Atomic sources can be built with filament heaters, or for microwave excitation. Filament lamps are commercially available. Sodium, mercury, and cadmium line lamps are commercially available. The power output per atomic line depends on the operating power and the lamp pressure. Low pressure mercury lamps emit up to 80% of all light in the 184.9 nm and 253.7 nm lines. High pressure mercury lamps emit largely visible and infrared light. Thus, a 150 W medium pressure A4/T mercury lamp (AH-4) is a better ultraviolet photolysis source than an AH-6 high pressure lamp with a 1 kW power supply.

All light sources dissipate substantial amounts of heat. Commercial lamps are often not well mounted. It is therefore well worthwhile to build an adequately designed air- or water-cooled housing, which also shields the lamp for experiments with weak luminescence. Microwave lamps can be built easily in the laboratory. For line sources, the lamp pressure must be kept at or below a few torr, and a rare gas starter at 0.1 to 1 torr is necessary. If the pressure is higher, molecular emission prevails.

Lasers concentrate so much power in a small volume and a small spectral region and are already so cheap that it is well worth considering a laser source whenever an absorption is anywhere near an available laser line.

Table 7.14

Selected Continuous and Atomic Emission Sources

(a) Continua

Continuum Sources	Wavelength Range (nm)	Remarks
High pressure mercury	245–IR	253.7 line is self-reversed
High pressure xenon	150–900	
High pressure xenon-mercury	150–1400	Lines above 400
Hydrogen	170–400	
Deuterium	170–400	Ten times brighter than H_2
Xenon	147–210	
Krypton	125–180	
Argon	107–160	
Neon	75–100	
Helium	60–100	
Tungsten	300–1200	
Zirconium	550–1200	
Carbon arc	300–IR	
Heavy metal (uranium, etc.)	5–visible	Pulsed
Continuum spark	190–600	Pulsed
High pressure helium or argon	200–700	Pulsed
Lyman continuum	27–900	Pulsed

(b) Lasers:

Line Sources	Wavelength	Remarks
Ruby	694.3	Pulsed
Neodymium	1060 (IR)	Pulsed
Helium–neon	632.8	
Argon ion	457.9, 476.5, 488.0, 496.5, 501.7, 514.5, 528.7	
Krypton ion	476.2, 520.8, 530.9, 568.2, 647.1	
CO_2	10600 (IR)	
N_2	337	Pulsed
HCN	33700 (IR)	

Table 7.14 (continued)

(c) Atomic Resonance Lines

Element	Wavelength (nm)	Element	Wavelength (nm)	Element	Wavelength (nm)
A(I)	104.826	Si(I)	288.1578	Pb(I)	405.7820
Si(II)	153.355	Os(I)	290.9061	Cb(I)	405.8938
Hg(I)	184.96	Pt(I)	306.4712	Sr(II)	407.7714
As(I)	189.05	Bi(I)	306.7716	N(I)	409.994
Se(I)	196.02	V(II)	309.3108	Ga(I)	417.2056
Zn(II)	202.551	Cb(II)	309.4183	Pr(II)	417.9422
Sb(I)	206.838	Be(II)	313.0416	Ce(II)	418.6599
Cu(II)	213.5976	Ir(I)	322.0780	Eu(II)	420.5046
Zn(I)	213.856	Cu(I)	324.7540	Ca(I)	422.6728
Te(I)	214.275	Ag(I)	328.0683	Cr(I)	425.4346
Cd(II)	214.4382	Ta(I)	331.1162	Sm(I)	429.675
Sn(II)	215.222	Ti(II)	334.9035	W(I)	430.2108
Pb(II)	220.3505	Zr(II)	339.1975	Nd(I)	430.3573
W(II)	220.449	Pd(I)	340.4580	V(I)	437.9238
Co(II)	228.6156	Ni(I)	341.4765	Sm(II)	442.4342
Ni(II)	228.7084	Rh(I)	343.4893	In(I)	451.1323
Cd(I)	228.8018	Co(I)	345.3505	Ba(II)	455.4042
Pd(II)	229.653	Re(I)	346.047	Eu(I)	459.402
Be(I)	234.8610	Ru(I)	349.8942	Sr(I)	460.7331
Fe(II)	238.2039	Zr(I)	360.1193	Y(I)	467.4848
Au(I)	242.795	Sc(II)	361.3836	Br(II)	470.486
Ag(II)	243.7791	Yb(II)	369.4203	Ra(I)	482.591
C(I)	247.8573	Y(II)	371.0290	Ti(I)	498.1733
B(I)	249.7733	Fe(I)	371.9935	Tl(I)	535.046
Mn(II)	257.6104	Mo(I)	379.8252	Ba(I)	553.5551
Lu(II)	261.543	Ra(II)	381.442	Na(I)	588.9953
Hf(II)	264.1406	Tm(II)	384.802	La(I)	624.9929
Ge(I)	265.1178	He(I)	388.8646	Li(I)	670.7844
Al(II)	266.9166	Sc(I)	391.1810	K(I)	766.4907
Mg(II)	279.553	Ca(II)	393.3666	O(I)	777.1928
Mo(II)	281.6154	La(II)	394.9106	Rb(I)	780.0227
Cr(II)	283.5633	Al(I)	396.1527	Cs(I)	852.110
Sn(I)	283.9989	Yb(I)	398.7994		
Mg(I)	285.2129	Mn(I)	403.0755		

The only drawback is that a laser can overheat, decompose, or vaporize low temperature samples. However, with appropriate care, fluorescence and Raman spectra can be successfully recorded in rare gas matrices at 4°K to 20°K.

Molecular sources are normally broad. Only nitrogen is commonly used to stimulate emission. It emits over the entire 280–400 nm region; thus, most emission is wasted, instead of being absorbed by a narrow absorber.

b. x-Rays, α, β Radiation. High energy radiation and particles can be used to excite electronic states of low temperature solutes. It is explained in Chapter 5 that x-ray, electron bombardment, and ion bombardment transfer energy into the sample lattice, where it quickly relaxes to the lowest exciton band. From there, energy can migrate into solute traps from which radiative decay occurs. The only disadvantage of high energy excitation is that host and guest can suffer radiation damage and chemical decomposition. In dilute solids, however, direct guest excitation is relatively unimportant.

c. Photolysis Sources. If the quantum energy of a light source is larger than the dissociation energy of the absorber, chemical reactions can be induced. The efficiency of photolysis sources depends on the energy of light and the dissociation mechanism of the absorbing molecules. Photolysis work differs from fluorescence mainly in the sample cell design. Any light source is suitable for photolysis, but, since photochemists are frequently interested in the quantum efficiency of a process, sources must be steady emitters so that they can be calibrated. The traditional mercury discharge is still the only well established source. There is ample need for development and commercial progress for this type of source.

C. Light Guides

Laser light is intrinsically directional. Therefore, the entire light beam can be used to illuminate a sample. In contrast, a large fraction of light from conventional light sources is lost before it ever reaches its destination. With these, the best light yield obtains when the source is directly in front of the sample. If this is not practical, the light yield must be increased by the use of light guides such as lenses. It is advantageous to use only the minimum number of lenses, filters, and windows. Long light paths increase stray light losses due to dust in the air and imperfections in all media. If mirrors are used, one must remember that reflection is wavelength dependent. Surface mirrors inflict smaller losses than normal mirrors, but are much more sensitive to mechanical damage. For work in the vacuum UV, mirrors should be coated with a thin film of magnesium oxide.

If nondirectional light has to be transferred from a weak source to a far away detector, as in the case of Zeeman experiments of luminescence pulses (Bajema, 1970), light is best channeled through fiber optics or light pipes. Fiber optics retain some image quality, but they are limited to short lengths and are expensive. Light pipes do not preserve the image. They are, however, comparatively cheap. They can be made from optical grade acrylic by polishing rods on all surfaces. Light transmission is best if the tubes are not in contact with any surface, but if they are wrapped with aluminum foil covered with black masking tape the loss is not severe. This surface treatment also prevents entrance of stray light. Light pipes can be bent and individual sections can be joined with optical silicone grease. Light transmission over a 10-meter section can be as high as 98%.

D. Monochromators and Filters

Individual spectral regions can be isolated with grating monochromators, prism monochromators, absorption filters, and interferometers. Each method has its own advantages and disadvantages, and a large choice of instruments of each type is commercially available. The choice of the most suitable equipment depends on the sample and the properties to be studied. Low temperature solution spectra have a line width of 0.2 cm^{-1} and more. Thus, high dispersion generally is not critical. However, speed is a significant factor because scattering losses on solid samples are substantial and emission is usually weak.

1. Grating Monochromators

These monochromators are most popular because for most practical purposes, their wavelength dispersion is nearly linear. Commercial instruments use different types of optical arrangements. Figure 7.28 shows four common choices, one employing a concave grating, the others based on plane gratings. Diagram A shows an Eagle mount in which the position of the grating is fixed. The detector is moved to scan the spectrum. Such spectrographs are still in wide use for medium to high resolution work, especially in the vacuum UV, but they suffer from several disadvantages. They require considerable space; gratings cannot be easily exchanged because of changes in focus; and concave gratings are more difficult to manufacture and are, therefore, either of lesser quality or more expensive. The advantage of the Eagle mount is that no mirrors are needed. Therefore it will retain the usefulness of this type of spectrometer in the vacuum UV, where mirror reflectivity is poor. Another advantage of the concave grating is that reflected monochromatic light is automatically focused. Thus, the usable free spectral range is almost a half sector. In medium-high dispersion spectrometers this fact can weigh heavily because it reflects in the time needed to record a given part of the spectrum. A 21-foot concave grating with a circular plate holder can be used over an angle of 120° or more to simultaneously

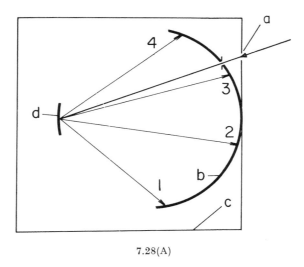

7.28(A)

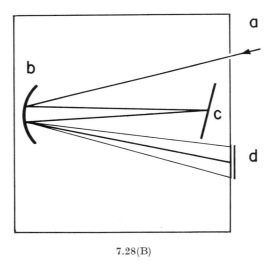

7.28(B)

FIG. 7.28. Basic spectrometer designs: (A) Eagle mount: *a*, entrance slit; *b*, plate circle; *c*, dark grating room; *d*, concave grating; *1st, 2nd, 3rd, 4th* indicates the order of the reflected light. (B) Ebert mount: *a*, entrance slit; *b*, concave mirror; *c*, plane grating; plate. (C) Crossed beam Czerny-Turner mount: *a*, entrance slit; *b*, concave mirror; *c*, plane grating; *d*, plate; *e*, exit slit (after McPherson Co. No. 214 UV spectro spectrograph). (D) 0.5 Spectromer f = 1.5 (after Professor K. Clark, University of Washington): *a*, collimating quartz lens; *b*, transmission grating; *c*, 37 mm camera.

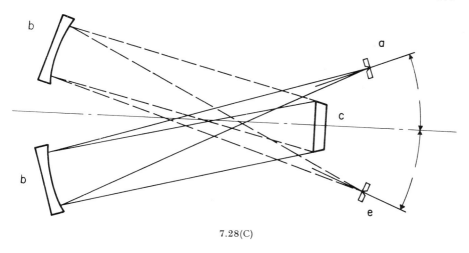

7.28(C)

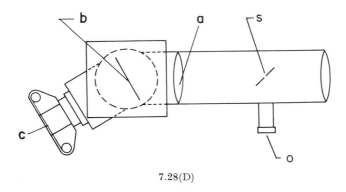

7.28(D)

photograph light between 200 and 1200 nm, if the recorded spectrum allows. When overlapping orders of the source interfere with each other, predispersing prisms or filters can be inserted. Thus, different orders can be simultaneously recorded.

Figures 7.28 B and C show the Ebert mounting and Czerny-Turner mounting. Both use plane gratings and concave mirrors. The difference between the two mountings is in the number of mirrors used. The advantage of the plane grating spectrometers is flexibility. Gratings can be rotated to select different wavelength regions and can be used in instruments with different focal lengths and gratings. They can be changed when different dispersions or blaze angles are desired. Replica gratings are cheap and accurate. A wide range of blaze angles are available which are equally good for low or high dispersion work and for use with camera or photomultiplier detectors.

For high efficiency of light use, high speed instruments with short spectral lengths, large mirrors, and large gratings, used in first and second order, are advisable. For high resolution, gratings should be used in higher orders. Figure 7.28 D shows a schematic of an f-1.5 photographic spectrometer that is not commercially available. Four-inch or larger lenses are used to collect light on an adjustable slit. After passage through a transmission grating, monochromatic light is focused with a Pyrex or quartz lens onto the camera. The spectrum can be photographed on a Polaroid film or regular optical plates. This high speed spectrometer is useful for recording weak phosphorescence.

A simple, superior, and cheap high resolution spectrometer using Czerny-Turner design has been perfected by Davis[*] and co-workers. It uses a 10×25 cm replica plane grating blazed for use in 25th to 30th order and two concave mirrors that can be positioned 10, 20, or 40 feet away. The resolution is close to 500,000; i.e., the line width of solids, and Doppler width of gas lines are the limiting factor for resolution. The price for the fabulous dispersion of 0.02 nm/mm with a 20-foot mirror is, however, the free spectral range, which for a 10-inch camera, is only 0.5–2 nm. This is narrower than a normal vibrational band. An additional inconvenience is that overlapping orders must be separated by predispersion with a supplemental spectrometer placed before the entrance slit.

Predispersion is also necessary for excitation of emission. The many different commercial models of 10–30 cm focal length monochromators are usually based on a Czerny-Turner mount with a 5×5 cm plane grating. The performance of the different models varies widely. The speed changes between f/2 and f/12 for otherwise similar design, and the percentage of stray light superimposed on the monochromatized light changes drastically.

2. Prism Spectrometers

Prism spectrometers have the advantage that a given wavelength appears only under one angle and not in various different higher orders. This makes prism instruments ideal for isolating parts of the UV spectrum. Prism dispersion decreases with increasing wavelength, and the useful prism range is limited by the transmission of the prism material; glass transmits between 280 nm and 1.3 μm. Fused quartz is useful to 230 nm, single crystal quartz to 190 nm, and Suprasil or similar high grade quartz to 170 nm. Until 1963, most commercial infrared spectrometers were based on dispersing prisms.

---

[*] S. P. Davis, Physics Department, University of California, Berkeley.

In the last few years advanced filters have become available, and most IR instruments are now built with gratings.

For high speed UV work requiring high resolution, double and triple prism instruments are still superior to any other monochromators. However, high quality prism instruments are heavy and expensive and useful only for special purposes, such as Raman work with mercury lines.

3. Absorption Filters

Absorption filters are ideal for the separation and isolation of larger portions of the spectrum, a task monochromators cannot fulfill. Gases, liquids, and solids can be used, but the most commonly used filters are dyed glasses or organic dyes dissolved in gelatin films. A wide selection of glass and Wratten filters allow separation of different spectral regions. There are three basic types of filters: blue cutoff filters, red cutoff filters, and filters with spectral windows, so-called band-pass filters.

For many applications commercial filters are not available. One unfulfilled notable need frequently encountered is a red cutoff filter, eliminating all visible light but transmitting the UV. Fortunately solution filters can be prepared for this purpose. Table 7.15 lists various common solution filters and their spectral range. Other frequency ranges can be isolated with the help of gas filters. For some special applications, filters and monochromators have been superseded by cheaply available interference filters.

Interference filters are normally narrow band-pass filters. A wide choice of commercial filters is available for many band-pass regions and in many band widths. Entire sets matched for the selection and separation of the different mercury lines are available.

For quantitative work, spectra are photographed with a step weakener. This is a device that contains strips of neutral, "gray" filters of successively larger density. Figure 7.29 shows that the useful range of such filters is restricted to the region between 300 nm and 1000 nm.

E. Light Detectors

In the UV and visible part of the spectrum photographic plates and photo-electric detectors are the most common light detectors. For some spectral regions chemical actinometers are available. In the far infrared, bolometers and thermopiles are commonly used. These different detectors have different and selective spectral responses. Figure 7.30 shows the spectral ranges for photographic emulsions, photomultipliers, and actinometers. The figure does not provide an exhaustive review of all the available emulsion detectors. Further information may be found in manufacturers' handbooks.

Table 7.15

Solution Filters for Isolating Mercury Lines[a]

Hg Lines	Cell A	Cell B	Cell C	Cell D
253.7	$NiSO_4 \cdot 6H_2O$, 27.6 g/100 ml aqueous solution; 5 cm path	$COSO_4 \cdot 7H_2O$, 8.4 g/100 ml aqueous solution; 5 cm path	I_2, 0.108 g + KI, 0.155 g/l water, 1 cm path	Cl_2 gas, 1 atm, 25°C; 5 cm path
265.2, 265.5	—	—	KI, 0.170 g/100 ml aqueous solution; 1 cm path	—
289.6, 303.0	—	—	Oxalic acid, 20 g/l aqueous solution, 1 cm; or $CuSO_4 \cdot 5H_2O$, 15g/l aqueous solution; 1 cm path	—
312.6, 313.1	$NiSO_4$, 0.178 M aqueous solution; 5 cm path	K_2CrO_4, 5×10^{-4} M aqueous solution; 5 cm path	Potassium biphthalate, 0.0245 M aqueous solution; 1 cm path	Corning glass filter 7–54 (9863); 0.3 cm path
334.1	$NiSO_4 \cdot 6H_2O$, 10.0 g/100 ml aqueous solution; 5 cm path	Corning glass filter 7–51 (5970); 0.5 cm path	Naphthalene in isooctane 1.28 g/100 ml; 1 cm path	—
365.0–366.3	$CuSO_4 \cdot 5H_2O$, 5 g/100 ml aqueous solution; 10 cm path	Corning glass filter 7–37 (5860); 0.5 cm path	2,7-Dimethyl 3,6-diazocyclohepta-1,6-diene perchlorate, 0.010 g/100 ml H_2O; 1 cm path	—

Table 7.15 (continued)

Hg Lines	Cell A	Cell B	Cell C	Cell D
404.5–407.8	$CuSO_4 \cdot 5H_2O$, 0.44 g/100 ml, 2.7 M NH_4OH; 10 cm path	I_2, 0.75 g/100 ml CCl_4; 1 cm path	Quinone hydrochloride, 2.00 g/100 ml H_2O; 1 cm path	—
435.8	$CuSO_4 \cdot 5H_2O$, 0.44 g/100 ml, 2.7 M NH_4OH; 10 cm path	$NaNO_2$, 75 g/100 ml aqueous solution; 1 cm path	—	—
546.1	$CuCl_2 \cdot 2H_2O$, 20.0 g + $CaCl_2$ (anhyd), 27.0 g/100 ml aqueous, very dilute HCl; 1 cm path	Neodymium nitrate, 60 g/100 ml aqueous solution; 5 cm path	—	—
577.0, 579.0	$CuCl_2 \cdot 2H_2O$, 10.0 g + $CaCl_2$ (anhyd), 30.0 g/100 ml aqueous, very dilute HCl; 1 cm path	$K_2Cr_2O_7$, 3.0 g/100 ml aqueous solution; 10 cm path	—	—

[a] Data from Calvert (1966).

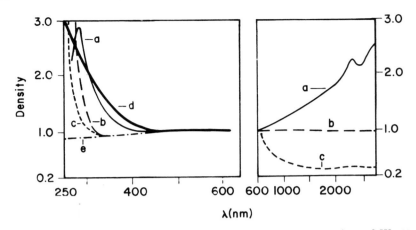

FIG. 7.29. Absorption edges of neutral filters; *a*, silver; *b*, inconel; *c*, carbon; *d*, Wratten; and *e*, inconel on quartz.

1. Photographic Plates and Films

Normal silver-based emulsions are dispersed in gelatin and mounted on glass or plastic sheet. Silver bromide is sensitive below 400 nm, as shown in Fig. 7.30 for O-type plates. Sensitivity in other spectral ranges is achieved with the help of sensitizers. This subject, as well as other details on photographic processes, is explained by Mees and James (1966). Practical aspects of photography are covered in handbooks (Kodak and Engel, 1968).

Below 230 nm, normal emulsions are limited by the absorption of the gelatin, but specially prepared plates in which the silver halide is on the surface of the carrier are available. Normal plates can be sensitized for use in this range by coating with sodium salicylate or other phosphorescent sensitizers. This type of sensitization can be used between 50 and 230 nm.

Emulsions for the visible and red portion of the spectrum contain organic dye sensitizers. The sensitivity of these materials varies significantly with wavelength. Photographers use filters to compensate for color distortions. Above 700 nm all photographic emulsions are a hundredfold less sensitive. In this range sensitivity is enhanced by washing in ammonia–alcohol solution or in water. Above 1200 nm, plates are useless. In the infrared, photoelectric devices and thermopiles must be used. The red blindness of plates is an advantage during development because UV plates can be developed in the presence of red light. This makes visual control of the processing of such film possible, allowing optimum use of stored images. Red sensitive plates cannot, however, be developed in blue light because all plates remain blue sensitive.

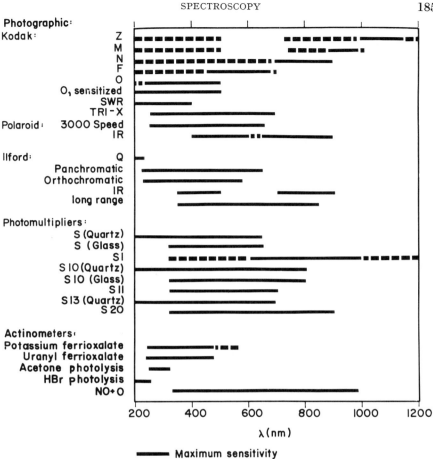

FIG. 7.30. Spectral sensitivity ranges of photographic plates, photomultipliers, and actinometers.

For quantitative work, plates have to be calibrated at each wavelength. Typical sensitivity versus wavelength curves have a minimum because of gelatin absorption at about 400–450 nm. It is best to calibrate the components of the assembled optical train in one operation. For this a calibrated standard tungsten light source and the unknown sample should be photographed alternately so that individual differences between plates are minimized. The optical density for a given source and a given emulsion depends on temperature at exposure time, age of the plate, preexposure, developer concentration, time, temperature, and agitation in developer.

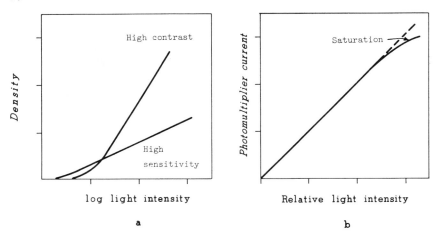

FIG. 7.31. Intensity *vs.* signal curves for (a) photographic plate, and (b) photomultiplier. The curve *a* is on a logarithmic scale.

The quantum threshold of photographic plates can be a nuisance for low light level work because the first light quanta are used to "saturate" the plate and do not yield linear darkening. Figure 7.31 shows the response of a photographic plate and a photoelectric device as function of light quanta. Since emulsions are integrating detectors, the threshold can be overcome by fogging. For this, the entire film surface is exposed to a pulse of weak white light. A 1-second pulse of light from a 40-W light bulb in a black box with a 1-mm hole is a convenient fogging source. An effect similar to fogging can be achieved by overdeveloping the emulsion, either by using a temperature 5° above normal or by developing two or three times longer.

The logarithmic response of plates is limited by saturation. For quantitative work one should always work within the "linear region." The speed of a photographic emulsion is related to the grain size. The grain size affects, therefore, both exposure time and resolution. Since low temperature samples scatter light, high speed is desirable. For this, Kodak 103a type emulsions and Polaroid 3000 film are ideal. For high resolution work, the much smaller grain size of a II-type emulsion is preferable, despite the hundredfold lower speed. The grain size of this emulsion is so small that resolution is limited by the dimensional accuracy and linear stability of the carrier, therefore all spectral emulsions are available on glass plates. Emulsions on Estar, a strong and tough plastic film, are much cheaper. It is reproducible to at least 0.05 inch. This is more accurate than is necessary for most low temperature work. Polaroid film is convenient. Polaroid red film records spectra up to 850 nm. Normal Polaroid film is sensitive between 220 nm and 550 nm. Type 3000 film has about three times higher speed than a 103a emulsion. It yields excellent contrast.

Photographic work has the great advantage that a wealth of primary data is stored. When and if better evaluation of the original data becomes desirable, old plates can be retrieved and remeasured after any number of years. This is not true for photoelectric recording, where the original signal is integrated, treated, amplified, and diluted before it can be stored and read. Another peculiarity of spectrophotographic work is that signals are automatically integrated over time. If a signal changes intensity or composition with time, a photographic plate records the sum of all signals, at an observed point of the spectrum over the entire time. This is very convenient for observation of samples during warming, where spectra can change abruptly and irreversibly because of diffusion. This can cause emission of light flashes, changes in absorption spectra, and other time-dependent effects that might be missed with photoelectric detection. On the other hand, photoelectric detectors are advantageous for observing the same effects because they can be used to measure the time dependence of individual features if the spectra are already known.

2. Photoelectric Detectors

A large number of different types of photomultipliers and photocells are available. Manufacturers' descriptions are the best guide to this type of equipment. Basically, all photoelectric devices are based on photoemission or photoconduction.

a. PHOTOMULTIPLIERS. Characteristic photoemission energies for metals are of the order of 2–5 eV. The spectral sensitivity range is similar to that of photographic emulsions. For practical purposes three other characteristics are equally important in choosing a tube. These are amplification, signal-to-noise ratio, and dark current.

The price for a high amplification factor is that in high-gain tubes dark current is intrinsically high and the signal-to-noise ratio low. The dark current is due to thermal emission from the cathode. This can be significantly reduced by cooling the tube. Cooling becomes imperative for IR tubes and for work at low light levels. Cooling to $-78°C$ reduces the dark current by a factor of 10^3 and increases the sensitivity correspondingly. To a certain degree, dark current can be suppressed by compensation with an auxiliary source. Therefore, many amplifiers, such as the Keithley 417, have built-in compensators. However, compensation has only limited value because noise, which increases with dark current, cannot be canceled. Noise is due to cosmic rays, stray light, and stray signals. High gain tubes collect more stray signals; therefore it is advisable to select tubes not primarily for gain but for low noise. Commercial selection of low noise tubes is made by using special designs and selection of the best individual tubes from a batch. The same holds for low dark current tubes, which are selected by trial and error and sold for premium prices under special designations. The EMI 9502 S-tube is an example. It is an experimentally selected tube from normal 9502 stock.

A wide variety of near infrared detectors exist. They are quite wavelength sensitive. All must be cooled. The technology in this field is at an extremely advanced stage, but much of the knowledge will remain classified for many years because of military use.

b. PHOTOCELLS. CdS and many other sulfides and selenides can be used as photoconductive cells which are light sensitive in the infrared part of the spectrum. The dark current of such cells is very large unless the sensitive surface is cooled. IR detectors are commercially available mounted in sealed Dewar flasks, which can be as small as a fountain pen. However, the response time of cold sulfides is large, often of the order of milliseconds. Photocells have little importance for electronic spectroscopy, except for silicon solar cells and gallium arsenide cells, which are sensitive to $^1\Delta$ oxygen emission.

F. Decay Time Analyzers

Measurement of time dependence of light signals is used to determine the lifetime of excited molecular states. It also serves spectroscopy in other ways. It makes possible the analysis of weak emission in the presence of stray light if the source is pulsed or modulated and it allows separation of monochromatic short-lived and long-lived emission from molecules in different states.

Lifetime measurement of molecules can be made in two ways. The first method is based on excitation of the molecule with a pulse that is shorter than the lifetime of the emission. Section VII, B, 2 describes pulsed sources that are suitable for this purpose. Mechanical shutters, stoppers, and rotating gratings can be used to modulate continuous light. Flashbulbs with nanosecond pulse width provide continuous wavelength sources.

The time dependence of the emission intensity can be recorded on an oscilloscope. Continued pulsing makes possible integration of signals with nuclear multichannel counters or wave form eductors. The time resolution of this method can be made 10^{-8} sec. If the exciting wavelength cannot be produced with a pulsed source, up to 40% of the light from a continuous source can be modulated with a Kerr cell. The decay time of molecular states is determined by measuring the phase shift between exciting and fluorescent light. This method is not suitable for nonexponential decays. Therefore, it is not desirable for solid state work. If a laser source is used, the signal may be strong enough to photograph the spectrum with a rotating mirror. Time resolution, depending on mirror, shutter speed, and sensitivity of the film, may reach 10^{-6} sec. For very short pulses very small time delays can be mechanically effected by splitting a light beam and crossing the parts after different path lengths. A typical use of this very elegant method was demonstrated by Windsor (Novak, 1968), who excited an organic molecule with half of the light from a laser beam, then used the other half, after a short detour, to record the absorption spectrum of its excited singlet state.

G. Polarizers

Circular polarization can yield information about sites in matrices. However, description of the method exceeds the scope of this book. Parallel and perpendicular polarization helps identify the character of electronic states, and loss of polarization indicates energy migration via excitons. In the visible, light can be polarized with polarizers made from organic molecules. UV polarizers employ Glenn prisms, which depend on splitting of light beams by anisotropic calcite. The light transmission of these prisms is limited by the transmission of the glue which keeps the parts together and must have a refractive index between those of the two calcite axes.

Recommended Reading

Engel, C. E., ed., *Photography for Scientists*, Academic Press, New York, 1968.

English, W. D., ed., *Cryogenic Technology*, Journal of the Cryogenic Society of America, Value Engineering Publications, Los Angeles, 1964 to present.

Hamilton, C. B., ed., *Cryogenics and Industrial Gases* (formerly Cryogenic Engineering News), Business Communications, Cleveland, Ohio, 1965 to present.

Macleod, H. A., *Thin-Film Optical Filters*, Elsevier, New York, 1969.

Mees, C. E. K., and T. H. James, eds., *The Theory of the Photographic Process*, Macmillan Co., New York, 1966.

Scott, R. B., *Technology and Uses of Liquid Hydrogen*, Pergamon Press, New York, 1969.

Scott, R. E., *Cryogenic Engineering*, Academic Press, New York, 1959.

CHAPTER 8

Properties and Production of Samples

I. PHYSICAL PROPERTIES OF MATRICES, ORGANIC GLASSES, AND POLYMERS

This section is devoted to the selection of host media. It is not a critical review of physical properties. In the first part, gaseous, liquid and solid matrix materials are described. Since many are also useful for forming organic glasses by slow cooling, Table 8.1 contains data for both types of samples. The data are arranged in the order of increasing chemical complexity: (a) rare gases, (b) diatomics, (c) triatomics, (d) polyatomics, (e) fluorocarbons and other halogen derivatives, (f) hydrocarbons, (g) alcohols and ethers, (h) aliphatics containing N, O, S, and, since they are useful for some special applications, (i) inorganic salts. The most important of these materials are the rare gases.

A. Rare Gas Matrices

Neon, argon, krypton, and xenon are chemically inert and optically transparent. Their intermolecular forces are small. The properties of rare gases have been well studied and reviewed in detail (Pollack, 1964; Cook, 1961; Claassen, 1966; Baldini, 1962).

X-ray diffraction studies have shown that the rare gases normally crystallize in a cubic close-packed (ccp) structure with a face-centered cubic (fcc) unit cell. In this geometry, the lattice can be pictured as consisting of layers of atoms stacked one on the other. Figure 8.1 shows a sketch of a layer of atoms as they occur in the ccp structure. Each atom in the lattice has six nearest-neighbors in each layer. In the ccp structure the layers are stacked in such a way that the interstitial volume is minimized and each atom is in contact with three others in the plane below and in the plane

Table 8.1

Physical Properties of Matrix Materials

Substance	Melting Point	Boiling Point	Temperature (°K) Vapor Pressure					Molecular Weight
			10^{-7} Torr	10^{-5} Torr	10^{-3} Torr	10^{-1} Torr	10 Torr	
(a) Rare Gases								
He	—	4.216	—	0.486	0.658	0.980	1.738	4.003
Ne	24.57	27.1	7.87	9.19	11.05	13.85	18.45	20.18
Ar	83.85	87.29	28.6	33.1	39.2	48.2	62.5	39.944
Kr	115.95	119.93	39.3	45.5	53.9	66.3	85.9	83.80
Xe	161.3	165.1	54.2	62.7	74.4	91.5	118.5	131.30
Rn	202	211.3			96.9	137.5	160.0	222.00
(b) Diatomics								
H_2	13.96	20.39^a	4.03	4.84	6.05	8.03	11.70	2.016
N_2	63.15	77.34	25.2	29.0	34.1	41.7	54.0	28.02
O_2	54.40	90.19	29.9	34.1	39.8	48.1	62.7	32.00
CO	68.10	81.66	28.4	32.5	38.0	45.8	57.9	28.01
NO	109.51	121.4	50.9	57.6	66.3	78.1	95.0	30.01
(c) Triatomics								
H_2O	273	373	153.0	173.0	198.5	233	284.4	18.016
CO_2	—	195	80.6	91.5	106.0	125.0	153.5	44.01
N_2O	182.2	184.66	75.5	85.7	99.0	117.5	144.0	44.02
(d) Polyatomics								
CH_4	90.68	111.7	34.2	39.9	47.7	59.2	77.7	16.04
SF_6	209.4 (subl.)	—	62.5	72.8	87.0	108.3	—	146.07

a Sublimes under normal conditions.

Table 8.1 (continued)

(e) Fluorocarbons and Other Halogen Derivatives

Name	Formula	Temperature (°K)				Molecular Weight
		Melting Point	Boiling Point	Vapor Pressure 1 Torr	Vapor Pressure 10 Torr	
Fluoromethane	CH_3F	131.2	195.0	125.9	141.6	34.03
Chloromethane	CH_3Cl	175.44	249.2	—	180.8	50.49
Bromomethane	CH_3Br	178	276.8	176.9	200.4	94.95
Iodomethane	CH_3I	106.5	315.6	—	227.4	141.95
Methylene fluoride	CH_2F_2	—	213.1	—	—	52.03
Methylene chloride	CH_2Cl_2	176	313.9	203.2	229.9	84.94
Methylene bromide	CH_2Br_2	221	371.8	238.1	270.8	173.86
Fluoroform	CHF_3	113	190.8	116.3	134.5	70.02
Chloroform	$CHCl_3$	109.5	334.5	215.2	243.5	119.39
Bromoform	$CHBr_3$	281.3	423.7	—	307.2	252.77
Iodoform	CHI_3	393	—	—	—	393.78
Freon 22	$CHClF_2$	127	232.5	—	—	86.48
Freon 14	CF_4	89.47	145.5	—	104.9	88.01
Freon 12	CCl_2F_2	118	243.1	—	—	120.92
Carbon tetrachloride	CCl_4	250	349.9	223.2	253.6	153.84
Carbon tetrabromide	CBr_4	363	462.7	302.3	341.1	331.67
Carbon tetraiodide	CI_4	444	580	404	445	519.69
Ethyl fluoride	C_2H_5F	129.8	241.2	156.2	175.5	48.06
Ethyl chloride	C_2H_5Cl	134.3	285.5	183.4	207.4	64.52
Ethyl bromide	C_2H_5Br	154.1	311.6	198.9	225.7	108.98
Ethyl iodide	C_2H_5I	165	345.6	218.8	248.9	155.98
Perfluoroethylene	C_2F_4	130.7	196.7	—	140.8	100.02
Perchloroethylene	C_2Cl_4	251	394.0	252.6	287.0	165.85
Freon 116	C_2F_6	173.1	194.4	—	—	138.02
Perchloroethane	C_2Cl_6	460	458.8	305.9	348.7	236.76
Perfluoropropene	C_3F_6	116.8	242.9	—	—	150.03
Freon C-318 (Perfluoro cyclobutane)	C_4F_8	233	266.6	—	—	200.04
Perfluoropentene	C_5F_{10}	—	271.0	—	—	250.05
Perfluoro-n-pentane	C_5F_{12}	320(?)	302.6	—	—	288.05
Perfluoro-n-hexane	C_6F_{14}	—	330.3	—	—	338.06
Hexachlorobenzene	C_6Cl_6	595	—	—	—	284.80
Perfluoro-1-hexane	C_6F_6	352	—	—	—	186.06
Perfluorocyclohexane	C_6F_{12}	330	326.0	217.7	246.1	300.06

Table 8.1 (continued)

(f) Hydrocarbons

Name	Formula	Temperature (°K)					Molecular Weight
		Melting Point	Boiling Point	Vapor Pressure			
				10^{-3} Torr	1 Torr	10 Torr	
Methane	CH_4	90.52	111.7	48.2	67.3	77.7	16.04
Ethane	C_2H_6	89.89	184.6	83.4	113.7	130.3	30.07
Ethane	C_2H_4	103.97	169.3	79.5	104.9	120.0	28.05
Acetylene	C_2H_2	91.2	189.2	98.6	130.3	145.0	26.04
Propane	C_3H_8	83.1	231.1	105.4	144.3	164.7	44.09
Cyclopropane	C_3H_6	146.4	240.1	115.5	151.9	173.0	42.08
Butane	C_4H_{10}	134.7	272.7	127.7	171.7	195.4	58.12
Cyclobutane	C_4H_8	—	286.1	—	181.2	205.3	56.10
n-Pentane	C_5H_{12}	143.28	303.2	147.5	197.0	223.1	72.15
Cyclopentane	C_5H_{10}	—	322.4	—	205.2	232.8	70.13
n-Hexane	C_6H_{14}	178	341.9	—	219.3	248.2	86.17
Cyclohexane	C_6H_{12}	266.5	353.9	—	227.9	253.3	84.16
Benzene	C_6H_6	267.5	353.2	—	236.5	261.6	78.11
n-Heptane	C_7H_{16}	182	371.6	—	239.2	271.2	100.20
Toluene	C_7H_8	178	383.8	—	246.5	279.5	92.13
n-Octane	C_8H_{18}	116.5	398.8	—	259.2	292.4	114.23
Cyclooctane	C_8H_{16}	276.5	424.3	—	—	—	112.21
n-Nonane	C_9H_{20}	222	424.0	—	275.6	312.3	128.25
n-Decane	$C_{10}H_{22}$	243.3	447.3	—	290.3	330.9	142.28

(g) Alcohols and Ethers

Name	Formula	Temperature in °K				Molecular Weight
		Melting Point	Boiling Point	Vapor Pressure		
				1 Torr	10 Torr	
Methanol	CH_4O	175.4	337.9	229.2	257.0	32.04
Ethanol	C_2H_6O	155.9	351.6	241.9	270.9	46.07
Propanol	C_3H_8O	146	371.0	258.2	287.9	60.09
Butanol	$C_4H_{10}O$	184.0–183.4	390.7	272.0	303.4	74.12
Pentanol	$C_5H_{12}O$	194.7	411.0	286.8	318.1	88.15
Hexanol	$C_6H_{14}O$	221.6	430.2	297.6	331.4	102.17
Phenol	C_6H_6O	314	454.9	313.3	343.7	94.11
Heptanol	$C_7H_{16}O$	238.6	449.0	315.6	347.9	116.20
Octanol	$C_8H_{18}O$	256.9	468.4	327.2	361.5	130.23
Nonanol	$C_9H_{20}O$	268	486.7	332.7	372.9	144.25
Dimethyl ether	C_2H_6O	134.6	249.5	157.5	179.9	46.07
Diethyl ether	$C_4H_{10}O$	157	307.7	198.9	225.2	74.12
Ethyl propyl ether	$C_5H_{12}O$	∼196	337.1	208.9	238.2	88.15
Dipropyl ether	$C_6H_{14}O$	151.1	362.1	229.9	261.4	102.17

Table 8.1 (continued)

(h) Aliphatics containing N, O, S

Name	Formula	Temperature in °K				Molecular Weight
		Melting Point	Boiling Point	Vapor Pressure		
				1 Torr	10 Torr	
Phosgene	CCl_2O	155	281.5	—	203.9	98.92
Acetyl chloride	C_2H_3ClO	161	324.7	117.4	205.6	78.50
Methylmercaptan	CH_4S	150.1	280.0	182.5	205.7	48.10
Ethylmercaptan	C_2H_6S	152	308.2	196.5	223.0	62.13
Dimethyl sulfide	C_2H_6S	190.0	309.2	197.6	224.0	62.13
Diethyl sulfide	$C_4H_{10}S$	171.1	361.2	233.6	265.2	90.18
Thiophene	C_4H_4S	234.85	357.6	232.5	262.3	84.13
Diethyl disulfide	$C_4H_{10}S_2$	—	427.3	276.5	313.1	122.24
Thiophenol	C_6H_6S	—	442.3	291.8	329.2	110.17
Diphenyl sulfide	$C_{12}H_{10}S$	233	565.7	369.3	418.2	186.26
Diphenyl disulfide	$C_{12}H_{10}S_2$	334	583.2	404.8	453.2	218.32

(i) Salts

Formula	Temperature (°K)						Molecular Weight
	Melting Point	Boiling Point	Vapor Pressure				
			10^{-5} Torr	10^{-3} Torr	1 Torr	10 Torr	
LiF	1115	1952	—	—	1321	1482	25.94
LiCl	887	1653	—	—	1058	1207	42.40
LiBr	820	1584	—	—	1020	1159	86.86
LiI	723	1443	—	764	997	1114	133.86
NaF	1261	1950	879	1011	1300	1500	44.00
NaCl	1074	1740	760	872	1136	1287	58.45
NaBr	1028	1665	718	825	1078	1223	102.91
NaI	924	1577	663	751	1041	1176	149.92
KF	1119	1776	749	865	1157	1311	58.10
KCl	1049	1679	730	839	1092	1238	74.55
KBr	1003	1659	702	805	1067	1212	119.01
KI	959	1596	670	767	1020	1159	166.02
RbF	1048	1682	—	—	1100	1245	104.48
RbCl	988	1653	702	807	1064	1209	120.94
RbBr	955	1625	693	797	1050	1192	165.40
RbI	915	1579	—	—	1022	1160	212.40
CsF	955	1525	—	—	983	1117	151.91
CsCl	919	1574	—	770.4	1018	1155	168.37
CsBr	909	1576	667	763	1021	1158	212.83
CsI	894	1553	651	744	1010	1145	259.83

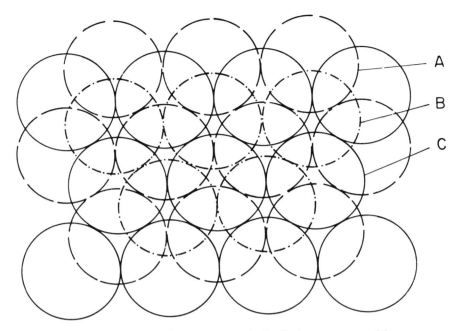

FIG. 8.1. Rare gas lattice structure; *A*, *B*, *C* gives sequence of layers.

above. Each atom has a total of twelve nearest-neighbors. The layers are arranged in the sequence ABCABC.... The projection of every third layer coincides. Lattice parameters for rare gases are listed in Table 8.2.

When the layers of atoms are stacked in the arrangement ABABAB..., a hexagonal close-packed (hcp) structure results. This structural arrangement is very similar to ccp except that one-third of the gaps are aligned and form tunnels through the lattice. This structure has been observed in H_2 and N_2. On the basis of computation taking into account long-range interactions, it was long predicted that argon should have an hcp allotrope. This has recently been observed in crystals containing impurities and crystals frozen from the liquid (L. Meyer, 1964).

Vapor-deposited matrices do not form perfect crystals. The average density of vapor-deposited solids is about 1% less than the solid grown from the liquid (Pollack, 1964). This indicates that vapor-deposited solids are porous. Matrices contain unoccupied sites and imperfections. It is likely that guests form centers for imperfections.

Pollack (1964) has reviewed the theories on the structure of the rare gas solids. The presently known potential functions do not fit all rare gas

Table 8.2

Lattice Parameters of Rare Gases[a]

Rare Gas	0°K	4.2°K	10°K	20°K	30°K	40°K	50°K	60°K	80°K	100°K	120°K	140°K	160°K
						Lattice Parameter (nm)							
Neon	0.4462	0.4462	0.4467	0.4504	0.4532[b]								
Argon	0.5312	0.5312	0.5313	0.5318	0.5328	0.5343	0.5366	0.5397	0.5470[b]				
Krypton	0.5643	0.5645	0.5647	0.5653	0.5663	0.5676	0.5692	0.5708	0.5748	0.5789	0.5820[b]		
Xenon	0.6131	0.6131	0.6132	0.6136	0.6143	0.6154	0.6165	0.6180	0.6210	0.6240	0.6273	0.6310	0.6352[b]

[a] Data from Pollack (1964).
[b] Lattice parameter at triple point.

properties. To a good approximation, the forces in the rare gas can be represented by the Lennard-Jones (6,12) potential where the attractive force is an induced dipole interaction, r^{-6} term and the repulsion is given by an r^{-12} term. The potential has the form:

$$\phi = 4\varepsilon \left[\left(\frac{\sigma}{r} \right)^{12} - \left(\frac{\sigma}{r} \right)^{6} \right]$$

where ε and σ are numerical constants determined by experiment. The shape of the curve obtained is shown in Fig. 8.2 as a plot of ϕ/ε versus r/σ. Values of ε and σ are tabulated in Table 8.3. The Lennard-Jones potential is a convenient model for deriving interaction between neutral atoms. The model fails to predict the stability of fcc structure over that of hcp, and several other properties (Boato, 1964). The low lattice energies of rare gases cause only very small host-guest interactions. Therefore, the optical properties of guests are less influenced than in any other solvent.

Figure 8.3 shows the vapor pressures of neon, argon, krypton, and xenon as a function of temperature. Lower vapor pressures are extrapolated

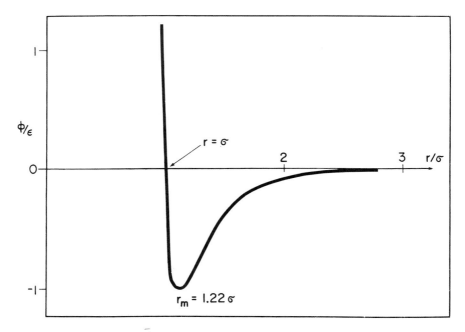

FIG. 8.2. Lennard-Jones potential.

(Honig, 1962). In matrix experiments, the host will sublime and is pumped off if its vapor pressure becomes comparable to the residual vacuum. This sets an upper limit to the sample temperature since vacuum is of the order of 10^{-7} torr. The upper temperature limits are indicated in Fig. 8.3 by a dashed line.

The thermal conductivities (λ) of neon, argon, and krypton are shown in Table 8.4 for some important temperatures. Only few data are available for λ of xenon. Xenon has a maximum λ of 24 mW/cm °K at 16°K (Pollack, 1964). All rare gases have low thermal conductivities compared to metals because in the absence of the free electrons heat must be transferred via lattice modes, or phonons. This type of heat transfer is small because only anharmonic terms contribute. In the harmonic oscillator approximation, heat is not transferred.

Table 8.3

Lennard-Jones Parameters and Polarizability of Rare Gases[a]

| Rare Gas | Lennard-Jones Parameters | | | Polarizability, α ($nm^3 \times 10^{-3}$) |
	ε (ergs $\times 10^{-16}$)	σ (nm)	Λ[b]	
He	14	0.256	2.68	0.204
Ne	49	0.275	0.59	0.392
Ar	165	0.341	0.18	1.63
Ke	230	0.368	0.101	2.465
Xe	311	0.407	0.062	4.01

[a] Data from A. C. H. Hallett in Cook (1961).
[b] $\Lambda = h/\sigma(me)^{1/2}$.

Table 8.4

Thermal Conductivity of Rare Gases[a]

| Rare Gas | Thermal Conductivity[b] | | | Maximum λ | |
	4.2°K	20.4°K	77°K	Value λ	T (°K)
Neon	41	37	—	47	3.4
Argon	17	12	3.4	38	8.2
Krypton	5.2	11	3.5	17	11.5
Xenon	—	—	—	24	16.1

[a] Data from G. K. White (1956) and Pollack (1964).
[b] λ in mW/cm · degree Kelvin.

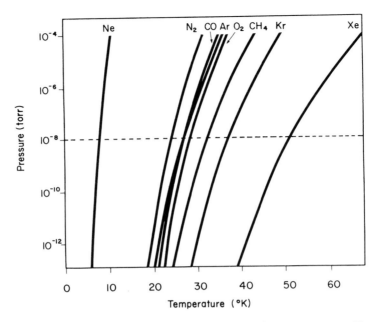

FIG. 8.3. Vapor pressure of matrix gases. Above about 10^{-8} torr the matrix will vaporize.

The sticking coefficient for argon, krypton, and xenon gas at $230°K$ on a target at $8°K$ is 0.95 ± 0.05 (Levenson, 1967). It is independent of impingement rate in the range of 5×10 to 9×10^{13} atoms/cm^2 sec. This value is compared to earlier measured rates of 10^{16} atoms/cm^2 sec for $\gamma < 1$. γ depends on the surface material; when xenon is deposited on krypton at $40°K$, γ is only 0.86.

Crystals or films of the rare gases at $4.2°K$ are brittle (Boato, 1964). They are highly susceptible to cracking and peeling when stress is applied. This is often observed during matrix experiments when sudden changes in temperature occur. As rare gas crystals warm up, they become soft, and near the triplet point the crystals are extrudable (Hallett, 1961a). This makes it difficult to compress rare gases, despite their low density and high compressibility which are tabulated in Tables 8.5 and 8.6.

The rare gas crystals are all optically transparent (Bolz, 1962; Pollack, 1964) from the far infrared to the vacuum ultraviolet. In the infrared, only the lattice frequencies appear, and these are at less than 100 cm^{-1} (Schnepp, 1961). Schnepp (1960b) and Roncin (1966) have reported the vacuum

Table 8.5

Density of Solid Rare Gases[a]

Rare Gas	Density (g/cm³)												
	0	4.2	10	20	30	40	50	60	80	100	120	140	160
Neon	1.508	1.508	1.504	1.468	1.394[b]								
Argon	1.769	1.767	1.765	1.762	1.752	1.738	1.717	1.689	1.620[b]				
Krypton	3.094	3.093	3.092	3.072	3.064	3.040	3.020	2.992	2.930	2.868	2.830[b]		
Xenon	3.782	3.781	3.780	3.774	3.762	3.742	3.720	3.693	3.640	3.587	3.533	3.471	3.400[b]

[a] Data from G. K. White (1964) and Pollack (1964).
[b] Density at triple point.

Table 8.6

Compressibility of Rare Gases[a]

Rare Gas	Compressibility[b]			
	0°K	4.2°K	20°K	77°K
Neon	10.1	10.1	—	—
Argon	4.0	4.0	4.2	7.5
Krypton	3.9	3.9	4.0	5.6
Xenon	2.8	2.8	2.9	3.7

[a] Data from G. K. White (1964) and Pollack (1964).
[b] In 10^{-13} cm²/dyne.

Table 8.7

Lowest Allowed Transition of Rare Gases
and Matrices

Gas	Wavelength (nm)	Frequency (μm^{-1})
He	58.43	17.114
Ne	73.59	13.589
	74.37	13.446
Ar	104.82	9.550
	106.67	9.375
Kr	116.49	8.585
	123.58	8.092
Xe	129.56	7.718
	146.96	6.804
SF_6	83	12.2
N_2	145	6.929
CO	153	6.507

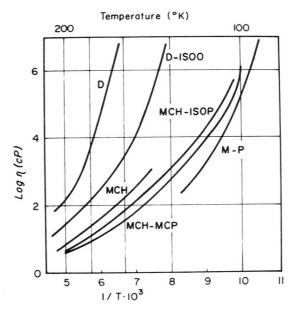

FIG. 8.4. Viscosity of organic glasses. After Schneider (1968). Abbreviations as in Table 8.8.

ultraviolet absorption of vapor deposited krypton and xenon samples in the region above 120 nm. The lowest excited states of rare gases are listed in Table 8.7. No argon absorptions occur in this region. The lowest rare gas singlet exciton bands are at 6.80 μm^{-1} in xenon, 8.09 in krypton, 9.37 in argon, and 13.4 in neon, well in the vacuum UV.

B. Organic Glasses

Frozen solutions of organic molecules have been used for over fifty years for phosphorescence studies. Many solvents do not crystallize, but form highly viscous glasses that remain transparent at 76°K and even at 20°K. Von Salis (1968) and Rosengren (1962c) have shown that several solvent mixtures remain Newtonian and have no miscibility gap. Figure 8.4 shows a viscosity versus temperature plot for several glasses. Methylcyclohexane crystallizes at 135°K. EPA has a high viscosity increase below the same temperature.

Table 8.8 lists some of the pure and mixed solvents that have been

Table 8.8

Commonly Used Organic Glasses

(a)

Pure Substances
3-Methylpentane (3MP)
Methylcyclopentane (MCP)
Nujol (paraffin oil)
Isopentane (ISOP)
Methylcyclohexane (MCH)
Isooctane (ISOO)
Boric acid
Sulfuric acid
Phosphoric acid
Ethanol
Isopropanol
1-Propanol
1-Butanol
Glycerol
Sugar
Triethanolamine
2-Methyltetrahydrogermane
Di-*n*-propyl ether
cis-trans Decalin (D)
Triacetin (TA)

Table 8.8 (continued)

(b) Organic Glasses

Components	Ratio A/B
3-Methylpentane/isopentane	1/2, 1/2
Isopentane/methylcyclohexane (MPH)	1/4 to 6/4
Methylcyclopentane/methylcyclohexane (PH)	1/1
Pentene-2(*cis*)/pentene-2(*trans*)	
Propane/propene	1/1
Isopropyl benzene/propane/propene	2/9/9
Ethanol/methanol	4/1, 5/2, 1/9
Isopropyl alcohol/isopentane	3/7
Ethanol/isopentane/ethyl ether (EPA)	2/5/5
Alphanol 79'/mixture of primary alcohol	
Isopentane/*n*-butyl alcohol	7/3
Isopentane/isopropyl alcohol	8/2
Isopentane/*n*-propyl alcohol	8/2
Ether/isooctane/isopropyl alcohol	3/3/1
Ether/isooctane/ethyl alcohol	3/3/1
Ether/isopropyl alcohol	3/1
Ether/ethanol	3/1
Isooctane/methylcyclohexane/isopropyl alcohol	3/3/1
Diethyl ether/toluene/ethanol	2/1/1
Isopropyl alcohol/isopentane	2/5/5
Propanol/ether	2/5
Butanol/ether	2/5
Diethyl ether/isopentane, dimethyl formamide/ethanol	12/10/6/1
Water/propylene glycol	1/1
Ethylene glycol/water	2/1
Trimethylamine/isopentane/ethyl ether	2/5/5
Triethylamine/isopentane/ethyl ether	3/1/3
Methylhydrazine/methylamine/trimethylamine	2/4/4
Diethylether/isopentane/ethanol/pyridine	12/10/6/1
n-Butyl ether/isopropyl ether/methyl ether	3/5/12
Diphenyl ether/1,1-diphenylethane/triphenylmethane	3/3/1
Diethyl ether/isopentane	1/1 to 1/2
Propyl ether/isopentane	3/1
Propyl ether/methylcyclohexane	3/1
Diethyl ether/pentene-2(*cis*)-pentene-2(*trans*)	2/1
Ethyl iodide/isopentane/ethyl ether	1/2/2
Ethyl bromide/methylcyclohexane/isopentane/methylcyclopentane	1/4/7/7
Ethanol/methanol/ethyl iodide	16/4/1
Ethanol/methanol/propyl iodide	16/4/1
Ethanol/methanol/propyl chloride	16/4/1
Ethanol/methanol/propyl bromide	16/4/1
Diethyl ether/isopentane/ethanol/1-chloronaphthalene	8/6/2/2
3-Methylpentane/isopentane	1/2
Propyl alcohol/propane/propene	2/9/9
Diisopropylamine/propane/propene	2/9/9
Diprobyl ether/propane/propane	2/4/4

used as optical solvents. Although EPA is by far the best known, many others are equally useful. It is important that all solvents be very pure and oxygen free. Otherwise emission effects can be severely perturbed. This is further discussed in Chapter 5 and in Chapter 8, Section III, A, 1. Organic glasses are not chemically inert. If UV light is used, solute hydrogen emission can lead to irreversible reactions between solute and solvent. Since organic glasses are metastable, their physical properties are ill defined and are time dependent. The optical properties of glasses are summarized in Fig. 7.21.

C. Polymer and Plastic Samples

Organic polymeric materials were originally introduced as matrices for the study of radicals by electron spin resonance (ESR) (Morawetz, 1960). Only since 1966 have they been used for the study of optical properties (Geacintov, 1968). Several "plastics" have now been used as matrices, but the most common is polymethyl methacrylate (PMMA). Table 8.9 lists several successfully used plastics. Figure 7.23 shows the approximate absorption spectrum for each material at 298°K and in the region 220–400 nm. Most of the plastics (Geacintov, 1968) show a weak phosphorescence when excited at 366 nm.

One drawback of organic polymers is their low thermal conductivity. For this reason, essentially all plastic matrix work has been performed at

Table 8.9

Optically Transparent Plastics[a]

Material	Softening Point (°C)	Low Wavelength Cutoff (nm)
Polystyrene (Pst)	65–85	280
Polymethyl methacrylate (PMMA)	65–85	250
Polyvinyl acetate (PVAc)	30	250
Polyvinyl chloride (PVC)	65–85	230
Polyvinyl alcohol (PVA)	Decomposes	<220
Polycarbonate (PC)	250	280
Polyethylene (PE)	90	<220
Polypropylene (PP)	90	<220
Ethyl cellulose (EC)	—	240
Cellulose acetate (CA)	60	250
Acrylamide gel (AAG)	50	270

[a] Part of data from Geacintov (1968).

77°K by immersion in liquid nitrogen. Achieving and maintaining a uniform temperature below 77°K within the plastics requires carefully designed equipment and cautious procedures.

Three methods are available for preparing polymer samples (Oster, Geacintov, 1968). Samples of other than the temperature sensitive polyvinyl alcohol, cellulose acetate, ethyl cellulose, and polyvinyl chloride can be prepared by melting. The solute and polymer are ground together in order to disperse the solute and then heated to melting. The best samples are obtained if pressure is applied after melting and during cool-down. This is accomplished by placing the mixed material between glass plates and compressing it when melting occurs. This is the only method suitable for polyethylene and polypropylene. It has the disadvantage that the solute is not uniformly dispersed and that aggregates form.

Homogeneous samples utilizing polystyrene, polymethyl methacrylate, or polyvinyl acetate can be prepared by *in situ* polymerization. The solute is dissolved in the monomer, which is then polymerized by any standard method. Polymerization can be carried out *in vacuo*, so that oxygen is excluded.

The third method of preparation is applicable to most polymers, except for polyethylene and polypropylene, and also yields a homogeneous sample. In this method, both the polymer and solute are dissolved in a suitable common solvent, which is then placed in a casting dish until the solvent evaporates. The best films are obtained when solvent evaporation is controlled at a slow rate. Geacintov *et al.* (1968) have used this method for preparing 20 μ-thick films of 1,2,5,6-dibenzanthracene in a variety of plastics.

All plastics are susceptible to oxygen penetration, and special care is required to exclude or remove oxygen prior to spectral observations. The only way to remove oxygen from already polymerized samples is to evacuate them. Thin films (20 μ) can be outgassed with about 4 minutes of evacuation time, whereas rods 1 cm in diameter require several days (Geacintov, 1968).

For water-soluble dyes, polyvinyl alcohols form excellent matrices and films. Thick transparent samples of dyes in 7.5% acrylamide gel can be made by reaction of acrylamide with tetramethylenediamine in the presence of N,N-methylene bisacrylamide.

II. SAMPLE PREPARATION

A. Vapor-Deposited Matrices

Matrices are formed by condensation of a gas beam on a cold target or window. The beam contains guest and matrix in the appropriate mixture.

Sample preparation involves control of gas flow and vaporization of materials. The gases are admitted through a controlled leak or generated at a controlled rate. In either case, the gases effuse from an orifice which is opposite the target. Figure 8.5 shows the cross section of two typical arrangements. In Fig. 8.5a, the jet is offset at an angle from the window. In the cryostat in Fig. 8.5b, the target can be rotated. During deposition it points at the furnace; for optical investigation it can be turned parallel to the window path; for fluorescence, set at an angle.

The beam characteristics depend on the size and properties of the orifice and the distance between orifice and target. The orifice size also determines the pressure gradient between the Dewar and the gas source. Orifice sizes between 0.01 mm and 2 mm diameter are suitable. We prefer a 0.5 mm hole 7.5 cm from the target. This gives an even beam over the entire width of a 2.5 cm diameter target, and it passes about 1 mmole of room temperature gas if the pressure in the gas line is 0.1–1 torr. If a larger orifice is used with a lower pressure, uneven samples are observed. It is advisable to have a magnetic mechanical shutter between the orifice and target so that the orifice can be purged with pure gas and the furnaces can be outgassed before deposition is started. At the start and end of a matrix preparation, we always

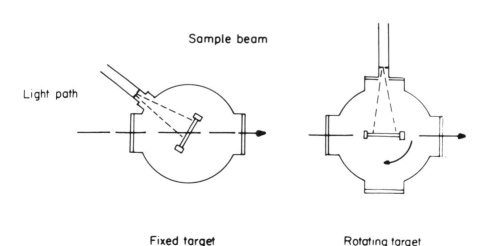

Fixed target   **Rotating target**

Fig. 8.5. Matrix deposition equipment: (a) cross section of Dewar with fixed angle target; (b) cross section of Dewar with rotating target.

deposit a thin layer of pure matrix. In this way the matrix is sandwiched between the pure matrix solid. This surpresses surface effects due to guest diffusion or impurity absorption.

1. Concentration

In order to stabilize free radicals or isolate stable species, the solute must be fully surrounded by host. Therefore, the concentration of the guest species must be kept small. This concentration is always expressed as a mole ratio of matrix to guest and abbreviated M/R (from ratio of matrix to radical). The selection of the best M/R depends on the oscillator strength of the guest's optical transition because the total amount of guest must be sufficient to allow observation of the desired properties. This is much easier in solids than in gases, but thick solid samples lead to considerable scattering of light. In the case of rigid solids such as Xe at $4°K$, the sample is usually opaque owing to formation of "snows," crystal imperfections, cracks, etc. In addition, xenon, sulfur hexafluoride, and perfluorocyclobutane tend to crack and peel. This can lead to loss of thermal contact and loss of sample when large amounts of gas are deposited. This limits the practical size of samples and establishes an upper limit for M/R for many systems.

The lower limits of M/R are determined by the nature of the guest. Spectroscopic experiments aimed at determining individual optical properties, such as lifetimes, transition energies, vibrational frequencies, and shifts, require isolation of the desired species. The presence of chemical and physical interactions between solute molecules influences the properties being observed. Under careful deposition conditions, M/R values of 1000–500 are adequate for isolation of 90% of the solute, although small species with tendencies to diffuse, such as Li, CH_2O, or C, require greater dilution. M/R values as high as about 10^5 are necessary to reduce recombination of small particles.

When the purpose of the experiment is to prepare a radical or unstable species *in situ*, through photolysis of a precursor, M/R ratios as small as 20–1000 are common. In three-component systems where two components serve as reactants for the preparation of the desired species, M/R is chosen in the order of $1000-100 : 1-10 : 1-10 = M : R_1 : R_2$. Experiments on emission might require a much larger M/R value, 10^5 or more, because Förster type excitons, between guests, extend over a length of 10 nm or even more.

2. Deposition Speed

The rate at which gases can be condensed on the target and, hence, the best rate of sample preparation is determined by the cooling capacity of the refrigerant or refrigerator, the thermal conductivity of the matrix material, the condensation characteristics of the gases, and the speed of the vacuum pump. In most cases, the thermal conductivity between refrigerant and condensing surface is critical. The thermal conductivity of the matrix gas is low compared to that of the target and holder material. Thermal conductivities for the various materials are discussed in Chapter 7. The thermal conductivities for the rare gases are temperature dependent. They have a maximum at temperatures below 20°K. Values of 10–20 mW/cm °K at 20°K are close to the amount of heat that must be removed to condense and cool a gas beam introduced at a rate of 1–2 mmoles/hour. The ability of the matrix to transfer heat from the condensing layer becomes even more critical as the matrix builds up. As discussed in Chapter 4, the rate of sample deposition affects the observed spectra. A rate of 1–2 mmoles per hour corresponds to an increase in sample thickness of about one molecular layer per second. This rate has been empirically established as an ideal compromise between the intrinsically opposite goals of forming a well annealed sample with minimum solute diffusion. It yields, for a given M/R, the sharpest lines and fewest dimers.

Exceptionally high flow rates can lead to considerable warming of the matrix gas, particularly near the surface. This results in localized annealing and diffusion. Excessive warming may lead to unrestricted diffusion, with the result that isolation is lost and aggregate formation dominates. The optical properties studied then resemble those of slow-frozen solids. Temperature measurements of the target during deposition have shown significant temperature gradients and temperature increases (Brabson, 1965b). It has been experimentally established that rates larger than 1 mmole per hour lead to a temperature increase of about 5°K at the surface of a sapphire window at 20°K. Relatively large guest molecules for the matrix can be annealed without guest diffusion.

Slow deposition rates cause amorphous solids, and crystal imperfections and thus yield multiple sites (Meyer, 1965). At slow deposition rates, both the solute and solvent are trapped at or near the point of contact with the cooled surface. This leads to crystal imperfections, lattice vacancies, or "snow." Solute molecules come to rest in unstable as well as stable sites, and the resulting spectra are usually broad and ill defined. This can be remedied by controlled annealing (see Chapter 6) by raising the temperature to ~ 0.4 of the melting point of the solvent for several minutes, but this is normally not as effective as annealing during deposition.

Only about 20 cal of heat are evolved during sample condensation. Therefore, the cooling capacity of the refrigerator or refrigerant is normally not a limiting factor in determining flow rates. Only in special cases, like the deposition of neon at 4°K, is this a critical factor. Refrigerators with less than 1.5 W capacity are unable adequately to maintain condensation at or close to 4°K.

Condensation characteristics play a major role in determining sample preparation and deposition rates. Although the sticking coefficient of most condensable materials approaches one, at 20°K and 4°K, neon and a few other gases may not condense efficiently. This can lead to a sequence of events that ultimately results in loss of sample. The rebounding gas collides with the oncoming beam. As a consequence the pressure builds up locally and the target warms. Target warmup causes a yet lower sticking coefficient, larger pressure buildup, and ultimately, thermal conduction between target and cryostat wall, with instant loss of sample. Since the process has a feedback loop, the critical flow rate has a very sharp threshold.

The tendency of SF_6, C_4F_8, C_6H_{12}, and other heavy solvents to form "snows" or highly scattering solids at 20°K requires careful annealing after deposition. The best target temperature for forming transparent matrices is above 25% or 35% of the matrix melting point. For emission studies it is often advantageous to permit "snow" formation, because such solids efficiently scatter the exciting light.

3. Preparation of Sample Beam

a. GASEOUS GUESTS. The use of gaseous materials as matrices for low temperature work requires external gas-handling apparatus in addition to the cryostat. Such a system does not need to be complex. A diagram of a simple gas inlet arrangement is shown in Fig. 8.6. This system consists of a bulb containing the matrix gas, a manometer for monitoring the pressure, a metering valve for regulating gas flows, a flowmeter of appropriate size to monitor the flow of gas, and a section of preferably flexible tubing joining the system to the cryostat. A bypass around the flowmeter makes it possible to evacuate the system quickly. The system in Fig. 8.6b can serve most deposition needs for gaseous and liquid matrices with a vapor pressure of more than 100 torr at room temperature.

Gaseous matrices can be deposited in several ways. The most convenient way is to premix the guest and matrix in the desired mole ratio prior to deposition. This can be done in the above system. If solute and solvent are reactive, an oil manometer or a quartz click gauge can be used for the control of the sample input.

b. LIQUIDS WITH VAPOR PRESSURE ABOVE 10^{-3} TORR. In another method suitable for substances with a vapor pressure of 1 torr or more at room temperature, the guest and matrix are premixed immediately prior to deposition, in the system shown schematically in Fig. 8.6c. The volume between

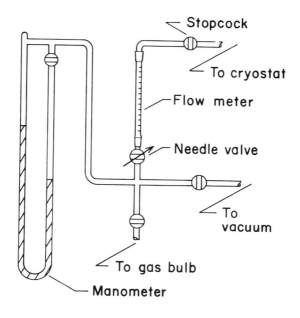

FIG. 8.6. Gas mixing system. (a) Mixing system for substances with vapor pressure above 100 torr.

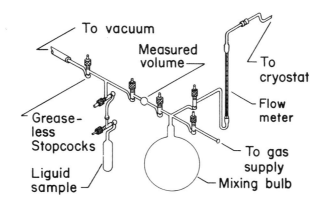

FIG. 8.6(b). Mixing system for substances with vapor pressure above 1 torr.

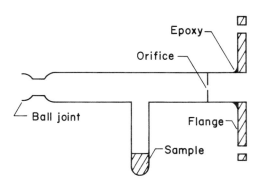

FIG. 8.6(c). Mixing system with sidearm for substances with vapor pressure below 1 torr.

valves or stopcocks a and b is filled with a known pressure of the sample from the sample bulb (g). The pressure and, hence, the amount of sample in this volume is regulated by the sample temperature in the tube (g), which is cooled with a suitable cold bath. The sample between a and b is then expanded through valve b into the evacuated bulb (f). The appropriate amount of solvent gas can then be introduced through valve c to achieve the desired M/R. After allowing time for mixing, the sample can be deposited through valve d. We always use a flowmeter (e) for monitoring the flow. This allows direct observation of the gas transfer.

The preparation method for guests with a vapor pressure above 10^{-3} torr at room temperature involves the sweeping of the matrix over low pressure vapors of the guest in a side arm (Fig. 8.6d) immediately prior to introduction into the cryostat. If desired, gaseous guests and matrices can be codeposited from separate inlets using two independent gas-handling systems. This arrangement is necessary for the preparation of samples containing two or more reactive substances and to prevent reaction between warm gases during deposition. The drawback of this method is that the relative flow of the two beams is difficult to control accurately.

The above methods can be used for gaseous, liquid or solid solutes if the vapor pressure of the material equals or exceeds 10^{-3} torr at room temperature. For reactive samples such as CS_2, thiazole, and S_2Cl_2, grease-free glass–Teflon gas systems must be used.

c. SOLUTES WITH LOW VAPOR PRESSURE. Several methods have been developed for vaporizing solutes with low vapor pressures. The most simple consists in warming the entire sample container.

i. *Quartz furnaces.* Figure 8.7 shows the schematic of a simple quartz furnace which can be used to deposit a wide variety of materials. The furnace consists of 15 mm o.d. quartz tubing approximately 15 cm in length. A 0.5 mm i.d. orifice in a 0.5 mm thick diaphragm is 8 mm behind the water condenser (*b*). The purpose of the latter is to establish a temperature gradient between the hot part of the furnace and the cryostat seal. Heating is accomplished by wrapping the quartz with nichrome or Kanthol resistance wire connected to a Variac. Quartz warts, 0.2 mm d., are used to space the wire coils, and quartz loops are used to secure the wire at both ends of the furnace. Thermocouples placed under the coils monitor the temperature of the furnace. Experience has shown that vaporization can be best controlled if a thermal gradient is established in the furnace. For this purpose, the front half and rear half of the furnace are wound and heated separately. The rear part of the double furnace is used to heat the sample to achieve the desired vapor pressure, i.e., 10^{-3} to 10^{-2} torr for matrix gas flow rates of 1 mM/hr, whereas the front portion is heated to a somewhat higher temperature to prevent plugging of the orifice and "creeping." Creeping occurs when samples diffuse two-dimensionally, i.e., along the furnace walls. If this effect is not prevented, some materials will migrate from the furnace without ever vaporizing, long before a beam can form. The rear portion of the furnace can be heated with wire. However, for maintaining even and steady temperature, liquid baths are greatly superior. Hot oil and molten Wood's metal are used up to 300°C.

For reactive materials, such as lithium, that cannot be handled directly in quartz, a modification of the above furnace has proved useful. The quartz tube shown in Fig. 8.7b has no jet. Instead, the sample is contained in a small stainless steel Knudsen cell. Such a cell is easily fashioned from a metal rod and an Allen screw containing an effusion hole. Quartz furnaces can be used up to about 1200°C; however, other furnace designs become equally practical at and above about 700°C.

ii. *Carbon resistance furnace.* A very versatile carbon resistance furnace for high temperature vaporization of samples is shown in Fig. 8.8 (Brabson, 1965b; Brewer, 1968; B. A. King, 1968). The body of the cell is 1.27 cm long by 3.2 mm in diameter and is threaded at both ends. Carbon rod electrodes are screwed into the body of the cell. The effusion hole, G, is normally 1 mm in diameter. Heating is accomplished by clamping the carbon electrodes of the assembled furnace into water-cooled copper jaws, D, which are connected to a transformer capable of delivering up to 5 V and 115 A. Temperatures between 600 and 2400°K can be maintained within $\pm 5°C$ without difficulty.

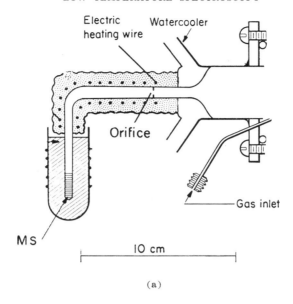

(a)

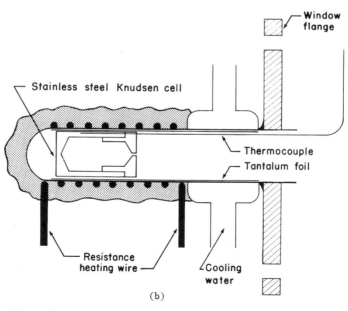

(b)

FIG. 8.7.   Quartz furnaces: (a) Knudsen cell with 0.5 mm diameter orifice (Meyer,
1960a); (b) Quartz tube with stainless steel cell (Currie, 1970).

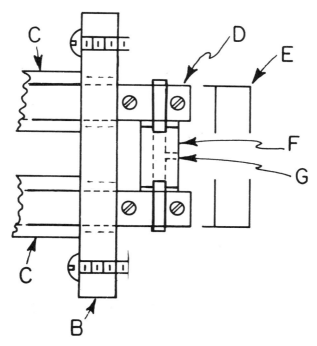

Fig. 8.8. Carbon resistance furnace; *B*, flange; *C*, hollow water cooled copper electrodes; *D*, copper jaws; *E*, tungsten heat shield and collimator; *F*, carbon Knudsen cell; *G*, 1 mm diameter effusion hole.

At temperatures above 1000°K, a heat shield is used to reduce radiative heat transfer to the target and to collimate the sample beam. Brabson (1965b) used this type of furnace for vaporizing carbon at 2700°C. Up to 1500°K the furnace temperatures can be measured with a thermocouple alone or with an optical pyrometer. Knudsen cells can be heated also by electron bombardment (B. A. King, 1968). Barger and Broida (1963) have used electron bombardment to heat a copper chamber to 550°C for the deposition of barium. The disadvantage of electron bombardment is that it works only at 10^{-5} torr or below. Above this pressure the electrons ionize residual gas, which forms a corona discharge.

Whenever a hot molecular beam source is used, the matrix target must be protected against thermal radiation. For this a tungsten or molybdenum heat shield must be used. Ingenious design of shields allows the bridging

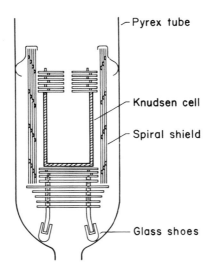

FIG. 8.9. Heat shield. Data adapted from Brewer (1944).

of very large thermal gradients over a short distance. An example of such
a design is shown in Fig. 8.9. This induction-heated Knudsen cell, designed
by Brewer (1944) allows the continued use of Pyrex tubing as a vacuum
shroud at a distance of 1 cm from a crucible at 3000°K.

iii. *Nonequilibrium sources.* Shirk (1968) has recently utilized a modified
"sputtering" technique in the study of a variety of metal atoms as well as
SiO. Positive ions of the matrix gas are produced by passing the gas through
a 2450 mHz microwave discharge at 0.005 to 10 torr. The ions then impinge
on the surface of the material to be deposited. In the case of metals, the
principal species are atoms. If the container wall is quartz, SiO is formed
in sufficient concentration to yield a matrix absorption spectrum.

Rice (1951 to 1953) used a microwave discharge to produce NH_2 radicals,
and Robinson (1958c) formed C_2 from C_2H_2. Discharges through gases or
mixtures of rare gases with reagents are efficient, but crude or capricious,
radical sources. The problem is that different products can result, and that
the product concentration depends on pressure, temperature, and time.
The discharge composition must be studied in a mass spectrometer before
meaningful matrix experiments can be performed.

B. Glasses

Glasses are formed by cooling solutions in a sample cuvette. The Dewar in Fig. 7.4a is ideal for making large samples. Small samples can be made by mounting a cuvette on a copper frame, or in a metal cell with sapphire windows. During freezing the glass contracts and loses thermal contact with the container. Sealed evacuated samples are therefore rarely in thermal equilibrium. This can be overcome by adding helium gas to the sample. Glasses can also be made by immersing the solution in a plastic tube into liquid nitrogen. If a sapphire or metal strip is tipped into the solution during cooling, the frozen glass can be extruded as a "popsicle" and mounted in a dry box on a coldfinger. Such windowless samples are very transparent.

The optical properties of glasses depend on concentration of the sample and on cooling. If the solute concentration is larger than 10^{-5} mole per liter, solute-solute energy transfer becomes significant. Above 10^{-3} mole per liter, aggregates cause fine structure and line shifts in the spectrum. Rapid cooling can cause cracking and shattering of the sample, but it has been shown that strain is present in all glasses. Strain relaxation can take weeks or longer. During this time the optical solute properties change. In addition, phase changes can occur during cooling. Experimental skill and practice are therefore essential for obtaining reproducible results, and it is not always easy to reproduce results of other workers. It has been stated many times above that all glasses must be carefully outgassed to remove oxygen, which would interfere with emission processes of all solutes.

C. Mixed Crystals

Mixed crystals of molecules in rare gases are formed by growing single crystals of rare gases from liquid containing small impurity concentrations. Mixed crystals can be grown only if the guest is soluble in the host. Argon in krypton is an example of this. The best studied mixed crystal systems involve aromatic molecules, for example naphthalene in durene. These crystals are formed by mixing host and guest in the appropriate ratio, and by growing single crystals of the mixture. Single crystals can be grown by slow cooling of a melted sample. To assure slow and even cooling, the heat capacity of the sample is increased by embedding the container in another material.

If a crystal undergoes a phase transition during cool down, it may have to be prepared from the vapor. For example, pyrene is known to crumble at low temperature, while hexamethylbenzene can be cycled through the phase transition without apparent damage.

Mixed crystals must be made from very pure material to reduce unwanted excitation drain and impurity emission. Also, the crystal must be very carefully mounted, because strain is known to affect the properties of luminescence centers. It is best to cool crystals by direct immersion in the refrigerant. However, bubbles of evaporating liquid disturb light emission studies. Normally, crystals are tacked onto a cooling surface with conductive grease, or mounted on a frame with indium washers.

III. EXPERIMENTAL PROCEDURES

In this section we discuss a few of the factors that can contribute to the success of an experiment. The selection is by necessity inadequate and somewhat arbitrary.

A. Purification

It has been pointed out throughout this book that high purity of materials is crucial. Since it is not possible to buy all necessary materials in the parts per million purity range, and since it is time consuming and often not feasible to purify all materials to semiconductor grade specifications, it is important to determine what impurities can be tolerated and which have to be removed. In free radical experiments a 50% yield of a side product is not uncommon and does not disturb most measurements, whereas traces of water can quantitatively destroy reagents, such as Li atoms, and traces of oxygen can alter the phosphorescence yield and lifetime by a large factor.

1. Removal of Oxygen

Molecular oxygen is an extremely efficient phosphorescence quencher and increases the absorption strength of forbidden transitions. It must be excluded from all samples before quantitative measurements are made. Organic solvents must be outgassed before use. This is best accomplished by vacuum. The solution is cooled to 195°K with a dry ice–acetone bath before evacuation of the optical cell. After evacuation, the cell is brought to room temperature. This cycle should be repeated twice. Final air traces can be removed by cooling. From matrix gases, oxygen is removed by chemical reaction with hot copper metal. For this purpose, gas is passed through a tube that is filled with copper turns and kept at 800°C. From plastic matrices and mixed crystals, oxygen is removed by evacuation to below 10^{-5} torr. If the vacuum must be broken, the sample should be first purged with dry nitrogen or hydrogen.

2. Removal of Moisture

Moisture is the most common impurity besides oxygen and dissolved gases. From liquids and solids, moisture can be removed fairly well by storing in a vacuum desiccator over a chemical desiccant. It is, however, better and quicker to dry a substance in a vacuum system. A liquid nitrogen trap is a convenient means to dry rare gases and removes most condensable impurities. As pointed out in Chapter 7, the trapping efficiency of a given coolant depends on design and operation. The active surface can be increased by molecular sieves or other adsorbents, and the effectiveness can be extended if the surface is cooled stepwise. In this way active surfaces can be produced during condensation and the last traces of moisture can be trapped better and quicker. From rare gases, residual moisture is removed by passing the gas through a cold trap. A dry ice–acetone trap is used for xenon; all others are dried in a liquid nitrogen trap.

3. General Purification Methods

There are numerous methods for purifying other materials. Basic chemical knowledge and intuition often can provide sophisticated, and sometimes simple, preparation methods that evade tedious and hazardous procedures and undesirable side products. Rubidium atoms, for example, are oxygen and hydroxide free when produced through decomposition of Rb_2CrO_4. S_2 free of other sulfur compounds can be produced by photolysis of S_2Cl_2, and CaF can be prepared by heating of CaF_2 with Ca. Consulting a book on preparation methods or discussion with a colleague in inorganic or organic chemistry often can lead to quick and elegant solutions. Many elements and compounds are now available in isotopically pure form. If only small quantities are needed, isotopically pure compounds are almost invariably cheaper and purer than electronic and semiconductor grade chemicals, which must be purchased in large minimum quantities.

Distillation is the most common method for purifying liquids. In distillation only the middle fraction should be retained. In fractional distillation, a fractionating column is used to increase the separation efficiency. Some mixtures cannot be separated by distillation. Ethanol and water, for example, form an azeotropic mixture containing 96% alcohol. The mixture boils at 78.15°C and cannot be further separated because pure alcohol boils at 78.50°C.

Recrystallization of solids is equally popular. It is, however, a poor method for preparing pure solids because small amounts of solvent are always occluded in the crystal. This small amount of solvent can cause stray spectral effects. CS_2 in S_8, for example, yields the strongest observed IR absorption bands. When possible, the solvent used for recrystallization should be the same as low temperature solvents.

Fractional condensation is a milder process, which is as selective as distillation and yields equally pure samples because it is based on the relative

Table 8.10

Constant Temperature Baths

Temperature (°C)	Slush or Bath[a]
0	Ice–water[a]
0 to −20	Ice–NaCl, HCl, or $CaCl_2$ solution[a]
−9	Methyl salicylate
−12.0	t-Amyl alcohol
−14.0	Benzaldehyde
−15.3	Benzyl alcohol
−22.9	Carbon tetrachloride[a]
−33 to −45	Liquid ammonia
−35.6	Ethylene dichloride
−45.2	Chlorobenzene
−50.0	Ethyl malonate
−63.5	Chloroform[a]
−78.5[b]	Dry ice–acetone
−83.6	Ethyl acetate
−95.0	Toluene
−96.7	Methylene chloride
−97.8	Methanol
−111.6	Carbon disulfide
−119.0	Ethyl bromide[a]
−126.3	Methylcyclohexane
−131.5	n-pentane
−138.7	Ethyl chloride
−150	Chloroform, 18.1%[a]; ethyl bromide, 41.3%; ethyl chloride, 8.0%; trans-1,2-dichloroethylene, 12.7%; and trichloroethylene, 19.9%
−160.5	Isopentane
−183[b]	Liquid oxygen
−185.7[b]	Liquid argon
−196[b]	Liquid nitrogen[a]

[a] Nonflammable.
[b] Temperature dependent on atmospheric pressure.

boiling points of the components. The crude material is vaporized *in vacuo* and passed through a series of traps maintained at successively lower temperatures. As with distillation, only a "middle" fraction should be retained. The trap used to collect the final product should not be the final trap in the series. In this way, any impurities more volatile than the product will be passed.

Cold baths and slushes. Table 8.10 lists several cold baths and slushes suitable for use in fractional condensation separations. The majority of these baths are used as slushes, mixtures of solid and liquid. The listed temperature is the normal melting point of the compound.

Zone refining is used commercially to purify semiconductors for use in transistors. However, the technique can be applied to any other material that can be melted without decomposition. A large number of organic substances have now been purified by the zone refining technique (Pfann, 1966). Repeated zone melting yields the purest material of any purification process. After hundredfold refining, impurity concentrations of 1 in 10^{10} can be achieved. In fact, the importance of impurities in determining the properties of certain organic substances was revealed by zone refining (Pfann, 1966; Schildknecht, 1964; Herington, 1963; Wilcox, 1964).

Gas chromatography. Although gas chromatography is used primarily as a qualitative and quantitative analytical separation procedure, it can be used also as a separation method for volatile substances. A wealth of information has been published on applications of this technique. For liquid stationary phases the liquid is commonly coated onto particles of diatomaceous earth. Adsorbants such as molecular sieves or silica gel are used as solid stationary phases. Gas chromatography can be practiced up to 575°K.

Adsorption is a very important method for the removal of moisture, gaseous materials and impurities from the refrigerant. Common adsorbants are activated alumina, silica gel, molecular sieves, and charcoal. Charcoal, silica gel, and molecular sieves are normally used at 77°K.

Vacuum sublimation is an important purification method for crystalline organic substances, and it can be used with materials that can be safely vaporized without decomposition. The refrigerant can be varied to suit the experiment. The colder the trap, the smaller the crystals formed. The use of liquid nitrogen increases the sublimation speed quite significantly because of cryopumping. Several sublimations are usually required to achieve the desired purity. It is best to continue pumping on the vessel during the sublimation in order to remove any volatile impurities.

B. Handling of Liquid Helium

1. Determination of Liquid Volume

For planning experiments it is important that stored refrigerant volumes be safely maintained at the required cooling volume. For hydrogen and helium the following measuring methods are commonly used: (1) weight of Dewar plus liquid; (2) depth gauge based on thermal acoustic or other effects; (3) measurement of escaped gas volume with gasometer gauge; (4) measurement of wall temperature at different heights in the storage wall; (5) differential pressure measurement between bottom and top of Dewar.

(1) Powder-insulated Dewars are relatively light and have a constant tare weight. Therefore, it is quite easy, even for liquid helium, to determine refrigerant levels by weighing. The easiest method of recording volume is, therefore, to store the Dewar on a cart with built-in balance. This method does not work well with the conventional Dewars with liquid nitrogen-cooled shields because their weight changes with time.

(2) Liquid hydrogen levels can be checked with a 1/8-inch diameter wooden stick. If the stick is fully inserted, the wood inserted into the liquid cools more quickly than that above. If the stick is then withdrawn and quickly whipped through the air to warm it up, snow condenses only on that part of the wood which was immersed in the liquid. With liquid helium this method is wasteful. Instead, a thermo-acoustical stick can be used. It consists of a thin-walled stainless steel tube, 1/8 inch in diameter, with a small funnel on one end. If the tube is inserted into the helium Dewar, gas vibrations set in when the tube reaches the liquid surface. A thin diaphragm fastened to the funnel with a rubber band makes the vibrations visible. Easier yet, the vibration can be felt if the thumb is pressed against the funnel. In order to detect the liquid level, one moves the tube up and down through the liquid–gas interface until the exact position is found.

(3) Helium and hydrogen evolve relatively large gas volumes on evaporation. Since both have to be carefully vented to prevent the formation of air plugs, the evolved volume of gas can be measured by inserting a gasometer into the vent. Old meters can be cheaply bought or rented from natural gas supply companies. One liter produces 700 liters of helium gas at STP or 790 liters of hydrogen gas. This method indicates the liquid volume continuously and, therefore, allows recording of boil-off rates. It indicates unusually large boil-off rates as they occur.

(4) Thermocouples and temperature-dependent resistors placed on storage walls indicate liquid levels via changes in electrical signals. If the monitors are placed on appropriate points, the signals can be used to activate refill

processes. Carbon resistors and copper-constantan thermocouple junctions are standard probes for such automatic liquid level control devices: one probe, at the lowest tolerable level, initiates transfer; another probe, at the highest desired level, stops transfer. A wiring schematic for such a system is in every cryogenic textbook.

(5) Differential pressure gauges can be inserted between the bottom of the liquid Dewar and the gas void. In large hydrogen storage Dewars, this constitutes a reliable and safe, nonelectrical means of level indication.

2. Cooling of the Sample

Figure 8.10 shows the heat capacity of copper versus temperature. If a 63-g (1 mole) copper window frame of a matrix Dewar is to be cooled to 4°K, 1223 cal must be removed by vaporization of refrigerant. This corresponds to 1.9 liters of liquid helium. At a price of 5 dollars per liter, this costs about 10 dollars. If the copper block is first cooled to 76°K with liquid nitrogen and liquid hydrogen is used as a second refrigerant to precool from 76°K to 20°K, the total cost is only six cents. Table 8.11 summarizes the net heat transfer involved. Obviously, heat loss in the transfer line costs more than cooling the target. The use of liquid could be further reduced if the cold vapor would pass through a heat exchanger. The heat capacity of helium vapor is used to cool heat shields in some large Dewars.

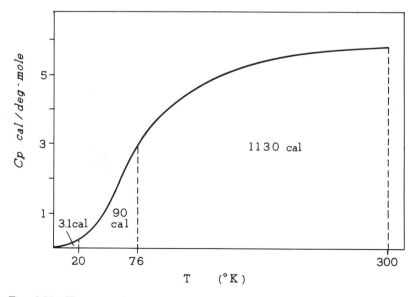

Fig. 8.10. Heat capacity of 63 g (1 mole) of copper between 4°K and 300°K.

Table 8.11

Use of Liquid Refrigerant and Cost of Cooling a 63-g Target (1 Mole Copper) Employing Different Cooling Techniques

Temperature Change (°K)	Liquid Nitrogen		Liquid Hydrogen		Liquid Helium		Approximate Total Cost (Dollars)
	Heat (cal)	Vol (ml)	Heat (cal)	Vol (ml)	Heat (cal)	Vol (ml)	
300–bp	1130	29	1220	160	1223.1	1900	10.00
77–bp	—	—	90	12	93.1	143	1.00
20–4	—	—	—	—	3.1	4.8	0.10

3. Liquid Helium Transfer

Since most heat losses occur during cooling, it is desirable to have short transfer lines and transfer all helium in one operation. In matrix work, transfer losses are always comparable or larger than the boil-off due to the sample and in the refrigerant can. It is not uncommon that 4 liters of helium are consumed for cooling a transfer line when one fills 1 liter of liquid into the matrix refrigerant vessel. This demonstrates the advantage of micro-refrigerators that produce liquid helium only as needed.

C. Safe Handling of Cryogenic Liquids and Gases

Liquid nitrogen vaporizes, forming an inert gas that is nontoxic but suffocating. Because of the large heat of vaporization of nitrogen one should be careful to avoid trapping liquid in shoes, pockets, gloves, and even hair; retention of liquid leads to severe and deep burns. If liquid nitrogen is stored in a closed container, pressure will build up and may lead to bursting of the container; this may result in secondary accidents. In an open container liquid nitrogen condenses oxygen, carbon dioxide, and moisture.

Liquid air, depending on age, contains 20–90% oxygen. During exposure to air the oxygen concentration increases steadily, as does the blue color. The liquid oxygen content makes liquid air a dangerous material. Its vapor can react spontaneously with hot pump oil, leading to vicious explosions. Since liquid nitrogen is readily available, liquid air should not be used.

Liquid helium and hydrogen. In most respects, helium and hydrogen are equally dangerous cryogenic liquids. The basic hazards are discussed below:

The heat of vaporization is very small. Minute heat and vacuum leaks lead to the release of large amounts of gases.

The boiling points are very low. Equipment must absorb large thermal gradients and large thermal mechanical stress. High vacuum insulation and heat shields are needed to maintain the gases in liquid form.

Because of the low boiling points, hydrogen and helium condense all other gases to form solids. This leads to air plugs whenever air comes in contact with cold gas or liquid. Therefore, open Dewar necks will frost very quickly and will seal with an "air plug." Air plugs and the small heat of vaporization cause rapid pressure buildup; this, if unchecked, leads invariably to explosion. During the explosion spilled liquid comes in contact with warm air and vaporizes instantaneously, providing continued pressure and thus, like rocket fuel, propelling parts. Figure 8.11 is a photograph of a 25-liter helium Dewar which plugged with about 4 liters of liquid helium remaining in it. All welding seams burst on the liquid container, liquid nitrogen shield, and protective shield. The upper half of the equipment, about 25 kg of metal, penetrated and stuck to the concrete ceiling. The bottom part and the cart were squashed flat to the floor.

D. Safe Handling of Glass Vacuum Equipment

Glass vacuum containers and vacuum lines are convenient because their content can be easily inspected visually. However, the handling of glass equipment needs some precautions. Mechanical stress of vacuum, especially in the presence of thermal stress easily leads to failure of joints and seals. Because of the vacuum, loose parts cave in and collide with other parts of the equipment; implosions always lead to secondary fragments and recoiling. Under mild conditions, implosions are much more devastating and dangerous than explosions.

Glass should always, after blowing and shaping, be annealed to relieve stress. Stresses can be identified with the help of polarizers. Since equipment containing sharp bends or curves and complicated seals is much more susceptible to stress, it is well worth the time and effort to design apparatus to have wide curves and bends. Generally, the most simple design is also the strongest and safest.

New vacuum equipment should always be tested with extreme caution. The operator must protect himself against possible fragments by wearing an unbreakable face shield. It is better to prevent parts from accelerating before they gather momentum. Wrapping new equipment in old lab coats is better than elaborate shields, which usually are not strong enough and, under certain conditions, can contribute an additional hazard either by providing secondary fragments or by restricting the operator so much that his actions become less efficient, or even clumsy.

FIG. 8.11. This 25 liter liquid helium Dewar contained 4
liters of liquid helium when it exploded because of an air
plug. Twenty-five kilograms of copper parts penetrated
in the concrete ceiling and cut all electricity to the
laboratory. Equipment in the laboratory was totally
destroyed. Fortunately, nobody was present at the time
of the explosion.

In a laboratory, glass equipment with vacuum spaces larger than 2 inches in diameter, including bulk cryostats and vacuum Dewars, should always be wrapped with masking tape. A crisscross pattern of coils with 1-inch tape spaced by 1 inch provides a good compromise between protection against debris and sufficient clearance for visual inspection of contents.

If gases are cooled or trapped in a vacuum system, large quantities of material can accumulate at low pressure. If the traps and other cool parts warm up, the pressure in the system will increase. If the gas is not released or cannot escape, explosions may result. This is a common cause of accidents.

E. Use of Liquid Hydrogen

The low boiling point, reasonably high heat of vaporization, and low price make hydrogen an ideal refrigerant. Unfortunately, the very dangerous handling characteristics make expensive safety precautions imperative. For the handling of hydrogen special laboratory construction, storage containers, and modified cryogenic equipment are necessary (see Section III, C).

Pure hydrogen gas burns safely. Pure liquid hydrogen burns very much like ether or benzene. However, mixtures of air (oxygen) and hydrogen explode violently. Solid oxygen in liquid hydrogen (in a leaky or insufficiently purged system) constitutes the most powerful explosive mixture known. Such oxygen-hydrogen bombs can be triggered by electrostatic sparks without any outside influence.

1. Laboratory Design

Liquid hydrogen should be used only in a closed metal piping system, and, even then, the laboratory should be designed and constructed as though for an open system. The room should be on an outside wall of the building, with at least one wall length consisting of blowout panels. Floor and ceiling must be reinforced concrete. The ventilation must be separate from that of the rest of the building and should replace air at a rate of one-fifth of the room volume per minute. The exhaust vents must be at the highest points in the room, where the hydrogen collects. If the ceiling is honeycomb concrete, each cubicle must be vented separately. A negative room pressure is desirable to keep hydrogen from leaking into the rest of the building. Vent heaters and all motors in the room must be three-phase spark-proof. Light fixtures must be vapor proof (not necessarily explosion proof), and wired independently of the rest of the room. Automatic emergency lights are needed.

In addition to the room vent, at least two separate vent chimneys are needed; one for the storage container and one for the experimental apparatus. It is often convenient to plan these chimneys as concentric tubes in one chimney stack. All metal parts, including doors, must be grounded, and a grounded 1/2-inch braided copper line should be anchored in the wall so that all mobile equipment can be easily grounded.

2. The Electric System

This system should consist of at least two independently fused circuits, each with a vaporproof master switch close to the room door. One system serves the pumps for mounting vacuum equipment on the Dewars and transfer lines, and the other serves all other experimental needs. In this way, all experiments can be stopped, at any sign of danger, without interrupting vacuum. This is important because vacuum failure, by itself, constitutes a great hazard by inducing explosion: a vacuum failure will lead instantaneously to the boil-off of all liquid hydrogen, which in turn leads to the abrupt release of large quantities of gas. This is the most undesirable event, especially in case of other potential dangerous situations. We use three levels of electrical safety: (a) All lights, vacuum equipment, and all equipment above the lowest level in the room ever reached by liquid hydrogen in transfer lines and apparatus are explosion proof; (b) All equipment that is ever operated in the room when hydrogen is present, either in storage or apparatus, is vaporproof; and (c) For repairs and equipment that is used only when no liquid hydrogen is in the room, normal electrical standards are applied.

In order to satisfy requirement (b), much normal equipment can be modified to achieve research grade safety; we find it useful to tape normal electrical plugs with insulating tape so that they cannot accidentally be disconnected. Electrical and electronic equipment are difficult to make vaporproof. We mount all equipment in large cabinets connected with separate vent inlet air. A flow-sensitive metal flapswitch in the air intake guarantees shutdown in case of overpressure failure. The same arrangement can be used for furnaces and other open hot filaments that cannot be excluded from the room. Hot filament ion gauges must be provided with automatic shutoff for high pressure so that a failure of the hydrogen container does not trigger an explosion.

Since hydrogen is lighter than air and escapes upward, we keep all electrical systems below the lowest hydrogen level. Thus hydrogen never reaches electrical equipment when small and medium gas leaks are present.

3. Hydrogen Container and Transfer Line

All apparatus, transfer lines, storage vessels, and vent lines should be closed systems, pressure tested, and metal-to-metal sealed, including the vent line from the room to the roof of the building. Transfer lines may be stainless steel double-wall evacuated, as for helium, but it is thermally as efficient, more convenient, and much cheaper to use stainless steel for the inner wall and heavy-wall Tygon tubing, with Teflon spacers, for the outer vacuum wall. Vent lines should be metal bellow and of larger diameter than the transfer line. All parts should be connected with metal-to-metal connections. The hydrogen vent is usually kept at somewhat higher pressure than the room pressure, so that air cannot enter and form air plugs on cold parts. Before use, all apparatus should be exposed to thermal shock by liquid nitrogen, and checked for vacuum and pressure leaks. Containers are best made of stainless steel and assembled by helium arc welding. If necessary, silver blazing and brass and copper can be used, but soft solder is not strong enough to meet hydrogen safety standards.

Most workers purge all hydrogen lines and apparatus with helium before use to remove air, which would condense in contact with liquid nitrogen. The liquid hydrogen level can be checked as for helium. The vent lines frost if cold vapor boils off. If the apparatus is overfilled and liquid splashes into vent lines, the room air will liquefy and clear liquid will drop from the metal hose.

4. Hydrogen Alarms

Various types of hydrogen alarms are commercially available. We recommend that thermal conductivity diffusion heads be placed 3 feet above storage Dewars and experimental Dewars. Alarm bells are the best warning signals. One can wire the alarms so that the electricity is automatically shut off when a chosen percentage of the dangerous hydrogen concentration is reached. This shutoff should, however, never include the pump circuit, or else all hydrogen will be released, because of vacuum failure, exactly when a leak springs.

We believe that hydrogen alarms are useful and necessary safety devices in that they are reliable when they signal leaks. However, our experience indicates that the absence of signal from a hydrogen alarm is not a sure sign of safe operation. Small leaks, and leaks at out-of-the-way, unsuspected places rarely release enough hydrogen to actuate an alarm. But it is exactly the latter type of failure that is most dangerous, because local concentrations might be high enough for ignition.

Small hydrogen explosions and hydrogen pressure explosions often lead to damage that can cause catastrophic secondary chemical hydrogen explosions. Fortunately, hydrogen gas emanating from leaks often burns, rather than detonates. It is then a matter of cool and decisive action to confine the flame and to prevent precipitous action that could cause more serious accidents.

Open-neck storage Dewars are not suitable liquid hydrogen storage containers: the loss rate is significant, and the insertion and removal of transfer lines creates dangerous contact between air and cold parts, leading possibly to air plugs. Superinsulated self-pressurized storage containers are safer and more practical. They operate without liquid nitrogen shield, using instead refractory ceramic in a vacuum space. The normal boil-off is used to pressurize the Dewar. A relief lake controls the pressure. Liquid withdrawal does not need auxiliary gas, and contamination is impossible.

5. Gaseous High Pressure Hydrogen

Since low temperature solution work has small cooling power requirements, normal cryostat operation, with transfer of cryogenic liquid from a storage Dewar into the apparatus, constitutes a very inefficient use of refrigerants. During the many small transfer operations, most loss occurs in the transfer line and in cycling normally warm parts of equipment. Therefore, micro liquefiers that condense only minute amounts of liquid directly in contact with the cold window are very convenient. Such liquefiers usually work with high pressure, normal cylinder hydrogen at 2200 psi (160 atm).

Operation is relatively simple and safe. Most chemistry departments have hydrogenation rooms which are much more dangerous, because in the cryogenic refrigerator equipment is never disassembled and hydrogen is always in a closed all-metal system. In our laboratory hydrogen is withdrawn from a storage rack containing several cylinders, passes immediately through a step-down pressure valve set at 1000 psi, and passes through a molecular sieve dryer and charcoal liquid nitrogen trap to remove argon, before it enters the expansion-compression or heat exchange parts. Spent hydrogen is released into a closed system with recycling compressor, or released to piping leading outside the building. All components for such systems are commercially available and are factory tested. The operation is certainly safer than operation of a natural gas kitchen range. The largest hazards lie in two areas: (1) The handling of hydrogen cylinders is a hard and tedious job. For an 8-W refrigerator, about 1 cylinder is consumed every 2 hours. If the connections are not carefully checked, leaks, and possible failures, might result. (2) The equipment is so simple that an untrained person might feel overconfident and be careless while maintaining and cleaning components. Thus, high pressure bellows, if broken, could lead to damage through whip — motions. This would also lead to the discharge of one or more hydrogen cylinders at a rate of about 750 liter or 50 scf per second. To reduce this risk, our hydrogen storage, a 30,000 scf cylinder trailer, is 50 ft from the laboratory, and a small orifice acts as a flow restriction in case of a pipe failure. The laboratory operates under liquid hydrogen safety rules, especially in regard to vent fan velocity, electrical connectors, fusing, and room lights. All equipment is fully grounded, and braided grounding wire surrounds the floor so that new equipment can be easily connected to a common ground.

Recommended Reading

Bailey, C. A., *Advanced Cryogenics*, Plenum Press, New York, 1971.

Claassen, H. H., *The Noble Gases*, Heath, Boston, Massachusetts, 1966.

Cook, G. A., ed., *Argon, Helium and the Rare Gases*, Vols. I and II, Interscience-Wiley, New York, 1961.

Gopal, E. S. R., *Specific Heats at Low Temperatures*, Plenum Press, New York, 1966.

Hingsammer, J., and E. Lüscher, Helv. Phys. Acta **41**, 657 (1968). "Edelgaskristalle, eine Übersicht."

Honig, R. E., *Vapor Pressure of Elements and Some of the Most Common Gases*, Radio Corporation of America, Princeton, 1962. (Unpublished report.)

Landolt-Börnstein, *Zahlenwerte und Funktionen aus Naturwissenschaften und Technik* (K.-H. Hellwege and A. M. Hellwege, eds.), Gruppe II, Band **3**: Luminescence of Organic Substances (by A. Schmillen and R. Legler), Springer, Berlin, 1967.

Nesmeyanov, A. N., *Vapour Pressure of the Elements* (Trans. from Russian edition and edited by J. I. Carasso), Academic Press, New York, 1963.

Pollack, G. L., Rev. Mod. Phys. **36**, 748 (1964). "The Solid State of Rare Gases."

Rosenberg, H. M., *Low Temperature Solid State Physics; Some Selected Topics*, Clarendon Press, Oxford, 1963.

Schnepp, O., Ann. Rev. Phys. Chem. **14**, 35 (1963). "Electronic Spectra of Molecular Crystals."

Seitz, F., and D. Turnbull, eds., *Solid State Physics; Advances in Research and Applications*, Vols. 1 ff., Academic Press, New York, 1955 ff.

CHAPTER 9

Spectra of Individual Systems

I. INTRODUCTION

In this chapter the spectra of individual guest atoms and molecules are discussed. The purpose is to give a more detailed assessment of present knowledge of the molecules, and to compare results from different sources. The literature search for this chapter was concluded in July 1969. Some newer references are included in the tables of Chapter 10. The discussion deals with the following groups of guests:

A. Atoms

B. Diatomics

C. Triatomics

D. Organic Molecules

Sections A through C contain a critical review of the literature up to 1969. For molecules with more than three atoms, a complete listing is not attempted, because the number of molecules studied is very large, while the data are often meager. For most organic molecules, only the wavelength dependence of the spectrum in a narrow range is known, and, perhaps, the lifetime of an excited state. Therefore, we restrict description to a few, relatively well studied species. Data for all molecules from this chapter are summarized in the tables of Chapter 10 and cross referenced in the Bibliography.

The molecules are listed in alphabetical order of the first chemical symbols. Subscripts are ignored; therefore, N_2 is before Na. Compounds of the same atom are arranged according to the alphabetical order of the partners. Thus SCl is before ScF. The order of organic molecules is explained in the introduction to Chapter 10.

II. LITERATURE REVIEW

A. Atoms

This section contains a discussion of the atoms listed in Table 9.1.

Ag Silver: $^2P \leftarrow\ ^2S$

Four absorption bands corresponding to this gas phase transition are found in all solids. The band width ranges from 170 to 300 cm^{-1}. The line position, width, and shape depend on matrix, concentration, and temperature, but the matrix yields in all cases a blue shift. On warm-up the four sublevels of the transition shift by different amounts and in different directions, and they exhibit different temperature coefficients. Below two-thirds of the matrix melting point the shifts are reversible; above this, diffusion sets in and new features appear, while the original absorption bleaches (Brewer, 1968).

Annealing within the reversible range does not alter the spectrum. Therefore, silver, like mercury, seems to trap at only one most stable site. In sulfur hexafluoride, the spectrum is broad. Similarly, the spectrum in $n \cdot C_7F_{16}$ is broad, but shows a distinct multiplet at the location of the gas phase transition (B. A. King, 1968). Zhitnikov and Melnikov (1965) produced silver atoms by freezing aqueous and alcoholic solutions of silver salts which were irradiated with x-rays for 3 hours. Large transparent matrix crystals were obtained by freezing the solution at $-20°C$ before cooling to 76°K.

Table 9.1

List of Matrix Isolated Atoms Covered in this Chapter

Symbol	Name	Symbol	Name
Ag	Silver	Li	Lithium
Au	Gold	Mg	Magnesium
Ba	Barium	Mn	Manganese
Cd	Cadmium	N	Nitrogen
Cs	Cesium	Na	Sodium
Cu	Copper	O	Oxygen
Fe	Iron	Rb	Rubidium
H	Hydrogen	Sc	Scandium
Hg	Mercury	Tl	Thallium
In	Indium	Zn	Zinc
K	Potassium		

The spectrum is broad, but contains a band with distinct but unresolved structure, which is similar to that in matrices.

The assignment of the sublevels is not conclusive, because, unlike gold or copper, silver phosphorescence is not observed. In silver ^2P is the lowest excited state because the ^2D-state is inverted and lies 700 cm^{-1} above ^2P whereas in copper and gold it leads to visible phosphorescence.

Au Gold: $^2P \leftarrow {}^2S$

Gold atoms were trapped in solid rare gases and SF$_6$ at 4° and 20°K by Morelle (1970) and Brewer (1970) from carbon furnaces. Since the vapor is mainly atomic, Au$_2$ spectra are observed only at low matrix ratios. At high dilution, a triplet absorption is observed, as in the case of silver. The triplet is assigned to lines corresponding to $^2P_{1/2} \leftarrow {}^2S$ and the two sublevels of $^2P_{3/2} \leftarrow {}^2S$ of which the degeneracy is removed in the low symmetry matrix field. Brewer (1970) studied the influence of solute-solute interactions on the spectrum by codepositing two molecular beams of silver and gold atoms; he concluded that spectra of the two atoms are not affected by each other's presence at concentrations below 1%. Gold fluoresces in the visible upon irradiation in the $^2P \leftarrow {}^2S$ system. Gold does not react with SF$_6$, and SF$_6$ makes an excellent matrix for gold atoms, which exhibit very sharp spectra, with a line width of only 75 cm^{-1}, in this environment. The gas-matrix shift is + 950 cm^{-1}, comparable to that in krypton and xenon. However, gold matrices show only two strong bands, the third being much weaker than in other matrices. Xenon bands are 450 cm^{-1} wide, broader than in any other matrix.

Ba Barium: $^1P \leftarrow {}^1S$; $^3P \leftarrow {}^1S$

Barger and Broida (1963) produced barium doped rare gas solids, using a copper Knudsen cell. The spectrum showed fifteen absorption lines, which were dependent on matrix and observation conditions. Time dependent effects, such as bleaching of the absorption, made the spectrum very complex. Electron bombardment led to the appearance of a new band. The strong overall features of the spectrum were assigned to transitions involving the $^1P_0$ and $^3P_1$ state, the fine structure being due to removal of orbital degeneracy, site effects, and impurities. At least part of the spectral complications are suspected to be due to impurities, perhaps BaOH.

Cd Cadmium: $^1P \leftarrow {}^1S$

In a study of cadmium and zinc in argon, krypton, and xenon at various temperatures, Duley (1966a, 1967b) reported that in all systems one triplet is observed in highly dilute systems. With increasing temperature, all features shift reversibly to the red. During temperature cycling, the triplet fine structure becomes more apparent because of increasing triplet splitting, but also because of a sharpening of the individual components. The appearance of a triplet is discussed in terms of removal of orbital degeneracy in a lattice site of low symmetry, and, alternatively, in terms of a Jahn-Teller distortion of the lattice. Bands outside the resonance region are explained as being due to metastable atoms, as proposed by Duley (1967c) for similar structure in the case of mercury, rather than due to aggregates. However, the presence of aggregates is discussed and acknowledged. A strong doublet appearing at moderately high concentrations is assigned to next nearest neighbor interactions, and the spectrum of Cd_2 is observed around 220 nm. Freedhoff (1967) discussed Cd_2 as an example of a van der Waals molecule for which excited state energy curves can be obtained from matrix observations. Blount (Merrithew, 1969) confirmed the formations of diatomics during bleaching of the matrix, and Shirk (1968) repeated xenon experiments and confirmed Duley's results.

Cs Cesium: $^2P \leftarrow {}^2S$

Weyhmann and Pipkin (1965) studied matrix isolated cesium in order to decide whether nuclear orientation could be achieved. They produced the matrix by depositing atomic beams of the alkali metal. Milligan and Jacox (1969b) produced cesium beams by decomposing Cs_2CrO_4 in the presence of silicon at 650°C. The matrix spectrum consists of two sets of triplets that behave in every detail like rubidium doped matrices.

Cu Copper: $^2P \leftarrow {}^2S$; $^4P \leftarrow {}^2S$; $^4D \leftarrow {}^2S$; $^2P \leftarrow {}^2S$; $^2D \leftarrow {}^2S$; $^2P \rightarrow {}^2D$

Copper atoms have been trapped in neon, argon, xenon, krypton, SF_6, CH_4, and N_2 by Currie (1970) and B. A. King (1968) by condensing copper beams from a Knudsen furnace. Shirk studied copper atoms by vaporizing the element from a filament, and by sputtering copper bombarded with xenon ions. As in the case of all atomic spectra in solids, the copper absorption is broad and structured. The multiplets are assigned to transitions to sublevels of the upper state which are nondegenerate in the presence of a matrix field. If the three sublevels are individually excited, a fluorescence can be observed. The emission depends on the multiplet sublevel stimulated, and the emission corresponds to the gas phase assignment of the levels, two corresponding to $^2P_{3/2} \rightarrow {}^2D$ and one to $^2P_{1/2} \rightarrow {}^2D$. As in the case of Cd, the emission is broader than the absorption and is not structured. On warming, the absorption broadens and shifts, and the sublevels resolve more clearly. This temperature effect is reversible up to two-thirds of the solvent melting point. The average temperature coefficient for the triplet in xenon is $+ 0.7$, $- 3.8$, and $- 5.2$ cm^{-1} per degree for the blue, center, and red peaks, respectively. Above 57°K, diffusion becomes significant and new spectral features appear. This temperature dependent behavior has been extensively studied for Hg, and also for silver, but it is not fully understood.

Copper spectra of solutions with more than 2% atom concentration show bands with vibrational structure to the red of the lowest atomic resonance transition. These bands can be tentatively assigned to Cu_2. Bass and Shirk (1970) successfully reacted copper atoms in matrices with oxygen atoms, produced by vacuum photolysis of O_2 impurities, to give CuO for which he reports both absorption and emission.

Fe Iron: $X \leftarrow {}^5D$

Matrices containing iron atoms were produced by sputtering an iron grid with xenon, argon, and krypton and trapping the gas mixture at 20°K. Iron atom beams from a Knudsen cell were trapped by Barger (1965), using matrices of astrophysical interest. However, iron reacts with several of these. The spectra show complicated fine structure; it is not clear which atomic states are responsible for absorption.

H Hydrogen: ${}^1P \leftarrow {}^1S$

Vegard (1924 to 1948) observed five lines belonging to the Balmer series when solid hydrogen was bombarded with electrons. Broida (1957b) and Bass (1958) repeated the experiment using discharges through hydrogen and observed that the glow originated at the solid surface, in the gas phase, and was possibly due to reflected light from the discharge. A weak greenish-blue continuum was observed, but not identified or assigned. Thus spectral proof of hydrogen atom emission in low temperature solids has not been brought. However, the existence of hydrogen atoms in matrices was demonstrated by Foner (1960) using electron spin resonance (ESR) techniques. He observed ESR signals which he explained in terms of at least two non-equivalent sites in argon, krypton, and xenon, at 4°K, while he found indication only of one site in solid neon. Atoms trapped from the vapor phase gave simpler spectra than those obtained from photolysis in the solid. HI photolysis in xenon gave especially complicated spectra. Foner assumed that both octahedral sites and substitutional sites were formed. D. Y. Smith (1964) confirmed this model by using a variational method for computing g-factors.

Baldini (1964) deposited argon-hydrogen and neon-hydrogen mixtures, which he passed through an rf-discharge in a capillary, on a LiF window at 4°K. The absorption spectrum showed strong absorptions in the 2p ← 1s region. In argon, the line was 2180 cm^{-1} wide and peaked at 85180 ± 100 cm^{-1}, 2920 cm^{-1} toward the blue of the gas phase transition at 82259 cm^{-1}. For the deuterium atom in argon, the line was 1850 cm^{-1} wide and located at 85300 cm^{-1}, with a shift of 3020 cm^{-1} from the gas phase line at 82281 cm^{-1}. Baldini pointed out that the half-width of the two isotopes seemed to be inversely proportionate to the fourth root of their masses. In solid neon, the absorption was too weak to be conclusive. It was, therefore, concluded that the hydrogen atom can diffuse in solid neon, at least during deposition. Roncin and Damany (1965a) observed the Lymann α line in argon with a shift of $+$ 2340 cm^{-1}. Their line width is 1300 cm^{-1} and assumed to be due to atomic motion.

Keil and Gold (1967) used the optical observations of Baldini to compute a four-mode model for hydrogen atoms in a octahedral and tetrahedral interstitial sites. They predicted IR modes of 260 cm^{-1} and 180 cm^{-1} for Ar-H and Ar-D, respectively, and suggested experiments to prove the absence of interstitial sites. They assumed Baldini's spectra to be due to occupation of only one single most stable site. This is in agreement with the earlier ESR work, which also indicated that only photolytically formed atoms occupy multiple sites, which anneal at 12° and 23°K, whereas atoms stabilized in trapped discharges were stable up to 39°K. It should be pointed out, however, that the conditions of the indicated stability range seem not well specified, and the range unreasonably large. It should be confirmed with more detailed work, because even much larger molecules, such as formaldehyde, have been observed to diffuse well below 39°K, and Pimentel (Andrews, 1967a) states for the heavier lithium atoms, "that dimerization of the incident atoms proceeds to a major extent except in very dilute samples of xenon deposited at 4°K."

Hg Mercury: $^3P_1 \leftarrow {}^1S$

Robinson's 1959 report on mercury atoms in xenon, krypton, and argon at 4°K constitutes the first report of the absorption spectrum of a matrix isolated atom. Roncin and Damany (1961a) studied mercury in argon at 20°K and reported a considerably different spectrum.

Brewer and co-workers (1965a) studied mercury in all the above-listed matrices plus neon, nitrogen, and oxygen and carefully observed the influence of concentration, impurities, deposition conditions, and other parameters. This study shows that the appearance of the mercury spectrum depends very significantly on experimental conditions, and that the apparent contradictions between the results of Robinson and those of Roncin were due to true differences in the spectrum. The transition energy of mercury follows the heavy atom effect except for neon, which yields shifts intermediate to those of argon and krypton. Xenon gives the most gaslike spectrum; all other matrices result in blue shifts. The line shift, line width, and line shape depend, among other factors, on the sample temperature. The temperature effects are partially reversible between 4°K and two-thirds of the matrix melting point. Xenon and krypton spectra showed clearly a triplet, while N_2 yielded a broad doublet. The individual multiplet components exhibit characteristic warm-up behavior. At concentrations above 1%, and at temperatures above two-thirds of the matrix melting point, new features appear because of aggregate formation. Unlike the case of trapped alkali metal atoms, the mercury spectrum does not indicate multiple trapping sites.

$^1P \leftarrow {}^1S$. Roncin and Damany (1961a) studied this transition in argon at 20°K. Although singlet-singlet, it also consists of a triplet. Brabson (1970) investigated several transitions over a large temperature range. Duley (1965) studied mercury transitions in argon, krypton, and xenon at 4°K and at about two-thirds of the matrix melting point. In a later paper (Duley, 1966b), he computed the crystal field parameters for Hg-rare gas, assuming D_{2h} symmetry. He treated the electrostatic potential around an impurity atom as a perturbation on the spin-orbit coupled states of the free atom, and selected a unique set by comparing the values derived from the $^3P_1 \leftarrow {}^1S$ transitions. The splitting parameters are about -200 cm^{-1} for argon, -170 cm^{-1} for krypton, and -140 cm^{-1} for xenon.

Forbidden transitions. Roncin and Damany (1961a) assigned the absorption at 227 nm to the transition $^3P_2 \leftarrow {}^1S$. Duley (1965) listed twelve absorption features in argon and krypton at two temperatures in the spectral range between 174 and 250 nm. He assigned most lines to transitions of atoms and assumed that several absorptions originate from the excited states $^3P_2$ and $^3P_0$ of the mercury atoms. The excited states are assumed to be populated via intersystem crossing from the ^1P level. This explanation warrants reconsideration, because the lifetime of these excited states would have to be very long to lead to the observation of absorption from such states, and because accumulation of atoms in excited states should lead to a reduction of ground state molecules resulting in a weakening of the ground state absorption. Also, the spectra assigned by Duley to atoms have been assigned to aggregates by other authors (Brewer, 1965a). Thus, the identity of the absorbing species is contested.

In Indium: $^2S \leftarrow {}^2P_{1/2}$; $^2P \leftarrow {}^2P_{1/2}$; $^4P \leftarrow {}^2P_{1/2}$

Duley (1967b) studied dilute solutions of indium atoms in three rare gas matrices at 4°K. In krypton the spectra exhibited a distinct crystal field splitting, while the argon spectrum showed many lines indicating multiple sites. The argon spectrum simplified through annealing. In xenon, the spectrum could not be correlated to that of the gas phase, because it consisted of weak and diffuse bands. The "resonance absorption $^2P \leftarrow {^2}P$" was not evident in any matrix and is much weaker, as was later established by Currie (1970). The assignment of the fine structure components of the various sublevels of ^2P and ^4P is not certain. The indium lines do not shift significantly with temperature, but they broaden (Currie, 1970).

K Potassium: $^2P \leftarrow {^2}S$

The spectrum of potassium is analogous to that of sodium atoms. Two pairs of triplets are observed in all matrices: one at about the gas phase location of the resonance doublet, one shifted toward the blue. As in the case of sodium and lithium, the spectrum always contains aggregate absorptions, and usually impurities, probably KOH or K_xO_y due to reaction of the atoms with matrix impurities or impurities from residual vacuum or the Knudsen furnace. The two triplets are assumed to be due to two different lattice sites, because the red set gains intensity from the blue set during annealing. On warming, the red set disappears slowly and broad aggregate bands appear in its vicinity. The spectrum was studied by Weyhmann (1965) and by Meyer (1965). The results were discussed by D. Y. Smith (1964).

Li Lithium: $^2P \leftarrow {^2}S$

Several authors have studied lithium atoms in various rare gas matrices (Andrews, 1967b; Belyaeva, 1968; Merrithew, 1968; Meyer, 1965). The atoms are produced by effusion from a Knudsen cell. Pure atomic lithium matrices are most difficult to obtain for two reasons: First, the vapor pressure is the lowest of all alkali metals. Therefore, the metal has to be heated to approximately 400°C to produce an adequate beam. At this temperature outgassing of metal containers becomes substantial, and only very carefully handled systems produce clear beams. In the absence of extraordinary care, lithium hydroxide is probably the most predominant species in the matrix. Second, lithium atoms are light and diffuse readily, thus highly dilute solutions should be made. However, as the ratio of rare gas to alkali atoms is increased, rare gas impurity concentration also increases at 100,000 : 1; for a rare gas of 99.99% purity, the matrix contains ten times more impurity than lithium. If it is oxygen or water, the atom concentration will be reduced drastically, and lithium oxide and hydroxide might absorb strongly.

Because it diffuses easily, Li will almost certainly react quantitatively under such conditions. Therefore, lithium atom spectra, in all reported cases, contain significant impurity bands. W. L. S. Andrews (1967) made a careful study of spectral changes as a function of many parameters, including matrix material, concentration, and temperature. He identified in argon, krypton, and xenon four to six absorptions with the resonance transition of lithium and observed in all cases a band attributed to Li_2. The band location and band structure are explained in terms of solute-solvent interaction responsible for the appearance of multiplet structure. Meyer (1965) studied lithium in neon, argon, krypton, and xenon and observed the temperature dependence of the absorption during annealing; he concluded that several features were caused by aggregates and LiOH. Belyaeva and co-workers (1968) also studied lithium in argon, krypton, and xenon between 4° and 40°K and commented on the overlap between the five strong broad features. As did the earlier authors, they observed redistribution of intensity between the features with changes of temperature, the two large wavelength bands disappearing more rapidly than the other bands. They attributed the appearance of a quintet, rather than two sets of triplets as observed for the other alkali atoms, to a site effect, and argued that lithium, being the smallest atom, can "penetrate into the rare gas lattice without perturbing it." Thus, it can occupy a site of higher symmetry, and the transitions can remain degenerate, as in the gas phase. They proposed two types of octahedral lattice sites, in addition to the "normal" site with low symmetry. Blount (Merrithew, 1968) restudied several atomic systems and assumed that "multiplet members are the result of transitions of isolated atoms and pairs of atoms trapped at non-nearest neighbor sites in the solid." They proposed that such solute-solute pairs can be treated qualitatively as a weakly bound diatomic. The different models and their merits are discussed in the section on solute-solvent interaction, and in the section on general observations on atoms in matrices.

It is remarkable that all authors list different absorption maxima. In fact, there is, among the three published reports, not one single absorption in any matrix for which the authors can agree on the line position to within their claimed accuracy. There are two reasons for this: First, the line position can indeed depend on experimental conditions. This fact has been carefully demonstrated in the case of mercury in argon (Brewer, 1965a) where it could be demonstrated that an apparent contradiction between two authors was in reality due to truly different spectra. However, a second reason could surely be a certain amount of euphoria of matrix spectroscopists about the accuracy that can be attained in measuring lines with a line width of 1500 cm^{-1} or more. A claimed accuracy of 5 cm^{-1} seems inappropriate for such lines with shallow maxima; instead it seems more likely that the authors think of the instrumental accuracy of their optical train. Obviously, more experimental work is needed before a meaningful interpretation can be sought.

It is interesting to note that alkali atoms in rare gases might presumably react with the matrix, perhaps under pressure, to give ionic compounds of the type Ne^-Li^+ with heats of formation of the order of 1 to 2 eV per molecule (Heller, 1967).

Mg Magnesium: $^1P \leftarrow {}^1S$

In a very thorough paper Schnepp (1961) studied the spectrum of magnesium and manganese in three different matrices. The magnesium gas phase line appears shifted in all matrices; it is broad and split into three components. Later Schnepp explained the splitting and line width with a quantitative model (Brith, 1963), which is discussed in Chapter 4. He realized, through comparison of Mg with Mn, that the splitting was due to an asymmetric lattice field causing removal of orbital degeneracy of the p-orbitals. Magnesium was later restudied by Brabson (1965b), who observed in the spectrum concentration and temperature dependent changes that he attributed to aggregates and reaction products with impurities. A band system around 240–290 nm with vibrational spacing of about 100 cm^{-1} and three intensity maxima at 255, 267, and 277 nm was tentatively assigned to MgOH. Wang repeated experiments on magnesium in three rare gas matrices, but also studied it in solid oxygen, nitrogen, SF_6, and other matrices in an attempt to produce MgO molecules by diffusing magnesium atoms and oxygen atoms under various conditions. The atomic spectra seem not to be seriously affected by the presence of impurities (Wang, 1969).

Mn Manganese: $^6P \leftarrow {}^6S$

Schnepp (1961) observed manganese atoms in three rare gases at 4°–50°K. This transition consists in the gas phase of two groups of triplets of which the individual components are too close to be resolved in a matrix. The matrix spectrum consists of two groups with five lines each. Schnepp attributed the lines to atoms in different sites, the transitions of subcomponents being resolved by the removal of degeneracy in the asymmetric environment of the lattice site. He deduced from the matrix shift and the line width that the crystal field seems to be two orders of magnitude weaker than in typical ion crystals. The level splitting seems too large for explaining matrix spectra by a Jahn-Teller distortion of the excited atom P state by the surrounding lattice. In this early paper, Schnepp discussed essentially all presently known effects observed for trapped atoms, except the temperature dependent transition energy shift, and he selected the asymmetrically distorted site model, which has been confirmed by all subsequent experiments and calculations. In the same paper, results on magnesium are discussed. In a later letter, Lee and Goutmacher (1962) reported the spectrum of manganese in argon at 4°K and demonstrated that they obtained a sharper spectrum by annealing the matrix. They also invoked multiple trapping sites but did not attempt a further analysis of the lines.

N Nitrogen: $^2D \rightarrow {}^4S$

Vegard, in the emission study of ion- and electron-bombarded solids, observed a complex spectrum that he assigned to nitrogen. In an extended series of papers he made a systematic investigation of the emission changing exciting source material, voltage, and current and any parameter affecting the solid, including temperature, solvent, concentration, and impurities. He assigned the spectrum to N atoms and N_2, but McLennan proved in 1928 that several lines, especially the auroral line at 557.7 nm, were due to oxygen impurities. Since much of the work was concentrated on the auroral line, details of this transition and the work will be discussed in the section on oxygen atoms. Besides oxygen atoms, oxygen molecules and NO have been identified as emitters in all but the most carefully purified nitrogen solids. Some of the N_2 emission features are discussed under that molecule.

Bass and Broida (1960a) re-examined Vegard's system very carefully and confirmed eight atomic nitrogen emission lines. Their nomenclature and Vegard's original designation are listed in Bass (1960b, p. 179). The emission of the atomic lines labeled N_2 and N_4 persists for several seconds after the excitation is interrupted and leads to an afterglow that has been carefully studied by several authors. The glow is observed only in α-nitrogen, the modification stable below 35.5°K. On warming, a light flash indicates that at this temperature the trapped excited energy is dissipated. This phenomenon has been recorded on film and is available as a demonstration movie from the U.S. National Bureau of Standards. A large number of other authors has studied frozen nitrogen discharges, but the nature of the glow and the mechanism of its production are not yet fully understood. Older work is summarized in the book by Bass (1960a). Brocklehurst (1962) restudied the system. A detailed analysis and isotope studies were performed by Schoen and Broida (1960a). Tinti and Robinson recently reported the $^2D - {}^4S$ bands in neon, argon, krypton, and xenon at 4°K. The gas to matrix shifts are -17, -42, -91, and -263 cm^{-1}, respectively.

Na Sodium: $^2P \leftarrow {}^2S$

Sodium was the second atomic matrix system studied, mercury being the first. Robinson reported the two D lines in argon, krypton, and xenon and correlated matrix shifts to the solvent heavy atom effect. The system was later restudied by Pipkin (Weyhmann, 1965), Meyer (1965), and Heller (1967) and was discussed by Blount (Merrithew, 1969). In all matrices the spectrum consists of two sets of triplets, one at about the free-atom value, the other shifted to the blue by roughly 1500 cm^{-1}. The relative intensity of the two triplets depends on deposition temperature, concentration, and speed. It has been postulated that each triplet corresponds to a different trapping site, because, on annealing, the red triplet gains intensity irreversibly from the blue triplet long before aggregate spectra appear. The triplet fine structure is assumed to be due to the transitions $^2P_{1/2} - ^2S$ and $^2P_{3/2} - ^2S$, where the latter is split into a doublet because of removal of degeneracy. Whereas Pipkin originally concluded that the trapping site was not substitutional, D. Smith (1964), in analogy to hydrogen atoms, assumed both substitutional and interstitial octahedral sites. Other models assume substitutional sites with low symmetry because of local lattice distortions and unoccupied neighboring lattice sites. Blount discussed atomic spectra in terms of nonnearest neighbor interactions corresponding to weakly bound diatomics. Interpretation of line width has been given by D. Y. Smith (1964), Schnepp (Brith, 1963), and others. The line width is dependent on deposition conditions, and for a given M/R it depends on deposition speed and sample thickness. Careful experiments on annealing indicated that this effect is due to the mechanism of the formation of the solid. On very slow deposition, a low density snowlike solid seems to form, where impinging atoms of solvent and solute solidify at highly metastable sites. This results in a broad spectrum due to superposition of absorption of atoms in a large number of different sites. During quick deposition, heat transport through the solid, especially in thick samples, becomes critical, and a temperature gradient is established, resulting in annealing of the most unstable sites, with survival of only the most stable site or sites.

O Oxygen: $^1S \rightarrow ^1D$

Pure oxygen luminesces only faintly, but matrix isolated oxygen emits quite strongly. Peyron, Schoen, and Broida, Harvey and Bass, and other workers at the National Bureau of Standards published observations on the emission that is largely due to molecular oxygen (Bass, 1960a). The most detailed report on oxygen atom emission, if not the most detailed report on any type of low temperature emission, was given by Vegard (1924 to 1948), who carried out a large amount of painstaking research on the $^1S \rightarrow ^1D$ line, which he originally believed was due to nitrogen. This green auroral line appears strongest on excitation by an electron beam operated at 430 V and 2 mA. The intensity seems temperature independent below 35°K. The transition energy depends on the environment. Figure 2.1 shows a plot of line position *vs.* wavelength. In pure nitrogen the line appears at 555 nm.

On dilution by neon or argon, the line shifts to the red. At about 30% dilution both curves show a kink; at dilutions exceeding 1% (not shown in figure) the line does not further shift. Vegard's interpretation was that above 30% the particle size depended on concentration, that the particle size reflected the line position, and finally, that below 1% nitrogen (i.e., oxygen) was isolated individually by the solvent. At such high dilution, the line position depended on "the specific influence of the rare gas." Figure 2.1 led him to conclude that the argon exerted noticeable influence, while "neon had a very small, or, perhaps, no specific influence on the position of the N band, and thus neon should be the very substance we want for obtaining a close approximation to the pseudogaseous state." In almost all points, this interpretation seems today correct. We know that above 20–40% spectra are those of pure solids, that below 20% the aggregate size is concentration dependent, and that spectra of concentrations smaller than 1% very often correspond to well isolated species. The matrix influence has now been recognized to be due to the heavy atom effect, which is connected with the polarizability of the solvent. Thus Vegard can be regarded as the discoverer and first practitioner of rare gas matrix spectroscopy. He was thirty years ahead of his time. Vegard also reported that, in addition to the line position, the line width and line shape also changed with concentration. This effect is generally observed for all matrix isolated species.

Rb Rubidium: $^2P \leftarrow {}^2S$

Weyhmann and Pipkin (1965) studied matrix isolated alkali atoms in the hope that radioactive nuclei could be oriented in the solid either by absorption of circularly polarized photons or by high magnetic fields. Their goal was to study beta and gamma emission. As in the case of sodium and potassium, they observed two sets of triplets, each of which was assigned to a different type of lattice site. Absorption lines are about 200 cm^{-1} wide at 4°K, and triplet members are split by 400 cm^{-1}. The blue triplet is shifted by almost 2000 cm^{-1}. Weyhmann and Pipkin treated line width and line shift with a configuration coordinate scheme and used crystal-field models to explain the line splitting. A restudy of rubidium in argon by Kupfermann and Pipkin (1968) indicated that the blue "triplet" contained in reality four lines. ESR spectra indicated at least three major trapping sites. The microwave and optical absorption sites were correlated by monitoring differential absorption of right and left circularly polarized light in the presence of a microwave field. This method is based on the fact that differential absorption of left and right circularly polarized light depends on the quenching of the angular momentum of the excited state by the crystal field. The interpretation of their data led the authors to the conclusion that (1) the majority of atoms were matrix isolated, rather than located on interfaces or dislocations, (2) the sites were well defined and loosely bound compared to normal substitutional sites, because the observed gas to matrix shift was small in terms of calculations based on a configuration coordinate model and the well known Lennard-Jones potential for alkali-rare gas atom interactions; (3) the stability of the triplet sites indicated that orbital degeneracy of the excited state was fully removed, while the circularly polarized light data showed that the orbital angular momentum of the excited state was only partially quenched. All these conclusions support a model of substitutional sites with unoccupied nearest neighbor site or sites. In such an arrangement the lattice will readjust, resulting in a characteristic distortion for each of the three excited state p-orbitals of the alkali atom. This model can be further developed if one takes into account atom-lattice coupling.

Heller (1967), analyzing data on alkali metal spectra in rare gases, concluded that, using simple Born theory of ionic crystals, known lattice parameters, and recently deduced electron affinities, one could predict the existence of noble gas-alkali metal salts.

Sc Scandium

Weltner (1967a) observed a spectrum assigned to scandium atoms in an argon matrix containing vapors condensed from a Sc_2O_3 beam. The solid contains mainly ScO. The spectrum was not correlated to the gas phase by Weltner but it consists of six lines, one of which weakens during annealing.

Tl Thallium: $^2S \leftarrow {}^2P_{1/2}$; $^2D_{3/2} \leftarrow {}^2P_{1/2}$; $^2S \rightarrow {}^2P_{3/2}$

Brabson (1965) studied thallium atoms in krypton at 20°K using quartz and stainless steel furnaces and discovered that the absorption depended strongly on preparation conditions, giving up to twelve absorption features under several conditions. Since thallium vapor is largely monatomic, Tl_2 seemed an unimportant impurity in highly dilute matrices. However, it is known that thallium reacts easily with oxygen, forming various oxides of which Tl_2O is more volatile than thallium metal.

Of all the observed absorption features, only the 375 nm line seemed to correlate with any certainty to the gas phase transition $^2S_{1/2} \leftarrow {}^2P_{1/2}$ at 377 nm. Excited with the mercury line 365 nm, a white fluorescence was obtained, which consisted of a continuum extending from 500 to 700 nm with a shallow maximum at 600 nm. It seems likely that this emission is due to atomic Tl, although Tl_2 could not conclusively be excluded as an emitter.

Zn Zinc: $^1P \leftarrow {}^1S$

Duley (1966a) observed zinc atoms in argon, krypton, and xenon at 4°K and at two-thirds of the matrix melting point. As in the case of cadmium, a triplet is observed in the region of the gas phase transition. At higher concentration other absorption features are also observed. The interpretation is analogous to that of cadmium, and references to interpretation and conclusions are contained in papers covering both atoms, which are discussed in the section on cadmium.

B. Diatomics

This section contains a discussion of the species listed in Table 9.2.

C_2

The spectrum of C_2 is of considerable astrophysical interest. Despite very extensive work on this molecule, the position, even of low lying energy

Table 9.2

Matrix Isolated Diatomic Species

Symbol	Name	Symbol	Name
C_2	Carbon	NF	Nitrogen fluoride
CH	Carbon hydride	NH	Nitrogen hydride
CN	Cyanogen	NO	Nitric oxide
CO	Carbon monoxide	O_2	Oxygen
CS	Carbon monosulfide	OH	Hydroxyl
ClO	Chlorine monoxide	PH	Phosphorous hydride
CuO	Copper oxide	S_2	Sulfur
GeS	Germanium sulfide	SCl	Sulfur monochloride
H_2	Hydrogen	ScF	Scandium fluoride
HBr	Hydrogen bromide	ScO	Scandium oxide
HCl	Hydrogen chloride	Se_2	Selenium
HF	Hydrogen fluoride	Si_2	Silicon
HfO	Hafnium oxide	SiO	Silicon oxide
HI	Hydrogen iodide	SnO	Tin oxide
I_2	Iodine	SnS	Tin sulfide
LaO	Lanthanum oxide	TaO	Tantalum oxide
LiF	Lithium fluoride	TiO	Titanium oxide
MgO	Magnesium oxide	WO	Tungsten oxide
N_2	Nitrogen	YO	Yttrium oxide
NBr	Nitrogen bromide	ZrO	Zirconium oxide
NCl	Nitrogen chloride		

levels, is not clearly known. Ramsey (Ballik, 1963) showed conclusively that the ground state is $X\,^1\Sigma_g^+$, not $X\,^3\Pi$. The two states are within 700 cm^{-1}. Several other low lying states are not known. This molecule should offer a unique opportunity for the matrix method to prove its worth, but experiments produced confusing data, especially regarding the Swan system, which still has not been fully interpreted. More than ten publications by seven different groups (see Milligan and Jacox, 1969b, c) deal with the visible spectrum, especially the Swan bands, but there is not yet final agreement on the observed effects or the interpretation. There are many reasons for the complexity: C_2 is a highly reactive high temperature molecule, it is not possible to prepare C_2 in high yield, and it cannot be purified. Thus, all C_2-containing systems contain other carbon compounds. UV and IR spectra indicate the presence of C_3, C_2H, or C_2H_2. A photoisomer of C_2H_2 is responsible for nonequivalent carbon stretches. C_2H has been found with the help of ESR, and carbon atoms have been found to absorb in the vacuum UV. In addition, polymers and IR bands of 2630, 1240, and 3325 cm^{-1} belonging perhaps to diacetylene, have been found. In x-ray emission work impurities are yet more important: rare gases show almost always NO, O_2, and atom emissions, and Zmerli (1959b) found even benzene phosphorescence. Very recent work (Milligan, 1969b) has shown that the spectrum is further complicated by C_2^- which forms in matrices containing C_2.

The following preparation methods were used: microwave discharges of acetylene, photolysis of acetylene in the gas phase and in the solid, photolysis of C_3O_2 in matrices, and molecular beams from graphite Knudsen cells. Many authors use ^{13}C and deuterium for isotope labeling in order to obtain indications about the type, number, and arrangement of atoms responsible for spectra.

Three systems of C_2 in matrices have been identified, and bands around 400 nm might belong to transitions that have not yet been observed in the gas phase.

$d\,^1\Sigma_u^+ \leftarrow X\,^1\Sigma_g^+$. The Mulliken bands have been reported by Milligan (1967a), Weltner (1962b, 1964a,b, 1966), and Brabson (1965). Because of the similar internuclear distance of the two states, only the (0,0) band appears normally, (1,0) being very weak. The system absorbs very strongly. It was observed in neon, argon, and N_2 at 4°K and 20°K. Bands are sharpest in neon, where triplet substructure becomes noticeable. This transition originates from the ground state, and its assignment seems now uncontested.

$b\,^1\Pi_u \leftarrow X\,^1\Sigma_g^+$. The Phillips system was reported in argon matrices. It consists of a progression with $2 < v' < 5$. This assignment is very plausible.

Other authors probably missed the system because of instrumental limitations in the near infrared. The lower state corresponds to the ground state of the molecule.

$A\ ^3\Pi_g \leftrightarrow X'\ ^3\Pi_u$. An extended series of partly contradictory papers deals with the matrix spectrum of the Swan bands (McCarty, 1959c; Barger, 1964). Many factors make the assignment ambiguous: First, the lower state of this transition is not the gas phase ground state, as is normally observed for matrix isolated species; second, the vibrational spacing is unusually large compared with the gas phase; third, the spectrum contains more bands than can be assigned to the Swan system; and finally, the system can be bleached with UV light while the two other C_2 transitions remain unchanged. A variety of convincing arguments has been presented; all aim at proving that the assignment of the system is correct, and that some peculiar circumstances lead to the observed effects. It is, for example, conceivable that the ground state, X, and $X'\ ^3\Pi_u$ reverse energies because of matrix fields. It is also possible that vibrational perturbations in this state are due to interaction with one or more of the many close lying, not yet observed states. The additional unanalyzed bands in the same spectral region may support this argument. However, the unanalyzed bands could be also due to impurities. The bleaching of the Swan bands is more difficult to explain. It has been proposed that it is due to slow depopulation of $X'\ ^3\Pi_u$ in the ground state. If $X'\ ^3\Pi$ is stabilized by cage or steric effects, this argument may hold, but Milligan's proposition is that the triplet state lifetime is unusually large. Since the absorption is observed at least during 15 hours, this explanation is improbable, because the $X - X'$ separation is only 700 cm^{-1} and nonradiative intersystem crossing would be expected to have a much shorter lifetime.

Each new publication on the Swan system of matrix isolated C_2 seems to add new evidence either supporting the assignment or contradicting it. However, Milligan and Jacox (1969b) found evidence that probably solved this riddle. They made observations that led them to propose that C_2^- is responsible for this absorption.

C_2^-

Herzberg and Lagerqvist (1968) observed recently in the gas phase a new system assigned to C_2^-. Milligan and Jacox (1969b) compared their spectrum of matrix isolated C_2 and observed that the origin and the vibrational spacing of the matrix "Swan" system fits the C_2^- spectrum. They observed that triethylamine and cesium atoms enhance the absorption strength of this system. Since both chemicals are electron donors, this observation supports their tentative new assignment. More work on this system is necessary. If, as now seems certain, their observation is correct, C_2^- is the first ion ever observed in a weakly interacting matrix.

CH

$B\,^2\Sigma \leftarrow X\,^2\Pi$; $A\,^2\Delta \leftarrow X\,^2\Pi$. Robinson and Keyser (McCarty, 1959c) produced CH by discharging a methane-argon mixture. The B ← X system consists of broad bands; the A ← X band shows fine structure which may be due to rotational motion.

CN

$B\,^2\Sigma \leftarrow X\,^2\Sigma$. Milligan (1967e) produced CN by photolyzing HCN in solid nitrogen at 15°K. A large progression of bands confirms the identity of this system.

CO

Information on five states of CO is available. All but two publications deal with the pure solid, which shows astonishingly gaslike transitions.

$a\,^3\Pi_2 \leftarrow X\,^1\Sigma^+$. Hexter (1967) observed the first five members of the progression $(v', 0)$ of Cameron bands in pure CO at 20°K. The crystal splitting is explained by spin-orbit coupling of the a state with the state $A\,^1\Pi_1$. Calculations indicate that the splitting is due either to vibronic interaction or to triplet excitons, but probably not to Davydov splitting, which could conceivably be caused by gain in electric-dipole character. The bands are quite broad, having a half-width of about 500 cm^{-1}. The solid-gas phase shifts are smaller than 80 cm^{-1}, i.e., less than 0.5% of the transition energy, but the vibrational frequencies differ by 4% and more from the gas phase.

$d\,^3\Delta \leftarrow X\,^1\Sigma$. A long progression in the 125 nm region of solid CO was assigned to a triplet-singlet transition. Schnepp (Brith, 1965) measured relative absorption coefficients, and established the vibrational numbering in the Franck-Condon maximum region. The bands are split by about 450 cm^{-1}, which has been explained in terms of Davydov splitting. The system is partly overlapped by the transition A − X.

$A\,^1\Pi \leftarrow X\,^1\Sigma^+$. Absorption in the fourth positive group of CO in solid α-CO at 10–30°K has been reported by Schnepp (Brith, 1965), by Hexter (1967), and by Roncin (1965c, 1966, 1967b, 1968). The bands form a long progression. The resolution of individual levels depends on temperature. The Franck-Condon curve and the potential energy curves are very similar to those of gaseous CO. Davydov splitting is observed, proportional to the Franck-Condon factor. In argon and neon the bands are very sharp. Roncin reports that the Rydberg state $B\,^1\Sigma^+$ is totally suppressed. Matrix shifts increase for $T_{0,0}$ and v' from neon to xenon, toward the red. Since no fine structure is observed, Roncin, assuming a lattice site symmetry of C_{2v}, C_{3v}, or C_{2v}, concluded that all energy levels are lowered, i.e., that matrix interaction is attractive with all states even in neon.

$C\ ^1\Sigma^+ \rightarrow A\ ^1\Pi$. Emission from CO_2 in rare gas matrices exposed to x-rays has been tentatively assigned to the Herzberg bands. Normally, x-ray excitation is believed to decay very efficiently on nonradiative paths to the lowest singlet exciton band of the solid. Energy is then transferred to lower-lying impurity traps, which may radiate. However, the exciton bands of krypton and xenon are at 8.06 μm^{-1} and 6.80 μm^{-1}, respectively, while the state C is at 9.20 μm^{-1}. Thus, coemission from the C-state would have to be due to direct excitation of CO formed by decomposition of CO_2. The lower state of the green emission lies, if the assignment is correct, at 6.50 μm^{-1}. Emission of this type is conceivable and was observed in the case of the isoelectronic molecule N_2. But in the latter case it is observed only when the exciton states are above the emitting states; and the emission is absent in xenon, where the exciton band lies below. Since x-rays notoriously stimulate impurity emission, and many rare gas and atmospheric impurities emit in the green, isotope work will be needed to confirm the assignment.

$X\ ^1\Sigma^+$. Several authors (Anderson, 1966; Ron, 1967; Leroi, 1964) have studied ground state molecules. Pimentel (Leroi, 1964) reported C–O stretches for $^{12}C^{16}O$, $^{13}C^{16}O$, $^{14}C^{16}O$, and $^{12}C^{18}O$ in various rare gas solids. He noted concentration-dependent aggregate formation, with aggregate frequencies shifted to 2138.0 and 2148.8 cm^{-1}. Half-widths vary from 1.5 to 3.5 cm^{-1} depending on temperature and concentration. The shifts indicate tighter bonding in dimers than in monomers.

GeS

$B\ ^1\Pi \leftarrow X\ ^1\Sigma$. Meyer (1970c, d) observed this system in xenon, krypton, and nitrogen matrices containing GeS. The spectrum corresponds to the gas phase spectrum and exhibits vibrational fine structure with a half-width of 40–80 cm^{-1}, depending on matrix.

$D\ ^1\Sigma \leftarrow X\ ^1\Sigma$. The system is very weak in matrices and appears to be without any discernible fine structure.

$a\ ^3\Pi \rightarrow X\ ^1\Sigma$. On excitation into the B and D state, a sharp green phosphorescence with a lifetime of 20 msec at 20°K in argon is observed. Comparison of the behavior and transition energy indicate that this transition corresponds to the Cameron bands of CO which are also responsible for the emission of matrix isolated SnS and SnO.

H_2

In the early work on high energy cathode ray bombardment of condensed gases, Vegard and Keesom (1930b) found in H_2 at 4°K an afterglow that persisted for more than a minute. Bass and Broida (1958) discovered that most of the intensity of the glow is due to hydrogen atomic lines. They observed 26 lines of which five were identified as members of the Balmer series. They noted, however, that the glow originates from the surface, and not from the solid.

HBr, HF, and HI

Mann, Acquista, and White (Mann, 1966) reported IR spectra for HBr and HF in rare gas matrices. The sharp lines can be attributed to translation-rotation around an interaction center. HBr, as HCl, exhibits reversible temperature-dependent spectra. HI photolyzes easily under formation of iodine atoms. Foner (1960) used this reaction to prepare hydrogen atoms.

HCl

Spectra of HCl and DCl in argon at 4° and 20°K were reported by Schoen, Mann, Knobler, and White (Schoen, 1962b) to be due to rotation-vibration in a substitutional site. The authors compared the gas phase and solid spectrum and assigned R(0) and P(1) bands. Matrix lines were less than 0.15 cm wide at 20°K. Much experimental and theoretical work followed in the next years, leading to a thorough review of the different parameters observed and pertinent for explanation. Robinson and co-workers (Kwok, 1962; Keyser, 1966a,b) studied the spectrum in several rare gas solids and in liquid xenon. Their conclusion was that the best description of the system results if the theoretical model of Friedmann and Kimel (1964, 1965) is used. In this model HCl is assumed to rotate in a substitutional site, with simultaneous translation. The best description of the system is given in terms of a *center of interaction*, which is the center of electrical symmetry of the molecule. In HCl the center of interaction, because of symmetry, does not coincide with the center of mass. This model of interaction between rotation and localized lattice vibration leads to astonishingly accurate correlation between observation and calculation. Transition energies, intensities, and temperature effects, as well as matrix interaction with different solvents, are correctly predicted, much better than with models assuming hindered rotation or libration. Argon constitutes an especially interesting case in that HCl and matrix have nearly resonant masses.

The extensive work on HCl (see Chapter 10, Section II, B) has led to the discovery of dimers and polymers. It seems that a cyclic dimer, a trimer and other well defined polymers can be identified by their near IR and far IR properties.

HfO

The gas spectrum of HfO is not well known. Weltner (1965d) prepared $Hf^{16}O$ and $Hf^{18}O$ in neon and argon by vaporizing Hf_2O_3. The vapor contains substantial quantities of HfO. Twenty absorption peaks and six emission peaks were recorded. On the basis of oxygen isotope shifts, the authors assign the absorption bands to seven different electronic systems, which all correspond to systems proposed in the gas phase. They suggest that the emission may be due to two new transitions of HfO that they correlate to known systems of ZrO. It should be pointed out that in several cases only one band of a system was observed. In these cases, the lack of an isotope shift need not conclusively indicate that the absorption corresponds to the origin (0,0) of an HfO transition. It is equally possible that these absorbers contain no oxygen, and are impurities, for example, hafnium halides that are difficult to separate from the oxides.

$A \leftarrow X$ $(^1\Sigma^+)$. Only the origin of this system is observed. The gas-solid neon shift is 300 cm^{-1}.

$B \leftarrow X$ $(^1\Sigma^+)$. Two bands are assigned to the B system, which is 300 cm^{-1} shifted. The matrix frequency is 1% larger than that in the gas phase.

$D \leftarrow 23830$ $(^1\Sigma^+)$. Six vibrational bands are observed. The bands exhibit peculiar warm-up behavior, which is discussed by Weltner (1965d). For emission, see system $D' - x'$.

E $(^1\Pi) \leftarrow X$ $(^1\Sigma^+)$. Three bands between 360 and 390 nm are analogous to those of ZrO and therefore are tentatively assigned to this electronic transition.

F $(^1\Sigma^+) \leftarrow X$ $(^1\Sigma^+)$. Four bands are drawn together in this system. The electronic characteristics are tentative.

$G \leftarrow X$ $(^1\Sigma^+)$. The author correlates three gas bands to the gas state G.

$D' \rightarrow x'$. The emission almost coincides with the $D - X$ absorption, but the lower state frequency is 6% smaller than that of the X state as observed in the IR. Weltner (1965d) presents a convincing argument, which supports an assignment to a triplet-triplet transition. The case cannot be decided at this time, but the correlation also fits energy transfer considerations. An alternate explanation would be that the emitter assumes a different geometry than the absorbing state reaching the same energy level.

I_2

B $^3\Pi_0 \leftarrow X$ $^1\Sigma_g^+$. Robinson (unpublished), Voigt and Meyer (1968), Broida and Phillips (unpublished), and probably many others, studied matrix isolated I_2. The spectrum is very broad and usually weak. Therefore, heavily doped solids must be studied, and the matrix assumes a deep red tint due to aggregates before the absorption appears in a medium-resolution spectrograph. The explanation for this peculiar behavior might be found from recent gas phase work which indicates that iodine dissociates efficiently by excitation in this absorption band. This could be tested by search for atomic iodine in matrices. The intensity of the atomic line could be used to measure the quantum yield of the photolysis. The matrix line width and line shift would further reveal whether the atom formation is enhanced by rare gas–iodine interaction.

Several solvents form charge transfer spectra with iodine. The iodine benzene spectrum exhibits strong CT bands. Voigt and Meyer (1968) found vibrational structure with a spacing of about 180 cm^{-1} in these bands. This frequency corresponds to the iodine molecule.

LaO

Weltner (1967a) studied the trapped vapor of La_2O_3 in solid neon and argon at 4°K. He observed the visible absorption spectrum and ESR parameters for ground state molecules. The matrix spectra show unusually large blue shifts, of about 500 cm^{-1} in neon. On illumination all bands slowly bleach and new absorption peaks appear. The authors studied this effect for ScO, YO, and LaO. They conclude that with increasing concentration, and with increasing N_2, H_2O impurities, the diatomic bands fade quicker while atoms do not seem to be affected. The thermodynamic data seem to confirm that dimer formation is preferred in comparison to atom-diatomic reactions. Annealing of the matrix does not seem to have immediate effects on the spectra, but the above-mentioned photosensitization apparently leads to new bands of LaO that are closer to the gas phase spectrum. A site effect is rejected for explanation. In view of the observation of C_2^- (Milligan, 1969b), formation of LaO^- ions should be considered, because LaO^- could be expected to be quite stable.

$A\ ^2\Pi_{3/2,1/2} \leftarrow X\ ^2\Sigma$. Four bands in the 680–720 nm region are assigned to (0,0) and (1,0) of the two sublevels of the $^2\Pi$ state. The bands are broad and blue shifted by 300–400 cm^{-1}. The origin of the transition was supported by isotope shifts. The doublet splitting is 935 cm^{-1}, as opposed to 860 cm^{-1} in the gas; bleaching leads to new bands, closer to the gas phase value.

$B\ ^2\Sigma \leftarrow X\ ^2\Sigma$. Three bands between 500 and 540 nm are identified as belonging to this system. The bands are originally broad, and blue shifted by 500 cm^{-1}. On illumination new sharp lines appear at 559 nm which are closer to the gas phase transition. They are assigned to molecules located in more gaslike sites.

$C\ ^2\Pi \leftarrow X\ ^2\Sigma$. As in the case of the A-X system, the doublet splitting in the matrix is larger than in the gas, the values being 485 cm^{-1} and 237 cm^{-1}, respectively. As in the B-system, bleaching leads to more gaslike spectra, but the bands remain broad.

N_2

Vegard's work (1924a–1948) on nitrogen and hydrogen at 4°K opened the way to low temperature spectroscopy because Vegard invented the matrix isolation method while studying the spectrum of N_2. Rarely has anybody since performed more careful work than Vegard and his co-workers, who observed emission spectra and changed every conceivable parameter, including deposition temperature, annealing, concentration, and impurities. In the classic series of papers a large number of emission systems were reported. His work was repeated and expanded by Broida and co-workers at the National Bureau of Standards (Bass, 1960a). The nitrogen glow can be produced by trapping active nitrogen, or bombarding solid nitrogen with electrons, ions, or x-rays. Much of the nitrogen emission is due to nitrogen and oxygen atoms produced during irradiation. Part of the emission observed by Vegard is due, however, to the A → X system of N_2, which he named M system. Today these bands are generally called the Vegard-Kaplan bands.

Astonishingly, the most prominent glow of solid N_2 is due to the O(I) auroral oxygen(I) line at 557.7 nm, which corresponds to a ¹S — ¹D transition. The emission also contains the α and β lines of atomic nitrogen, and some molecular bands, including the Vegard-Kaplan bands and the Herzberg bands of oxygen that occur as an impurity (Bass, 1960a). The spectra change with temperature (Vegard, 1924). A long-lived glow persists after the irradiation is terminated. On warming to 35.5°K a flash of light is emitted. Above this temperature glow is not further noted. It is now certain that atom recombination causes the glow. Brocklehurst and Pimentel (1962) studied the mechanism of the glow, which they explained in terms of ⁴S atom recombination.

$A\,^3\Sigma_u^+ \to X\,^1\Sigma_g^+$. The Vegard-Kaplan system was first observed by Vegard during his studies of irradiation of solid nitrogen and nitrogen in neon and argon matrices at 4° and 20°K. Tinti and Robinson (1968b) observed this system in the same matrix and analyzed and assigned 67 vibrational levels in argon. This makes it probably the best known and best studied matrix spectrum of any diatomic so far observed. The bands belong to long progressions in v'' with v' between zero and six. The presence of higher v' indicates that vibrational relaxation is slow compared to electronic decay. It was found that at concentrations above 0.1% N, higher v' levels emit weaker with increasing concentration. With heavy solvent atoms, high v' levels become stronger. Bands with $v' > 6$, however, are not observed.

Temperature changes below 0.3 of the matrix melting point lead to reversible line broadening and changes in line shape, but the relative intensity of different v' is not temperature dependent. The line width increases from neon to xenon from 10 cm^{-1} to 40 cm^{-1}. In argon each band consists of a doublet. In neon, at low concentrations, weak satellite bands appear on both sides of the absorption maximum. These lines which might be due to restricted translation, or lattice effects, are weaker at increasing distance to the main line.

Lifetimes for individual vibrational levels of the Vegard-Kaplan system were measured in four matrices at different temperatures and for different concentrations. The lifetimes vary from 33 sec for $v' = 0$ of 0.1% N_2 in neon at 4°K, to 2.8 sec for 0.6% N_2 in neon at 1.7°K, to less than 5 msec for 1% N_2 in xenon at 4°K. The initial decay is exponential within 10%, the stated experimental accuracy. A weak, but long-lived, tail in the I vs t curve is probably due to repopulation of A $^3\Pi$ due to atom recombination. In neon, excited vibrational levels do not emit. The neon lifetime of 3.3 sec constitutes a lower limit for the gas phase lifetime of the A state.

$C\,^3\Pi_u \to B\,^3\Pi_g$. The second positive system of N_2 was discovered by Robinson (Tinti, 1968b) in neon solids irradiated with x-rays. This system is blue shifted by 76 cm^{-1} from the gas phase. The system is more than a hundred times weaker than the Vegard-Kaplan bands, but Tinti and Robinson succeeded in observing fifteen bands which they analyzed as originating from $0 < v' \leqslant 2$. Obviously, $v' = 0, 1, 2$ decay slowly, with decay times comparable with the electronic decay C → B. $v' > 0$ is either not populated or decays more quickly. The second positive system is not observed in heavier rare gases. This is not astonishing, as the C-state of N_2 lies above the lowest exciton bands of these solids. Radiative decay of $C\,^3\Pi_u$ cannot compete with the nonradiative quenching by interaction with host states.

The observed slow vibrational relaxation of excited states A and C confirms similar observations in other molecules such as OH, CH, O_2, S_2, and probably C_2. In all these cases vibrational relaxation is comparable with electronic decay. It is interesting to consider the effect of matrices on vibrational and electronic quenching. The latter depends strongly on the matrix environment and often changes by a factor of a hundred or more from neon to xenon. An analysis of the available data shows that high v' population is favored in xenon, but rarely observed in neon. Therefore, vibrational decay in neon is quicker, and in xenon slower, than electronic decay. Thus, the matrix affects the vibrational quenching less than electronic decay. This is due to the different nature of the two processes. Vibrations relax purely nonradiatively, while electronic energy can be dissipated on radiative as well as nonradiative paths. Absorption studies have proved that the heavy atom affects the oscillator strength significantly, and it is obviously the contribution of the radiative heavy atom effect that makes observation of excited v' possible. In all matrices, the vibrational relaxation time of A and C states in N_2 molecules is at least 10^{10} times longer than the often quoted time of 10^{-13} sec.

$a\,^1\Pi \leftarrow X\,^1\Sigma_g$. This system was studied in absorption by Dressler (1962), who observed ten bands of the $v'' = 0$ progression between 140 and 160 nm. They studied the shape of the potential curve in the solid and observed attractive perturbations at high v'. Brith and Schnepp (1965) observed this transition in solid nitrogen at 20° and 30°K. The intensity was 10^{-4} times that of the corresponding transition A-X of CO. Eight vibrational levels of the upper state were reported. The bands are about 200 cm^{-1} wide and split in a doublet separated by 150 cm^{-1}.

$\omega\,^1\Delta_u \leftarrow {}^1\Sigma_g{}^+$. The above authors also observed 11 vibrational levels of the ω-state. The bands are 390 cm^{-1} wide, and are split by 130 cm^{-1}. The splitting is explained as Davydov splitting. Roncin has reported (1967b) that this transition is at least 1000 times stronger in pure N_2 than in the gas phase. In solid neon, the bands remain weak. The Rydberg state $C\,^3\Pi_u$ is suppressed in the matrix.

NBr, NCl, NF

Milligan (1964c) produced all three molecules by photolyzing the corresponding azide, N_3X. Isotope substitution was used, all reagent spectra are recorded, and intermediates and impurities are listed. The infrared spectra of all molecules are very strong, with frequencies of 693 cm^{-1} for NBr, 818 cm^{-1} for NCl, and 1115 cm^{-1} for NF. The NBr frequency is in excellent agreement with gas phase data.

NH

In their pioneering work, Rice and Freamo (1951, 1953), discovered that hot hydrazoic acid, and sulfur vapor gave colored products when trapped at 77°K. Rice and Grelecki reported the blue substance to have the stoichiometric composition of NH_4N_3, indicating that the metastable blue component was NH. Mador and Williams (1954) and later Dows (1955a) studied IR spectra, and found various, partly contradicted frequencies in regions possibly related to NH. Dows' band at 3126 cm^{-1} was later confirmed by gas phase work on NH. Later work by Rice and Gager indicated substantial ESR activity, but mass spectra of the hot vapor by Foner failed to show NH (Bass, 1960).

Robinson (1957b, 1958b–d, 1960b) and McCarty (1959b,c) trapped rare gas discharges that contained hydrazoic acid, ammonia, hydrazine and various impurities containing nitrogen and hydrogen. They found an absorption at 338 nm, which deuteration confirmed to arise from NH. Schnepp (1960b) and Dressler reported NH after UV photolysis of NH_3.

$A\,{}^3\Pi \leftarrow X\,{}^3\Sigma$. The absorption spectra are exceptionally sharp and show well resolved fine structure, which Robinson assigned to the P, Q, and R branches of a rotating molecule. Since this early discovery of rotational motion of NH, other molecules have been shown to perform more or less restricted rotation, often combined with translation in the cavity.

$^1\Delta_g \leftarrow X\,{}^3\Sigma$. After the discharge is interrupted, a weak band at 3.047 μm^{-1} disappears quickly. Robinson suggested that it could be due to molecules trapped in the long-lived $^1\Delta_g$ state.

NO

$a\,{}^4\Pi \rightarrow X\,{}^2\Pi$. In his studies on nitrogen emission, and emission from nitrogen in neon and argon matrices, Vegard (1926) discovered a set of bands, which he called M bands. Broida and Peyron (1960), using $^{15}N_2$ and $^{18}O_2$, demonstrated conclusively that the bands are due to NO. They correlated this state to the $^4\Pi$ state which Mulliken (1932) predicted at 4.5 eV. Robinson (Frosch, 1964) reported bands assigned to a progression $(0, v'')$ with $3 \leqslant v'' \leqslant 11$. He also measured the lifetime of the emission in neon, argon, and krypton and found that the transition is forbidden. The assignment to $^4\Pi - X\,{}^2\Pi$ as a spin forbidden transition is supported by the observation of the solvent heavy atom effect on intensity and lifetime, and by the vibrational frequency of X, which coincides with the ground state vibration of NO. Lefebvre—Brion (1968) discussed the lifetime data and electronic character of the state, considering spin orbit coupling with B' $^2\Delta_{5/2}$ and A $^2\Sigma^+$.

$B\,{}^2\Pi - X\,{}^2\Pi$. Bands with $3 \leqslant v'' \leqslant 13$ of the β bands were observed by several authors. The gas-matrix shift is $- 160$ cm^{-1} in argon and $- 330$ cm^{-1} in krypton. The $w_e x_e$ value is almost identical with that of the gas phase. Broida studied this system with isotopes. Several attempts have been made to observe this system in absorption, but satisfactory results have not yet been reported. It seems that two problems arise: first, the bands are apparently broad, perhaps because of matrix perturbations; and second, it is not easy to prepare NO-doped solids, because NO dimerizes on cooling.

Roncin, Damany, and Romand (1967b) studied the absorption spectrum of NO in the pure solid and in neon, argon, krypton, and xenon matrices. While the pure solid shows only the broad absorption of N_2O_2, the matrices show three progressions consisting of a total of 40 sharp bands. The bands are evenly spaced and can be assigned to transition from the ground state to B $^2\Pi$, B' $^2\Delta$ and G $^2\Sigma^-$, all of which are valence states. The Rydberg states are completely suppressed, and the band structures of the valence transitions show no perturbations. This is entirely different from the gas phase, where Rydberg and valence transitions overlap in the same energy range and yield severe perturbations that make analysis very difficult. The transitions to B' $^2\Delta$ and G $^2\Sigma$ are sharp in solid neon, B $^2\Pi$ is sharper in argon. The explanation for the observed drastic simplification of the NO spectrum in matrices is that the observed matrix effects depend on changes in electron configurations between lower and upper states of a transition. In valence transitions, the electron configuration does not change drastically, although internuclear distance increases. Therefore, both upper and lower states are equally influenced and shifted, and the resultant spectrum is sharp and has an unchanged transition energy and probability and behaves generally gas—like. In Rydberg states, molecular orbitals of NO are much larger than those of the ground state, and thus environmental interaction changes during the transition; the results are drastically broadened and weakened lines, which make the transition appear forbidden. Roncin (1968) made qualitative correlations between the lattice site and shifts of energy levels. He also discussed site symmetry and concluded that the sharp lines, with no fine structure, indicate that NO is in a substitutional rare gas site with O_{4h} symmetry.

O_2

The visible absorption of liquid and solid oxygen has been extensively studied (Tsai, 1969). Several broad absorptions are reported. The spectrum is due to absorption of monomeric O_2 and simultaneous absorptions by two neighboring molecules. Such simultaneous transitions, for example a $^1\Delta$, a $^1\Delta \leftarrow$ X'X'; b $^1\Sigma$, b $^1\Sigma \leftarrow$ XX; and a $^1\Delta$, b $^1\Sigma \leftarrow$ XX, are responsible for bands in the visible which cause the blue color of solid and liquid. The forbidden fundamental frequency of 1449 cm^{-1} is observed in the IR because of matrix interactions (Cairns, 1965). Various other IR bands are assumed to be due to O_2–O_2 interaction, and lattice effects. β–O_2 and β–O_2 show different IR spectra.

B $^3\Sigma_u^- \leftarrow X$ $^3\Sigma_g^-$. In matrices, the Schumann-Runge bands consist of a long progression of well resolved bands. Schnepp and Dressler (1965) used $^{16}O_2$ and $^{18}O_2$ to confirm the assignment of this system. Potential energy curve computations indicate that in nitrogen and argon the curves are shifted only at large internuclear distances. The result is an apparent increase of the dissociation limit.

$A\ ^3\Sigma_u^+ \to X\ ^3\Sigma_g^-$. The Herzberg bands are observed throughout the visible region whenever oxygen-containing solids are bombarded with electrons. Schoen and Broida (1960a) analyzed this transition in krypton, argon, and xenon at 4°K. In xenon six bands with $v' = 1$ have been measured. Some of these are split into doublets. The emission from excited vibrational levels of the A state indicates that vibrational relaxation in xenon is a slow process. It took many years before other cases of similarly slow relaxation were observed, but it is now certain that OH, N_2, CH, S_2, C_2, and other molecules listed in Table 5.1 exhibit the same behavior. In nitrogen, the Herzberg bands are sharper than in any rare gas solid. The half-width is less than 5 cm^{-1}. In neon, the emission is different from all other solids. It resembles the second negative system of O_2^+.

$b\ ^1\Sigma^+ \to X\ ^3\Sigma_g^-$. In neon at 4°K the (0,0) band of the atmospheric band is observed at 759.4 nm.

OH

The OH-radical is found in solids formed by all discharges containing traces of oxygen and hydrogen. Robinson (1957a, 1958b–d, McCarty, 1959c) used microwave discharges through rare gas-water mixtures for preparation. Acquista, Schoen, and Lide (1968) used *in situ* vacuum UV photolysis. Tinti (1968a) irradiated rare gas-water solids with x-rays, and Matheson and Smaller (1955) irradiated ice and formic acid with x-rays. In all cases the spectrum shows a series of bands in the 310 nm region.

$A\ ^2\Sigma^+ \leftrightarrow X\ ^2\Sigma_i$. In three papers Robinson (1958b–d) reported strong bands assigned to OH in Ar. Partly resolved fine structure was tentatively assigned to rotational modes. A more recent study by Tinti (1968a), using H_2O and D_2O in neon proved the existence of rotational structure in neon at 40°K and led to a partial rotational analysis.

The neon spectrum is shifted by 70 cm^{-1} to 120 cm^{-1} to the red of the gas phase, but vibrational and rotational constants excited astonishingly small perturbations. Although the relative intensities are different, gas and spectra in neon show the same general rotational transitions. P_1, R_1, O_1, O_2 and S_1 are all assigned, with lines having half-widths of less than 5 cm^{-1}. The $J''_{3/2} - J''_{1/2}$ was found to be 51 cm^{-1}, compared with 61 cm^{-1} for the gas phase. For $R_1 + R_{21}$ two lines are observed. It seems likely that this is due to matrix-OH interactions. The author considers both crystal field effects and translation-rotation coupling about the interaction center, and mentions lattice phonon coupling as a third type of interaction to be considered.

Acquista, Schoen, and Lide (1968) found in argon that the IR frequencies of OH are shifted by 129 cm^{-1}, or 3.5% of the gas phase value. Such large shifts are rare, but are known to occur. The observation of a doublet is discussed in detail. The authors observed no change with temperature, and, assuming that the spin coupling should not be strongly affected by the matrix, conclude that the doublet is due to OH in two different sites.

PH

Robinson (McCarty, 1959c) observed one broad band at 341 nm in products condensed from a discharge of phosphine in argon. The absorption was so broad that no wavelength measurements were taken.

S_2

In their series of trail-blazing, exploratory experiments, Rice and co-workers (1953c,d) trapped hot sulfur vapor at 77°K. They found green and violet products, depending on the deposition conditions. This system was later studied by Meyer (1960a,b, 1962), who found that an IR band at 663 cm^{-1} appeared at low temperatures. It disappears with an activation energy of 14.1 kcal/mole. The ESR spectrum of the solid showed less than 10^{15} free spins. The electrical conductivity was 10^{12} times higher than that of normal orthorhombic sulfur. A broad absorption minimum at 500 nm was found in colored films only, but not in films annealed at room temperature. The system is very complex because it contains all the sulfur gas phase components $1 < S_x < 12$ plus the reaction products formed during quenching of the mixture. However, S_2 can be produced in matrices by several other reactions, for example, when H_2S is photolyzed in the vacuum UV (Milligan, 1964b), when S_2Cl_2 is photolyzed at 253.7 nm (J. Smith, 1968c), and when molecular beams of S_2 are trapped (Brewer, 1965b). Brewer, Brabson, and Meyer (1965b) studied S_2 in rare gas matrices and observed the system B ← X which corresponds to the Schumann-Runge bands of oxygen.

SCl

Snowden and Davidson (1958) photolyzed S_2Cl_2 in a 5 : 1 isopentane-3-methylpentane matrix at 77°K. They found a new UV absorption at 237 nm which they assigned to SCl. The S_2Cl_2 photolysis was later studied in solid rare gases at 20°K by Meyer (J. Smith, 1968c) using IR and UV methods. The latter results showed that the photolysis products in rare gases contain mainly S_2, and that the UV bands in hydrocarbon solids are probably due to reaction of halogen and sulfur atoms with the matrix. Several studies indicate that the S–Cl bond is weaker than the S–S bond. Thus, it is likely that products trapped from gas phase discharges through S_2Cl_2 contain SCl.

$B\,^3\Sigma_u^- \leftrightarrow X\,^3\Sigma_g^-$. This system is the only absorption and emission reported in matrices between 220 and 900 nm. The absorption in neon, argon, krypton, xenon, SF_6, CO, N_2, and methane consists of more than 20 members of the $(v', 0)$ progression. Predissociation, which is observed in the gas phase, is suppressed in matrices. Brewer (1965a) observed matrix shifts and matrix induced changes in anharmonicity. Nitrogen matrices are peculiar in that S_2 seems to behave like a harmonic oscillator. The shape of potential curves in matrices was explored by Brabson (1970). In all matrices an IR band in the 650–750 cm^{-1} region is observed. It is not clear whether it is due to S_2, as isotope experiments seem to indicate (Meyer, 1962) or to a sulfur-containing impurity. While the absorption bands are 100 cm^{-1} wide, or more, the B–X system in emission consists of much sharper lines. In argon, bands emitting from $v' = 1$ and $v' = 0$ were found. Thus, the vibrational relaxation times must be comparable to electronic relaxation time. Similar cases of slow vibrational relaxation have been reported for N_2, O_2, and C_2. In all cases, the emission from excited vibrational states depends on matrix material and temperature.

ScF

Weltner (McLeod, 1966) prepared neon matrices containing ScF by condensing the vapor of a mixture of ScF_3 and Sc. Bands between 220 nm and 800 nm were assigned to at least three electronic transitions of ScF, and to Sc atoms.

$B\,^1\Pi \leftarrow X\,^1\Sigma$. Six bands between 710 nm and 940 nm seem to form a progression with $0 < v' < 6$, but since the origin region is weak, it is possible that the v' numbering is too low by one or more vibrational quanta. Gas–solid shifts are 30 cm^{-1} for the band origin in neon, and 10 cm^{-1}, i.e., 2% of the transition energy, for the vibration quantum.

$C\,^1\Sigma \leftrightarrow X\,^1\Sigma$. Weltner observed this system in absorption and in emission. The bands have a half-width of 20 cm^{-1}. Eight absorption and seven emission bands are reported. If the assignment is correct, the vibrational relaxation of C is so slow that emission from $v' \leqslant 4$ is observed. Emission from excited vibrational states with v' up to 6 has been reported. However, in the case of ScF the lack of bands from excited v' to v'' levels other than zero is astonishing, because $v' = 0$ shows a clear progression with $0 \leqslant v'' \leqslant 2$. The C-system weakens upon exposure to light, but annealing leads to recovery of the absorption. The authors conclude that this is due to formation of different sites, i.e., photo-induced metastable secondary sites that can be depopulated by thermal activation. Accordingly, the authors believe that emission originates from activated sites. They quote the shift between absorption and emission bands as supporting this assumption.

The fact that fluorescence is observed shows either that nonradiative electronic excitation transfer is inefficient, or that the emitting B-state belongs to an impurity rather than to the same molecule. Careful study of the emission as a function of exciting frequency would be necessary to understand the emission mechanism.

$E\ ^1\Pi \leftarrow X\ ^1\Sigma$. Four bands have been assigned to this system. The gas-solid shift is large, 500 cm^{-1}, and the bands are broader than those of C–X, their half-width being 60 cm^{-1}. The authors used relative absorption intensities to compute the Franck-Condon factor for this system.

UV bands. Absorption in the UV can be assigned to scandium atoms. A progression of bands between 280 nm and 320 nm has similarities to the 370 nm gas phase system of Barrow, but the shift of over 4200 cm^{-1} makes this assignment unattractive. It is more probable that these bands belong to another molecule, perhaps ScF_2.

The large shifts and irregularities in the gas phase–solid correlation of ScF can stem from several sources. First, the gas phase spectra may not be correctly analyzed, second, the matrix interaction of a molecule with so many close-lying energy levels might lead to unusually large secondary, internal perturbations, and finally, the matrix spectrum might overlap with that impurity.

ScO

Weltner (1967a) studied matrix isolated ScO in neon trapped from Sc_2O_3 vapor. Under these conditions scandium atoms are also trapped, and their spectrum has been observed. Two systems were attributed to ScO.

$A\ ^2\Pi_{3/2;1/2} \leftarrow X\ ^2\Sigma$. Four bands have been analyzed as (0,0) and (1,0) of the two sublevels of the A state. The bands are unusually broad, with half-widths of up to 400 cm^{-1} in neon, and bleach within 4 hours if exposed to light from a tungsten lamp. A study with oxygen impurities and various vapor concentrations and condensation temperatures indicates that O_2 reacts with ScO.

$B\ ^2\Sigma \leftarrow X\ ^2\Sigma$. The first three bands of this transition are reported in argon and neon. As in the case of A — X, the origins are blue shifted by 400 cm^{-1} in neon, are broad, and bleach on illumination. It is likely that diffusion in the neon matrix leads to dimer formation and aggregates that have no band spectrum.

Se_2

Diatomic selenium is the predominant species in overheated selenium vapor at 1000°K. The spectrum is very complex in the gas phase, partly because the element has five almost equally abundant stable isotopes.

However, it was shown by Barrow (1966) that the entire visible spectrum is part of the Schumann-Runge system. Accordingly, all matrix bands belong to only one system.

$B\ ^3\Sigma_u^- \leftarrow X\ ^3\Sigma_g^-$. Eighteen bands of $^{78}\text{Se}_2$ and $^{80}\text{Se}_2$ in argon and xenon were assigned to this transition. The vibrational spacing and the Franck-Condon intensity fits this system, but the $(v', 0)$ progression is long and the origin region is too weak to be observed. Therefore, the vibrational numbering is not certain. Numbering based on isotope labeling is insecure, because the shifts are small and the bands are broad. It is not clear whether the band width is due to the unusually large triplet splitting of Se_2, or whether it is due to the matrix broadening observed for absorption of all diatomics. Magnet deflection experiments of hot Se_2 beams by Meschi and Searcy (1969) indicate that the triplet sublevels are at least 2000 cm^{-1} apart. Therefore, matrix bands must all originate from the 0^+ sublevel of $^3\Sigma$ (Meyer, 1970).

Si₂

The vaporization of silicon leads mainly to atoms, but the gas also contains Si_2, Si_3, and Si_4. Silicon vapor trapped in solid near 40°K shows three absorptions, one of which was assigned by Weltner (1964c) to Si_2.

$H\ ^3\Sigma_u^- \leftarrow X\ ^3\Sigma_g^-$. This system is known from the gas phase. It consists of a large progression, with the origin at 2.458264 μm^{-1}, if the vibrational numbering is correct. In the matrix the origin appears at 2.5156 μm^{-1} but bands in this region are weak, and insufficient material was collected to establish the (0,0) band. The vibrational spacing and the anharmonicity are similar to the gas phase, but the bands have a half width of 140 cm^{-1}. The observation of the H − X system in a matrix indicates that X is the ground state of the molecule. If the gas phase analysis of the electronic character is correct, the ground state of Si_2 is $^3\Sigma_g^-$. However, it should be pointed out that Si_2 is isoelectronic with C_2, which has a′ ground state.

SiO

If a rare gas discharge in a quartz tube is trapped at 4°K, several impurity spectra can be observed. Six absorption bands in the 210–240 nm region belong to SiO.

$A\ ^1\Pi \leftarrow X\ ^1\Sigma^+$. This system has been observed by Shirk and Bass (1968) in argon, krypton, and xenon. In all solids, the Franck-Condon curve is very similar to that of the gas phase. The gas-solid shifts increase with increasing solvent atomic weight, and the origins appear red shifted, except for argon. The anharmonicities increase from argon to xenon. The matrix experiment confirms that the origin of the transition is at 4.2657 μm^{-1}.

SnO

SnO vapor at 600°C is mainly diatomic. In matrix isolated molecular beams, J. Smith and Meyer (1968a) observed two systems.

$D\,^1\Pi \leftarrow X\,^1\Sigma$. In all matrices bands extended to the red of the reported (0,0) band origin. Therefore, the gas phase data need to be converted and the numbering should be changed by one unit of v'. The spacing and the intensity of the progression show abrupt changes indicating strong perturbations of this state, at least at $v' = 2$. There are so many close-lying states predicted, that an assignment seems impossible. The D-X system is the only strong absorption system observed in the 200–600 nm region.

$a\,^3\Pi \rightarrow X\,^1\Sigma$. In the gas phase SnO shows resonance fluorescence. However, if SnO in a matrix is excited in the D state, red phosphorescence is observed. Analysis of the system leads to the assignment a → X, in analogy with SnS. The system corresponds to the Cameron bands of the isovalent molecule CO. The a state is the lowest excited state of the molecule. It is populated by nonradiative decay from higher excited states through internal conversion and intersystem crossing. This type of excitation transfer, leading to phosphorescence, occurs only in the solid.

SnS

$D\,^1\Pi \leftarrow X\,^1\Sigma$. Trapped molecular beams of SnS in argon, krypton, and xenon show absorption by the 310–370 nm region (J. Smith and Meyer, 1968a). Band origin and vibrational spacing indicate assignment to D-X which was analyzed in the gas phase with the help of pure tin isotopes. In the matrix the progressions undergo a drastic intensity change at $v' \geqslant 6$. This might be due to another overlapping transition with similar v' value, or due to strong perturbation by a close-lying state.

$a\,^3\Pi \rightarrow X\,^1\Sigma$. Excitation of SnS with light with energy above 25000 cm^{-1} leads to strong red emission. As in the case of SnO, this is due to intersystem crossing. This effect consists of matrix-induced nonradiative energy transfer from all higher excited states to the lowest excited triplet state. The latter decays nonradiatively, and by emitting light. The quantum yield of the triplet emission in SnS must be very high, because the system can be easily observed in very small samples. Meyer (1970c, d) measured a lifetime value of 0.5 msec for the $^3\Pi \rightarrow {}^1\Sigma$ transition in argon and SF$_6$.

TaO

Tantalum oxide vapor, Ta$_2$O$_5$, contains TaO and TaO$_2$ in comparable amounts. Weltner (1965c) studied Ta ^{16}O and Ta ^{18}O in argon at 20°K and near 4°K. The absorption spectrum is very complicated, showing about thirteen different types of bands. The spectrum is sharpest in neon. The structure is simplified appreciably when neon solids are annealed. The tentative assignment is included in the diatomics table of Chapter 10. Three of the reported transitions, listed below, correspond to gas phase spectra:

$b \, {}^2\Pi_{1/2} \leftarrow a \, {}^2\Delta_{3/2}$. This transition, in the matrix called L-X system, consists of a progression of five bands with a spacing of 887 cm^{-1}. Since the system is observed in matrices, the authors assume that it connects with the ground state.

$d \, {}^2\Phi_{5/2} \leftarrow a \, {}^2\Delta_{3/2}$. The matrix system M-X, is observed in emission and absorption. Vibrational levels with $v = 889$ cm^{-1} are reported.

$c \, {}^2\Delta_{3/2} \leftarrow a \, {}^2\Delta_{3/2}$. This is system P in the matrix. It consists of five vibrational bands. This system is observed only in absorption.

TaO is a heavy molecule, with a complicated electron configuration. It cannot be easily prepared, and it cannot be purified. Thus, a more detailed analysis of its spectrum might prove to be very difficult.

TiO

The spectrum of TiO in neon and argon at 4° and 20°K was reported by Weltner (1965d). It shows three absorption systems. The emission is reported to be very weak. The molecule can be prepared by vaporizing TiO_2 at 1900°K. The resulting vapor contains also TiO_4 and probably some impurities from TiO_2 and the container.

$A \, {}^3\phi_2 \leftarrow X \, {}^3\Delta_1$. This transition is also called γ system. It consists of five vibrational bands. Since it is observed in absorption, Weltner assumes that it originates in the ground state. However, the lowest excited state of TiO is estimated to be only 500 cm^{-1} above the ground state, and such close-lying levels can lead to interactions that allow absorption from several levels. This effect is reported for the case of C_2, where Swan bands are observed, although the corresponding lower state is 700 cm^{-1} above the ground state.

$\gamma' \, {}^3\Pi_0 \leftarrow X \, {}^3\Delta_1$. The assignment of a progression with four bands originating at 16330 cm^{-1} is ambiguous, because the gas phase analysis is uncertain. It seems that three systems are observed in the gas phase, but different authors come to different conclusions.

$C \, {}^3\Delta_1 \leftarrow X \, {}^3\Delta_1$. This is called the α system. In the matrix five bands appear. The assignment seems unambiguous. All three transitions were confirmed with [18]O isotopes. The ground state frequency was observed in the IR.

WO

The spectrum of this molecule is not well known. It can be expected to be complicated, and, indeed, gas phase results are not conclusive. So far not even one transition has been rotationally analyzed. As in the case of other high temperature molecules, matrix spectra are complicated by the presence of impurities and other molecular species. Since heavy diatomics have many close-lying and low-lying energy levels, the advantage of low vibrational excitation at low temperatures is insufficient to lead to an unambiguous assignment. WO occurs together with WO_2 in the vapor of WO_3. The complex spectrum was studied with ^{18}O isotopes, and the analysis led Weltner (1965c) to propose seven observed transitions. One transition is very weak, and all others, except the D system, are vibrationally perturbed. Also, the two oxygen isotopes give in many regions a different number of bands.

$A, B, C \leftarrow X$. Weltner grouped bands between 470 nm and 580 nm into three systems. Four bands, with $4 \leqslant v' \leqslant 7$, are assigned to system A; B consists of $0 \leqslant v' \leqslant 3$, and the first three levels of C were observed. The authors justify the analysis with detailed arguments. As usual in matrix experiments, the spectra are complicated by fine structure which depends on matrix material and temperature.

$E, F, G \leftarrow X$. E and F are badly perturbed and overlapped, and transitions to G are very weak. A detailed discussion of the system and its tentative interpretation is given in the above-mentioned reference.

$D \leftarrow X$. This system corresponds very closely to the gas phase spectrum. The first three vibrational levels in neon at 4°K coincide, for all practical purposes, with gas phase transitions. They are reported to have gas–solid shifts of less than 0.01% of the transition energy.

YO

This molecule is prepared by vaporizing Y_2O_3 (Weltner, 1967a). The gas contains measurable amounts of Y atoms and O atoms. In addition, furnace materials and rare gas impurities may be present. The spectrum shows only five bands.

$A\ ^2\Pi_{3/2}, {}^2\Pi_{1/2} \leftarrow X\ ^2\Sigma$. Weltner reported ESR data supporting the $^2\Sigma$ character of the ground state. In the visible, he assigned three bands to transitions to the A state; one being (0,0) of $^2\Pi_{1/2}$, and the other corresponding to the first two upper state quanta of $^2\Pi_{3/2}$. In neon the bands are 700 cm^{-1} blue-shifted and unusually broad. Another peculiar property is that all YO bands bleach within half an hour when the matrix is exposed to the light of a tungsten lamp. This behavior is reminiscent of the Swan system of C_2, and a satisfactory explanation must await further experiments.

$B\ ^2\Sigma \leftarrow X\ ^2\Sigma$. Weltner observed two bands of this transition. The characteristics are very similar to those of the system A-X.

ZrO

Weltner (1965a,d) trapped ZrO in neon and argon at 4°K and 20°K using a Knudsen cell with ZrO_2 and $Zr^{18}O_2$. The absorption spectrum consists of 16 bands in the 330–650 nm region; in emission eight bands were observed.

$A\,{}^1\Sigma^+ - X\,{}^1\Sigma$. This system is observed in emission and absorption. Bands have half-widths of 70 cm^{-1} and are moderately shifted from the gas phase. Oxygen isotopes confirm the assignment to the gas phase A-X transition.

$B\,{}^3\Pi_0 \to S\,{}^3\Delta_1$. These four bands are observed only in emission. The vibrational spacing indicates that the lower state is not the ground state, and that the system corresponds to the gas phase B bands. The fact that this system emits is rather unusual. One would expect ZrO to have quite efficient intersystem crossing because there is a great wealth of close-lying energy levels that could interact. In view of the similarity of the lower state frequency with the IR frequency of ZrO_2 the triatomic could be responsible for this emission. In emission even minute quantities of other impurities could easily dominate and account for the spectrum.

Table 9.3

Matrix Isolated Triatomics

Al_2O	Cl_3	HO_2	SO_2
BO_2	Cl_2O	$HOBr$	S_2O
BaF_2	ClO_2	$HOCl$	ScF_2
$BeBr_2$	$ClOO$	$HgCl_2$	SeO_2
$BeCl_2$	$CoCl_2$	KrF_2	Si_3
BeF_2	$CrCl_2$	Li_2O	SiC_2
BeI_2	FCO	LiO_2	Si_2C
C_3	FNC	$LiON$	SiF_2
CCO	$FeCl_2$	MgF_2	SrF_2
CCl_2	GeF_2	$MnCl_2$	TaO_2
CF_2	HC_2	NCN	WO_2
CH_2	$HCCl$	NCO	$XeCl_2$
CNN	HCF	NH_2	XeF_2
COS	HCO	N_2O	$ZnBr_2$
CS_2	HNC	$NiCl_2$	$ZnCl_2$
CaF_2	HNF	NiF_2	ZnF_2
$CdCl_2$	HNO	O_2F	ZnI_2
$ClCO$	HNS	PH_2	

C. Triatomics[†]

In this section data on triatomic matrix isolated species are discussed. The literature is so large, and grows at such a fast rate, that it is virtually impossible to offer here a complete coverage of the present status. The reader will find that in some cases the data are not reliable enough to warrant claims of discovery of the indicated species, but we include those cases to allow the reader to form his own judgment, and to see whether earlier work exists and what it is worth.

Al$_2$O

Linevsky *et al.* (1963) have reported the infrared spectrum of Al$_2$O in argon and krypton matrices at 4°K. In dilute samples, only one prominent absorption is observed, but in more concentrated samples several bands appear. The former appears at 994 cm^{-1} in argon and 988 cm^{-1} in krypton and is assigned to ν_3. Bands at 715 cm^{-1} in argon and 709 cm^{-1} in krypton are assigned to ν_1. Results with ^{18}O substitution are consistent with the assignments. The observed shifts suggest a molecular bond angle of near 150° and a ν_2 bending frequency of 238 cm^{-1}. Also observed in the spectrum is a band near 1870 cm^{-1} which is assigned to an overtone of ν_3.

BO$_2$

Boron dioxide has been prepared for observation in matrices by Sommer (1963) through the oxidation of B$_2$O$_3$ with ZnO. Mass spectroscopic analysis, however, shows BO$_2$ to be a minor constituent (BO$_2^+$/B$_2$O$_3^+$ = 0.10), so that spectral observation is limited to those regions unmasked by B$_2$O$_3$. The visible absorption spectrum of BO$_2$ in argon consists of a series of bands in the 380–580 nm region. The majority of these bands can be assigned to the transition A $^2\Pi_u \leftarrow$ X $^2\Pi_g$ through comparison with the gas phase, high resolution work of Johns (1961). The gas to matrix shift is about 400 cm^{-1}, and all but three bands appear to originate from the $^2\Pi_{3/2}$ sublevel. Two bands near 410 nm cannot be fitted to the Π-Π transition, but correlate closely with the (0,0,0) transition of the B state, B $^2\Sigma_u^+ \leftarrow$ X $^2\Pi_g$. These bands, along with three from the Π-Π transition, appear to originate in the $^2\Pi_{1/2}$ sublevel.

The infrared spectrum of the molecule shows absorptions at 1276 and 1323 cm^{-1}. These bands are assigned to the asymmetric stretching frequency, ν_3, of the species ^{11}BO$_2$ and ^{10}BO$_2$, respectively. The additional fundamental frequencies were not observed because of overlap from the spectrum of B$_2$O$_3$.

[†] The author thanks Dr. J. Smith who assisted by collecting data on triatomics and by drafting the text of this section.

BaF₂

The infrared spectrum of barium fluoride in the region from 4000 to 200 cm^{-1} was reported by Snelson in 1966. BaF_2 is believed to have a symmetrical F—Ba—F structure because the dissociation energy for the alternate Ba—F—F structure would be too high. The symmetry must, therefore, be C_{2V} or $D_{\infty h}$ depending on whether the molecule is bent or linear. Two infrared absorptions attributable to BaF_2 substantiate the bent structure. These bands, at 400 and 425 cm^{-1} appear in neon, argon, and krypton and are assigned to ν_3 and ν_1, respectively, on the basis of relative intensity. The appearance in the infrared of ν_1 requires the bent structure. The ν_2 bending mode was not observed; presumably it lies below 200 cm^{-1}. A weak band at about 325 cm^{-1} appears in neon and argon matrices and is assigned to polymeric or agglomerate material. As the matrix is changed from neon to argon to krypton, the external heavy atom effect on both vibrational frequencies causes increasing red shifts.

BeBr₂

$BeBr_2$ has been deposited directly from the solid into neon and argon matrices at 4°K by Snelson (1968). The vapor is superheated to 975°K to reduce polymer concentrations. Infrared observations give two bands in neon at 993 and 207 cm^{-1}, but only one in argon, 985 cm^{-1}. The band near 990 cm^{-1} is assigned to ν_3, and the low frequency band to ν_2. The latter is presumably shifted below the detection limit of 200 cm^{-1} in argon. The frequencies are consistent with a linear structure for the molecule. A calculation of ν_1 using the valence force field approximation gives a value of 230 cm^{-1}.

BeCl₂

Beryllium chloride, in the rare gases at 4°K, shows two absorption bands, at approximately 1120 and 240 cm^{-1}, in the infrared (Snelson, 1966, 1968). These bands are assigned to the asymmetric stretching vibration, ν_3 and the bending mode, ν_2, respectively. The former correlates closely with the gas phase value for ν_3 of 1113 cm^{-1} (Buchler, 1961). The gas phase band at 482 cm^{-1} previously assigned to ν_2 is not observed at low temperatures and is probably in error. Estimation of ν_1 suggests a value of 390 cm^{-1} (Snelson, 1968). The absence of ν_1 is consistent with a linear structure for $BeCl_2$. Force constants are also reported.

BeF₂

Monomeric beryllium fluoride, unlike the chloride, shows two strong infrared absorption features (Snelson, 1966). These bands, at 1542 and 330 cm^{-1} in neon at 4.2°K, are assigned to ν_3, the asymmetric stretching mode, and ν_2, the bending mode, respectively. No bands corresponding to ν_1 are observed, and the molecule is presumably linear. Additional weak bands at 830, 790, and 1250 cm^{-1} are attributable to dimers and polymers of BeF_2. Mass spectroscopic data (Hildenbrand, 1964) indicate that up to 1 mole percent of dimers may be present in the vapor at 600°C. Gas phase values for ν_3 and ν_2 are reported to be 1520 and 825 cm^{-1}, respectively (Buchler, 1961). The value for ν_3 in the gas phase and in matrices is consistent; however, the results for ν_2 are in disagreement. It is possible that the gas phase band at 825 cm^{-1} is due to a polymeric species. Force constants and the symmetric stretching vibration, $\nu_1 = 680$ cm^{-1}, have been calculated using a valence force field method.

BeI_2

Only one vibrational fundamental of BeI_2 has been observed in matrices following vaporization of the solid (Snelson, 1968). In both neon and argon at 4°K, a band of multiplet structure appears near 870 cm^{-1}. The fine structure is presumed to be due to matrix effects. The band is assigned to ν_3 of the molecule. A calculated value of 160 cm^{-1} for ν_1 is obtained using the valence force field approximation.

C_3

The molecule C_3 has been studied extensively by several workers (Weltner, 1962, 1964a,b, 1966; Barger, 1962, 1964, 1965; Brabson, 1965) in a variety of solids. All workers have used trapped carbon vapor as the C_3 source. The vapor concentration of C_3 depends on the nature of the source. A tantalum Knudsen furnace has been reported by Weltner (1964a) to give 50% C_3, 7% C_2, 38% C, and 4% Tr at 2430°C. Langmuir sources at 2500°K give a composition of about 25% C_3, 25% C_2, and 50% C atoms.

The gas phase "4050 A system" of C_3, assignable to the $A^1 \Pi_u \leftarrow X^1 \Sigma_g^+$ has recently been analyzed by Gausset et al. (1963, 1966). The molecule has a very low ground state bending mode (63 cm^{-1}) and a large Renner effect in the excited $'\Pi_u$ state ($E = + 0.537$). The gas phase analysis also indicates that the upper state is also linear and that Franck-Condon factors allow transition involving v_1' and $2v_2'$, and $2v_3'$ if observed in this system.

The matrix absorption spectrum of C_3 also consists of the $A'\Pi_u \leftarrow X'\Sigma_g^+$ system. Table 9.4 gives the origins as well as other pertinent data on this system in each of the matrices studied. The appearance of the bands, as evidenced by the half-widths, depends on the matrix. Neon, argon, and oxygen were all observed to give sharp structure. Neon and argon apparently give additional multiple sites on initial condensation. Weltner (1966) reports that annealing of the C_3—neon system at 11–12°K for 0.5 hour leads to

Table 9.4

Characteristics of C_3, A $^1\Pi_u \leftarrow$ X $^1\Sigma_g^+$ Absorption in Various Matrices

Matrix	λ (nm)	Transition Energy (μm^{-1})	Half-width (cm^{-1})	Gas to Matrix Shift[c] (cm^{-1})	References
CO_2	398.5	2.5085	500	-410	Barger (1962, 1964, 1965)
Ne[a]	405.7	2.4642	12–30	33	Weltner (1962b, 1964a,b, 1966)
N_2	405.8[b]	2.4635	250	40	Barger (1962, 1964, 1965), Brabson (1965b)
SF_6	407.0	2.4565	200	110	Barger (1962, 1964, 1965)
Ar	410.2	2.4370	11–50	305	Barger (1962, 1964, 1965), Brabson (1965b)
O_2	410.2	2.4370	40	305	Barger (1965), Weltner (1965)
Kr	410.6	2.4350	200	325	Barger (1962, 1964, 1965), Brabson (1965b)
Xe	423.4	2.3610	100	1065	Barger (1962, 1964, 1965)

[a] After annealing.
[b] Brabson reports a value of 419.9 nm for the 0,0,0 band in N_2.
[c] Gas phase value 404.98 nm = 2.46755 μm^{-1}.

considerable simplification of the spectrum. It is noteworthy that, before annealing, the first strong band in neon occurs at 407.2 nm with the multiplet structure extending to about 405.0 nm and includes the strong band at 405.7 nm. Emission of this system (discussed below) also shows the first band at 407.2 nm, but the band structure is not a mirror image of the absorption (0,0,0) band, and little other structure is present. Annealing leads to a loss of all structure with only the 405.7 nm band remaining. The annealing effect on emission was, unfortunately, not reported. It is not clear why the multiple sites are observed in absorption, but not in emission.

The absorption bands show progressions in v_1' and weakly $2v_2'$ in line with expectations. The values of v_1' and v_2' depend to a certain extent on the matrix environment. Values reported for v_1' are 1125 cm^{-1} in neon and 1095 cm^{-1} in argon. The upper state bending frequency v_2' varies between 302 and 314 cm^{-1}. The values of v_2' are less clear because the large Renner effect leads to uneven spacing of the vibrational levels in the upper state. Renner parameter calculations from the observed band positions are $+ 0.52$ by Brabson, 0.566 by Weltner, and 0.55 by Barger.

Assignments are made by considering this splitting $(v_1', V_2^+{}', 0)$ and $(v_1', V_2'^-, 0)$ bands are tabulated in the original references. The agreement between authors is excellent except for the assignment of the $(0, 6^+, 0)$ band in argon in which Brabson and Weltner disagree. The value of the latter appears more probable. The assignments correlate well with calculated wavelengths based on the gas phase Renner parameter $E = +0.537$ and upper state bending mode $v_2' = 307.9$ cm^{-1}. Although bands involving $2v_3'$ are not forbidden, transitions involving this vibration are either not present or very weak. Weltner does, however, report two bands in neon at 379.8 and 364.7 nm which seem related but do not fit into the assignment scheme. These are proposed to involve v_3' with the 379.8 nm band $(0,0,2)$ and the 364.7 nm band $(1,0,2)$. This yields a value of 840 cm^{-1} for the v_3' vibration. This value is extraordinarily low and is rationalized on the basis of similar anomalies in like molecules such as BO_2, CO_2^+, and CNN, where large interaction force constants are observed. In addition, Douglas' (1951) measurements of ^{13}C isotope shifts of the $(0,0,0)$–$(0,0,0)$ C_3 band in the gas phase requires a value for v_3' of about 900 cm^{-1}.

When C_3 in Ne or Ar is excited with light of 404.7 nm or 365.0 nm wavelength, two distinct emissions are obtained (Weltner, 1965; Brabson, 1965). The bluest emission has its origin near 407.2 nm and is assigned to the fluorescence associated with the $'\Pi_u - X'\Sigma_g{}^+$ transition. This emission is characterized by a short progression with frequency differences of about 170 cm^{-1}, a second series of bands located about 1230 cm^{-1} away, and a third weak band 4046 cm^{-1} away. The difference of 1230 cm^{-1} is assigned to v_1''; the 170 cm^{-1} difference represents $2v_2''$ giving a v_2'' value of 85 cm^{-1}, and the 4046 cm^{-1} difference belongs to $2v_3''$ giving v_3'' the value 2023 cm^{-1}. Direct infrared observations give a v_3'' value of 2042 cm^{-1} thereby giving weight to the $2v_3''$ assignment.

The second emission originates at 585.6 nm in neon and 590.5 nm in argon. It shows progressions almost identical with the A → X system. The low frequency differences are 158, 164, 178, and 191 cm^{-1}, and the higher frequency is 1223 cm^{-1}. It is therefore likely that this system terminated in the C_3 ground state. Weltner determined the lifetime of this emission in neon. The value of 0.02 sec indicates that the transition is forbidden. The upper state is proposed to be the a $^3\Pi_u$ state, associated with the electronic configuration of the $^1\Pi_u$ state. Population of the $^3\Pi_u$ state, because of excitation conditions, presumably comes about via intersystem crossing from the $^1\Pi_u$ state.

Although attempts were made to observe other transitions in the molecule, in particular, the $^1\Sigma_u{}^+ \leftarrow {}^1\Sigma_g{}^+$, none were found, at least in the region down to 195 nm. Barger and Weltner have computed oscillator strengths for the $^1\Pi_u \leftarrow {}^1\Sigma_g^+$ system. The values of 6×10^{-2} and 10^{-3}, respectively, were reported for the 410.2 nm band in argon. In view of the inherent difficulty involved in measurements of this type in matrices, the agreement is excellent.

Barger and Broida (1965) suggested the possibility of the presence of excited ground state vibrational levels of v_2'', in particular, levels 3, 4, and possibly 7. The suggestion is based on the presence of unassigned bands which fit the difference $(0,3,0) - (0,0,0)$, $(0,7,0) - (0,3,0)$ and $(0,4,0) - (0,0,0)$.

CCO

The free radical CCO has been prepared in sufficient concentration for direct spectroscopic observation in two ways. Carbon atoms, produced in the photolysis of matrix isolated cyanogen azide at wavelengths shorter than 280 nm, were observed to react with carbon monoxide in the matrix with little or no activation energy, yielding directly CCO. The exact mechanism of CCO formation is not known, but several deductions can be made regarding it. Milligan showed in 1965 that NCN is the initial photolysis product of N_3CN with radiation of wavelengths greater than 280 nm. Subsequent photolysis of NCN at wavelengths shorter than 280 nm yields N_2 and carbon atoms. The electronic state of the carbon atoms is not clear although it is rationalized that with ^3P and ^1D states atoms may be produced, depending on the energy of the incident radiation. Either is capable of reacting with CO to form CCO. Because of the nature of the CCO synthesis, this system also contains undesired impurities. Other species known to be present include: NCN, N_2, CO, N_3CN, and C_3O_2. The latter is apparently formed through direct reaction of CCO with CO with little or no activation energy. The half-life of CCO in CO is about 3 minutes.

Vacuum ultraviolet photolysis of C_3O_2 also produces observable quantities of the radical CCO. Photolysis is effected using a xenon resonance lamp and wavelengths below 280 nm. This system has the advantage of fewer impurities than the above system; however, CO and unphotolyzed C_3O_2 as well as CCO are known to be present.

The CCO radical shows three distinct absorptions in the infrared. The three vibrational fundamentals attributable to CCO in an argon matrix occur at 381, 1074, and 1978 cm^{-1}. The use of carbon and oxygen isotopes confirms the identification. The data are consistent with a linear structure, as proposed by Walsh (1953a,b). The ground state is probably $^3\Sigma$.

A continuous absorption assigned to CCO occurs in the visible region near 500 nm. The absorption appears as a broad structureless band and evidently results in the photodissociation of CCO:

$$CCO\ (^3\Sigma) + h\nu \rightarrow C(^3P) + CO.$$

CCl₂

Milligan (1967) and Andrews (1968), used two different methods for preparing CCl_2 in matrices for spectroscopic observation. Milligan reacted carbon atoms produced by the photolysis of cyanogen azide with chlorine in argon and nitrogen matrices at 14°K to form directly CCl_2. This method has the disadvantage that several unwanted species are simultaneously produced, thereby limiting the useful spectral range to those areas where overlap does not occur. The experiments consist of simultaneous depositions of $Ar : Cl_2$ and $Ar : N_3CN$ samples. The resulting solid is photolyzed with the entire spectrum of a cadmium lamp, with glass envelope removed. This treatment is known to result in the formation of excellent yields of the free radical NCN. The carbon atoms, used to form CCl_2 through reaction with Cl_2, are then produced through photolysis of the intermediate NCN with the full spectrum of a medium pressure mercury arc.

Andrews reported a more direct, but not less sophisticated, method involving the reaction of lithium atoms with carbon tetrachloride in argon matrices at 15°K. Lithium is deposited from a Knudsen cell while the carbon tetrachloride–argon mixture is deposited through a second jet. The reaction yields CCl_3 and LiCl as primary products. The CCl_2 is formed by secondary reaction of CCl_3 with excess lithium. This method suffers from the presence of intermediates and impurities, which are inevitably present in a lithium beam. Thus, the spectral features of CCl_2 must be sorted from those of other constituents.

Two infrared absorptions are reported for CCl_2. Andrews' assignments are based on isotope shifts and normal coordinate calculations. The bands at 746 cm⁻¹ and 720 cm⁻¹ are assigned to ν_3 and ν_1, respectively, of the $^{12}C^{35}Cl_2$ species in argon. These frequencies shift to 754 and 725 cm⁻¹ in N_2. The assignment of ν_3 to the highest frequency band is consistent with previous observations for OCl_2, $HBCl_2$, and H_2CCl_2, where ν_3 is also higher than ν_1, and so it is not without precedent. It should be noted that $\nu_1 > \nu_3$ occurs in CF_2 and OF_2. The presence of ν_1 in the infrared requires a bent structure for the molecule, with an almost certain symmetry C_{2v}. The calculation of the valence bond angle using ν_3 for $^{12}CCl_2$ and $^{13}CCl_2$ gives a value of $100° \pm 9°$. From his data, Milligan estimated the angle to be 90°–110°. The ν_2 bending mode is not observed.

In the visible region, 16 bands occurring between 440 and 560 nm are observed in absorption. These bands, because of analogous behavior with that of the infrared absorptions, are also assigned to CCl_2. The average spacing between bands is 305 cm^{-1}, and the system probably is a progression in v_2'. By analogy with CF_2, the lower state is concluded to be the $^1A_1$ ground state; the upper state is probably the first excited electronic configuration and presumably $^1B_1$, although $^1A_1$ is also possible. Herzberg tentatively lists $^1A_1$ for CF_2.

CF_2

Photolysis of CF_2N_2 in matrices, reactions of carbon atoms from the photolytic decomposition of NCN_3 with molecular fluorine, and condensation of the products of a discharge (2450 megacycles) through C_4F_8/argon mixtures have all yielded sufficient quantities of the CF_2 radical for low temperature spectroscopic observation (Bass, 1962; Milligan, 1964, 1968).

Only one absorption system of CF_2 is observed in the region 190–540 nm. This system, which corresponds to the gas phase transition A ($^1A_1$) ← X $^1A_1$, originates at 3.739 μm^{-1} and consists of at least 16 distinct bands. The transition consists of a single progression in v_2' with a vibrational spacing of 500 cm^{-1} and resembles the gas phase spectrum quite closely. The Franck-Condon maximum occurs near 248 nm, at the seventh band. Intensity in the origin region is sufficient to allow clear observation of the (0,0,0), (0,0,0) band. Only in the case of the $NCN_3/F_2/Ar$ system is the spectrum overlapped. This is due to the CNN absorption in the same region.

The ground state vibrational frequencies of the radical have been observed directly by infrared spectroscopy. All these vibrational modes appear as is consistent with the C_{2v} structure. Frequencies for $^{12}CF_2$ in argon are: $v_1 = 1222$ cm^{-1}, $v_2 = 668$ cm^{-1}, and $v_3 = 1102$ cm^{-1}. Yields of the radical are sufficient to allow observations of v_1 and v_3 at 1191 and 1073 cm^{-1}, respectively, for the $^{13}CF_2$ species from ^{13}C natural abundance. These assignments have been confirmed using ^{13}C enriched samples. The frequencies are virtually identical in N_2 matrices. The 1222 cm^{-1} v_1 band in argon does, however, appear as a doublet, whereas only a single peak occurs in N_2. The doubling is not totally clear, although it may be due to sites. Results in CO and CO_2 matrices are essentially the same, indicating that CF_2 does not react with either under these conditions. Warm-up leads to the formation of C_2F_4. The dimerization of CF_2 to C_2F_4 is apparently accompanied by chemiluminescence, because a "straw-yellow" glow is observed when diffusion becomes important.

Impurities or unwanted products depend on the preparative method; they include CF_3, C_2F_4, C_2F_6, $CF_2N_2CF_2$, which is called perfluoroformadezine, and $(CF_2N)_2$.

A bond angle of 108° is calculated for CF_2 from the observed $^{13}CF_2$

isotope shifts. This agrees favorably with Walsh's prediction that the molecule would prove to be strongly bent. CF_2, like several other halogen-containing species, has the asymmetric stretching fundamental at a lower frequency than the symmetric stretching fundamental. Force constants and thermodynamic functions are tabulated in the original references.

CH_2

Numerous attempts have been made to prepare and stabilize the methylene radical in low temperature matrices for spectroscopic studies (Milligan 1958, 1962a, 1967b; Goldfarb 1960a,b; DeMore 1958; Moore 1964a, 1965; Robinson 1960c; Jacox 1963b). Most of these attempts have centered on the photolysis of diazomethane CH_2N_2 which was expected to fragment into CH_2 and N_2. It was hoped that the back reaction between methylene and nitrogen would not occur or would proceed slowly at 20°K or below. No unambiguous optical spectral observations on trapped CH_2 have been made. There are, however, several observations on reactions at low temperatures which indicate the formation of CH_2 from some photolytic processes. The CH_2 radical apparently has a very high reactivity in all systems yet studied.

CNN

Robinson and McCarty (1960) made the first tentative spectroscopic identification of the radical CNN, when they suggested that bands at 424.8 and 423.4 nm produced in the photolysis of diazomethane in a krypton matrix might be due to CN_2 or HCN_2. Goldfarb (1960) at the same time studied the photolysis of diazomethane in nitrogen matrices and reported unassigned bands at 396.8 and 418.2 nm. The warm-up behavior suggested that these bands were due to a reactive species, and it was proposed that the methylene radical could be responsible for one or both. The 418.2 nm band presumably correlated with Robinson's 423.4 nm band. The 396.8 nm feature, however, could only be correlated to a band at 317.4 nm in krypton which Robinson has assigned to CH. Milligan et al. (1965c), in a study of the photolysis of N_3CN in N_2, reported bands at 418.9 and 396.4 nm. These correspond very closely with those of Goldfarb and Pimentel, and a tentative assignment to CNN was made. A conclusive assignment could not be made on the basis of the data. In a subsequent investigation of the photolysis of N_3CN, aimed specifically at the identification of CNN, Milligan (1966b) confirmed the assignment of the 396.4 and 418.9 nm features to CNN. The spacing between the bands corresponds to 1355 cm^{-1}, ν_3 of the upper state. The considerable intensity of the 396.4 nm band suggests that only a small change in bond length occurs in the transition. Weltner (1964) reported the presence near 420 nm of bands containing carbon and associated with depositions of carbon in neon and argon matrices. These bands were later (Weltner, 1966) shown to be due to CNN formed through the reaction of carbon atoms, from vaporized carbon, with N_2 which had entered the system through a vacuum leak. Bands occur at 421.0–419.6 nm and 398.8–397.6 nm in neon and argon containing N_2. Weltner (1966) reported an upper state vibrational frequency of 1325 cm^{-1}. ESR observations have led to the conclusion that the radical CNN is linear and that the ground state is triplet (Wasserman, 1965), probably $^3\Sigma^-$.

Infrared observations (Milligan, 1966b) have led to the assignment of all three fundamentals of the radical. Frequencies observed in an argon matrix and their assignments are $v''_1 = 1241$ cm^{-1}, $v''_2 = 393$ cm^{-1}, and $v''_3 = 2847$ cm^{-1} for the $^{12}C^{14}N^{14}N$ species. A frequency of 1235 cm^{-1} was observed in fluorescence in neon by Weltner (1966) and correlates well with the v''_3. This frequency is a counterpart of the 1325 cm^{-1} upper state frequency, therefore strengthening the latter assignment as v'_1. Identification of the absorber and the assignments are consistent with the observed isotope shifts on substitution of ^{13}C and ^{15}N atoms. A comparison of band structure on ^{15}N substitution in argon with substitution in nitrogen leads to the conclusion that CNN is formed from the reaction of carbon atoms with N_2. The asymmetric stretching frequency of 2847 cm^{-1} is anomalously high. This leads to the conclusion that the carbon-nitrogen bond has substantial triple bond character. Overtones or combination bands are ruled out as being responsible for this band by isotope substitution so that the assignment to v''_1 seems assured.

CNN is also observed in the vacuum ultraviolet photolysis of C_3O_2 in nitrogen matrices (Milligan, 1966b; Moll, 1966). The latter reports infrared absorptions of 2858, 1252, and 394 cm^{-1} for the species.

COS

Carbonyl sulfide has been studied in several matrices in the infrared (Venderame 1966; J. J. Smith 1968c) and in the vacuum ultraviolet (Roncin, 1969). The vibrational frequencies observed directly in the infrared are $v''_1 = 2050$, $v''_2 = 518$ and $v''_3 = 857$ cm^{-1}. The former is in krypton and the latter two are for the pure solid, but the values in CO are essentially the same.

The vacuum ultraviolet absorption spectrum appears to consist of three separate transitions, two in the region 160–180 nm, and the third between 115 and 145 nm, with origins at 5.54, 5.96, and 6.75 μm^{-1}. The vibrational intervals for the three are 760, 495, and 511 cm^{-1}, respectively. The transition at 6.74 μm^{-1} appears Rydberg-like; the other two are assigned to valence transitions. The bands are diffuse in neon, but sharper on going to argon or krypton.

CS_2

The electronic spectrum of CS_2 is complex and not well understood in the gas phase. Furthermore, the matrix spectrum has not completely clarified the situation. CS_2 has been studied in the rare gases and nitrogen and methane between about 2° and 20°K (Roncin, 1969; Bajema, 1970). Observations in the vacuum ultraviolet reveal a series of bands between 135 and 152 nm with an origin at 6.60 μm^{-1}. The best spectra are obtained in argon and krypton. The bands in neon are broadened to the point that they are nearly inseparable and xenon shows only one band. A vibrational spacing of 540 cm^{-1} occurs in neon and argon at the red end of the system. The assignment of the frequency has not been made. The Rydberg series appears to be suppressed.

A complex series of absorptions is observed in the near ultraviolet and visible region of the spectrum. The bands appear to result from the overlap of three separate transitions having vibrational spacings of 560, 580, and 575 cm^{-1} and origins at 3.10, 3.081, and 3.078 μm^{-1}, respectively. The transitions have been tentatively assigned as $^1B_2 \leftarrow {}^1\Sigma_g^+$, $^1A_2 \leftarrow {}^1\Sigma_g^+$, and $^1A_2 \leftarrow {}^1\Sigma_g^+$. In emission, a weak broad phosphorescence with two lifetime components, $\tau_1 = 0.8$ msec and $\tau_2 = 2.6$ msec in argon, is observed. This transition appears near 1.82 μm^{-1} and is tentatively assigned as $^3B_2$ or $^3A_2$.

CaF_2

Snelson isolated (1966), calcium fluoride in neon, argon, and krypton. Only one absorption in the infrared can unambiguously be assigned to the monomeric species. This band occurs at 581 cm^{-1} in neon, 561 cm^{-1} in argon, and 565 cm^{-1} in krypton. Other bands, in argon, are observed at 370, 489, and 528 cm^{-1}. These bands are significantly weaker than the absorption at 561 cm^{-1}. The relative intensity of the bands at 370 and 528 cm^{-1} depends on deposition conditions and is attributed to aggregates of CaF_2. Inasmuch as mass spectroscopic studies reveal the absence of polymers in the high-temperature vapor of CaF_2, these aggregates must form during deposition. The band at 489 cm^{-1} parallels the strong feature at 561 cm^{-1} and may be assigned to monomeric CaF_2 although the assignment is far from certain. Based on expectation and on the results of ^{40}Ca and ^{44}Ca isotope experiments, the strong feature at 561 cm^{-1} is assigned to the asymmetric stretching frequency, ν_3, of CaF_2. The 489 cm^{-1} peak, assuming it to be a fundamental, is assigned to ν_1. This observation requires a bent geometry for the molecule. The weak intensity of ν_1, suggests a large apex angle, and calculations based on v_3 isotope shifts give 145° as a value.

$CdCl_2$

Deposition of $CdCl_2$ can be accomplished from a Knudsen furnace at 400–500°C. Infrared spectra of $CdCl_2$ in argon, krypton, and xenon matrices at 20°K show only one band attributable to the monomeric species in the region 280–4000 cm^{-1} (McNamee, 1962). A band assignable to v_3 appears at 420 cm^{-1} in krypton. This band is shifted to 427 cm^{-1} in argon and 411 cm^{-1} in xenon. Other absorptions at 369 and 364 cm^{-1} in krypton have been attributed to dimers.

The data are consistent with a linear structure in the ground state. The dimers are proposed to have a bridge structure, with two chlorine atoms bonded to the Cd atoms. The molecule has a D_{2h} symmetry.

$ClCO$

Chlorine atoms produced through the photolysis of a suitable precursor are found to react with CO in argon matrices with little or no activation energy to give the radical ClCO (Jacox, 1965b). Sources of Cl atoms reported were HCl, Cl_2, Cl_2CO, and $(ClCO)_2$. Hydrogen chloride was observed to give the most satisfactory yield of ClCO. Infrared spectra of the solids show the presence of HCO when HCl is used, and phosgene and oxalyl chloride when the other Cl precursors are used. The vibrational fundamentals of ClCO are observed at 281, 570, and 1880 cm^{-1}. The use of ^{13}CO, and identical results with and without hydrogen present confirm the assignment to ClCO. $Cl^{13}CO$ frequencies in agreement with observed values have been computed using a valence angle of 120° or 135° and bond lengths of $r_{C-Cl} = 0.175$ nm and $r_{C=O} = 0.117$ nm based on the values for phosgene. The computed force constant for the C=O stretching mode is significantly greater than that for phosgene. This leads to the conclusion that the carbonyl bond possesses some triple bond character. Similar behavior is observed in the radical HCO. Some thermodynamic properties of the radical have been calculated using the vibrational fundamentals and the estimated structural parameters. No ultraviolet absorption for ClCO is observed in the region between 250 and 450 nm.

Cl_3

Nelson and Pimentel (Nelson, 1967b) have proposed that bands occurring between 365 and 375 cm^{-1} in the infrared spectra of samples of Kr : Cl_2 mixtures (Kr : $Cl_2 = 50$–100) subjected to a microwave discharge before deposition are due to the radical Cl_3. The bands are explained as the v_3 fundamental of a linear but slightly asymmetric ($C_{\infty v}$) species.

Cl_2O

Two structural isomers of the species Cl_2O have been investigated in the infrared at low temperatures by Rochkind (1965, 1967b). Spectra of symmetric Cl_2O, tabulated as OCl_2, have been recorded in N_2 and argon matrices at 20°K and in the pure solid at 77°K. The pure solid shows all three normal modes; the symmetric stretching vibration, ν_1, and the bending mode, ν_2, are observed in N_2 matrices. The values reported for the fundamentals are: $\nu_1 = 631$ cm^{-1}, $\nu_2 = 296$ cm^{-1}, and $\nu_3 = 671$ cm^{-1}. Under high resolution, the ν_3 band is observed to be a triplet. In a nitrogen matrix, ν_1 occurs at 640 cm^{-1} and ν_3 at 680 cm^{-1}. The frequency ν_1 is shifted to 639 cm^{-1} in argon. The bands are sufficiently sharp in matrices to reveal isotope shifts. In addition to the fundamental frequencies, overtone bands are observed in pure Cl_2O at 965 cm^{-1} ($\nu_2 + \nu_3$), 1294 cm^{-1} ($\nu_1 + \nu_3$), 1328 cm^{-1} ($2\nu_3$), and 1976 cm^{-1} ($3\nu_3$). All these bands show multiplet structure. The assignments are based upon isotope shifts, band contours, intensity and separate observations on rotational structure in the gas phase. The assignments differ from earlier references quoted by Rochkind, particularly as relates to ν_3. The band at 972 cm^{-1} previously assigned as ν_3 is calculated to be due to the combination $\nu_3 + \nu_2$. This reassignment results in a lower value for the force constant associated with the Cl—O stretching mode. This force constant, Kr = 27.5 mdyn per nanometer, correlates with the relatively long Cl—O bond length of 0.170 nm. As a further result, revision of the calculated thermodynamic functions has been carried out on the basis of the new assignment.

When Cl_2O is photolyzed in N_2 in argon matrices, several new bands near 960 cm^{-1} and 375 cm^{-1} occur. Growth plots of these bands indicate that three different molecules are produced. One species proposed to account for some of the bands between 952 and 962 cm^{-1} and 368—377 cm^{-1} is the ClClO molecule, with the nitrosyl halide type structure. The multiplet structure of the absorptions is presumably due to the $^{35}Cl/^{37}Cl$ natural abundance. The magnitudes of isotopic shifts as well as relative intensities are consistent with the assignment to ClClO. The bands at 368–377 cm^{-1} are assigned to the Cl—Cl stretching vibration in the molecule. The bands at 952–962 cm^{-1} are assigned to the Cl—O stretching motion. The bonding in the molecule is apparently quite weak and resembles that in other molecules, such as O_2F, FNO, and $(NO)_2$. The assignments must be considered tentative at best, because ClClO as well as the other species present are as yet uncharacterized. As in most other photolysis experiments, several "impurities" are present in addition to the desired product. Definitely identified as being present are the molecules: N_2O, O_3, and unphotolyzed Cl_2O. In addition, the presence of $(ClO)_2$ is suggested to account for other observed spectral features.

ClO_2

The ground state vibrational frequencies for symmetrical chlorine dioxide, OClO, have been reported in argon and nitrogen matrices at 4° and 20°K, respectively, by Arkell (1967), and Rochkind (1967) as parts of photolysis studies. The observed infrared absorptions are very close to the gas phase values determined from electronic spectra (Herzberg, 1961). ν_1 equals 940 cm^{-1}, ν_2 is 448 cm^{-1}, and ν_3 is 1100 cm^{-1} in argon at 4°K. The ν_1 and ν_3 bands appear as quartets, and ν_2 is a single band. The asymmetric stretching frequency, ν_3, is shifted to 1105 cm^{-1} in N_2 at 20°K. The other frequencies, although presumably observed, were not reported. The corresponding gas phase frequencies occur at 946, 447, and 1111 cm^{-1}.

No report of the UV-visible spectrum of chlorine dioxide was made in the above studies. Norman and Porter (1955) did, however, report a UV absorption of ClO_2 in an isopentane, methylcyclohexane glass at 77°K. In the liquid solution, the absorption consisted of distinct sharp bands between about 430 and 300 nm at 77°K. The structure of the absorption is retained, but appeared almost entirely diffuse. Warm-up and melting of the solvent again led to the original structure. The transition observed is surely $A \leftarrow X\ ^2B_1$. Herzberg lists the symmetry of the upper state as $^2A_2$. Because the purpose of the work was to look for ClO from the photolysis of ClO_2, no specific optical data were presented.

$ClOO$

Asymmetric chlorine dioxide, ClOO, has been proposed as a precursor in the formation of ClO from Cl_2 and O_2 in the gas phase by Porter (1953), but only later trapping experiments provided evidence for the existence of the ClOO molecule. Benson and Anderson (1959) reported indirect and inconclusive evidence for ClOO. Mixtures of measured amounts of Cl_2 and O_2 were subjected to neon UV radiation and then trapped at 77°K. The amount of "trapped" oxygen over and above residual amounts was considered to exist as chlorine oxides. This amount of O_2 was determined by warming the sample to room temperature followed by direct measurement. Oxygen in amounts of 6–8 times of the blank runs was observed. Calculations based on estimated rate constants and activation energies seemingly rule out Cl_2O and OClO as being responsible for the "trapped" oxygen. The results can be interpreted in terms of either ClOO or ClO.

More recently, an infrared study (Arkell, 1967) of the photolysis of Cl_2 and O_2 mixtures and photolysis of OClO has resulted in direct observation of vibrational frequencies assignable to the fundamentals of ClOO. The photolysis of Cl_2, O_2 mixtures alone and in argon matrices at $4°K$ led to a band near 1440 cm^{-1} showing ^{16}O, [18]O isotope shifts appropriate for a O—O stretching vibration. Other fundamentals were too weak for observation in this system. Greater amounts of the desired species were obtained through photolysis of OClO in argon, nitrogen, or oxygen at $4°K$. Intensity versus temperature characteristics of the observed peaks led to the assignment of bands at 373, 407, and 1441 cm^{-1} at $4°K$ in argon as the three fundamentals of ClOO, ν_3, ν_2, and ν_1, respectively. The assignments are strengthened by observation of isotope shifts and normal coordinate calculations. The low frequency, 407 cm^{-1}, for ν_2, and the Cl—O stretching frequency confirm the earlier suggestion of a weak Cl—O bond (Benson, 1957). In addition to the absorptions assigned to ClOO, unassigned bands at 1415 cm^{-1} and 435 cm^{-1} in argon appear during the early part of the photolysis. Isotopic and decay-growth data led to the assignment of these bands to an intermediate designated ClOO* in the formation of ClOO. ClOO* is proposed to be a structural isomer of ClOO, which, because of the solid environment, is prevented from assuming its stable configuration.

Rochkind and Pimentel (1967) while looking at the photolysis products of Cl_2O in N_2, also photolyzed OClO as an impurity in the Cl_2O, and by itself. Two bands that could be correlated to ClO_2 photolysis appeared at 1438 and 1428 cm^{-1}. These were tentatively assigned to the O—O stretching frequency in ClOO. These can be compared to the bands reported by Arkell (1967) in N_2 at 1424 and 1445 cm^{-1}. A band at 1438 cm^{-1} observed by Arkell in argon, however, was not seen in N_2. The two results are therefore not in agreement on this point. The cause of discrepancy between these studies is difficult to determine because of the complexity of the systems on which the observations were made. Both studies report absorptions which cannot be unambiguously assigned. Furthermore, several "impurities" resulting from photolysis fragments and secondary reactions are present. Identified impurities include O_3, N_2O, α—O_2, Cl_2. It appears unlikely that experimental errors are to blame for the differences. It is conceivable that differences in photolytic procedures, wavelengths and temperatures result in the formation of different products. Also not totally ruled out are site effects.

$CoCl_2$

Matrix isolation spectra of $CoCl_2$ in the ultraviolet visible and infrared regions have been reported (Clifton, 1969; DeKock, 1968; K. Thompson, 1968; Jacox, 1969b). The molecule can be deposited by direct vaporization of the solid. The ligand field model gives a $^4\Phi_g$ ground state for the gaseous species. Strong transitions at 3.08, 3.20, 3.37, 3.50, and 3.64 μm^{-1} and weaker transitions at 3.95, 4.20, and 4.58 μm^{-1} were reported by DeKock and Gruen at 4.2°K, but only the 3.37 region, the 3.50 band, and the weak absorption at 4.20 μm^{-1} were observed by Jacox and Milligan at 14°K. The 3.37 μm^{-1} system appears as a series of bands with a vibrational spacing of about 230 cm^{-1} and is assigned to a progression in ν_1 of the upper state. The number of transitions observed is not consistent with the number expected from the ligand field model for a $^4\Phi_g$ ground state. Therefore, either the model, or the state designation or both may be in error. Clifton and Gruen (1969a) have obtained fluorescence spectra in argon and nitrogen.

CoCl$_2$ gives two bands in the infrared. A multiplet feature at 490 cm^{-1} corresponds to the asymmetric stretching vibration, ν_3, with the strongest component corresponding to $^{59}Co^{35}Cl_2$ at 493 cm^{-1} in argon. The bending mode ν_2 occurs at 95 cm^{-1} in argon. The frequency ν_3 shows a heavy atom effect, shifting from 493 to 484 to 468 cm^{-1} from argon to krypton to xenon.

CrCl$_2$

The ultraviolet and infrared spectra of CrCl$_2$ isolated in argon at 14°K have been reported by Jacox and Milligan (1969b). Samples of CrCl$_2$ can be obtained by either direct vaporization of the solid or via the reaction of chlorine with a hot chromium surface at 1035–1095°K immediately prior to deposition. Samples were observed to strongly absorb at wavelengths shorter than about 260 nm. Thick deposits show, in addition, a weak absorption near 307 nm. Both absorptions appear unstructured. The gas phase systems reported at 3.623 μm^{-1} and 4.960 μm^{-1} (DeKock, 1966) do not appear in the matrix.

The infrared spectrum, down to 250 cm^{-1}, shows a strong complex group of bands near 490 cm^{-1} and several weak absorptions near 470 cm^{-1}. The former agree well with the spectrum expected from the natural isotopic abundance for the asymmetric stretching frequency ν_3 of a linear CrCl$_2$. The latter bands are attributed to site effects. No evidence for a frequency assignable to ν_1 was obtained.

FCO

Fluorine atoms have been observed to react with CO at 4, 14, and 20°K to give sufficient quantities of FCO for spectroscopic investigation (Milligan, 1965d). In addition, photolysis of F$_2$CO or HFCO in CO or Ar gives FCO. Molecules known to give fluorine atoms on photolysis are t$-$N$_2$F$_2$, OF$_2$, and NF$_2$.

An extensive series of absorptions occurring between 220.0 and 340.0 nm can be attributed to the radical FCO. Of the forty-three bands reported, eighteen occur with a regular spacing of 650 cm^{-1} and are believed to constitute at least a portion of one progression in the upper state bending mode. (Not totally ruled out is an assignment to the $C-F$ stretching mode, but the bending mode is predicted.) The bands are all relatively broad, with measured half-widths of from 250 to 400 cm^{-1}. Most of the intense peaks are accompanied by weaker secondary peaks 240 cm^{-1} toward the blue. It is not clear whether this secondary sequence is intrinsic or constitutes multiple sites.

The three ground state vibrational fundamentals of the FCO radical in CO matrices occur at 1855 cm^{-1}, ν_1, 1018 cm^{-1}, ν_3, and 626 cm^{-1} for ν_2. ^{13}C and ^{18}O isotopic substitution coupled with the wide variety of circumstances in which these bands were observed confirm the assignments. Force constants and thermodynamic functions have been calculated assuming a valence angle of 135° and bond lengths of 0.118 nm and 0.134 nm for $C-O$ and $C-F$, respectively.

FNC

Milligan and Jacox (1967a) have reported experimental evidence that indicates the formation of the species XNC, where X = F, Cl, Br, during the vacuum ultraviolet photolysis of matrix-isolated halogen cyanides. The data are incomplete, particularly with reference to the lower frequencies, so that the existence of these molecules is not yet proved. Infrared features which are consistent with assignment to these species are given below:

	(C$-$N stretch)	(X$-$N stretch)
FNC	2123	928
ClNC	2074	—
BrNC	2067	—

FeCl$_2$

FeCl$_2$ can be isolated in argon matrices either by direct vaporization of the solid or by the reaction of chlorine with hot iron metal surfaces at 1085°K, followed by condensation on a cooled target (DeKock, 1968; K. Thompson, 1968; Jacox, 1969b).

In the spectral range 200–550 nm, several broad, structureless bands have been observed. At 4°K, band maxima occur at 3.750, 3.980 (shoulder), 4.160, 4.410 (shoulder), and 4.760 μm^{-1} (DeKock, 1968). At 14°K the bands are apparently less well resolved and the spectrum appears as a broad peak at 4.170 μm^{-1} superimposed on an increasing absorption below 4.000 μm^{-1}. Ligand field models predict a $^5\Delta_g$ ground state for FeCl$_2$ and five allowed one-electron transitions to $^5\Pi_u$, $^5\Delta_u$, and $^5\Phi_u$ states (DeKock, 1968). Assignment to transitions is not, however, possible on the basis of the data.

Infrared observations yield directly 88 and 493 cm^{-1} for the ν_2 and ν_3 frequencies of the molecule. The asymmetric stretching frequency, ν_3, shifts to 447 cm^{-1} in N_2, an unexpectedly large shift. This has been rationalized in terms of N_2—$FeCl_2$ interactions. All evidence favors a linear ground state for the molecule.

GeF_2

Infrared vibrational spectra of GeF_2 have been observed in neon and argon at 4.2°K following direct deposition of the vapor from a Knudsen furnace (Hastie, 1968). The molecule can be prepared from GeF_4 and Ge at 300°C. The spectrum shows several groups of bands between 500 and 850 cm^{-1}. The general appearance is the same in neon and argon; however, the band widths in neon are less than in argon. Two vibrational fundamentals are observed; ν_1 at 655 cm^{-1} and ν_3 at 685 cm^{-1} in neon. These bands shift to 648 and 676 cm^{-1} in argon. The bands both show fine structure due to the germanium isotopes, and the above frequencies are for the strongest component. Matrix bands are shifted from the gas phase by about 8 cm^{-1} and 15 cm^{-1} to the red in neon and argon, respectively. The assignments are based on relative intensities and the computed bond angle for the molecules, 94°.

Other bands near 600 cm^{-1} and 670 cm^{-1} are assigned to dimeric and polymeric species. A group of bands near 800 cm^{-1} is assigned to unreacted GeF_4. Since dimers and polymers exist in equilibrium with the monomer in the vapor phase, their appearance does not necessarily occur from poor isolation.

HC_2

The species HC_2 has been shown by ESR to be produced when acetylene is photolyzed with vacuum ultraviolet radiation in an argon matrix (Cochran, 1964). Very little, however, is known about the optical spectrum of the species. Milligan et al. (1967) have reported one vibrational fundamental of 1848 cm^{-1} assignable to HC_2 when mixtures of acetylene and argon or nitrogen are photolyzed with microwave or radiofrequency excited H_2 or Kr discharge lamps. These sources are rich in vacuum UV light. Deuterium and ^{13}C substitution confirms the assignment of the IR band at 1848 cm^{-1} to HC_2. Observations on the band indicate that HC_2 is stable to further photolysis with wavelength greater than 200 nm. Brabson (1965) suggests that a band at 405.4 nm, observed when carbon vapors are trapped in argon, may be due to HC_2.

HCCl

The A ($^1A''$) ← X ($^1A'$) transition of the radical HCCl in the gas phase at 550–820 nm has been reported by Merer and Travis (1966). Jacox and Milligan (1967) have prepared HCCl in argon and nitrogen matrices at 14°K through the reaction of carbon atoms with HCl. The carbon atoms are produced by the photolysis of N_3CN.

The A ← X absorption system is also observed in the solid, appearing as a series of bands between 560 and 750 nm. This observation confirms that the gas phase lower state is the ground state of the molecule. These bands are relatively broad and weak and appear, in argon, to be shifted with respect to the gas phase by about 250 cm^{-1} toward the blue, but if the gas phase numbering is wrong, a red shift of 640 cm^{-1} could also explain the results. Six of the bands can be correlated closely with the gas phase values. At 1.5000 μm^{-1}, unassigned features appear between the principal bands. The bands show vibrational perturbations, as in the gas phase. The observed frequency is ∼ 860 cm^{-1} corresponding most likely to v'_2.

In the infrared, two fundamental vibrational modes are observed. These occur at 815 cm^{-1} for v_3 and 1201 cm^{-1} for v_2 in argon. The results of ^{13}C and D isotope substitutions are consistent with the assignment of these bands to HCCl. In addition to HCCl, bands at 753 and 1270 cm^{-1} attributable to CH_2Cl_2 are observed. These bands undergo considerable increases in intensity when diffusion is allowed to occur. The CH_2Cl_2 presumably results from the reaction of HCCl and HCl with little or no activation energy.

HCF

Vacuum ultraviolet photolysis of Ar : CH_3F or N_2 : CH_3F yields HCF (Jacox, 1969a). A series of four related bands between 470 and 546 nm correspond well with the most prominent gas phase band heads, reported for HCF (Merer, 1966). The argon matrix shifts are approximately 30 cm^{-1} toward the blue from the gas phase bands of the A ($^1A''$) — X ($^1A'$) transition. The bands are assigned to the progression $(0,v'_2,0) - (0,0,0)$ and yield a value for v'_2 of about 1010 cm^{-1}. Satellite bands associated with the two strongest bands at approximately 110 cm^{-1} toward the blue are attributed to site effects.

HCF in argon shows an infrared band at 1182 cm^{-1} which can be assigned to v''_3 of HCF on the basis of ^{13}C and D substitution. A band at 1405 cm^{-1} is assigned to v''_2. The latter assignment is based on the known v''_2 derived from the gas phase by Merer (1966). Additional absorptions at 2918 and 3262 cm^{-1} both in the C—H stretching region show behavior expected for a fundamental of HCF, but an assignment is not possible on the basis of the data. Force constant calculations indicate a C—F band somewhat stronger than normal approaching the strength observed for CF.

HCO

The formyl radical, HCO has been produced via the photolysis of HI, HBr, or H_2S in CO matrices at 14–20°K (Ewing, 1960; Milligan, 1964a) by condensation of the products of a discharge through methane–argon–oxygen mixtures (Robinson, 1958) or by condensation of the products of the reaction of atomic oxygen with C_2H_2 (McCarty, 1959). The corresponding DCO can be produced using the appropriately deuterated precursor. More recently, Milligan and Jacox (1969a) have succeeded in preparing HCO in argon matrices by reaction of H atoms with CO, using as precursors HCl, H_2O, and CH_4, all of which photolyze in the vacuum ultraviolet to produce H atoms.

The UV and visible spectrum consists of a series of broad bands between 510 and 670 nm corresponding to the $^2A''\mathit{\Pi} - {}^2A'$ gas phase system (Johns et al., 1963; Ramsay, 1953; Herzberg, 1955) and a complicated series of absorptions between 210 and 260 nm corresponding to the hydrocarbon flame bands (see Vaidya, 1964; Dixon, 1967). The former spectrum consists of a progression in v_2' with a vibrational spacing of about 800 cm^{-1}. It involves the ground state, in which HCO is bent, and a linear upper state. The matrix bands, in CO, appear shifted by about 220 cm^{-1} to the blue from the gas phase bands. The shift is about 400 cm^{-1} in krypton. The origin is not observed, so the assignments can be considered to be only tentative. The lowest energy band reported in the matrix corresponds to the (0,8,0) — (0,0,0) band. The "hydrocarbon flame bands" show simultaneous progressions in the upper state bending and C—O stretching vibrations in line with expectation from the gas phase rotational analysis by Dixon. The matrix spectrum leads to a new value for the origin of the transition.

HNC

Milligan and Jacox (1963, 1967b) have reported the infrared spectrum of the HNC molecule prepared by the vacuum ultraviolet photolysis of HCN in argon and nitrogen at 14°K and from the prolonged photolysis of methyl azide, CH_3N_3, in argon at 4°K.

The three fundamental vibrations of the molecule are observed and appear at 477, 2029, and 3620 cm^{-1} in argon at high dilution. The presence of nitrogen in neighboring lattice sites apparently perturbs the (N—H) stretching frequency and the HNC bending mode of the molecule. Frequencies obtained at low M/R's or in N_2 matrices are shifted to vary significantly between 478 and 538 cm^{-1} for the bending mode and 3567 and 3620 cm^{-1} for the (N—H) stretching frequency.

Isotope shifts for ^{13}C, D, and ^{15}N substituted species are consistent with the assignments. HNC is predicted (Walsh, 1953) to possess a linear ground state, and the computed isotope shifts suggest such a geometry. The computed force constants indicate that the carbon–nitrogen bond is a triple bond.

No ultraviolet visible transitions have been observed. The photolysis of HCN does, however, lead to sufficient CN concentrations for the observation of the (0,0) and (0,1) bands of the CN B $^2\Sigma^+ \leftarrow$ X $^2\Sigma^+$ system at 385 nm.

HNF

Jacox and Milligan (1967a) have produced the radical HNF by the reaction of fluorine atoms with NH in argon matrices at 14°K. Fluorine atoms can be produced by the photolysis of F_2 or N_2F_2 and NH is prepared by the photolysis of HN_3. The wavelength dependence of the process suggests that both F and NH are required for HNF formation. Other species known to be present include NF, NF_2, NF_3, HNF_2, HF, NH, N_2H_2, as well as precursors.

HNF shows an electronic transition between 390 and 500 nm consisting of a progression of six bands in v_2' with a frequency of 1033 cm^{-1}. Walsh (1953) suggested that the progression is caused by the bending mode of the transition $^2A' \leftarrow {}^2A''$. The origin of the system appears at 20,340 cm^{-1}. The same system for DNF originates at 20,360 cm^{-1} and shows a progression with a frequency of 798 cm^{-1}.

Two vibrational fundamentals for HNF are observed in the infrared. The N—F stretching mode occurs at 1000 cm^{-1} and the HNF bending mode at 1432 cm^{-1}. The N—H stretching mode should occur between 2700 and 4000 cm^{-1}, but it is not observed. Presumably this mode is very weak. Deuterium and ^{15}N isotope shifts confirm the identification. The HNF bond angle is about 105°, in analogy with NH_2 and NF_2. Force constants and thermodynamic properties have been computed.

HNO

The HNO molecule was among the first trapped free radicals (Robinson, 1958a,b). It was obtained as a by-product following condensation of the products of a discharge through hydrazine, argon mixtures containing water as an impurity. Shortly thereafter, the sustained photolysis of nitromethane and methyl nitrite in argon was found to give observable amounts also of HNO (H. W. Brown, 1958). Subsequently, other systems have been found to give HNO, often as the result of impurities (Robinson, 1958; Harvey, 1959; Baldeschwieler, 1960; Milligan, 1962). Of particular note is its formation in the photolysis of HN_3 in CO_2 (Milligan, 1962) via the reaction of NH with CO_2. This system gives a moderately clean sample, spectroscopically.

Eight bands of HNO are observed in the visible spectrum originating at 13,120 cm^{-1} and extending to 17,400 cm^{-1}. Only the first three have significant intensity. These bands correlated well with the gas phase bands initially reported by Dalby (1958). The bands are assigned to the transition $^1A'' \leftarrow X\,^1A_1$ and involve simultaneous progressions in v'_2 and v'_3. The observed frequencies are $v'_2 = 1422$ cm^{-1} and $v'_3 = 982$ cm^{-1}. The matrix bands are shifted from the gas phase bands by about 54 cm^{-1} toward the red.

The infrared spectrum of HNO has been reported by several workers (H. W. Brown, 1958; Harvey, 1959; Milligan, 1962). Agreement in regard to the v_2 and v_3 fundamentals, the molecular bending mode, and the N=O stretching frequencies is in all cases excellent, and the values observed in argon are: $v_2 = 1570$ cm^{-1} and $v_3 = 1110$ cm^{-1}. The use of deuterium and oxygen isotopes conforms to these assignments. There is, however, a discrepancy regarding the value for v_1, the H—N stretching mode. Brown and Pimentel (1958) observed a band at 3300 cm^{-1} which they tentatively assigned to HCO; Milligan et al. (1962d) reported a value of 3380 cm^{-1} for v_1 in CO$_2$ and N$_2$O, whereas Harvey and Brown (1959) reported a value of 3592 cm^{-1} in argon. In all cases, deuterium substitution has been used. Deuterium shifts are all within reasonable limits. There is no aspect in any of the experiments that would tend to reject the observations. All systems are complex, however, and contain species other than HNO. The value reported by Harvey and Brown of 3592 cm^{-1} does correlate best with the gas phase value, 3596 cm^{-1} (Herzberg, 1967).

The high frequency observed for v_2 indicates a molecular angle of 110°. This is in good agreement with the 109° from the gas phase (Herzberg, 1967).

HNS

Irradiation of SiH$_3$N$_3$ in argon near 4°K with a high pressure mercury lamp is reported to produce infrared observable quantities of the species HNSi (Ogilvie, 1966). Frequencies assigned to the molecule are $v_1 = 3583$ cm^{-1}, $v_2 = 523$ cm^{-1}, and $v_3 = 1198$ cm^{-1}. Calculated and observed isotope shifts with deuterium are consistent. The structure is linear and a large k_2 force constant is taken as an indication of a singlet ground state. The (N—H) stretching frequency, v_1, is identical with the equivalent mode in the species HNC in argon, containing nitrogen (Milligan, 1963a, 1967e).

HO$_2$

Milligan and Jacox (1963b, 1964d) have succeeded in observing the infrared vibrational fundamentals of the species HO$_2$ following the reaction of H atoms, produced in photolysis of HBr or HI, with oxygen in argon matrices at 4°K. Yields of the radical are apparently greater when HI is used compared to HBr. Bands attributable to HO$_2$ are observed at 1101,

1389, and 3414 cm^{-1}. The use of ^{18}O and D isotopes as well as comparisons with spectra of H_2O_2 lead to the assignments $\nu_1 = 3414$, $\nu_2 = 1389$, and $\nu_3 = 1101$ cm^{-1}. The spectrum indicates that the oxygen atoms are non-equivalent, casting doubt on an isosceles triangle structure. The data is insufficient to permit the calculation of an accurate value for the molecular angle. At wavelengths < 220 nm, HO_2 appears to also undergo photolysis.

Giguère (1954) had earlier assigned a band observed at 1305 cm^{-1} to HO_2 following condensation of the products of a discharge through water vapor. He subsequently showed (1956) that the band was due to N_2O_3 produced from nitrogen as an impurity.

HOBr

Photolysis of argon, HBr, and O_3 at 4.2°K yields HOBr (Schwager, 1967) presumably by the reaction $O_3 + HBr + h\nu \rightarrow HOBr + O_2$. No evidence for intermediates such as OH is obtained so that a detailed mechanism is not available.

All three fundamental vibrational frequencies are observed. For H^{16}OBr these appear at: $\nu_1 = 3590$ cm^{-1}, $\nu_2 = 1164$ cm^{-1} and $\nu_3 = 626$ cm^{-1}. The DOBr counterpart bands appear at 2153, 854, and 621, respectively. Oxygen-18 isotopic substitution in both HOBr and DOBr has been used to assist in the assignments. The molecular bond angle was estimated to be 110° for the calculation of force constants and isotopic frequencies.

HOCl

Similarly to HOBr, HOCl has been prepared in argon matrices via the photolysis of Ar—HCl—O_3 mixtures at 4.2°K (Schwager, 1967). The vibrational fundamentals of HOCl, ν_1, ν_2, and ν_3 appear at 3581, 1239, and 729 cm^{-1}, respectively. Oxygen-18 isotopic substitution was used to verify assignments and to calculate force constants. The molecular bond angle is 113°, as determined from the gas phase data (Herzberg, 1951).

HgCl$_2$

The infrared spectrum of $HgCl_2$ in argon, krypton, and xenon has been investigated by McNamee (1962) following condensation of $HgCl_2$ vapor from a Knudsen furnace. Only one vibrational mode, ν_3, the asymmetric stretching frequency, is observed. This absorption appears as a doublet in all matrices and at 411 and 407 cm^{-1} in krypton. The splitting is consistent with the isotope shift for ^{35}Cl, ^{37}Cl, but the expected intensities are not. For this reason, the assignments of the subbands to isotopic species is tentative. A moderately intense band appearing at 402 cm^{-1} in krypton is assigned to dimers.

KrF$_2$

Infrared absorptions at 580 cm^{-1} and 236 cm^{-1} occurring when 1 : 70 : 220 mixtures of F$_2$: Kr : Ar are condensed at 20°K and photolyzed with an AH-4 medium pressure mercury lamp, have been assigned to ν_3 and ν_2 respectively of the molecule KrF$_2$ (Turner, 1963a,b). At higher F$_2$: Kr ratios, these bands shift to 575 and 245 cm^{-1}. The shifts are believed to be due to aggregations. Force constants derived for the molecule indicate that the bond energies are similar to those in XeF$_2$.

Li$_2$O

Condensation of the vapors from solid Li$_2$O with krypton under conditions where the vapor consists predominantly of Li$_2$O yields infrared bands at 112 and 987 cm^{-1} assignable to ν_2 and ν_3 of the molecule (Seshadri, 1966; White, 1963b). Substitution of ^{6}Li in the molecule shifts the bands to 118 cm^{-1} and 1029 cm^{-1}, respectively. Isotope ratios are consistent with a linear structure for the species, but the accuracy of measurements is not sufficient to make the conclusion unambiguous. It suffices, however, to exclude large deviations from linearity. On the basis of force constant data, a value for ν_1 of 685 cm^{-1} is calculated.

LiO$_2$

Low frequency infrared bands at 231 and 685 cm^{-1} appearing in the spectrum of matrix isolated Li$_2$O vapors under conditions where the predominant vapor species is Li$_2$O$_2$ have been assigned to the ν_2 and ν_3 fundamentals of the species LiO$_2$ (White, 1963b; Seshadri, 1966). Isotope substitution indicates the presence of only one lithium atom in the species, and calculated isotope ratios are consistent with the assignment to LiO$_2$. Best fit is obtained when a symmetrical molecule with an angle of 170° is assumed. It is conceivable that the molecule is linear. A calculated value for ν_1 of 340 cm^{-1} is reported.

LiON

Andrews and Pimentel (1966) report the appearance of new infrared bands when codeposition of lithium, nitric oxide, and argon are made at 15° and 4°K. The isotope shifts with ^{6}Li, ^{18}O, and ^{15}N are consistent with their assignment to a triatomic species containing one each Li, O, and N atoms. The observed isotope shifts and a normal coordinate analysis favor the molecular arrangement LiON in which the molecule is bent with an angle of 100 ± 10°. The observed frequencies for the natural isotopic species, assuming the structure LiON, are: ν_1, the NO stretching motion, 1352 cm^{-1}; ν_2, the bending mode, 333 cm^{-1}; and ν_3, the LiO stretching frequency, 650 cm^{-1}. The latter is the strongest of the three bands. The NO stretching frequency suggests a bond order of about 1.7. The bonding of the species is not clear. The molecular arrangement is not unambiguous and must be considered tentative.

MgF_2

Magnesium difluoride can be deposited by direct vaporization from a Knudsen furnace at temperatures in the range 1500–1575°K (Snelson, 1966; Mann, 1967). The infrared spectrum of MgF_2 in krypton shows several bands between 200 and 900 cm^{-1}. Bands at 478, 242, and 837 cm^{-1} are assigned to ν_1, ν_2, and ν_3, respectively, of the most abundant species of the molecule. Isotope shifts for ^{25}Mg and ^{26}Mg are in agreement with the assignments. The direct observation of ν_1 requires that the molecule be bent. The apex angle giving the closest agreement between observed and calculated isotope shifts is in the range 145°–160°, the most probable value being 150°–155°. Spectra in neon and argon appear essentially the same, but the frequencies are shifted as expected.

Other bands occurring in the spectrum are assigned to other species. A band at 740 cm^{-1} is assigned to MgF and bands near 450 and 480 cm^{-1} are assigned to polymeric species.

$MnCl_2$

$MnCl_2$ can be deposited for matrix spectral studies either by direct vaporization of the solid or via the reaction of chlorine with manganese metal surfaces at 995–1085°K (DeKock, 1968; K. Thompson, 1968; Jacox, 1969b).

The UV-visible spectrum of $MnCl_2$ in argon gives three broad unstructured bands at 4.39, 4.57, and 5.00 μm^{-1}. $MnCl_2$ is linear and is suggested to have a $^6\Sigma_g^+$ ground state (DeKock, 1968). The transitions may involve upper $^6\Sigma_u^+$ and $^6\Pi_u$ states, but no definite assignments have been made. The asymmetric stretching frequency, ν_3, and the bending mode, ν_2, appear in an argon matrix at 477 and 83 cm^{-1}, respectively.

NCN

The free radical NCN has been prepared by the photolysis of cyanogen azide N_3CN in a variety of different solvents. IR observations yielded two of the three vibrational fundamentals. The third was then deduced from the first two. The gas phase bands at 329 nm (Herzberg and Travis, 1964) and a new UV absorption system between 240 and 300 nm were observed by Milligan (1965a, 1966).

The gas phase rotational analysis of the (0,0,0) band of the 329 nm system shows the molecule to be a linear symmetric molecule with a $^3\Sigma_g^-$ ground state (Herzberg, 1964).

Cyanogen azide, N_3CN, has two distinct UV absorptions at 275 nm ($E = 103$) and 220 nm ($E = 2157$) (Marsh, 1964), and irradiation of the molecule in either band leads to photolytic cleavage to give NCN and N_2. Because of the characteristics of the absorption, the 228.8 nm line of a cadmium lamp has proved to be the best photolysis source for the production of NCN. Its yield is, for all practical purposes, quantitative. If light of 250 nm is used, NCN itself will also photolyze, but photolysis apparently does not occur with the 228.8 nm cadmium line.

The 329 nm gas phase $^3\Pi_u \leftarrow {}^3\Sigma_g^-$ absorption system is, in the solid, shifted to 330.4 nm in nitrogen and to 334.4 nm in argon. This system normally appears as a broad single nonstructured band. In solids containing large amounts of NCN, an additional band appears at about 1140 cm^{-1} toward the blue. Considering this band as belonging to the transition, the frequency of 1140 cm^{-1} is assigned to v_1 of the $^3\Pi_u$ state.

In addition to the $^3\Pi_u - {}^3\Sigma_g^-$ transition, a second and previously unreported transition occurs. This system consists of a series of bands extending from 300 nm to 240 nm and separated by about 1040 cm^{-1}. Each major absorption is accompanied by a weaker second component located 35 cm^{-1} toward the blue in argon, or 50 cm^{-1} toward the blue in N_2. The exact cause of the substructure is not known. The 1040 cm^{-1} vibrational frequency, assignable to v_1', and the number of vibrational bands observed, about 10, suggest that the upper state is also linear and involves an appreciable change in the carbon-nitrogen bond length. Using the arguments of Walsh (1953a) the transition is assigned to B $^3\Sigma_u^- \leftarrow$ X $^3\Sigma_g^-$.

Infrared observations give directly the frequencies 423 cm^{-1} for v_2'' and 1475 cm^{-1} for v_3''. Samples containing large amounts of NCN also show a band at 2672 cm^{-1} which is assignable to the combination band ($v_1 + v_3$). This then gives a value of v_1'' equal to 1197 cm^{-1}. The use of the isotopes ^{13}C and ^{15}N supports all assignments. Force constants and thermodynamic functions for the species have been calculated. The C—N stretching force constant is near that of a carbon-nitrogen double bond.

Small amounts of NCN have also been reported from the reaction of CCO produced from the vacuum ultraviolet photolysis of C_3O_2 in N_2 (Moll, 1966).

NCO

Robinson (1958) and McCarty (1959) tentatively observed a band near 440 nm in the condensation products of a methane-argon discharge containing nitrogen and oxygen impurities. They analyzed it as $(0,0,0) \leftarrow (0,0,0)$ band of the A $^2\Sigma^+ \leftarrow$ X $^2\Pi$ transition of NCO. This band was shifted by about

70 cm^{-1} toward the blue from the gas phase band (Holland, 1958). In light of more recent work (Milligan, 1967c), this assignment of Robinson and McCarty is questionable. However, there is no doubt now that NCO has been isolated in low temperature matrices.

Two transitions of the radical have been observed (Milligan, 1967c) in neon, argon, nitrogen, and carbon monoxide matrices at 4.2 and 14°K. The first of these is the A $^2\Sigma^+$ ← X $^2\Pi$ transition originating near 2.28 μm^{-1}. The bands correlate with the more recent gas phase data of Dixon (1960a,b). The matrix spectra are shifted with respect to the gas phase with neon showing a − 38 cm^{-1} shift, argon − 64 cm^{-1}, N_2 + 156 cm^{-1}, and CO + 119 cm^{-1} for the (0,0,0) band. Band half-widths vary from 40 cm^{-1} in neon to 500 cm^{-1} in CO. All three frequencies for the upper state (A $^2\Sigma^+$) can be derived from the spectra. They are, in neon $v'_1 = 2325$ cm^{-1}, $v'_2 = 687$ cm^{-1}, and $v'_3 = 1270$ cm^{-1}. The second system observed is the B $^2\Pi$ ← X $^2\Pi$ system with its origin near 31,600 cm^{-1}. The matrix bands are shifted from the gas phase bands by − 122 cm^{-1}, − 301 cm^{-1}, − 400 cm^{-1}, and − 768 cm^{-1} in neon, argon, nitrogen, and CO, respectively. Vibrational frequencies observed for the B $^2\Pi$ state are approximately 2300 for v'_1 and 1040 cm^{-1} for v'_3. The B ← X transition is a much more extensive band system than the A ← X transition. Nearly 40 bands are observed in neon for B ← X vs. 5 bands for the A ← X system.

Analysis of the spectra is complicated by an appreciable Renner effect for the NCO ground state. In addition, the molecule has a large spin splitting (Dixon, 1960). As a result, transitions are expected from the $^2\Pi_{3/2}$ level only, at 14°K when paramagnetic impurities are present to depopulate the $^2\Pi_{1/2}$ level.

Infrared observation on NCO produced by several reactions has led to the assignment of all three vibrational fundamentals of the ground state. These appear at 1275, 487, and 1922 cm^{-1}, respectively, for v_1, v_2, and v_3. The assignments are consistent with ^{13}C and ^{15}N isotopic substitution. Force constant calculations indicate that the CO bond is somewhat stronger than the CN bond.

Continued photolysis of NCO at wavelengths near 254 nm led to disappearance of the molecule. It is concluded that NCO photolyzes to give N atoms and CO. No evidence for the species with atomic arrangement CNO was obtained.

NH_2

The electronic spectrum of the radical HN_2 has been carefully investigated in argon matrices at 4.2 and 14°K and to a lesser extent in Kr and N_2

(Robinson, 1958a–d, 1959, 1962b; Keyser, 1960; Milligan, 1965c). NH_2 appears following discharges through nearly any system containing nitrogen and hydrogen, for example, N_2H_4 in argon, following vacuum UV photolysis of NH_3 in argon, or via photolysis of HN_3 in matrices. The spectrum in argon appears as an extensive series of 67 sharp band absorptions between 345 nm and 790 nm. The bandwidth of many of the "lines" is less than 3 cm⁻¹, suggesting that the radicals are situated in equivalent, and possibly, well ordered lattice sites. In N_2 the absorption appears as a series of broad features with bandwidths of nearly 100 cm⁻¹. The principal transition involved is A $^2A_1(\Pi)$ ← X $^2B_1$.

Clearly visible in the spectrum in argon are transitions involving rotational levels as well as vibrational levels. This has led to the conclusion that NH_2 undergoes nearly free end-over-end rotation in the matrix. In the ground state of the molecule the four lowest rotational levels are: O''_0 at 0.00 cm⁻¹; $1''_{-1}$ at 21.11 cm⁻¹; $1''_0$ at 31.87 cm⁻¹, and $1''_{+1}$ at 36.65 cm⁻¹. At 4.2°K, approximately 99.9% of the molecules are in the lowest rotational level, O''_0. As a result, the strongest features in the absorption spectrum involve transitions from this level (Ramsay, 1957). The matrix spectrum correlates very closely with the gas phase spectrum (Ramsay, 1957; Dressler, 1959) and shows a progression in the excited state bending mode $(0,v'_2,0)$ ← $(0,0,0)$. Only those bands where v'_2 is even are observed with significant intensity, and the first strong band is assigned to 0,4,0. The alternating appearance of the spectrum results from the fact that odd v'_3 levels cannot combine with O''_0.

The upper state of NH_2 apparently consists of vibronic levels with Π vibronic bands for even v'_2 and Δ subbands for odd v'_2. Robinson (1959) has given a tentative rotational assignment for the strongest bands observed. The results of Milligan and Jacox (1965c) are in excellent agreement with the results of Robinson. Many of the weaker lines observed can be attributed to transitions from excited ground state rotational levels such as $1''_0$. The observed intensities are somewhat greater than expected on the basis of thermal distribution alone. The excess population can be rationalized in terms of optical pumping via either absorption followed by emission to levels other than O''_0 or via direct absorption of and transitions between rotational levels.

In addition to the principal progression, bands attributable to $(1,6,0)$ — $(0,0,0)$ and $(1,8,0)$ — $(0,0,0)$ transitions are observed. These transitions arise via Fermi resonance with the $(0,10,0)$ and $(0,12,0)$ band, respectively. Measurements of the relative intensities have led to calculated values for the interaction constants of $W_{1,6,0} = 72$ cm⁻¹ and $W_{1,8,0} = 76$ cm⁻¹. These values are in excellent agreement with the gas phase values of Dressler (1959).

An extrapolated origin of about 1.0200 μm^{-1} is obtained, and a vibrational frequency v'_2 of 680 cm^{-1}; because the origin region is not observed, these values are highly tentative.

Two of the three ground state vibrational fundamentals of NH_2 have been directly measured by Milligan (1965e). The use of ^{15}N and D isotopes confirmed the assignment of bands appearing at 1499 cm^{-1} and 3220 cm^{-1} in argon following the vacuum UV photolysis of NH_3 to v_2 and v_3, respectively, of NH_2. These results contradict an earlier tentative assignment of 1290 cm^{-1} for v_2 (Becker, 1957). The complexity of the absorption pattern near 1499 cm^{-1} is consistent with the conclusion that NH_2 is free to rotate in the solid.

N_2O

Several ultraviolet absorption systems of N_2O have been reported, both for the pure solid and in neon, argon, and krypton matrices over the temperature range 1.5–63°K (Sibleyras, 1968; Romand, 1952; Granier-Mayence, 1953). The A system, appearing in the gas phase near 3.8500 μm^{-1} appears in the solid at 20°K also as a broad, structureless feature (half-width of 3000 cm^{-1}) but reportedly shifted toward the blue by 1500 cm^{-1}. The gas phase system B at 5.9540 μm^{-1} appears in the solid shifted by 2500 cm^{-1} toward the blue. This system shows vibrational structure; however, the origin of the system is not observed, and the upper state vibrational frequency cannot be deduced with accuracy. An average spacing of 590 cm^{-1} is observed for those bands appearing in the solid. The progression appears to be in v'_2.

The B band as well as four other systems further in the vacuum ultraviolet are observed in matrices (Sibleyras, 1968). The B system shows more extensive vibrational structure than in the pure solid. Fifteen bands are reported in argon. As in the pure solid all transitions are reported to have very large gas to matrix shifts varying from 2000 to 5400 cm^{-1}. The transitions can be correlated to the gas phase systems B, C, D, E, and F (Hermann, 1970) appearing at 5.9590, 6.8950, 7.7900, 8.4900, and 8.6800 μm^{-1}, respectively. Bands C and D are both continua.

Infrared spectra give the values for v_1 and v_3 of the ground state molecules as 2222 and 1290 cm^{-1}, respectively, in nitrogen (DeMore, 1959c).

$NiCl_2$

The matrix spectrum of $NiCl_2$ in argon consists of at least six distinct electronic transitions in the region from 260 to 500 nm (Milligan, 1965e; Gruen, 1968; Jacox, 1969a; K. R. Thompson, 1968; DeKock, 1968). Structural progressions are observed with origins near 2.02, 2.13, 2.05, 3.35, and 3.69 μm^{-1} as well as a broad unstructured band at 2.12 μm^{-1}. In addition a very weak structureless feature at 4.15 μm^{-1} has been reported by DeKock and Gruen. The system appearing at 3.05 μm^{-1} is the most intense, with the bands at 3.35 and 3.69 μm^{-1} somewhat weaker. The bands at 2.02, 2.13, and 2.12 μm^{-1} are observed only after long depositions. The observed vibrational frequencies for each of the three bands, 3.05, 3.35, and 3.69 μm^{-1}, are near 250 cm^{-1}, the individual average values being 256, 249, and 283 cm^{-1}, respectively. These values are assigned to ν'_1 of the excited state. The system at 2.02 μm^{-1} shows four bands with an average spacing of 114 cm^{-1}. This frequency is unassigned.

The band at 2.13 μm^{-1} shows a vibrational spacing of 350 cm^{-1}, also assigned as a ν_1 frequency. This transition also shows fine structure, with three apparent parallel progressions. The second most intense features are shifted with respect to the strongest by $-$ 95 cm^{-1}, while the least intense bands appear at approximately 55 cm^{-1} higher energy than the strong bands. The exact reason for this is not clear, but it may be due to multiple sites, overlap of transitions, or Renner splitting in a linear degenerate upper state.

A detailed assignment of the absorption spectrum of NiCl$_2$ is not possible, even in the gas phase work (DeKock, 1968). Previously, the observed matrix spectrum (DeKock, 1967) had been interpreted in terms of an axial ligand field model including spin-orbit coupling. The transitions at 3.05, 3.35, 3.69, and 4.15 μm^{-1} were believed to correspond to the four lowest allowed one-electron allowed transitions to the $^3\Sigma_u^+$, $^3\Sigma_u^-$, $^3\Pi_u$ and $^3\Delta_u$ molecular states. The observation by Jacox and Milligan (1969a) of the bands at 2.02, 2.13, and 2.12 μm^{-1} cannot, however, be interpreted easily with this model. Consequently, Jacox and Milligan (1969a) have proposed a revised energy relationship between the orbitals on the nickel and chlorine atoms in a molecular orbital treatment based on a covalent NiCl$_2$. This treatment results in four low lying allowed transitions not involving charge-transfer and therefore likely to show structure ($^3\Pi_u$, $^3\Sigma_u^+$, $^3\Sigma_u^-$, and $^3\Delta_u$). Two of these states, $^3\Pi_u$ and $^3\Delta_u$ might be expected to show Renner splittings. The transitions at 2.02, 2.13, and 2.12 μm^{-1} presumably involve these states. Two higher energy transitions are also predicted, these being $^3\Sigma_u^+$ and $^3\Pi_u$ states. The model falls short, however, because four transitions are observed. Expansion to include all the transitions involves other possible levels due to different electron configurations and possible spin forbidden transitions.

Irradiation of NiCl$_2$ in argon at 3.20 or 2.70 μm^{-1} is observed to result in green emission from the molecule. Three band systems have been reported

(Gruen, 1968) although only two could be reproduced (Jacox, 1969a). These band systems originate near 2.13 and 1.95, with a very weak one near 1.72 μm^{-1}. The first two show clear vibrational frequencies of 360 cm^{-1}, very close to the expected ground state frequency ν_1''. The appearance of three absorption systems in this region, particularly the two at 2.02 and 2.13 μm^{-1} suggests that the two stronger emission systems may be the corresponding fluorescences. Gruen (1968) postulated that all but four of the observed bands resulted from emission from a $^3\Sigma_g^+$ upper state to various lower-lying states.

Infrared observations have yielded directly two of the three ground state vibrational frequencies. The band attributable to ν_3 of the most abundant species appears at 521 cm^{-1}. The bending mode, ν_2, is at 85 cm^{-1}. Additional bands near 440 cm^{-1} have been assigned to the dimer $(NiCl_2)_2$. Calculations of ν_1 based on the values for ν_2, ν_3 and the isotope spacings give a value of 351 cm^{-1} in good agreement with the 360 cm^{-1} observed in the emission spectrum.

NiF_2

The asymmetric stretching fundamental of the molecule NiF_2 appears near 780 cm^{-1} in argon at 14°K, the most intense component corresponding to the most abundant isotopic species at 780 cm^{-1} (Milligan, 1965c). The failure to observe ν_1 along with the correlation between observed spacings to those calculated tends to support the hypothesis that NiF_2 is linear. A group of bands near 715 cm^{-1} is tentatively assigned to dimers. A calculated value for ν_1 of 606 cm^{-1} is obtained from ν_3.

No absorption in the region 220–500 nm attributable to NiF_2 has yet been observed in matrices.

O_2F

The infrared spectrum of the radical O_2F has been observed following photolysis of OF_2—O_2 or F_2—O_2 mixtures in N_2, Ar, or O_2 at 4.2° and 20°K (Arkell, 1965b; Spratley, 1966; Noble, 1966). All three vibrational fundamentals have been reported. All observations give essentially the same results. The results give values of 1495 cm^{-1} for ν_1, 585 cm^{-1} for ν_2, and 376 cm^{-1} for ν_3. The early interpretation of the spectral features was complicated by the results observed on ^{18}O substitution (Arkell, 1965b; Spratley, 1966). Instead of the expected quartet features, the ν_1 band near 1500 cm^{-1} showed a triplet whereas the ν_2 mode at 585 cm^{-1} gave a doublet. Normal coordinate analysis showed that the observed bandwidths could exceed the isotope splitting, thereby leading to unresolved structure. Later experiments (Noble, 1966) confirmed this behavior.

The bonding in O_2F apparently is the same as in O_2F_2. The $O-O$ bond is essentially the same as in O_2. The $O-F$ bond distance is unusually long as in O_2F_2, and the bond angle is 109.5°.

PH_2

McCarty and Robinson (1959c) have reported five bands in the spectrum of condensed products from a discharge through argon-phosphine mixtures which correlate well with the gas phase bands of PH_2 (Ramsay, 1956; Herzberg, 1967). These bands show matrix shifts of about 80 cm^{-1} toward the red with regard to the gas phase. They have been assigned to a progression in v'_2 with the first band observed at 1.91 μm^{-1} corresponding to $(0,1,0) - (0,0,0)$ of the A $^2A_1 \leftarrow$ X $^2B_1$ transition. The observed vibrational frequency is 930 cm^{-1}. They have estimated $v'_1 = 2320$ cm^{-1} from a force constant calculation. The data indicate an upper state angle of approximately 125°, and a ground state angle of 97°.

SO_2

Sulfur dioxide has been studied in a wide variety of matrices and in a solid film over the temperature range of 4.2° to 110°K. Infrared observations on SO_2 in krypton matrices give the three ground state vibrational fundamentals as: $v_1 = 1150$, $v_2 = 519$, and $v_3 = 1351$ cm^{-1}. Sulfur-34 and oxygen-18 isotopic substitution verify the assignments (Allavena, 1969). The v_1 and v_2 frequencies are also observed in the phosphorescence spectrum of the molecule (Meyer, 1968; Phillips, 1969).

The ultraviolet absorption spectrum consists of several bands attributable to the A $^1B_1 \leftarrow$ X $^1A_1$ transition in the region 280–310 nm (Phillips, 1969). The origin of the system is not observed; the first band corresponds to $(2,4,0) - (0,0,0)$. The system consists of overlapping progressions in v'_1 and v'_2. The frequency differences are 720 and 220 cm^{-1}, respectively, for the first bands, but because of the failure to observe the origin, these cannot be compared to the gas phase $^1B_1$ frequencies. The origin is estimated to occur at about 2.96 μm^{-1}. In addition, estimates for the origins of the C and D systems are 4.15 and 4.23 μm^{-1}, respectively.

Excitation of SO_2 with ultraviolet light into the systems A, C, or D with x-rays leads to strong phosphorescence, a $^3B_1 \rightarrow$ X $^1A_1$, in the region 390–470 nm. The lifetime of this phosphorescence varies from 0.55 msec in O_2, where strong quenching occurs, to 17.5 msec in neon. The lifetime is relatively independent of temperature over the range 4.2°–110°K, but the phosphorescent intensity decreases by a factor of up to 100 over the equivalent range. This intensity decrease is interpreted in terms of a temperature dependent intersystem crossing rate (Meyer, 1968). A completely analogous behavior is observed with $^{34}S^{18}O_2$. The emission bands are well resolved in SF_6 and can be assigned to progressions in v''_1 and v''_2 with the values equal to 1126 and 518 cm^{-1}, respectively. Other matrices do not yield separation of the two frequencies. Synthesized spectra based on the observed values of v''_1 and v''_2 in other matrices are consistent with the observed spectra. Both v''_1 and v''_2 shift from matrix to matrix, but the shifts do not show the same trend. The origin of the system appears at 2.56 μm^{-1}. The intensity and lifetime measurements lead to the conclusion that radiationless processes in SO_2 are very small under the conditions of the experiments. Even pure SO_2 and SO_2 in oxygen show phosphorescence.

Zeeman experiments on the phosphorescence of SO_2 produce two lifetimes and a broadening of several emission bands (Conway, 1969). At fields greater than 20 kG, a second, about 15% longer lifetime component representing 20–30% of the total intensity appears. The contribution of this component is independent of field up to 90 kG, however at about 80 kG a Poschen-Bach effect occurs. The results are believed to be due to a combination of factors, including spin lattice relaxation, kT imbalance, and triplet level splitting.

S_2O

The ultraviolet absorption spectrum of the molecule S_2O has been observed in argon, krypton, xenon, and nitrogen matrices at 20°K, and the infrared spectrum in a solid film at 77°K (Phillips, 1969; Blukis, 1965). S_2O can be prepared by passing a mixture of $SOCl_2$ in rare gas through a column of Ag_2S heated to 160°C. In absorption, only one transition of S_2O is observed. The spectrum consists of a progression of 18 bands originating near 2.9000 μm^{-1} with a vibrational spacing of 415 cm^{-1}. All 18 bands fit the formula

$$G(v'_3) = 29{,}070 + 426(v'_3 + \tfrac{1}{2}) - 4.80(v'_3 + \tfrac{1}{2})^2 + 0.075(v'_3 + \tfrac{1}{2})^3$$

The matrix spectrum is very similar to that of the gas phase (Herzberg, 1967). The predissociation limit, however, is suppressed in the solid. Two bands toward the red of the reported gas phase origin are observed, indicating that the gas phase numbering is incorrect, if the heavy atom effect holds. A reevaluation of the gas phase data in light of the matrix observations leads to estimated excited state frequencies $v_1 \sim 720$ and $v_2 \sim 286$ cm^{-1}. In addition some previously unassigned bands are accounted for.

Infrared observations in solid films of S_2O give directly values for the three vibrational fundamentals in the solid at 77°K. These values are $v_1 = 1165$ cm^{-1}, $v_2 = 388$, and $v_3 = 679$ cm^{-1}.

ScF$_2$

McLeod and Weltner (1966) have reported the observation of a series of ultraviolet absorption bands and several infrared bands, following condensation of vaporized ScF$_3$ into a neon matrix at 4°K, which they have tentatively assigned to ScF$_2$, ScF$_3$, or both. The UV band system extends from 280 to 320 nm with the origin at 318 nm and a vibrational frequency of 580 cm^{-1}. Five infrared bands appear at 726, 709, 661, 482, and 446 cm^{-1}. It is proposed that the bands at 726, 482, and 446 might be due to ScF$_3$(D$_{3h}$) and the bands at 709 and 661 cm^{-1} to ν_3 and ν_1, respectively, of a slightly bent ScF$_2$.

SeO$_2$

The UV-visible spectrum of selenium dioxide has recently been reported by Voigt (1969) in argon, krypton, xenon, SF$_6$, CH$_4$, and C$_4$F$_8$ matrices at 20°K. Two absorption regions are observed. A strong absorption originating at about 3.10 μm^{-1} shows fine structure in argon and xenon, but appears as a broad, unresolved system in SF$_6$, CH$_4$, and C$_4$F$_8$. The resolved spectrum consists of vibrational bands forming an extended Franck-Condon curve with two close-lying maxima. The data do not allow distinction of the cause of band doubling, which could result from two different progressions or from overlap of bands. Site effects are ruled out because the structure is identical in all matrices. If the spectrum consists of two progressions, it can be due to absorption in two electronic transitions, both with progressions in v'_1, or a single transition involving progressions in $(v',0,0)$ and $(v',1,0)$. The spacing between adjacent bands averages 308 cm^{-1} and between alternate bands 612 cm^{-1}. This transition is tentatively assigned to the gas phase B state (Herzberg, 1967), which is analogous to the C state of the isoelectronic molecule SO$_2$.

A second, considerably weaker absorption appears in the region between 320 and 410 nm as a broad system with no distinct Franck-Condon maximum. It may involve more than one transition, with at least one origin below 2.40 μm^{-1}. This transition is tentatively assigned to S$_1$ ← S$_0$, where S$_0$ represents the ground state and S$_1$, the first excited singlet state in the molecule.

The latter state is in all likelihood analogous to the A ^{1}B$_1$ state of SO$_2$. It is also believed that the lowest triplet state, T$_1$, may contribute to the absorption in this region. The weak intensity of this absorption leads to the conclusion that S$_1$ and T$_1$ are very strongly mixed.

Depending on the wavelength of excitation, two emissions from SeO$_2$ are observed. With excitation into the strong absorption near 275 nm, or with x-rays, a weak, blue, generally structureless emission originating at 3.10 μm^{-1} appears. This emission is interpreted as resonance fluorescence of the strong absorption. With light of 365 nm wavelength, a strong yellow emission with origin at 2.20 μm^{-1} is obtained. The system appears as an extensive progression in v''_2 with vibrational spacing of 365 cm^{-1}. The lifetime of this transition has been measured in Xe, SF$_6$, and C$_4$F$_8$ and found to be less than 2, 2.5, and 2.0 msec, respectively. This transition is assigned to the phosphorescence $T_1 \rightarrow S_0$ with T_1 corresponding to the gas phase C state and analogous to the a ^{3}B state of SO$_2$. Population of T_1 occurs either via direct excitation through $T_1 \leftarrow S_0$ or by intersystem crossing following the weak $S_1 \leftarrow S_0$ absorption. $S_3 \rightsquigarrow T_1$ intersystem crossing apparently is absent.

Si$_3$

The trapping of silicon vapors in a neon matrix has given between 420 and 470 nm a series of 7 weak bands which do not fit the scheme of Si$_2$ absorptions. These bands have tentatively been assigned to a $^3\Sigma_u^- \leftarrow {}^3\Sigma_g^-$ transition of Si$_3$ (Weltner, 1964c). The bands appear in groups of three separated by 310 cm^{-1}. The separation of individual components in a group is 110 cm^{-1}. The 110 cm^{-1} splitting within groups has been attributed to site effects. The frequency of 310 cm^{-1} is suggested to be v'_1. This value is not unreasonable when compared with a value for the ground state v''_1 of 358 cm^{-1} as computed by Drowart (1958).

SiC$_2$

Weltner and McLeod (1964c) reported the appearance of 11 bands assignable to SiC$_2$ in the absorption spectrum of silicon carbide vapors trapped in neon or argon at 4°K and 20°K. The bands appear in the same region as the previously observed blue-green stellar bands (Kleman, 1956). The bands originate at 497 nm in neon and extend to about 400 nm. The intensity is highest near the origin and decreases abruptly at higher energies, indicating little change in internuclear distance. In analogy with C$_3$ (Weltner, 1964a,b), the molecule is expected to be linear in both the ground state and the excited state. Transitions occur in which Δv_1 and Δv_3 take integral values and $\Delta v_2 = 0,2,4$, etc. The vibrational frequencies derived from the spectrum are: $v'_1 = 1461$, $v'_2 = 230$, and $v'_3 = 1015$ cm^{-1}. The vibrational structure in the upper state apparently requires positive values for x'_{13} and x'_{23}. That is, the frequency v'_3 increases with higher vibrational quanta of v'_1. No evidence for Renner splittings, as in C$_3$, was observed. The transition is assumed to be $^1\Pi_u \leftarrow X\,^1\Sigma_g^+$.

The emission spectrum of this same system has been recorded, but a complete interpretation is not clear. Vibrational frequencies for the ground state of 836 cm^{-1} and 1745 cm^{-1} are obtained from the emission. The former is assigned to ν_3 and the latter to ν_1. The remaining frequency, ν_2, is listed as 300 cm^{-1} as obtained from the gas phase data.

Infrared measurements confirm the ν''_1 and ν''_3 frequencies, giving 1751 and 835 cm^{-1}, respectively, in neon. No observation of ν''_2 was made. All features are also observed in argon.

Si$_2$C

A few bands appearing in the absorption spectrum of silicon carbide vapors trapped in neon and argon have been proposed to arise from the molecule Si$_2$C (Weltner, 1964c). These bands overlap the long wavelength end of the A bands of SiC$_2$. The bands originate near 530 nm in argon and near 510 nm in neon. Nearly all the intensity appears in the first three bands. The bands are separated by about 500 cm^{-1}, and the assignment is made to ν'_1 on the basis that the molecule is symmetrical and the transition is $^1\Pi_u \leftarrow X\,^1\Sigma_g^+$. A calculated value for ν''_1 of 672 cm^{-1} is obtained if all assumptions are correct. The analysis and even the assignment to Si$_2$C are very tentative. This is particularly true in light of the number of species known to be present in silicon carbide vapor (Drowart, 1958).

SiF$_2$

One electronic transition and all three vibrational modes of the species SiF$_2$ have been observed in several matrices at 4.2° and 14°K by Milligan (1968a). Difluorosilane, SiH$_2$F$_2$, photolyzes readily with vacuum ultraviolet radiation, for example, the hydrogen 121.6 nm Lyman line, to yield directly SiF$_2$. The molecule has also been prepared and trapped via the reaction of SiF$_4$ with solid silicon at 1150°C (Bassler, 1966). Ratios of SiF$_2$ to SiF$_4$ in the final products are about 3 : 2, so that the latter system is far from spectroscopically clean. The SiF$_4$ infrared ν_3 absorption occurs in the same region as the absorptions of SiF$_2$ making observations more difficult.

In both neon and argon, ultraviolet absorptions corresponding to the gas phase $^1B_1 \leftarrow {}^1A_1$ transition at 44,000 cm^{-1} are observed (Khanna, 1967). In argon, the absorption appears as a structureless feature, 7.5 nm in half-width, and centered at about 220 nm; while in neon, a progression of 8 distinct bands with an average separation of 253 cm^{-1}, the gas phase value is obtained for the upper-state bending mode of SiF$_2$. The bands can be correlated with the $(0,\nu'_2,0) - (0,0,0)$ bands of the gas phase spectrum by assuming a matrix red shift of 130 cm^{-1}. The origin is not observed, and the first band at 4.44 nm is assigned to the (0,2,0) level.

Infrared observations in an argon matrix yield the following frequencies for the vibrational modes: the bending mode, ν_2, appears at 343 cm^{-1}; the symmetric stretching fundamental, ν_1, at 843 cm^{-1}, and the asymmetric stretching vibration, ν_3, at 855 cm^{-1}. Warm-up behavior and isotopic substitutions are consistent with the assignments.

The use of a CO matrix has shown that H atom photodetachment is an important step in the photolysis process, whereas little or no F atom fragmentation occurs.

Numerous infrared bands not attributable to SiF$_2$ are observed. Some can be assigned to dimers or aggregates, others to unreacted precursors. Some, however, remain unexplained.

SrF_2

The infrared spectrum of SrF$_2$ in argon at 4°K shows a moderately strong doublet absorption with components at 447 and 450 cm^{-1}, and much weaker bands at 303 and 356 cm^{-1} (Snelson, 1966). The latter bands are assigned to aggregates. It is not clear from the spectrum whether the doublet at 450 cm^{-1} is due to matrix splitting or to two fundamentals of nearly equal frequency. Doublets appear also in neon and krypton at 468, 471 and 439, 443 cm^{-1}, respectively. This favors the second interpretation. Assuming this to be the case, the band at 447 cm^{-1} would most likely correspond to ν_1 and the band at 450 cm^{-1} to ν_3. This would require a bent molecule.

TaO_2

The molecule TaO$_2$ has been observed in neon and argon matrices at 4° and 20°K following vaporization of tantalum oxide at 2270°K or via reaction of oxygen with tantalum metal at 2270°K (Weltner, 1965b).

TaO$_2$ shows two absorptions in the visible part of the spectrum. In neon, a strong system of bands originates at 861 nm and a second, weaker series of bands appears at 616 nm. The former transition, designated A, consists of a progression of bands with a vibrational spacing of 285 cm^{-1}. The short wavelength portion of the system is overlapped by a second progression starting at 797 nm with the same vibrational frequency. The shift between the progressions is 937 cm^{-1}. In argon, much of the structure is lost and the bands appear broad. The principal progression frequency of 285 cm^{-1} corresponds to ν''_2, the upper state bending frequency. The system shows a long Franck-Condon envelope indicating a significant change in angle in the upper state. The second progression has been assigned as $(1,\nu''_2,0) - (0,0,0)$ giving a value for ν'_1 of 937 cm^{-1}. The second system, designated B, also shows a progression in ν'_2 with a value of 281 cm^{-1}. Because it is significantly weaker, ν'_1 is not observed.

The ground state vibrational frequencies $\nu''_1 = 971$ and $\nu''_3 = 912$ cm^{-1} have been determined by infrared analysis of the same system. The assignments were made on the basis that $\nu'_1 = 937$ cm^{-1} is normally smaller than ν''_1. This does, however, result in ν''_1 being greater than ν''_3, a situation, which in light triatomics almost never occurs. Thus, these assignments are not without suspicion.

A molecular orbital scheme somewhat similar to Walsh's treatment for BAB molecules has been used to derive the term symbols for the ground state and the lowest allowed transitions. The ground state is suggested to be $^2B_1$ and the observed transitions may involve the upper states $^2A_1(2)$ and/or $^2A_2$.

WO₂

Vaporization of either yellow WO_3 or blue $WO_{2.96}$ at 1600°K or the reaction of oxygen with hot tungsten at 1900–2950°K yields several tungsten oxide species including WO_2 in sufficient yields for direct spectral observations in neon or argon matrices at 4°K and 20°K (Weltner, 1965e).

Two electronic transitions of WO_2 are observed in the visible portion of the spectrum. A strong system A, originating at 1.2670 μm^{-1} and a weaker system, B, with an origin near 1.2800 μm^{-1} both show long progressions in the bending mode, ν'_2, of the upper state. The A system also shows a simultaneous progression in ν'_1, the symmetric stretching frequency of the excited state. The observed vibrational frequencies for the system A are $\nu'_1 = 972$ and $\nu'_2 = 300$ cm^{-1}, while the ν'_2 frequency of the B transition is 287 cm^{-1}. Oxygen-18 isotope shifts have been used to aid the analysis. The extended ν'_2 progression leads to the conclusion that the upper state molecular angle differs significantly from that of the ground state. The transitions are assigned as A $(^3B_1) \leftarrow$ X $(^3A_1)$ and B $(^3B_2) \leftarrow$ X $(^3A_1)$, respectively.

Infrared observations on tungsten oxide deposits give several bands in the region 600–1100 cm^{-1}. Of these, bands appearing at 928 and 992 cm^{-1} have been assigned to ν''_3 and ν''_1, respectively, of the ground state WO_2 molecule. These assignments are consistent with the observed ^{18}O substituted isotope shifts. Most of the remaining bands have been assigned to higher oxides such as W_2O_4, W_3O_9, W_4O_{12}.

XeCl₂

Nelson and Pimentel (1967b) report the preparation and isolation of the species $XeCl_2$ in sufficient quantities to record a complex infrared band assignable to ν_3 of the species. The band appears as a broad structured feature near 313 cm^{-1}. The observed absorption can be fitted closely with a calculated spectrum based on the available xenon and chlorine isotopes. The species is concluded to have a D_{Oh} symmetry. No additional data on the molecule is available, therefore the identification should be regarded as tentative.

XeF_2

Photolysis of fluorine, xenon, argon mixtures at 20°K with the full light of an AH-4 medium pressure mercury lamp gives sufficient XeF_2 for the observation of two of the three infrared fundamentals (Turner, 1963b). A weak band at approximately 510 cm^{-1} assignable to ν_1 and an intense absorption at 547 cm^{-1} assigned to ν_3 are observed. At an F_2 : Xe ratio of 5 : 1 evidence for the formation of XeF_4 is obtained.

$ZnBr_2$, $ZnCl_2$, ZnF_2, and ZnI_2

The infrared spectra of all the zinc halides have been investigated at 4° and 20°K in argon, krypton, and xenon matrices (McNamee, 1962; Loewenschuss, 1968). Each of the species, ZnF_2, $ZnCl_2$, $ZnBr_2$, and ZnI_2 can be vaporized directly from a Knudsen furnace, however, monomer yields appear to be greatest with a double furnace arrangement (Loewenschuss, 1968). Direct observations of ν_2 and ν_3 have been made. In addition, bands attributable to dimers are observed. The latter are found to depend significantly on the vaporization conditions. The bands assignable to monomers all show the multiplet structure expected from the natural isotopic abundance of Zn isotopes. In addition, splittings appropriate for $^{35}Cl-^{37}Cl$ isotopes are also observed. A band at 425 cm^{-1} for $ZnCl_2$ has been assigned to the ν_{12} vibration of the dimer (McNamee, 1962), assuming a D_{2h} symmetry for the species with two chlorine atoms binding the Zn atoms.

Several other bands also appear in the spectra. These are in the range 450 cm^{-1} for ZnF_2 to 170 for ZnI_2. Bands at 334 cm^{-1} and 297 cm^{-1} for $ZnCl_2$ have also been tentatively assigned to dimer frequencies, ν_9 and ν_{11} respectively.

All data are consistent with a linear structure for all the halides. Thermodynamic properties have been computed from the data (Loewenschuss, 1968).

D. Organic Molecules

Many hundreds of organic molecules have been studied in low temperature glasses. It is impossible to provide here a detailed discussion of all literature data because literature appears at a higher rate than it can be abstracted. Even if practical, such a review would be of very limited value because usually only meager data are available, and the experiments vary so widely in sophistication and accuracy that one has to check the original literature in almost every case to establish how trustworthy are the data. Therefore, it was decided to omit a detailed review, except for benzene and naphthalene. These two molecules demonstrate the immense wealth of experiments that have been reported for aromatics. Aromatics have served as a vehicle for theoreticians to study all possible electronic properties. Thus, these molecules are a laboratory standard for correlation of data deduced for other molecules. More detailed reviews of organic low temperature spectra are contained in recent books by Parker (1968), McGlynn (1969), and Becker (1969).

Benzene

The fluorescence and phosphorescence of benzene in solid solutions was reported first by Kowalski in 1911. He studied benzene and nine of its simpler derivatives in frozen solutions of ethanol at 76°K and discovered that all emit bluish or green phosphorescence. The absorption and emission of this system was restudied in 1941 by Lewis and Kasha (Lewis, 1941), who assigned the lowest transition to T_1. In 1949, McClure reported that the lifetime of benzene in EPA was 7.0 sec at 77°K. Since then, benzene has been studied as a pure solid, in chemically and isotopically pure crystals, in crystals doped with isotopes, oxygen, and other impurities, and in a variety of solid solutions of solvents, such as rare gases, cyclohexane, and many others.

It is not our intention to present a full review of all work on low temperature solutions of benzene. Instead, we list only selected examples to discuss spectra in three types of solvents: (a) rare gas matrices; (b) frozen hydrocarbon glasses, and (c) crystals.

Rare Gas Matrices.   Leach (1958) was the first to report on the benzene spectrum in rare gas matrices. Robinson (1961b) reported the absorption, fluorescence, and phosphorescence of benzene in argon, krypton, and xenon. All matrix spectra are red-shifted in regard to the gas phase, the vibrational structure is clearly resolved, with crystal vibrations of 20 cm^{-1} and 80 cm^{-1} superimposed. C_6D_6 and the solvent heavy atom effect were used to observe intensity perturbations. With increasing heavy atom effect, the transition $^3B_{1u} - {}^1A_{1g}$ is strongly enhanced and phosphorescence lifetimes are shortened. C_6D_6 shows, however, an almost purely radiative lifetime of 25.8 sec. Energy transfer from S_1 to T_1 was found to be solvent dependent, the efficiency being highest, close to 100%, for xenon and predicted to be lowest in solid hydrogen.

Diamant, Hexter, and Schnepp (1965) restudied the absorption spectrum and phosphorescence in argon, krypton, xenon, nitrogen, CO_2, and methane at 4° and 20°K. They observed that all, except the spectra in nitrogen, consisted of multiplet absorption lines, and they concluded that the solute was located in several well defined lattice sites, with the solvent possibly consisting of two separate cubic and hexagonal zones. Concentration studies indicated that at high dilution the fine structure was simpler. Blount and co-workers deposited benzene–nitrogen mixtures at 4°, 17°, and 20°K and observed in absorption sharp doublets at the lowest temperature, but only a single line corresponding to the red component for each vibrational level at 20°K. The lines seem to shift between 4° and 20°K by less than 0.005%. Gas phase-nitrogen matrix shifts were less than − 0.5% of the transition energy. Voigt and Meyer (1969b) studied the fine structure of the $S_1 \leftarrow S_0$ transition and varied deposition speed as well as concentration and deposition temperature. They reproducibly produced at will matrices with one to four lines in nitrogen. In high dispersion, argon lines after annealing have a half-width of less than 0.1 cm^{-1} at 4°K.

In thick samples, even dilute solutions show a broad satellite shoulder toward the red of the strong and sharp line. This shoulder is reversibly temperature dependent in that its intensity increases above 4°K.

The $S_1 \leftarrow S_0$ bands of benzene are also noted in matrices containing benzene-I_2 charge transfer complexes.

Faure, Valadier, Bergeon, and Janin (1967) codeposited benzene with active nitrogen in nitrogen and argon matrices at 4 and 20°K. They observed that benzene strongly emits via $T_1 \rightarrow S_0$, with three fine structure components for each vibrational level. The spectrum and the emission intensity were found to depend on temperature and concentration.

GLASSES AND FROZEN SOLUTIONS. Sponer and Rousset (1958) studied at the same time independently the emission spectrum of benzene in cyclohexane glasses at 4°K and presented a vibrational analysis. Zmerli (1959a–c) used C_6D_6 and tested oxygen quenching. Kanda (1961c) used carbon tetrachloride and dioxane matrices at 90°K. In the latter solvent very sharp spectra were obtained. He explained the strongly enhanced emission deformation of the benzene ring in the solvent field. In 1968, Spangler restudied the cyclohexane matrix absorption, fluorescence, and phosphorescence and concluded that slowly cooled samples undergo a phase transition forming the low temperature monoclinic structure which gives fewer bands and a simpler spectrum than cubic crystals. The latter are formed when cyclohexane solutions are rapidly quenched. These authors presented a detailed analysis of the spectrum and reported phosphorescence lifetimes, at 77°K, of 4.6 sec for monoclinic solvent and 1.1 sec for cubic solvent. Absorption and fluorescence are reported to be equally efficient in both solids, but phosphorescence yields are higher in monoclinic cyclohexane. Kembrovskii (1968) concluded that benzene preserves D_{6h} symmetry in cyclohexane at 77° and confirmed the excited state symmetries $^1B_{2u}$ for S_1 and $^3B_{1u}$ or $^3B_{2u}$ for T_1. Martin and Kalantar studied benzene and four differently deuterated benzenes in cyclohexane and methylcyclohexane and analyzed the lifetime of individual multiplet components, confirming that the nonexponential decays are the result of emission from molecules in different lattice sites. Quantitative analysis of the decay curves confirmed the two-site model, with the cubic site yielding shorter lived emission.

CRYSTALS. While rare gas matrices and frozen solutions contain randomly oriented molecules, benzene-doped or pure benzene crystals have a high degree of orientation. Benzene crystals are orthorhombic-bipyramidal with four molecules per unit cell. In 1926, Pringsheim and Kronenberger (1926b) showed that benzene single crystals give sharp spectra closely related to the gas phase. Early work on crystals was on exciton bands, by Fox (1954) and Schnepp (1957), and on infrared spectra by Hexter (1959a), Pimentel (Dauben, 1955), and Broude (1957). Recent far-infrared data by Harada on translational lattice vibrations were used to determine intermolecular force constants. Hochstrasser (1967) used the internal heavy atom effect of p-dihalogenated benzene crystals to observe UV $T_1 \leftarrow S_0$ absorption at 4.2°K. He discussed the observed spectra in terms of the oriented gas model, triplet-exciton interaction, and Davydov splitting. Polarized absorption and emission gives sharp bands with a pure exciton origin, with an alternating intensity pattern indicating that T_1 is slightly distorted into a trans-chair form. Temperature dependence indicates small changes in crystal structure. Colson and Bernstein (1965) doped benzene and C_6D_6 crystals with oxygen and reported absorption spectra of T_2 ($^3E_{1u}$) $\leftarrow S_0$ and T_1 ($^3B_{1u}$) $\leftarrow S_0$. The oxygen-doped crystals were compared with large crystals of ultrapure benzene. The oxygen perturbation enhances the transition drastically, but shifts it by only $+ 20$ cm^{-1}, namely 0.1% of the transition energy, from 29657.1 to 29675 $\pm$ 25 cm^{-1}.

Moross (1966) reported the temperature dependence of NQR spectra of single crystals. Colson (1966) studied the effects of strain on optical properties, and van der Waals (1967a) discussed the influence of geometry on phosphorescence effects in terms of a pseudo Jahn-Teller interaction between the four lowest excited states. Later, the same group used ESR spectra to demonstrate that the vibronic states of the phosphorescent molecule are nonhexagonal and influenced by the environment. Nieman and Tinti (1967), using C_6D_6 as a host crystal for seven isotopic benzenes with symmetries lower than D_{3h}, observed that phosphorescent emission has eight times larger line splitting than fluorescence. They concluded that the $^3B_{1u}$ state is distorted, at least partly for intrinsic reasons, and not entirely, or predominantly, because of the crystal field. This model agrees with van der Waals model of a distorted $^3B_{1u}$ state in a preferentially oriented site. Concentration dependence of relative intensities indicates solute-solute exciton migration. Gee and Robinson (1967) studied the Raman spectrum of benzene and C_6D_6 at 77°K and 2°K. Maria and Zahlan (1963) noticed in hexamethylbenzene different temperature dependence of intensity and line width of the $S_1 \leftarrow S_0$ (0,0) band between 4 and 70°K, which they attributed to phonon effect on oscillator strength. Colson and Robinson (1968b) used two different isotopic molecules as solute in C_6D_6, to form a three-component system, for which they studied phosphorescence and fluorescence as a function of temperature, solute concentration, and intensity of the exciting light source. They concluded that few or no solute-solvent excitons result from intersystem crossing. When 30 kT was smaller than the solute-solvent energy gap, triplet-triplet excitation transfer occurred from the solute with higher lying T_1 to that with the lower T_1. This transfer corresponds to predictions of the Perrin model, excitation migration being restricted to less than 2 nm. At high lamp intensities excitation-annihilation becomes important and photolysis is observed. Bernstein, Colson, Tinti, and Robinson (1968b) also studied high dispersion spectra of emission and absorption of four isotopically different benzenes in C_6D_4. Two site effects were noted, namely, orientational effects and splitting of degenerate fundamentals. The first occurs for isotopes with less than a 3-fold axis of rotation, the second occurs for those with such an axis. Both types of splitting occur for vibronic and vibrational bands in mixed isotopic crystals, and an empirical rule correlating magnitude of site splitting, orientation effects and gas-crystal energy shifts for in-plane and out-of-plane modes is deduced. In a later paper, exciton-exciton band transitions were observed for S_1 and state density functions were computed. Temperature effects were used to deduce phonon contributions. Colson (1968c) reexamined the method of energy variation to determine the fourth forbidden factor group component of $^1B_{2u}$, and concluded that the band structure of S_1 indicates negligible mixing of this state with ion-pair states. Sommer and Jortner (1969a) used one-particle Green's functions to compute density of state functions for the triplet and excited singlet state in crystals.

The occurrence of phosphorescence is due to intermolecular and intra-molecular effects which lead to $S_1 \rightarrow T_1$ energy transfer; this intersystem crossing is discussed in Chapter 5. Robinson discussed such radiationless transitions for gaseous benzene as well as benzene in solid solution. He assumed that benzene constitutes an intermediate case between small molecules and large molecules in that no $S_1 \to T_1$ relaxation occurs in the gas phase, but that only small perturbations are needed to induce highly efficient intersystem crossing.

Benzene forms charge–transfer complexes with iodine and bromine. Person (1967) studied solids formed from mixtures of benzene and bromine. Margolis (1966) deposited iodine-benzene mixtures and observed broad spectra. Voigt and Meyer (1968) prepared argon, krypton, xenon, SF_6, and CH_4 matrices containing iodine–benzene complexes that give a broad but structured UV band corresponding to the charge–transfer transition.

Spangler (1968) and Martin (1968a–e) reexamined the relative contribution of radiative and nonradiative triplet decay in the cubic and monoclinic cyclohexane site at 77°K and concluded that benzene, otherwise remarkably sensitive to its environment, has a site-independent $T_1 \to S_0$ radiative lifetime. Therefore, observed lifetime changes are due to nonradiative contributions, which are four times larger in cubic sites than in monoclinic sites. For C_6D_6, nonradiative decay is slower, the site effect being twice as large in cubic sites as in monoclinic sites. Hatch, Erlitz, and Nieman (1968b) measured benzene triplet decay time in several solvents at 4.2°K and temperatures up to 77°K. Typical lifetimes are listed in Table 5.7. They deduced activation energies from the lifetime vs. temperature curves and concluded that various models could be invoked as explanation. A more detailed discussion of temperature dependence of lifetime and intensity is given in Chapter 5 in the sections on energy transfer and environmental effects.

Naphthalene

The information on naphthalene is so extensive that this section can hardly point to all areas of knowledge. It certainly cannot do justice to all the beautiful detailed work in the literature. Naphthalene constitutes in many respects a joining point between different fields of spectroscopy. Shpol'skii-type frozen solution spectra yielding quasi-line spectra are well established and can be compared with matrix spectra, more commonly used for study of small radicals, which are prepared by condensing molecular beams of solvent and solute on a cold window, and a very extensive literature is available on single crystal work of more or less pure naphthalene. All techniques and frequency ranges of spectroscopy have been used to explore the properties of this molecule. Despite this, most information is not yet as reliable as the techniques would allow. In recent years, ESR spectra of this molecule have proved the power of this technique for the study of excited triplet states. Application of this technique to other molecules in solids will contribute invaluable understanding to our knowledge of intersystem crossing.

Many effects observed first for naphthalene are of general importance. A more thorough discussion of these cases is given in the sections dealing with lifetimes, Zeeman effect, temperature effects, etc.

Matrices. Frosch (1966) was the first to report the spectrum of naphthalene in rare gases at 4°K. The absorption spectrum consists of a progression of sharp vibrational bands with fine structure dependent on concentration, and matrix material. Metzger (1969) studied the fluorescence and phosphorescence in argon, krypton, xenon, methane, and SF_6 between 20°K and two-thirds of the matrix melting point, reporting that the ratio of fluorescence to phosphorescence decreases with increasing heavy atom effect: methane solutions emit only fluorescence, argon fluoresces and phosphoresces, and xenon and krypton solutions phosphoresce only. With increasing heavy atom effect, total emission increases while the phosphorescence decay time decreases. After annealing, reversibly temperature dependent intensity changes of phosphorescence were observed, but $T_1 \rightarrow S_0$ decay times appeared to be unchanged.

The results for naphthalene, phenanthrene, porphyrins, and thiazole demonstrate that rare gas matrices yield very sharp spectra for large organic molecules. In benzene–argon, the line width is < 0.2 cm^{-1} at 4°K. This proves that the Shpol'skii effect is not restricted to hydrocarbon chain solvents. We recommend SF_6, CH_4, and rare gas matrices for the study of all organic molecules which can be vaporized without decomposition. Naphthalene lifetimes in various solvents and at several temperatures are listed in Table 5.8.

FROZEN HYDROCARBON GLASSES. Ermolaev reported (1959b) spectra of naphthalene and its halogen derivatives in frozen hydrocarbon glasses. In 1965 Mikhailenko studied the phosphorescence in pentane, hexane, and heptane at 77°K and obtained sharp quasi-line spectra. An extensive study of naphthalene in pentane at 77°K is reported in the doctoral thesis of Bolotnikova (1959b), who established and assigned vibrational modes of 1386 cm^{-1} and 495 cm^{-1}, the latter corresponding to a not fully symmetric vibration β_{1g}. Both frequencies correspond to data deduced from vapor studies of Craig. A more detailed discussion of line spectra is given in Section 4.III.D. In recent years, intensive pulsed sources made it possible to observe excited singlet state absorption. Bonneau (1968) determined the fluorescence lifetime, $S_2 \leftarrow S_1$ absorption, and intersystem crossing of naphthalene in cyclohexane, but the system has not yet been studied below room temperature.

DURENE, PLASTICS, AND MIXED CRYSTALS. In 1951, Pimentel studied the IR spectrum of naphthalene in anthracene. Naphthalene is isomorphous with tetramethylbenzene (durene). Dilute solutions give, therefore, "oriented gas"-like spectra. McClure (1955a) was the first to study the phosphorescence in this system. Similar solutions have since been investigated by Kellogg and Schwenker (1964), Jones (1966), Kanda and Shimada (1959), McGlynn, Daigre, and Smith (1963), and Ferguson, Iredale, and Taylor (1954). Jones and Siegel studied naphthalene in polymethyl methacrylate and determined the phosphorescence lifetimes and intensity as a function of temperature. The great wealth of data available on these systems covers absorption and emission transition energies, solvent shifts, energy transfer and solute-solute and solute-solvent interaction. Durene–naphthalene at 77°K was the first system for which Hutchison and Mangum (1958) observed the ESR spectrum of T_1, thus proving experimentally, unambiguously, that the phosphorescent state belongs to a triplet state and was part of the solute. Jen, Aamodt, and Piksis (1967) showed with ESR experiments that the lifetime of naphthalene in the two different durene sites was different, and that the individual Zeeman levels have different radiative transition probabilities to the ground state. Port and Wolf (1967) calculated the hyperfine interaction of α and β protons and deuterons in the triplet state from ENDOR spectra taken at 4°K. Port and Wolf (1968) studied phosphorescence and delayed fluorescence of naphthalene-h_8 and -d_8 and located the emitter as solute, or solute-disturbed solvent exciton. Temperature dependence between 1.4 and 50°K indicates that delayed fluorescence is mainly due to thermally activated triplet-triplet annihilation, with triplet energy transferring from the solute-trap to the annihilation partner via the solvent exciton band. From this mechanism, spectroscopic and thermal energy gaps between solute-trap and solvent exciton were measured. Harrigan and Hirota studied solvent and temperature effects on the lifetime of naphthalene (1968) and discussed solute-solute and solute-solvent triplet energy transfer for various naphthalenes (1967). They concluded that lifetimes in any given system depend on the site of the solute, and that the radiationless $T_1 - S_0$ transition can be temperature dependent at higher temperature. Temperature effects, energy-transfer and decay mechanisms are discussed in Chapter 5.

Pure Crystals. Naphthalene crystals are monoclinic with two molecules per unit cell. After Prikhotko (Obreimov, 1932), McClure and Schnepp (1955) were the first to observe the absorption of crystalline naphthalene and naphthalene-d_8. Fluorescence was first studied by Obreimov and Shabaldas (1943). Sponer, Kanda and Blackwell reported, in 1958, that the fluorescence lifetime of naphthalene at 4°K was $> 10^{-3}$ sec. The lifetime is now known to be much shorter, but early work on pure organic crystals is generally troubled by the presence of unknown inadvertently present impurities. Shpak (1961) showed that all fluorescence spectra published before 1961 contained peaks due to β-methylnaphthalene, thionaphthalene, and similar impurities. The IR spectrum was investigated by Person (1952, 1955), Pimentel (1952, 1955), and McClellan (1955). Hanson and Robinson (1965) observed the Davydov splitting of T_1 in pure naphthalene and obtained excellent agreement with computations. Castro and Robinson (1969) studied the $T_1 - S_0$ absorption at 4°K in high resolution and analyzed the strong Ag modes which exhibit factor-group splitting polarized normally to the molecular plane. They also observed antisymmetric modes which were 100 times weaker than (0,0). The lack of ESR and phosphorescence of pure crystals is explained because T energy is delocalized in the T exciton bands. Schwoerer and Sixl (1968b) used ESR spectra to measure the lifetime of intersystem crossing. Schwoerer and Wolf (1966) measured exciton and optical spin polarization with the help of ESR, and Gallus and Wolf (1968a) measured the diffusion length of singlet excitons in evaporated naphthalene films at 77°K as 25 nm, and at 150°K as 50 nm. In addition to naphthalene fluorescence, such films show increasing emission from lattice effects with decreasing temperature. Surface quenching of singlet excitons was observed, and it was found that energy migration is more efficient in these films than in crystals. El-Kareh and Wolf (1967) studied the fluorescent lifetime of naphthalene crystals as a function of film thickness between 1 μ and 1 cm, and of temperature between 4 and 300°K. The lifetime of the lower Davydov level A is 115 ± 5 nsec. The lower, B state, value is deduced to be 20 ± 10 nsec.

Since temperature effects are caused not only by thermal population changes, but also by density changes in the crystal, it is of interest to compare the influence of high pressures on pure naphthalene crystals and naphthalene solutions. At 300°K and 50 kbar, an irreversible decrease of fluorescence intensity is accompanied by the appearance of a broad emission at $- 3000$ to $- 6000$ cm^{-1} of the fluorescence. Jones and Nicol (1968a,c) assign this red-shifted emission to excimer fluorescence. The emission disappears after annealing. Offen has studied naphthalene in polymethyl methacrylate and various other polymer matrices. In all systems, increased pressure shortens the lifetime and transitions appear red-shifted. Heavy atom substitution on naphthalene reduces this effect significantly. Effects at 77°K are similar.

Recommended Reading

Becker, R. S., *Theory and Interpretation of Fluorescence and Phosphorescence*, Interscience (Wiley), New York, 1969.

Berlman, I. B., *Handbook of Fluorescence Spectra of Aromatic Molecules*, Academic Press, New York, 1965.

Falk, J. E., *Porphyrins and Metalloporphyrins*, Elsevier, Amsterdam and New York, 1964.

Hallam, H. E., Mol. Spectrosc. (The Institute of Petroleum) **22**, 329 (1968). "Recent Advances in the Infrared Spectroscopy of Matrix-Isolated Species."

Kallmann, H. P., and G. M. Spruch, eds., *Luminescence of Organic and Inorganic Materials* (*Int. Conf., N. Y. Univ.*), Wiley, New York, 1962.

Konev, S. V., *Fluorescence and Phosphorescence of Proteins and Nucleic Acids*, Plenum Press, New York, 1967.

Kropp, J. L., and W. R. Dawson, *Int. Conf. Molecular Luminescence, Loyola University, Chicago, 1968.* "Fluorescence and Phosphorescence of Aromatic Hydrocarbons in Poly-Methylmethacrylate as a Function of Temperature."

Lower, S. K., and M. A. El-Sayed, Chem. Rev. **66**, 199 (1966). "The Triplet State and Molecular Electronic Processes in Organic Molecules."

McGlynn, S. P., T. Azumi, and M. Kinoshita, *Molecular Spectroscopy of the Triplet State*, Prentice-Hall, Englewood Cliffs, New Jersey, 1969.

Milligan, D. E., and M. E. Jacox, in *Physical Chemistry: An Advanced Treatise*, Vol. 4: *Molecular Properties* (H. Eyring, ed.), Chapter 4, Academic Press, New York, 1969c. "Spectra of Radicals."

Parker, C. A., *Photoluminescence of Solutions with Applications to Photochemistry and Analytical Chemistry*, Elsevier, New York and Amsterdam, 1968.

Schumacher, E., Chimia **15**, 471 (1961). "Untersuchungen an eingefrorenen, reaktionsfähigen Substanzen."

Thomas, A., in Oxidation Combustion Rev. **2**, 257 (1968). "Trapped Radicals and Combustion."

Wolf, H. C., Solid State Phys. **9**, 1 (1959). "The Electronic Spectra of Aromatic Molecular Crystals."

CHAPTER 10

Tables of Molecular Data

I. INTRODUCTION

This chapter consists of tables with data on low temperature spectra of guest molecules. While Chapter 9 is a detailed review of the properties of some individual species, this chapter provides a summary and a reference guide to the literature up to July 1969. A few references to papers published between July 1969 and July 1970 were added in the proofs.

The tables contain the name of the molecule, the name and character of the states, the energy of the states, the observed transition, the conditions under which the sample was studied, the sample preparation, the name of the first author appearing on the publication, and the last two digits of the publication year. Vibrational frequencies, decay times, and other optical properties are indicated when available.

The use of different energy units is explained in Chapter 1, Section II. As throughout this book, the ground state is listed last, and the upper state of a transition is listed first, regardless of whether absorption or emission was observed.

Only transitions observed in low temperature samples are listed. States and transitions observed in the gas phase are reviewed in G. Herzberg's three volumes on *Molecular Spectra and Molecular Structure* (Herzberg, 1961, 1967), and in the *Berkeley Spectroscopic Newsletter* (S. P. Davis, Physics Department, University of California, Berkeley; 1964 to present).

It was found convenient to prepare separate tables for each group of molecules consisting of a given number of atoms. Thus, the following tables were made:

A.   Atoms
B.   Diatomics
C.   Triatomics
D.   Polyatomics
E.   Organic Molecules
F.   Organic Radicals

Details of the order of listings are explained at the beginning of each table. It was not convenient to use exactly the same format for all tables.

In the atomic table, the elements are listed in alphabetical order of the chemical symbols. Diatomics and triatomics are in the alphabetical order of the symbol of the first atom listed. Since the sequence of atoms in triatomic and polyatomic formulas is not always based on the relative position in the periodic table, but often follows the order in which atoms are chemically bonded, the alphabetical order of first elements does not give a consistent grouping of molecules. Therefore, NCN and CNN are not listed jointly, although their overall formulas are identical. In the organic tables, the order is determined by the number of carbon atoms present. For a given number of carbon atoms, molecules are listed according to other elements present. The simplest formula comes first; all elements except CH are listed in alphabetical order. Thus, metal organic compounds are listed with the metal last.

In order to find the data for a given molecule in the tables, it is necessary to know the group to which it belongs. If a triatomic or polyatomic seems to be missing, each atom of the molecule should be checked against the alphabetical listing, because naming in the literature is inconsistent. Generally, the formula of the original paper was adapted.

II. TABLES

A. Atomic Tables

The first column lists the chemical symbol in alphabetical order. The second indicates the states involved in the observed transition. The excited state is always listed first. An arrow pointing to the left indicates absorption; an arrow pointing to the right identifies emission. Transition energies are listed in μm^{-1} (1 μm^{-1} = 10,000 cm^{-1}). We believe that this unit, already widely used by organic spectroscopists, is clear and allows simpler and more legible tabulation of transition energies than the use of cm^{-1}. The use of μm^{-1} follows the recommendation of international unit committees, which try to discourage the use of kiloKeyser (1 kK = 1000 Keyser = 10^3 cm^{-1}; 1 kK = 0.1 μm^{-1}), which, among atomic spectroscopists, is presently still more widely used. The number of digits of a figure indicates the claimed accuracy: 4.0 stands for 4.0 ± 0.05, and 4.000 indicates 4.000 ± 0.0005, unless otherwise indicated.

The column on matrix materials lists all materials in sequence. Not all listed transitions have been observed in all given matrices. The matrix temperature range indicates the largest range ever used. The symbol m* stands for upper matrix limit; i.e., the highest temperature for a given material where processes are fully reversible; i.e., diffusion is negligible. This is normally 0.4 of the matrix melting point, or less. The preparation methods refer to the solute and sample preparation. Usually the solvent is separately added as an independent beam. The references are listed in alphabetical order of the first author. The year of publication is abbreviated to two digits. When an author published more than one paper in a year, an identifying letter is added.

Atom	Transition		Matrix	Temperature (°K)	Preparation	References
	State	Energy (μm^{-1})				
Ag	$^2P \leftarrow ^2S$	3.1	Ar, Kr, Xe, SF$_6$, ice	20-m*	atomic beam, x-ray from AgNO$_3$	Brewer 1968 King 1968 Zhitnikov 1965
Au	$^2P \leftarrow ^2S$	3.7; 4.1;	C$_4$F$_8$, CH$_4$, N$_2$,	20-m*	atomic beam	Brewer 1970 King 1968 Morelle 1968 Shirk 1969
	$^2P \rightarrow ^2D$	3.0; 2.0; 1.6	Ar, Kr, Xe, SF$_6$			
Ba	$^1P \leftarrow ^1S$	1.8	Ar	4	atomic beam	Barger 1963
	$^3P \leftarrow ^1S$	2.5				
Cd	$^1P_1 \leftarrow ^1S_0$	4.3	Ar, Kr, Xe	4-20	atomic beam, sputtering	Duley 1966a, 1967a Freedhoff 1967 Merrithew 1969 Shirk 1969
Co	$^4F \leftarrow ^4F$	2.8	Ar	4	beam	Mann 1970
	^4G	2.9				
	^4D	2.93				
	^4D	3.20				
	^4F	3.28				
	^2G	3.34				

Co	^4F	3.35	(Continued)			
	^4D	3.96				
	^4F	4.12				
	^4G	4.15				
	^4F	4.19				
	^4G	4.23				
	^4F	4.33				
Cr	$^7P^0 \leftarrow {}^7S$	2.96	Ar	4	atomic beam	Mann 1970
	$^5P \leftarrow {}^7S$	3.33				
Cs	$^2P \leftarrow {}^2S$	2.1	Ar, Kr	4,15	atomic beam $Cs_2 CrO_4$+Si	Milligan 1969b Weyhmann 1965
Cu	$^2P \leftarrow {}^2S$	3.0	Ne, Ar, Kr, Xe,	4-m*	sputtering	Currie 1970 King 1968 Shirk 1969 Chang 1970 Mann 1970
	$^4P \leftarrow {}^2S$	3.9	CH_4, SF_6, N_2		and filament	
	$^2D \leftarrow {}^2S$	4.4			beam	
	$^2P \leftarrow {}^2S$	4.6				
	$^2D \leftarrow {}^2S$	4.6				
	$^2P \rightarrow {}^2D$	1.8				

Atom	Transition State	Transition Energy (μm^{-1})	Matrix	Temperature (°K)	Preparation	References
Fe	$^5D \leftarrow {}^5D_4$	2.6	Ar, Kr, Xe, H_2O	4	sputter, atomic	Barger 1965
	$^5F \leftarrow {}^5D$	2.68	N_2		beam	Mann 1970
	^5P	2.9				Shirk 1968
	^5D	3.3				
	^5F	3.3				
	^5P	3.6				
	^5D	3.9				
	^5F	4.0				
H(D)	$^2P \rightarrow {}^2S$	8.5	H_2, Ne, Ar, Kr,	4	discharge	Baldini 1964
	$^2P \rightarrow {}^2S(?)$		Xe		HI + hν	Bass 1958
						Broida 1957
						Foner 1960
						Keil 1967
						Roncin 1965a, 1967b
						Smith 1964
						Vegard 1925

Element	Transition	Value	Gas	Temp	Phase	References
Hg	$^3P_1 \leftarrow {}^1S_0$	4.0	Ne, Ar, Kr, Xe	4,20 -m*	vapor	Brabson 1970
	$^1P \leftarrow {}^1S$	5.4				Brewer 1965
	$^1P_1 \leftarrow {}^3P_0(?)$	3.7				Duley 1965, 1966b, 1967
	$^3P_2 \leftarrow {}^1S_0(?)$	4.4				Robinson 1959
						Roncin 1961a
						McCarty 1970
In	$^2S \leftarrow {}^2P$	2.4	Ar, Kr, Xe	4-m*	atomic beam	Currie 1970
	$^2P \leftarrow {}^2P$	3.8				Duley 1967b
	$^4P \leftarrow {}^2P$	3.6				
K	$^2P \leftarrow {}^2S$	1.3	Ar, Kr, Xe	4	atomic beam	Meyer 1965
						Weyhmann 1965
Li	$^2P \leftarrow {}^2S$	1.5	Ne, Ar, Kr, Xe, N_2	4-m*	beam	Andrews 1967
						Belyaeva 1968
						Merrithew 1969
						Meyer 1965
Mg	$^1P \leftarrow {}^1S$	4.0	Ar, Kr, Xe	4-m*	beam	Brabson 1965
	$^3P \leftarrow {}^1S$	4.7				Brith 1963
						Schnepp 1961
						Wang 1969
Mn	$^6P^0 \leftarrow {}^6S$	2.486	Ar, Kr, Xe	4-50	beam	Lee 1962
	$^4P \leftarrow {}^6S$	3.1				Mann 1970
	$^6P \leftarrow {}^6S$	3.57				Schnepp 1961

Atom	Transition		Matrix	Temperature (°K)	Preparation	References
	State	Energy (μm^{-1})				
N	$^2D \rightarrow {}^4S$	1.9	Ne, Ar, Kr, Xe	4-40	x-ray of N_2 electron bombardment	Bass 1958, 1960a Tinti 1968 Vegard 1929
Na	$^2P \rightarrow {}^2S$	1.7	Ne, Ar, Kr, Xe, N_2	4-m*	beam	Heller 1967 Jen 1967 Merrithew 1969 Meyer 1965 Robinson 1959 Weyhmann 1965
Ni	$^5F \rightarrow {}^3F$	3.03	Ar	4	beam	Mann 1970
	^3F	3.12				
	^3G	3.14				
	^1F	3.14				
	^3F	3.49				
	^3D	3.53				
	$^3?$	4.31				

O	$^1S \to {}^1D$	1.8	N₂, Ne, Ar, Kr, Xe	4-40	electron bombardment x-ray	Bass 1960 Harvey 1959 Peyron 1959 Schoen 1960b Tinti 1968 Vegard, 1924, 1948
Pb	$^3P \to {}^3P$	3.77	Xe, Kr, Ar, SF₆	4, 20, warm-up		Chang 1970 Duley 1966
Pd	$^3P \to {}^1S$ $^3D \to {}^1S$ $^1P \to {}^1S$	2.96 3.12 3.19	Ar	4	beam	Mann 1970
Rb	$^2P \to {}^2S$	1.2	Ar, Ke, Xe	4-20	beam	Kupfermann 1968 Weyhmann 1965
Sc	$^4D \to {}^2D(?)$	1.6 – 2.9	Ne	4	Se₂O₃ beam	Weltner 1967
Sn	$^3P \to {}^3P$ ^1P ^3D	3.58 3.83, 3.92, 4.05 4.34, 4.58	Ar	4	beam	Mann 1970

Atom	Transition		Matrix	Temperature (°K)	Preparation	References
	State	Energy (μm^{-1})				
Tl	$^2S \leftarrow {}^2P$ $^2S \rightarrow {}^2P_{3/2}$(?)	2.6 1.6	Kr	20	beam	Brabson 1965
Xe	$^1P \leftarrow {}^1S$	6.0	Kr	4	vapor	Roncin 1963, 1964, 1967b Schnepp 1960a
Zn	$^1P \leftarrow {}^1S$	4.7	Ar, Kr, Xe	4-m*	beam	Duley 1966a, 1967a

B. Diatomics

The tables are organized as in the case of atoms. Subscripts are neglected. Thus, N_2 is before Na. The format of the table is self-explanatory. Transition energies, T_e, usually refer to (0,0) peak intensities. Since the line width varies significantly, these values are not always equally accurate and dependable. Electronic energies are listed in μm^{-1}. As explained for atoms, this unit is now considered more desirable, and, for matrices, is more convenient than cm^{-1}. 4.000 indicates 4.000 $\pm$ 0.0005; 4.0 indicates 4.0 $\pm$ 0.5. The vibrational frequency, ω_e, is listed in cm^{-1} because the use of μm^{-1} would lead to clumsy figures.

State	T_e (μm^{-1})	ω_e (cm^{-1})	Observed Transition	Remarks	T (°K)	Matrix	Preparation	References
BN								
A $^3\Pi$	2.79	1288	A ← X		4	Ne, Ar	H_3BNH_3 photolysis	Mosher 1970
X $^3\Pi$								
C$_2$								
d $^1\Sigma_u^+$	4.197 (Ar) 4.304 (Ne)	1839 ?	d ← x	Mulliken bands	14 4	Ne, Ar, N_2	C_2H_2 photolysis, C_3O_2 photolysis, carbon vapor, x-rays, $(C_2D_2, ^{13}C_2H_2)$	Brabson 65 Frosch 64 Milligan 67f, 69b,c Robinson 60 Weltner 62b, 64a,b, 66
b $^1\Pi_u$	0.842	1530	b ← x	Phillips system				
A $^3\Pi_g$ (?)	+2.300	1600	A ↔ X	Swan bands (?)				
?			a,b → n					
x $^1\Sigma$	0							
C$_2^-$								
Y	2.300	1939	A ← X	Swan bands	4–14	Ne, Ar	C_2+Cs	Milligan 69b
X	0	1600						

CH								
B $^2\Sigma^-$	2.572	2540	B→X	broad bands	4	Ar	CH$_4$ discharge	Keyser 65
A $^2\Delta$	2.310	2920	A←X	rotation ?				McCarty 59c
X $^2\Pi$	0							
CN								
B $^2\Sigma^+$	2.570	2160	B←X	progression of band	15,	N$_2$, Ar,	HCN photolysis	Milligan 67e
X $^2\Sigma^+$					4	Ne		Easley 70
CO								
C $^1\Sigma^+$	2.717		C → A	Herzberg bands (?)	4–30	Ar, Kr,	CO$_2$ x-rays,	Anderson 66
A $^1\Pi$	6.383	~1480 kV	A ← X	4th positive group		Xe, pure	^{13}C^{18}O	Brith 65
d $^3\Delta_i$	6.430	1569 Co	d ← X	origin not observ. Davidov splitting 450 cm^{-1}		solid		Dressler 62
	?							Frosch 65
a $^3\Pi_2$	4.840	1750	a ← X	Cameron band 0 v' 5 exciton splitting due to a-A spin-orbit mixing				Hexter 67
								Leroy 64
X $^1\Sigma^+$		2138.1	IR					Roncin 65c, 66, 67b, 68

State	T_e (μm^{-1})	ω_e (cm^{-1})	Observed Transition	Remarks	T (°K)	Matrix	Preparation	References
CS								
$A\ ^1\Pi$	3.860	1070	$A \leftarrow X$	3 vibrational levels	77	glass	CS_2 photolysis	Norman 54
$X\ ^1\Sigma^+$	0							
ClO								
?	?		255–300 nm				ClO_2 photolysis	Norman 54
CuO								
$B\ ^2\Sigma$	2.49	624	$B - X$	$Cu\ ^{16}O$ and $Cu\ ^{18}O$	4	Ar, Kr	$Cu + O_2$ photolysis	Shirk 70
$A\ ^2\Pi$	0.39	605	$A \leftarrow X$					
$X\ ^2\Pi$	0	665						
GeO								
$A\ ^1\Sigma$	3.66	630	$^1\Sigma \leftarrow {}^1\Sigma$		20	Xe, Kr, CH_4, O_2, SF_6, N_2, **Ar**	GeO vapor $t(20°K,Ar) =$ 1.6 msec	Meyer 70c,d Ogden 70
$a\ ^3\Pi$	2.60		$^3\Pi \rightarrow {}^1\Sigma$	Cameron bands				
$X\ ^1\Sigma$	0	973.4	IR	$(Ge_2O_2$ impurities)				

GeS					20	Xe, Kr	GeS vapor	Meyer 70c,d
$^1\Pi$	4.000		$^1\Pi \rightarrow {}^1\Sigma$	broad, continuous (?)				
$^1\Sigma$	3.300	350	$^1\Sigma \rightarrow {}^1\Sigma$	6 bands			$t_{(20°K, Ar)} =$ 2.4 msec	
a $^3\Pi$	2.250	550	$^3\Pi \rightarrow {}^1\Sigma$	Cameron bands				
X $^1\Sigma$	0							
GeSe					20	SF$_6$, Kr	GeSe vapor	Spitzer 70
$^1\Sigma$	3.04							
a $^3\Pi$	2.05							
X $^1\Sigma$	0							
H$_2$			IR					Bass 58 Vegard 30c Vu 63
HBr								Kwok 62 Mann 66 Pandey 66 Schnepp 69

State	T_e (μm^{-1})	ω_e (cm^{-1})	Observed Transition	Remarks	T (°K)	Matrix	Preparation	References
HCl					4–50	Ar, Kr Xe		Acquista 68a
X			IR	rotation,				Atwood 67
								Flygare 63
								Friedmann, 64, 65
								Katz 69
								Keyser 66a,b
								Kwok 62
								Pandey 68
								Schoen 62b
								Verstegen 66
								Whyte 66
HF								Pandey 66
HI								Kwok 62
HS								
A $^2\Sigma$	3.04	1850	A ← X		20	Ar	photolysis of H_2S	Acquista 70
X $^2\Pi$	0	2540	IR	HS, DS				

HfO

				vapor composition unknown	4	Ne, Ar	HfO₂ vapor	Weltner 65d
G	3.009	861	G ← X					
F($^1\Sigma^+$)	2.745	838	F ← X					
E($^1\Pi$)	2.555	874	E ← X					
D$_{D'}$	2.383	862	D ← X					
	2.237		(D'→ x')?					
B	1.785	906	B ← X					
A	1.692		A ← X					
x' $^3\Delta$	?	929	Emission					
X($^1\Sigma^+$)	0	974	IR					

LaO

					4	Ne, Ar	La$_2$^{18}O$_3$, La + La$_2$O$_3$	Weltner 67a
C $^2\Pi$	2.460	–	C ← X	La impurity				
	2.400			broad bands, blue shifted by ~500 cm⁻¹				
B $^2\Sigma$	1.837	720	B ← X	photosensitive				
A $^2\Pi_{3/2}$	1.291	752	A ← X					
X $^2\Sigma$	0	810	IR					

State	T_e (μm^{-1})	ω_e (cm^{-1})	Observed Transition	Remarks	T (°K)	Matrix	Preparation	References
LiF								
X		917		$(LiF)_n$ $1<n<3$			^7LiF; ^6LiF Molecular beams	Snelson 63, 67b
LiO								White 63b
N$_2$								
$\omega\ ^1\Delta_u$			$\omega \leftarrow X$					Broida 60
$a\ ^1\Pi$			$a \leftarrow X$					Peyron 59a,b
$C\ ^3\Pi_u$			$C \rightarrow B$	Ne only	4–30	Ar, Kr, Xe, Ne	Gas	Pilon 59
$B\ ^3\Pi_g$								Ron 67
								Roncin 65c, 67b, 68
$A\ ^3\Sigma_u$			$A \rightarrow X$	Vegard-Kaplan				Schnepp 65
$X\ ^1\Sigma_g^+$								Schoen 60
								Tinti 68b
								Vegard 24 to 48
								Kuan 70
NBr								
$X\ ^3\Sigma$		693	IR	^{74}NBr, ^{15}NBr	4,20	Ar, N$_2$	BrN_3 photolysis	Milligan 64c

Species / State		Freq	Transition	Notes	Temp	Matrix	Production	References
NCl		818	IR	$N^{35}Cl$, $N^{37}Cl$	4,20	Ar, N_2	ClN_3 photolysis	Milligan 64c
NF		1115	IR	FN_3, NF_2, ^{14}NF, ^{15}NF	4,20	Ar, N_2	FN_3 photolysis	Milligan 64c
NH								
$^1\Delta_g$	3.047(?)		$^1\Delta \leftarrow x$	**vw**, disappears when discharge is interrupted	40	Ar, Kr, Xe	NH_3, HN_3, H_nN_m discharge	Dows 55a, McCarty 59b,c, Milligan 64e, Rice 51, 53, Robinson 57a, 58d, 60b, Rosengren 65
A $^3\Pi$	2.958	2211(Ar)	$A \leftarrow X$	>20% yield, also NH_2, etc.				
X $^3\Sigma^-$								
NO								
a $^4\Pi_{5/2}$	3.794	1895	$a \leftarrow X$	often with N_2, O_2, N and O emission; $\tau=0.16$ sec in Ne; $\tau=0.09$ sec in Ar; $\tau=0.04$ sec in Kr	4–30	Ne, Ar, Kr, Xe, N_2	NO, N_2, O_2 solid rare gas with x-ray, electron	Broida 60, 63, Frosch 64, Lefebvre 68, Roncin 67a, 68, Vegard 26a
B $^2\Pi$	4.533	1902	$B \leftarrow X$					
X $^2\Pi_{1/2}$	0	1874	β-bands					
$^2\Pi_{3/2}$		1868						

State	T_e (μm^{-1})	ω_e (cm^{-1})	Observed Transition	Remarks	T (°K)	Matrix	Preparation	References
NaCl								Snelson 63
O_2								
B $^3\Sigma_u^-$	5.218	819	B ← X	Schumann-Runge bands	4 liq.	N_2, Ar, Kr, Xe,	O_2, electron bombardment,	Bass 60a
A $^3\Sigma_u^+$	~3.400	1	A → X	O-atom emission NO neon only		N_2O,	$O_2(^1\Delta)$ gas	Broida 60a,b
b $^1\Sigma_g^+$	1.320	1432	b - X			$\alpha, \beta\ O_2$		Cairns 65
a $^1\Delta$	0.77		a → X					Schnepp 65
X $^3\Sigma_g^-$	0	1548	IR					Schoen 60b
								Graham 70
								Akimoto 70
$\underline{OH}$				impurities: Vegard-Kaplan and 2nd position system of N_2 Slow vibrational relaxation in emission	4	Ne, Ar	H_2O, D_2O x-rays; H_2O_2 H_2O-Ar discharge; vacuum UV photolysis	Acquista 68
A $^3\Sigma^+$	3.246	3145.5	A↔X					Matheson 55
	3.235							McCarty 59c
X $^2\Pi_i$	0	3735.5	Ne					Robinson 57a, 58b,d
								Tinti 68a

PH								
A $^3\Pi_i$	~2.950(?)	-	A ← X(?)	broad band	4	Ar	phosphine discharge	McCarty 59c
X $^3\Sigma^-$	0							
Pb₂								
A	1.91 (-2.02)	168	A ← X	9 bands	20	Xe, Kr, Ar, SF₆	beam	Chang 70
X	0							
S₂								
B $^3\Sigma_u^-$	3.180	440	B ↔ X		4	Ne, Ar, Kr, Xe, N₂, CO, CH₄, SF₆	S₂ vapor, ^{34}S₂, S₂Cl₂ and H₂S photolysis	Brabson 65a, Brewer 65b, Meyer 60a,b, 62, Milligan 64b, Petropoulos 67, Smith,J. 68c
X $^3\Sigma_g^-$	0	760						
SCl								
			? ← X	UV and IR in rare gas matrices show only S₂	77	hydro-carbon glass	S₂Cl₂ photolysis	Smith,J. 68c, Snowden 5

State	T_e (μm^{-1})	ω_e (cm^{-1})	Observed Transition	Remarks	T (°K)	Matrix	Preparation	References
ScF								
E $^1\Pi$	2.086	605	E ← X		4-11	Ne	Sc + ScF$_3$	McLeod 66
C $^1\Sigma$	1.605	580	C↔X	photoinduced secondary sites				
B $^1\Pi$	<1.063							
X $^1\Sigma^+$	0	719						
ScO								
B $^2\Sigma$	2.091	822	B ← X	Sc-atom impurities bleaches in 4 hr	4, 33	Ne, Ar	Sc$_2$O$_3$ vapor	Weltner 67a
A $^2\Pi_{3/2}$	1.706	840	A ← X					
A $^2\Pi_{1/2}$	1.681	847						
X $^2\Sigma$		963	IR					
Se$_2$								
B $^3\Sigma_u^-$	2.600(?)	280	B ← X	origin not observed	200	Ar, Xe	^{78}Se$_2$, ^{80}Se$_2$	Meyer 70
X $^3\Sigma_g^-$	0							

Si₂								
D ³Π_u	3.47	530	D ← X		4,	Ne, Ar	Si vapor,	Weltner 64c
H ³Σ_u⁻	2.458(?)	260	H ← X	origin not certain	14		photolysis of SiH₄	Milligan 70
X ³Σ_g⁻	0			matrix confirms X is ground state				
SiH								
	0	1967	IR	(Si₂O₂ impurity)			photolysis of SiH₄	Milligan 70
SiO								
A ¹Π	4.266	830	A ← X		4	Ar, Kr, Xe	rare gas discharge in quartz tube; vapor	Shirk 68
X ¹Σ⁺	0	1223.9	IR	(Si₃O₂ impurity)				Anderson 69
SnO								
D ¹Π	2.902	780	D ← X	vibrational perturbations excited via intersystem crossing; not observed in gas phase	20	Ar, Kr, Xe	SnO vapor, Sn, $t_{(20°K,Ar)} =$ 0.24 msec	Smith,J. 68a
a ³Π	2.090	-	a → X					Meyer 70
X ¹Σ	0	~800						

State	T_e (μm^{-1})	ω_e (cm^{-1})	Observed Transition	Remarks	T (°K)	Matrix	Preparation	References
SnS								
D $^1\Pi$	2.800	350	D ← X	vibrational perturbations excited by intersystem crossing from D; not observed in gas phase	20	Ar, Kr, Xe	SnS vapor $t(20°K,Ar) =$ 0.52 msec	Smith,J. 68a Meyer 70
a $^3\Pi$	1.820	–	a → X					
X $^1\Sigma$	0	550						
TaO								
Q	2.924			$Ta^{16}O$, $Ta^{18}O$	4, 20	Ne, Ar	Ta_2O_5 vapor	Weltner 65c
$^2\Delta_{3/2}$ P=c	2.675	899						
N	2.562							
$^2\Phi_{5/2}$ M=d	2.415	889	M↔X	weak emission				
$^2\Pi_{1/2}$ L=b	2.340	887	L↔X	weak emission				
K	2.213	895						
I	2.089	944	I ← X					
H	2.080	910	H↔X	strongest emission				
G	1.801		G ← X					

TaO (Cont)								
F	1.672	922	F ← X					
E	1.599	925	E ← X					
D	1.439	941	D ← X					
C	1.370	931	C ← X					
B	1.299		B ← X					
A	1.215		A ← X					
$^2\Delta_{3/2}$ X=a	0	1020	IR					
TiO								
$\alpha = c\ ^3\Delta_1$	1.946	830	C ← X	$Ti^{16}O, Ti^{18}O$	4, 20	Ne, Ar	TiO_2 vapor (W_xO_y impurities)	Weltner 65d
$\lambda'\ ^3\Pi_0$	1.633	863	$\lambda' \leftrightarrow X$					
$A\ ^3\Phi_2$	1.407	855	A ← X	v perturbed in Ar				
$X\ ^3\Delta_1$	0	956(?) 1005	fluorescence IR					

State	T_e (μm^{-1})	ω_e (cm^{-1})	Observed Transition	Remarks	T (°K)	Matrix	Preparation	References
WO								
G	2.380	893		weak	4, 20	Ar, Ne	WO_2, WO_3 vapor	Weltner 65e
F	2.339	886		perturbed				
E	2.150	896		perturbed				
D	2.080	927		corresponds to gas phase				
C	1.919	874		perturbed				
B	1.728	883		perturbed				
A	-1.416	948		perturbed				
		1046						
X $^3\Sigma^-$	0	1055		IR				
		1064						
YO								
B $^2\Sigma$	2.152	772	4650	Ne:700 cm^{-1} blue shifted	4, 20	Ar, Ne pre-cooled	Y_2O_3 vapor	Weltner 67a
A $^2\Pi_{3/2}$	1.755	812	5700					
A $^2\Pi_{1/2}$	1.700	–						
X	0	853	5890	Y, WO impurities				

ZrO					4, 20	Ar, Ne	ZrO$_2$ vapor Zr ^{18}O$_2$	Weltner 65a,d
b $^1\Sigma^+$	2.723	807	b↔X	α-bands				
B $^3\Pi_0$	x'+1.833		B → x'	β-bands				
system 2	1.940	836	? ← X					
?	1.702	872	? ← X					
system 2	1.551	854	2 ← X					
X $^3\Delta_1$	?	886; 935 975		v: text error? IR				
X $^1\Sigma$	0							

C. Triatomics†

Molecules are listed according to the first element in the formula. Since the writing of formulas is not standardized, we quote the formula of the original publication. This leads to some inconsistencies. NCN and CN_2, for example, appear at far separated places. HCN, CH_2, and other hydrogen-containing triatomics may be listed under hydrogen, or any other atom which they contain. As in diatomics, subscripts are ignored. Therefore, N_3 is before NaF, etc.

---

† The author thanks Dr. J. Smith who assisted by collating data for this table.

Molecule and State	T_e	Observed Transition	ν_1	ν_2	ν_3	Remarks and Matrix	$T_{°K}$	Preparation	References
Al_2O X	0	IR	715	(238)	994	argon; ν_2 calc. overtone at 1867 cm^{-1}; ^{18}O Ar Kr	4.2	Al+Al$_2$O$_3$ 1465°K	Linevsky 64
BO_2 $B\,^2\Sigma_u^+$	2.14	B ← X				2 bands only Ar	4.2	vaporization ZnO$_{(s)}$+B$_2$O$_3$ 1825°K	Sommer 63
$A\,^2\Pi_u$	1.79	A ← X 400–565nm	930	465	2400	^{11}B			
$X\,^2\Pi_g$	0	IR			1276	^{11}B; $^2\Pi_{1/2}$ may be frozen out excess B$_2$O$_3$ masks low frequency region			
BaF_2 X	0	IR	390	(64)	413	neon; polymer peak at 325 cm^{-1} ν_2 calc. Ne Ar Kr	4.2	vaporization 1475–2125°K	Calder 69 Snelson 66
$BeBr_2$ X	0	IR	230	207	993	neon; ν_2 not observed in argon Ar polymer bands at 570 and 760 cm^{-1}; ν_1 calc. Ne Ar	4.2 20	vaporization 975°K	Snelson 68

Species	State	(eV)	Method	ν1	ν2	ν3	Comments	Matrix	T/K	Conditions	Reference
BeCl$_2$	X	0	IR	(390)	238	1122	neon; dimer bands at 870, 640 cm^{-1}; ν$_1$ calc.	Ne Ar Kr	4.2	vaporization 725–1275°K	Snelson 66,68
BeF$_2$	X	0	IR	(680)	330	1542	neon; aggregate bands at 790, 830 and 1250 cm^{-1}; ν$_1$ calc.	Ne Ar Kr	4.2	vaporization 875–1275°K	Snelson 66
BeI$_2$	X	0	IR	(160)		872	neon; ν$_3$ doublet ν$_1$ calc.	Ne Ar	4.2	vaporization 975°K	Snelson 68
C$_3$	A $^1\Pi_u$	2.46	A ↔ X 380–408nm	1125	305	(840)	neon; ν$_3$ tentative	CO$_2$ Ne	4.2 20	carbon vapor	Barger 62,64, 65 Brabson 65b Weltner 62b, 64a,64b,66
	a $^3\Pi_u$	1.71	a → X				neon; excited via A ← X at 405 or 365nm	N$_2$ SF$_6$ Ar			
	x $^1\Sigma_g^+$	0	IR	1235	(75)	2040	neon; average ν$_2$	O$_2$ Kr Xe			
CBr$_2$	X $^1A_1$	0	IR	595		641	numerous other species present; ν$_2$ probably 200 cm^{-1}	Ar	15	Li + CBr$_4$	Andrews 68c
CBrCl	X	0	IR	739		612	ν$_2$ not observed	Ar	15	1) Li + CClBr$_3$ 2) Li + CCl$_3$Br	Andrews 68c

Molecule and State	T_e	Observed Transition	ν_1	ν_2	ν_3	Remarks and Matrix	$T_{°K}$	Preparation	References
CCO ?	(2.00)	?←X (500nm)				broad, unstructured continuum Ar, N_2	4.2	1) C, from photolysis of N_3CN, +CO	Jacox 65b
$X^3\Sigma$	0	IR	1978	381	1074	Ar	14	photolysis of C_3O_2	
CCl_2 $A(^1A_1$ or $^1B_1)$	(1.78)	A←X 440–560nm		305		16 bands, prog. in ν_2 Ar, N_2	14	1) C, from photolysis of N_3CN+Cl_2	Andrews 68b,e Milligan 67c
X^1A_1	0	IR	720		746	most abundant species; CCl_4, CCl_3 and other impurities present	15	2) $Li+CCl_4$	
CF_2 $A(^1A_1)$	3.74	A←X 230–268nm	1222	500	1102	single prog. in ν_1; 16 bands observed Ar; ^{13}C; "impurities" present: $CF_2N_2CF_2$, C_2F_4', Ar, N_2, CO, CO_2	4.2	1) discharge through C_4F_8 in Ar 2) photolysis of CF_2N_2	Bass 62 Milligan 64c 68a
X^1A_1	0	IR		668		CF_4, CF_3, C_2F_6, $(CF_2N)_2$		3) photolysis of F_2, N_3CN and argon or N_2 mixtures	

Species	State	Transition	Frequencies	Assignment / Notes	Matrix	No.	Method	References
CH_2				indirect chemical evidence only				DeMore 58; Goldfarb 60a,b; Jacox 63a; Milligan 58, 62a,67d; Moore 64a,65; Robinson 60b
C_2H	0	IR	(1848)	no assignment; $^{13}C,D$	Ar	14	vacuum UV photolysis of C_2H_2	Brabson 65; Milligan 67a
CNN	?	? ← X 419–396nm	1355	2 bands	Kr, Ar	14	1) photolysis of N_3CN 2) photolysis of C_3O_2 in N_2 3) photolysis of CH_2N_2	Goldfarb 60b; Milligan 65c, 66a; Robinson 60b; Weltner 66
	$X^3\Sigma$ 0	IR	2847 393 1241	^{13}C, ^{15}N	N_2, N_2, Ar			
COS	6.74	? ← X 115–145nm	(760)	krypton; Rydberg like; mode not assigned;	Ne, Ar, Kr	2–80	1) direct deposition 2) photolysis of S_2Cl_2 in CO	J. Smith 68c; Roncin 69; Verderame 66
	5.96 5.54	? ← X ? ← X	(495) 511	krypton; argon; 15+ bands	CO			
	$X^1\Sigma^+$ 0	IR	2050 518 857	ν_3 argon; ν_1 and ν_2 argon; ν_2 pure solid	N_2, CS_2, COS			
CS_2	6.60	? ← X 135–152nm	(540)	neon; mode not assigned; 1st band; origin not clear; Rydberg series suppressed	Ar, Kr, Xe, Ne, N_2, CH_4	2–20	direct deposition	Bajena 70; Roncin 69

Molecule and State	T_e	Observed Transition	ν_1	ν_2	ν_3	Remarks and Matrix	$T_{°K}$	Preparation	References
CS_2 (continued)									
$(^1B_2)$	3.10	? ← X	560 290–330nm			argon; simultaneous progressions in v'_1 and v'_2; Renner-Teller splittings			
$(^3B_2)$ or $(^3\Lambda_2)$	1.82	? → X				two lifetime components $\tau_1=0.8$msec; $\tau_2=2.6$msec in argon			
$X\,^1\Sigma_g^+$	0								
CaF_2 X	0	IR	485	163	554	krypton; dimer bands at 528cm^{-1}, 370 cm^{-1}; Ne Ar Kr ^{40}Ca and ^{44}Ca	4.2	vaporization 1675–2175°K	Calder 69 Snelson 66
$CdBr_2$ $X\,^1\Sigma_g^+$	0	IR	(205)	62	319	dimer band at 270 Kr cm^{-1}; polymers at 190, 163 cm^{-1}; ν_1 calc.	4.2 20	vaporization	Loewenschuss 69
$CdCl_2$ $X\,^1\Sigma_g^+$	0	IR	(327)	89	420	krypton; bands at 371,364,357 cm^{-1} assigned to dimers Ar Kr Xe	4.2 20	vaporization	Loewenschuss 69 McNamee 62

CdF_2	$X^1\Sigma_g^+$	0	IR	(572)	123	662	polymer bands at 475, 384, and 377 cm⁻¹; ν_1 calc.	Kr	4.2 20	vaporization	Loewenschuss 69
CdI_2	$X^1\Sigma_g^+$	0	IR	(150)		270	dimer bands at 222, 217 cm⁻¹; polymers at 140, 127 cm⁻¹; ν_1 calc.	Kr	4.2 20	vaporization	Loewenschuss 69
Cl_3	X	0	IR	(273)		374	group of bands between 365-375 cm⁻¹; 35Cl, 37Cl ν_1 calculated linear, slightly asymmetric	Kr	20	discharge through Kr and Cl_2	Nelson 67b
ClCO	X	0	IR	1880	281	570	possible C-O triple bond 13C	Ar	14	Cl sources HCl, Cl_2, Cl_2CO, $(ClCO)_2$	Jacox 65a

Molecule and State	T_e	Observed Transition	ν_1	ν_2	ν_3	Remarks and Matrix	$T_{°K}$	Preparation	References
ClClO X	0	IR	960		372	quartets; ^{18}O isotope shift smaller than expected N_2	20	photolysis of Cl_2O in N_2	Rochkind 67b
ClO_2 $A(^2A_2)$	(2.30)	$A \leftarrow X$ 300-430nm				diffuse MPH	77	solutions	Arkell 67 Norman 55
X^2B_1	0	IR	940	448	1100	ν_1 and ν_2 appear as quartets Ar	4.2	direct deposition	Rochkind 67b
ClOO X	0	IR	1441	407	373	argon, O^{18} N_2 O_2 Ar	4.2	1) photolysis of Cl_2 and O_2 mixtures 2) photolysis of OClO in Ar, N_2, O_2	Arkell 67 Rochkind 67b
$CoCl_2$?	(4.58)	? ← X						vaporization	Clifton 69
?	4.16	? ← X				broad band Ar	4.2		DeKock 68
?	(3.95)	? ← X					14		Jacox 69b
?	(3.64)	? ← X				Kr			K. Thompson 68
?	3.50	? ← X 286nm	233			shoulder			
?	3.37	? ← X 290-320nm				single band Xe			
?	(3.20)	? ← X							
?	(3.08)	? ← X							
$X(^4\Phi_g)$	0	IR		95	493	most abundant species, linear			

Species	State	eV	Transition	Frequencies (cm⁻¹)	Notes	Matrix		Method	Reference
CrCl₂	?	3.85	? ← X 260nm down		strong, continuous below 260nm; gas phase bands at 3.62 and 4.96 μm⁻¹ not observed	Ar	14	1) vaporization 2) reaction of Cl₂ with hot Cr 1035-1095°K	Jacox 69b
	?	3.26	? ← X		weak, unstructured				
	X	0	IR	490	most abundant species; linear				
FCO	A	(3.00)	A ← X 220-340nm		43 bands; 18 appear in progression $(v_1',0,0)$; ^{13}C, ^{18}O	Co Ar	4 14 20	1) F+CO F from NF₂, OF₂ t-N₂F₂ 2) photolysis of F₂CO and HFCO	Milligan 65b
	X²A₁	0	IR	1855 626 1018					
FeCl₂	?	(4.76)	? ← X		Jacox 69 reports 4.16 superimposed on increasing continuum only band maxima	Ar	4.2 14	1) vaporization 2) reaction of Cl₂ with hot Fe (1085°K)	DeKock 68 Jacox 69b K. Thompson 68
	?	(4.41)	? ← X						
	?	(4.16)	? ← X 240nm						
	?	(3.98)	? ← X 250 down						
	X⁵Δg	(3.75)	? ← X IR	88 493	most abundant species, linear strong N₂ shift of ν₃ to 447 cm⁻¹				

Molecule and State	T_e	Observed Transition	ν_1	ν_2	ν_3	Remarks and Matrix	$T_{°K}$	Preparation	References
GeF$_2$ X^{1}A$_1$	0	IR	685	(263)	655	neon, strongest component; from gas phase; bands at 800 cm^{-1} due to GeF$_4$; bands at 600cm^{-1} and 670cm^{-1} due to dimers or polymers Ne Ar	4.2	vaporization at 425°K	Hastie 68
HCCl A^{1}A''	(1.25)	A ← X 560–750nm		860		argon; several perturbations Ar	14	C from N$_3$CN photolysis + HCl	Jacox 67**b**
X^{1}A'	0	IR		1201	815				
HCF A^{1}A''	1.73	A ← X		1010		argon; 0,0,0 not observed; progression (0,v$_2$',0) matrix shift ν_0+30 cm^{-1} Ar N$_2$	14	photolysis of CH$_3$F	Jacox 69a
X^{1}A'	0	IR		1405	1182	bands at 2918 or 3262 may be ν_1 ^{13}C,D			

Molecule	State		Transition / Method	ν_1	ν_2	ν_3	Remarks	K	Preparation	References
HCO	$B\,^2A'$	3.87	$B \leftarrow X$ 210–260nm	1375		1035	hydrocarbon flame CO bands; origin not observed	14	1) photolysis of HI,HBr or H_2S in CO 2) discharge through $CH_4/O_2/Ar$ mixtures 3) reaction of O atoms with C_2H_2	Ewing 60 McCarty 59b Milligan 64e 69a Robinson 58b
	$A\,^2A''$	(0.93)	$A \leftarrow X$ 510–670nm		(800)					
	$X\,^2A'$	0	IR	2488	1090	1861	1937,1800 and 852 cm^{-1} for DCO; $^{13}C, D$			
HNC	$X(^1\Sigma^+)$	0	IR	3620	477	2029	presence of N_2 in Ar neighboring site perturbs the normal modes. values shift to 535,2032,and 3583 in Ar when significant amounts of N_2 are present	4.2 14	1) vacuum UV photolysis of HCN 2) photolysis of CH_3N_3	Milligan 63b 67b
HNF	$A\,^2A'$	2.03	$^2A' \leftarrow {}^2A''$ 390–500nm		1033		progression in ν_2	14	reaction of F atoms with NH; F from photolysis of N_2F_2 or F_2; NH from HN_3	Jacox 67a
	$X\,^2A''$	0	IR	1432	1000		D, ^{15}N			

Molecule and State	T_e	Observed Transition	ν_1	ν_2	ν_3	Remarks and Matrix	$T_{°K}$	Preparation	References
HNO $^1A''$	1.31	A ← X 575–760nm		1422	982	argon progressions in $v'_2 + v'_3$	Ar N$_2$O CO$_2$	4.2 14 20	1)discharge through N$_2$H$_4$/ O$_2$/H$_2$O/Ar 2)photolysis of CH$_3$NO$_2$ or CH$_3$ONO 3)discharge through Ar/ H$_2$/NO 4)photolysis of HN$_3$ in CO$_2$ or N$_2$O	H. Brown 58 Harvey 59 McCarty 59b Milligan 62c Robinson 57a, 58a,b,c,d
X $^1A'$	0	IR	(3592)	1570	1110	argon angle ~110° disagreement regarding ν_1				
HOBr X	0	IR	3590	1164	626	natural isotopes O18, D; estimated angle 110°	Ar	4.2	photolysis of Ar/HBr/O$_3$	Schwager 67
HOCl X	0	IR	3581	1239	729	natural isotopic species;O18, D	Ar	4.2	photolysis of Ar/HCl/O$_3$ mixtures	Schwager 67
HO$_2$ X $^2A''$	0	IR	3414	1389	1101	argon oxygens non-equivalent	Ar	4.2	H, from photolysis of HI or HBr + O$_2$	Milligan 63a, 64a

HgBr$_2$ $X^1\Sigma_g^+$	0	IR	(219)	73	294	dimer band at 286 cm^{-1}; polymer at 261 cm^{-1}; ν_1 calc.	Kr	4.2 20	vaporization	Loewenschuss 69
HgCl$_2$ $X^1\Sigma_g^+$	0	IR	(348)	107	407	ν_3 triplet; unidentified band at 412 cm^{-1}; dimer at 402 cm^{-1}; ν_1 calc.	Ar Kr Xe	4.2 20	vaporization	Loewenschuss 69 McNamee 62
HgF$_2$ $X^1\Sigma_g^+$	0	IR	(588)	172	642	ν_3 doublet; dimer bands at 586 cm^{-1}; other bands at 660, 384 cm^{-1}; ν_1 calc.	Kr	4.2 20	vaporization	Loewenschuss 69
HgI$_2$ $X^1\Sigma_g^+$	0	IR	(158)	63	238	other bands at 229, 220, 234 cm^{-1}; ν_1 calc.	Kr	4.2 20	vaporization	Loewenschuss 69

Molecule and State	T_e	Observed Transition	ν_1	ν_2	ν_3	Remarks and Matrix	$T\ ^\circ K$	Preparation	References
KrF_2 X	0			236	580	aggregate bands at 575 and 245 cm^{-1}; bond strengths similar to XeF_2 Ar	20	photolysis of $F_2/Kr/Ar$ mixture	Turner 63a,b
LiO_2 X	0	IR	(340)	231	685	best fit for C_{2v}; ν_1 calculated angle = 170° Kr	20	vaporization	Seshadri 66 White 63b
Li_2O X	0	IR	(685)	112	987	probably linear; ν_1 calc. ^6Li Kr	20	vaporization 1640°K	Seshadri 66 White 63b
LiON X	0	IR	1352	333	650	molecular arrangement proposed LiON; ν_3 strongest band Ar	15 4.2	codeposition of Li and NO	Andrews 66a
MgF_2	0	IR	478	242	837	krypton; ^{24}Mg, ^{25}Mg, ^{26}Mg, Ne; bands at 450 and 480cm^{-1} assigned to polymers; angle 158° Ar Kr	4.2 20	vaporization 1500-1575°K	Calder 69 Mann 67 Snelson 66
$MnCl_2$ $X\,^6\Sigma_g^+$	5.00 4.57 4.39 0	? ← X ? ← X 250nm down ? ← X 228nm IR	83	477		all bands broad, unstructured shoulder most abundant species Ar	4.2 14	1) vaporization 2) reaction of Cl_2 with hot Mn surface 995-1085°K	DeKock 68 Jacox 69b K. Thompson 68

Molecule	State	T (eV)	Transition	ν_1	ν_2	ν_3	Notes	Matrix	Production	References
NCN	$B^3\Sigma_u^-$	3.31	B ← X 340–300nm	1040			argon; photolyzes with λ=2500Å; mean lifetime 500 μsec in N_2	N_2 14 CO 20 Ar	photolysis of N_3CN	Comeford 66 Milligan 65c, 66c,69c Moll 66a Schoen 66
	$^1\Delta_g$	3.00	$^1\Delta$ ← X 335nm							
	$^3\Pi_u$	2.99	Π ← X 300....	1140			argon; structureless			
	$X^3\Sigma_g^-$	0	IR	1197	423	1475	$(\nu_1+\nu_3) = 2672$; $^{13}C, {}^{15}N$			
NCO	$B^2\Pi$	3.16	B ← X 400–450nm	2295		1036	neon (R_2) ~40 bands	Ne 4.2 Ar 14 N_2 CO	1) $CH_4/Ar/N_2$ O_2 discharge 2) vacuum UV photolysis HNCO 3) vacuum UV photolysis HN_3 in CO 4) C (from N_3CN)+NO 5) O (N_2O) + CN (from HCN)	McCarty 59c Milligan 67c Robinson 58b
	$A^2\Sigma^+$	2.28	A ← X 240–320nm	2325	687	1270	neon (Q) 5 bands			
	$X^2\Pi_i$	0	IR	1922	437	1275	considerable spin splitting (A=956 cm^{-1}); transitions from $^2\Pi_{3/2}$ only at 14° K and below; large Renner splitting			

Molecule and State	T_e	Observed Transition	ν_1	ν_2	ν_3	Remarks and Matrix	$T_{°K}$	Preparation	References
NH_2 $A\,^2A_1$	1.02	A ← X 344-730nm	3350	680		$T_e+\nu'_2$ extrapolated; alternate bands; originates in 0"0. II and B vibronic sub bands; ν'_1 average value = $\Delta l/2W$ ~3cm⁻¹ Ar Kr N₂	4.2 14	1) discharge through N₂H₄/Ar 2) vacuum UV photolysis of NH₃ 3) photolysis of HN₃	Keyser 60 Milligan 65e Robinson 57c 58a,b,c,59, 62b
$X\,^2B_1$	0	IR		1499	3220	Possible free rotation in matrix			
N_2O F	9.20	F ← X				observed only in argon sol. Ne	1.5 63	direct deposition	Granier-Mayence 53 Romand 52 Sibleyras 68 DeMore 59a
E	9.01	E ← X				Ne Ar			
D	8.33	D ← X				Ne, continuous Kr			
C	7.34	C ← X				Ne, continuous N₂			
B	(6.20)	B ← X		(590)		progression in ν'_2 average spacing; origin not observed			
$A(^1\Sigma^+)$	(4.00)	A ← X				structureless b = 3600cm⁻¹			
$X\,^1\Sigma^+$	0	IR				in nitrogen; all transitions strongly blue shifted			

Molecule / State	E	Transition	ν_1	ν_2	ν_3	Comments	Matrix	Conc.	Conditions	References
NO_2 $A(^2B_1)$	1.12		(620)			argon; blue shifted from gas by 55–70 cm^{-1}	N_2	1.5		Becker 56
X^2A_1	0	IR	(1322)	750	1611	argon; numerous dimer bands	Ar	4		Fateley 59
							O_2	20		Robinson 57a
							CO_2			
							H_2			
							N_2O			
$NiCl_2$?	4.15	? ← X	283			very weak	Ar	4.2	1) vaporization, 675–800°K	DeKock 68
?	3.69	? ← X 265–290nm				extended progression		14	2) reaction of Cl_2 with hot Ni surface at <1375°K	Gruen 68
?	3.35	? ← X	249			extended progression				Jacox 69a,b
		290–325nm				extended progression				Milligan 65a
?	3.05	? ← X 330–370nm	256			extended progression				K. Thompson 68
?	2.13	? ← X 440–470nm	350			3 parallel progressions				
?	2.12	? ← X 470–500nm				featureless				
?	2.02	? ← X 480–500nm								
?	1.95	? → X 510–530nm				band separation 114 cm^{-1} (4 bands)				
?	1.72	? → X								
$X^3\Pi_g$	0	IR	360	85	521	most abundant species				
NiF_2 $X(^3\Pi)$	0	IR	(606)		780	most abundant species; peaks near 715 may be due to dimers; ν calculated	Ar	14	vaporization 1075–1175°K	Milligan 65a

Molecule and State	T_e	Observed Transition	ν_1	ν_2	ν_3	Remarks and Matrix	$T_{°K}$	Preparation	References
O_3 $X\,^1A_1$	0	IR	(1125)	702	1025	$\nu_1+\nu_3$ at 2150 N_2	20	direct deposition	DeMore 58
OCl_2 X	0	IR	631	296	671	pure solid $\nu_1 = 636$ in argon; bent ^{18}O N_2 Ar pure sol.	20 77	direct deposition	Rochkind 65
OF_2	0	IR	812	461	926	nitrogen; ν_3 doublet; ν_2 from gas phase N_2 Ar O_2	4.2 20	1) photolysis of F_2 and O_2 mixtures 2) direct deposition	Arkell 65a,b Spratley 66
O_2F X	0	IR	1495	585	376	resembles O_2F_2 angle $\sim110°$; ^{18}O N_2 O_2 Ar	4.2 20	photolysis of OF_2/O_2 matrix or F_2/O_2 matrix mixtures	Arkell 65b Noble 66 Spratley 66
PH_2 $A\,^2A_1$	1.82	$A \leftarrow X$ 436-522nm	(2320)		930	origin not observed; ν_1 estimated; 5 bands $(0,v,0)-(0,0,0)$ Ar	4.2	discharge through PH_3 argon mixtures	McCarty 59c
$X\,^2B_1$	0								
S_3 A	2.37	$A \leftarrow X$		390		isopentane-cyclohexane Kr	76 20	photolysis of S_3Cl_2	Meyer, J.Phys. Chem., in press
X	0								

		State	Energy	Transition				Notes	Matrix	Temp	Method	References
SO_2	D	D	(4.23)	D ← X								
	C	C	(4.15)	C ← X								
		A^1B_1	2.96	A ← X 280–310nm	(720)	(220)		Kr; origin not observed; 17 bands; frequency differences from first observed bands	Ne Ar Kr Xe CH$_4$ CD$_4$ SF$_6$ C$_4$F$_4$ N$_2$ O$_2$	4.2 to 110	direct deposition	Allavena 69 Conway 69 B. Meyer 68 Phillips 69 Voigt 70
		a^3B_1	2.56	a → X 390–470nm				SF$_6$; lifetime 13.5 msec at 4.2°K in SF$_6$				
		X^1A_1	0	IR	1150	519	1351	Kr; ^{34}S; ^{18}O; Zeeman effect				
S_2O		A	2.90	A ← X	(720)	(286)	415	xenon;new origin, previous gas phase origin in error (see Herzberg 67) ν_1 estimated; ν_2 reevaluation of gas phase	Ar Kr Xe N$_2$	20 77	SOCl$_2$/matrix gas + Ag$_2$S at 433°K	Blukis 65 Phillips 69
		X^1A	0	IR	1165	388	679	Pure solid at 77°K				
ScF_2			(3.14)	(? ← X)	(580)			neon; tentative may be due to ScF$_3$	Ne	4.2	vaporization of ScF$_3$ 1875°K	McLeod 66
		X	0	IR	(661)	(709)		not positively identified				

Molecule and State	T_e	Observed Transition	ν_1	ν_2	ν_3	Remarks and Matrix	$T_{°K}$	Preparation	References
SeO_2 B	3.10	$B \leftrightarrow X$ 242-322nm 310-520nm	(620)	(310)		complex absorption, possibly 2 transitions or 2 progressions in (v',0,0) and (v',1,0); resonance fluorescence — Ar Kr Xe SF$_6$ CH$_4$ C$_4$F$_8$	20	vaporization 409°K	Voigt 70
?	>2.20	$? \leftarrow X$ 320-410nm				weak absorption; may involve state C			
C	2.20	$C \leftarrow X$ 425-613nm				C is triplet state τ=<.2 msec in Xe; 2.5 msec in SF$_6$; 2.0 msec in C$_4$F$_8$; excited at 365nm			
X	0	--			365				
Si_3 $A(^3\Sigma_u^-)$	2.15	$A \leftarrow X$	310			7 bands tentative — Ne	4.2	vaporization of silicon 2175-2675°K	Weltner 64c
$X(^3\Sigma_g^-)$	0								
SiC_2 $A^1\Pi_u$	2.01	$A^1\Pi_u \leftrightarrow X^1\Sigma^+$ 400-497nm 500-550nm	1461	230	1015	possible positive X'13 absorption fluorescence little r_e change from fluorescence data(gas phs.853) — Ne Ar	4.2 20	vaporization 2775-3125°K	Weltner 64c
$X^1\Sigma_g^+$	0	IR	1742	300	853				

Molecule / State		Transition	Frequencies (cm⁻¹)	Notes	Matrix	Conditions	Reference
(Si₂C) $A\,^1\Pi_u$	1.89	$A \leftarrow X$ 450–500nm	500	very tentative	Ne	4.2 vaporization silicon carbide 2775–3125°K	Weltner 64c
$X\,^1\Sigma_g^+$	0		(672)	calculated	Ar	20	
SiCl₂	0	IR	502, 513	assignments tentative; may be reverse	Ar	14 vacuum UV photolysis of SiH₂Cl₂	Milligan 68c
SiF₂ $A\,^1B_1$	4.40	$A \leftarrow X$ 213–226nm	843, 253	neon	Ne, Ar	4.2, 14 1)vacuum UV photolysis of SiH₂F₂ 2)reaction of SiF₄ with Si at 1425°K	Bassler 66a
$X\,^1A_1$	0	IR	343, 855	argon	CO, N₂	20	Milligan 68d
SrF₂ $X(^1A_1)$	0	IR	(441), 82, (443)	argon; may be due due splitting; bands at 303 and 356 cm⁻¹ assigned to aggregates	Ne, Ar, Kr	4.2, 20 vaporization 1625°K	Calder 69, Snelson 66
TaO₂ $B(^2A)$	1.62	$B \leftarrow X$ 558–616nm	937, 281	weak	Ne, Ar	4.2, 20 1)vaporization 2)reaction with hot tantalum (2270°K)	Weltner 65a
$A(^2A)$	1.16	$A \leftarrow X$	285	progression in v'_2; also see $(1,v'_2 0) \leftarrow (0,0,0)$ assignment based on a decrease from $v'_1 \leftarrow v''_1$			
$X(^2B_1)$	0	IR	(971), (912)				

Molecule and State	T_e	Observed Transition	ν_1	ν_2	ν_3	Remarks and Matrix		$T^{\circ}K$	Preparation	References
WO_2 $B(^3B_2)$	1.28	$B \leftarrow X$		287		neon	Ne	4.2	1) vaporization WO_3 or $WO_{2.96}$ 1600°K 2) reaction of O_2 with tungsten at 1900–2950°K	Weltner 65b
$A(^3B_1)$	1.27	$A \leftarrow X$	972	300		neon; ^{18}O; extended progression in ν'_2	Ar	20		
$X(^3A_1)$	0	IR	992		928	neon; ^{18}O; numerous IR absorptions between 600–1000 cm^{-1} assigned to higher oxides				
$XeCl_2$ X	0	IR			313	complex absorption due to Xe isotopes	Xe	20	Xe + Cl_2 through microwave discharge	Nelson 67a
XeF_2 X	0	IR	(510)		547	high F_2:Xe ratios give XeF_4	Ar	20	photolysis of F_2 in Xe	Turner 63a
$ZnBr_2$ $X^1\Sigma_g^+$	0	IR		73	404	most abundant species in Kr; band at 326 assigned to dimers	Ar Kr Xe	4.2 20	vaporization	Loewenschuss 68 McNamee 62
$ZnCl_2$ $X^1\Sigma_g^+$	0	IR		103	508	most abundant species in Kr; bands at 425, 334 and 297 assigned to dimers	Ar Kr Xe	4.2 20	vaporization	Loewenschuss 68 McNamee 62

ZnF$_2$	X$^1\Sigma_g^+$	0	IR	151	758	most abundant species in Kr; band at 665 assigned to dimer	Ar Kr Xe	4.2 20	vaporization	Loewenschuss 68 McNamee 62
ZnI$_2$	X$^1\Sigma_g^+$	0	IR	62	346	most abundant species in Kr; band at 272 assigned to dimer	Ar Kr	4.2 20	vaporization	Loewenschuss 68 McNamee 62

D. Polyatomics†

The listing is entirely analogous to that of triatomics. Since the writing of formulas is not standardized, the formula of the original publication is used. Hydrogen containing molecules, for example, may be listed under hydrogen, or any other atom, depending on how the first paper spelled the formula.

---

† The author thanks Dr. J. Smith who assisted by collating data for this table.

Molecule and State		T_e	Observed Transition	Vibrational Frequency	Remarks and Matrix	$T\,^{\circ}K$	Preparation	References
AlF_3	X	0	IR	300 (ν_2) 965 (ν_3) 270 (ν_4)	Ne Ar Kr		4.2 vaporization of AlF_3 (s) at 1150–1875°K	Snelson 67b
Al_2F_6			IR	995 (ν_8) 340 (ν_9) 660 (ν_{13}) 805 (ν_{16}) 575 (ν_{17}) 300 (ν_{18})	Ne Ar Kr		4.2 vaporization of AlF_3 (s) at 1150–1875°K	Snelson 67b
$(BF_3)_2$	X	0	IR	662 674 1410 1460 1515	correlated to monomer bands	Ar 20 Kr 50		Bassler 66b
B_2O_2	X	0	IR	1921 (ν_3)	multiplet	Ar	4.2 vaporization of B_2O_3 + B 1450–1500°K	Sommer 63 Rentzepis 60
B_2O_3	X	0	IR	2128 (ν_1) 733 (ν_2) 536 (ν_3) 172 (ν_4) 260 (ν_5) 476 (ν_6) 2128 (ν_7) 1242 (ν_8) 471 (ν_8) 493 (ν_9)	$^{10}B_2O_3$; ^{11}B	Ar	4.2 vaporization 1400°K	Sommer 63 Weltner 62a

Species	X		Method	Frequencies	Notes	Matrix		Preparation	Reference
C_2Br_4	X	0	IR	595.0 (ν_1) 640.5 (ν_3^1)		Ar	15		Andrews 68c
CBr_3	X	0	IR	582 (ν_1) 773 (ν_3^1)	ν_2 and ν_4 not observed	Ar	15	reaction of Li atoms with CBr_4	Andrews 68c
CCl_3	X	0	IR	674 (ν_1) 898 (ν_3^1)	ν_2 and ν_4 observed	Ar	15	reaction of Li atoms with CCl_4	W.L.S.Andrews 67 L.Andrews 68a
CCl_3Li	X	0	IR	521 (C-Cl st) 429 (Li st)	Li	Ar	15	reaction of CCl_4 with Li atoms	Andrews 68d
CF_3	X	0	IR	1087 (ν_1) 703 (ν_2) 1251 (ν_3) 512 (ν_4)	^{13}C; other bands observed	Ar	14 20	photolysis of CF_2N_2/ and tN_2F_2	Comeford 66 Milligan 66b, 68a
CH_3	? X	6.65 0	? ← X IR	611 (ν_2) 730 (ν_2) 1383 (ν_3)	D; planar ν_3 not observed	N_2 Ar CO	14	photolysis of CH_4 and reaction of CH CH_3X with Li atoms	W.L.S.Andrews 66b L.Andrews 67b Milligan 67d
CH_4	X	0	IR	3037 (ν_3) 1306 (ν_4)	multiplets D	Ar Kr Xe	2- 40	direct deposition	Cabana 63 Frayer 68

Molecule and State	T_e	Observed Transition	Vibrational Frequency	Remarks and Matrix	$T_{°K}$	Preparation	References
$CH_2(CN)_2$ X	0	IR	2264 (ν_2) 887 (ν_4) 573 (ν_5) 2272 (ν_9) 974 (ν_{11})	overtones	Ar	20	direct deposition	Ames 63
CH_2CO X	0	IR	3043 (ν_1) 2133 (ν_2) 1374 (ν_3) 1131 (ν_4) 3140 (ν_5) 971 (ν_6) 440 (ν_7) 616 (ν_8) 529 (ν_9)	D	Ar	20	photolysis of acetone	Moore 63
C_6H_5CO ?	3.12μm^{-1} 2.22μm^{-1}	? ← X		ESR and optical study of acyl radicals; other radicals (R-CO) observed	organic glasses	77	frozen solutions	Noda 68
$CHCl_3$ X	0	IR	2500	D; bands widened in matrix	Ar CS_2 CCl_4	20 77	deposition of vapor mixtures of $CHCl_3$ and $(C_2H_5)_3N$	Denariez 65 S. King 68 W. Thompson 60
CH_3Cl X	0	IR		chlorine isotopic splitting patterns are determined	Ar	20	direct deposition	S. King 68

	X	0	IR	frequencies	notes	matrix		method	reference
CH_2F	X	0	IR	996, 1163 (C-F)		Ar, N_2	14	photolysis of CH_3F	Jacox 69a
CH_3F	X	0	IR	1041, 1463, 2866, 2972, 3022	correlate with gas phase	Ar, N_2	14	direct decomposition	Jacox 69a
CH_3Li	X	0	IR	2780 (ν_1), 1158 (ν_2), 530 (ν_3), 2820 (ν_4), 1387 (ν_5), 409 (ν_6)	^6Li, D	Ar	15	reaction of CH_3X with Li atoms	L. Andrews 67b,c; Tan 68
CH_3LiBr	X	0	IR	730	Li, Na, K, Br, I	Ar	15	reaction of CH_3X with M atoms	Tan 68
CH_2N_2	X	0	IR	3069 (ν_1), 2096 (ν_2), 1407 (ν_3), 1168 (ν_4), 3182 (ν_5), 1105 (ν_6), 420 (ν_7), 542 (ν_8), 427 (ν_9)	D, N^{15}	N_2, Ar	20		Moore 64a

Molecule and State	T_e	Observed Transition	Vibrational Frequency	Remarks and Matrix	$T_{°K}$	Preparation	References
$(CH_3)_3N$ X	0	IR	1475 (ν_3) 1470 (ν_4) 1187 (ν_5) 823 (ν_6) 365 (ν_7) 1456 (ν_{15}) 1440 (ν_{16}) 1405 (ν_{17}) 1098 (ν_{18}) 1037 (ν_{19}) 823 (ν_{20}) 421 (ν_{21}) 259 (ν_{22})	D; C_{3v}	Ar	20	direct deposition	Goldfarb 67a
CH_3OH X	0	IR	3660 (OH st)	polymers	N_2	20	direct deposition	Van Thiel 57a
C_2H_5O ?		$1.93\mu m^{-1}$? $\leftarrow$ X		violet color	organic glasses	77		Symons 56
$CH_3(SiH_3)_2N$			2891 (C-H st) 2179 (Si-Hst) 1470 (CH_3 def) 1200 (CH_3 rock) 1091 (C-N st) 986 (Si-Nst) 923 (SiH_3 def) 716 (SiH_3 rock)	planar multiplet multiplet multiplet multiplet multiplet multiplet	Ar	20	direct deposition	Goldfarb 67b

Species	X		Method	Frequencies	Notes	Matrix	Temp	Preparation	Reference
$(CH_3)_2SiH_3N$	X	0	IR	2872(C-Hst) 2196(Si-Hst) 1472(CH3def) 1295(CH3rock) 1187(C-Nst) 900(C-Nst) 990(Si-Nst) 965(SiH3def) 695(SiH3 rock)	multiplet multiplet multiplet multiplet multiplet multiplet pyramidal	Ar	20	direct deposition	Goldfarb 67b
CO_3	X	0	IR	568 593 972 1073 1880 2045 3105 3922	probably planar C_{2v} with one carbonyl bond	Ar	4.2	1) photolysis of CO_2 2) photolysis of O_3/CO_2 mixture 3) condensation of discharged CO_2	Moll 66
C_3O_2	X	0	IR	$2282\ (\nu_3)$ $1594\ (\nu_4)$ $536\ (\nu_6)$	linear symmetric; overtones	Ar	4.2 / 20	direct deposition	Ames 63 W.H.Smith 66
CX_3Li					see CCl_3Li				Andrews 68d
$(ClO)_2$	X	0	IR	951	multiplet	N_2	20	photolysis of Cl_2O	Alcock 68 Rochkind 67b

Molecule and State		T_e	Observed Transition	Vibrational Frequency	Remarks and Matrix	$T_{°K}$	Preparation	References
F_2CN $A(^2A_1)$	Π^*	2.76	$^2A_1 \leftarrow {}^2B_2$		fine structure N_2 Ar	14	photolysis of FCN and $t\text{-}N_2F_2$	Jacox 68a
F_2CO	Π^*	4.4	$n \to \Pi^*$		$(FCO)_2$ also produced; continuous absorption CO	4.2	photolysis of OF_2, N_2F_2 or tN_2F_2 in CO matrix	Milligan 65b
	X	0	IR	585 620 1913 1941				
FNCN	X	0	IR	873 2068	^{13}C, ^{15}N Ar	14	photolysis of $N_2CN{:}F_2$	Milligan 68b
$Fe(C_5H_5)_2$	F	5.00	$F \leftarrow X$		strong; allowed no structure Ar	20	vaporization 300°K	J. Smith 68a
	E	4.05	$E \leftarrow X$	400	cyclopentadienyl ring; perturbation at $v'=4$ Kr			
	D	3.50	$D \leftarrow X$	250	iron ring vibration; charge transfer Xe			
	C	2.90	$C \leftarrow X$	450	cyclopentadienyl ring N_2			
	B	2.50	$B \leftarrow X$		3d-3d transition no structure CH_4	77		
	A	2.00	$A \to X$		$\tau=1.25$sec excited via $C{\leftarrow}X$ EPA			
	X	0			no structure all bands broad at 77°K			

	X	O		Frequencies	Notes	Matrix	Conditions	Reference
$(HBr)_2$	X	0	(IR)	2433 2469 2500		Ar	83 from liquid solution 103	Atwood 67
H_2CN	X	0	IR	1338	uncertain	Ar	14 photolysis of HCN	Milligan 67d
$(HCN)_2$	X	0	IR	732; 792 797; 2090 2114; 3202; 3301	closely correlated to monomer peaks	Ar CO N_2	4.2 direct deposition 20	C. King 68
$(HCl)_2$	X	0	IR	232	argon; D	Ne Ar Kr Xe	4.2 deposition of HCl 20 103	Katz 67b Keyser 66b
HN_3	X	0	IR	3324 (ν_1) 2150 (ν_2) 1273 (ν_3) 1168 (ν_4) 527 (ν_5) 588 (ν_6)	dimer		20 direct deposition	Pimentel 66
HNCO	X	0	IR	460 (OCN) 1098 (OC) 1241 (OH bend) 2294 (C-N) 3506 (O-H)	N_2 D	N_2 Ar	14 vaporization of cyanuric acid	Jacox 64b
HNCS	X	0	IR	3505 (ν_1) 1979 (ν_2) 988 (ν_3) 577 (ν_4) 461 (ν_5)	D	Ar	20 direct deposition	Durig 67

Molecule and State	T_e	Observed Transition	Vibrational Frequency	Remarks and Matrix	$T °K$	Preparation	References
H_2O_2 X	0	IR	3417 (ν_1) 3578 (ν_5) 1292 (ν_6)	tentative overtone at 2750 several other unassigned bands N_2	4.2	direct deposition	Catalano 63b
Li_2F_2 X	0	IR	$^7Li_2F_2$ 641 (B_{3u}) 553 (B_{2u}) 287 (B_{1u})	^6Li Ne	20	vaporization of Li at 1175-1475° K; direct deposition F_2	Snelson 67b
N_3CN B	4.75	B ← X	444,450	broad band Ar	14	direct deposition	Milligan 65d, 66c
X	0	IR	865,923 1263,2101 2151,2163 2208,2249	no definite assignments N_2 CO CO_2			
NF_2CN X	0	IR	576 619 840 888 1021	^{13}C, ^{15}N Ar	14	photolysis of $N_3CN:F_2$	Milligan 68b
NH_3 A($^1A_2''$)	5.25	A ← X		fine structure dimers; D Ar N_2 CO_2	4.2 20 53	direct deposition	Dressler 60 Jacox 63b Milligan 61a Pimentel 62a
X	0	IR	3332 (ν_1) 970 (ν_2) 3440 (ν_3) 1632 (ν_4)	N_2			

Molecule	State	Value	Method	Frequencies	Notes / Gas	Matrix	Conc.	Conditions	Reference
N_2H_2	X	0	IR	1279 3074 1286 (ν_5) 1481 (ν_2)	ν_3 preferred; cis N_2 trans trans		20	photolysis of HN_3	Rosengren 65
N_2H_4	X	0	IR	3390 (ν_1) 1312 (ν_4) 1087 (ν_5) 832 (ν_6) 394 (ν_7) 3356 (ν_8) 3297 (ν_9) 1265 (ν_{11}) 982 (ν_{12})	N_2	N_2 Ar	4.2	direct deposition	Catalano 63a
$NbCl_5$	X	0	IR	444 (ν_3) 126 (ν_4) 396 (ν_5) 159 (ν_6) 99 (ν_7)	N_2	N_2 C_6H_{12}	5–10	vaporization	Werder 67
O_2F_2	X	0	IR	624 612 462 368		N_2 Ar O_2	20	photolysis of F_2 and O_2	Spratley 66
S_4	A X	1.9 0	B←A	continuum		isopentane-cyclohexane pure sulfur; Kr	76 20	photolysis of S_4Cl_2 or sulfur vapor	Meyer, J. Phys. Chem., in press

Molecule and State	T_e	Observed Transition	Vibrational Frequency	Remarks and Matrix	$T °K$	Preparation	References
$SiCl_3$　X	0	IR	470.2 (ν_1) 582.0 (ν_3)	$^{28}Si^{35}Cl_3$; $^{29}Si^{37}Cl$; $^{30}Si^{37}Cl$	14	photolysis of $HSiCl_3$	Jacox 68b
Si_2C_2　$(^3\Sigma^-)$	1.54	?← X		Ne Ar	4.2 20	vaporization of SiC(s) at 2600°K	Weltner 64c
X	0	IR	595(Si=Si st) 657(C=Si st) 994(C=C st) 1967(C≡C st)	argon; additional unassigned bands			
SiF_3　X	0	IR	832 (ν_1) 406 (ν_2) 954 (ν_3) 290 (ν_4)	argon; non planar Ar ^{29}Si, ^{30}Si N_2 CO	14	photolysis of $SiHF_3$	Milligan 68e
SiH_2Cl_2	0	IR	2210 948 877 584 523	Ar	14	direct deposition	Milligan 68c
SiH_3Cl	0	IR	2198 945 663 544	Ar	14	impurity	Milligan 68c
SiH_2F_2	0	IR	980 972 863 714	Ar N_2	14	direct deposition	Milligan 68d, 68e

SiH$_3$F	X	0	IR	890		Ar N$_2$	14	impurity	Milligan 68d, 68e
(SiH$_3$)$_3$N	X	0	IR	2174 (1) 2155 (2,14) 942 (3) 921 (4) 767 (5) 454 (7) 2193 (12) 2186 (13) 966 (15) 955 (16) 934 (17) 734 (18) 693 (19)	C$_{3v}$ pt. group overtones	Ar	20	direct deposition	Goldfarb 67a
WO$_3$	A	3.46	A ← X	894 (A'$_1$)	neon; tentative	Ne	4.2	1)vaporization of WO$_3$ or WO$_{2.96}$ at 1600°K 2)reaction of O$_2$ with tungsten at 1900-2950°K	Weltner 65b
	X	0	IR	1040 (E')					
XeF$_4$	X	0	IR	290 (ν_2) 568 (ν_6)		Ar	20	photolysis of F$_2$/Xe/Ar mixtures	Turner 63a

E. Organic Molecules

In these tables, molecules are arranged according to the number of carbon atoms. For a given number of carbon atoms, the order follows the number of hydrogen atoms. Deuterated compounds are listed immediately after the normal compounds. If atoms other than CH are present, all pure CH come first, followed by all others in alphabetical sequence of the symbol of the third type of atom.

To help in quick identification, for some compounds the structural formula is given. The solvent is occasionally abbreviated by a symbol:

EC = ethyl cellulose

EPA = ethanol/isopentane/ethyl ether

MCH = methyl cyclohexane

MPH = isopentane/methylcyclohexane

3MP = 3-methyl pentane

PMMA = polymethyl methacrylate

PVAc = polyvinyl acetate

A more complete list of glasses is given in Table 8.8. The absorption and emission columns list peak intensities. The claimed accuracy of the transition energy or lifetime is indicated by the number of digits listed.

Formula and Substance	Solvent	$T_{°K}$	Transition (μm^{-1}) Abs.	Emis.	τ sec	References
CH_2O Formaldehyde	xenon krypton SF_6	20 55		2.73 2.73 2.71	0.23 1.10 0.63	J. Smith 69
$C_2H_2N_4$ s-Tetrazine	hexane hydrocarbons	77 77	1.78	2.70		Chowdhury 63 Nurmukhametov 67
C_2H_4O Acetaldehyde	3-methylpentane/ isopentane	77	1.80	1.80		Longin 60
C_2Cl_4 Tetrachloroethylene	EPA	77		2.60		Kasha 47b
$C_3H_3N_3$ s-Triazine	EPA	77		2.22 2.64	0.44	Paris 61
C_3H_6O Acetone	EPA	83 77		2.20	$6 \cdot 10^{-4}$	Gilmore 55
$C_4H_3ClN_2O_2$ Amino-chloro-maleic imide	ethyl acetate CCl_4			1.90 2.19	0.04 0.39	Viktorova 61

$C_4H_4N_2$ Pyrazine	hexagon structure	3-methylpentane/ 77 isopentane 77 EPA 4.2 H_2 77 isopentane 4.2 cyclohexane; pure solid		2.63 2.60 2.66 2.60	II* $20 \cdot 10^{-3}$ II*	El-Sayed 61c, 67 Goodman 58 Kanda 58 Krishna 62
$C_4H_4N_2$ Pyrimidine	hexagon structure with N	3-methylpentane/ 77 isopentane 77 EPA 77 ethanol dioxane cyclohexane benzene		2.40 2.83		Goodman 58 Krishna 62 Shablya 61 Shimada 61
$C_4H_4N_2$ Pyridazine		pure solid 4.2	2.43		0.05	Hochstrasser 67
$C_4H_4N_2O$ 4(3H)-Pyrimidinone		ethylene glycol 77 or propylene glycol/H_3O		3.26		Longworth 66
$C_4H_4N_2O_2$ Uracil		ethylene glycol 77 or propylene glycol/H_3O		3.18		Longworth 66

Formula and Substance	Solvent	$T_{°K}$	Transition (μm^{-1}) Abs.	Emis.	τ sec	References
$C_4H_5N_3$ 2-Amino pyrimidine	ethylene glycol or propylene glycol/H_2O	77		2.88		Longworth 66
$C_4H_5N_3O$ Cytosine	ethylene glycol or propylene glycol/H_2O	77		3.21 2.50		Longworth 66
$C_4H_6N_4$ Dimethyl-g-tetrazine	3-methylpentane/ isopentane	77		1.71		Chowdhury 63
$C_4H_6O_2$ Diacetyl (2,3-Butanedione) H_3C-C, N, $C-CH_3$, N	EPA, 2-butanone crystal	77 20 20/4 20/4 4	2.23 2.29 2.04	1.96 2.01 2.29 1.98	$2.25 \cdot 10^{-3}$ S T S S T	L. Forster 60 Sidman 55
$C_4D_6O_2$ Diacetyl (2,3-Butanedione)-d_6	perdeuterated crystal	20/4 20/4 4	2.29 2.04	2.29 2.00 2.04	S S T T	Sidman 55
C_4H_8O Methylethylketone $H_3C-C-C_2H_5$, $\parallel$, O	EPA	83		2.13	$0.85 \cdot 10^{-3}$	McClure 49

Formula / Name	Solvent	Temp	Value 1	Value 2	T	Reference
C$_4$Cl$_6$ Hexachlorobutadiene	EPA			2.58	T	Kasha 47b
C$_5$H$_4$N$_4$ Purine	hexane	4	2.67	3.8	1.1	Tomlinson 68
	C$_6$F$_{12}$	4	2.65			
	nitrogen	4	2.68			
	methanol	4	2.62	3.85		
	CCl$_4$	4	2.62			
C$_5$H$_5$N Pyridine	EPA			(2.70)	T	Reid 53
C$_5$H$_5$N$_5$ Adenine	H$_2$SO$_4$	77	3.82	2.63	1.8	Bersohn 64
	H$_2$O/glycerin				3.0	Longworth 66
	neon	4				Rahn 66
	isopropanol	4	2.55	3.82		Reid 53
	nitrogen	4	2.60	3.52		Tomlinson 68
	hexane	4	2.67	2.74		Udenfriend 65
C$_5$H$_5$N$_5$O Guanine	H$_2$SO$_4$		3.68	2.78, 3.13, 2.78	1.42	Longworth 66, Udenfriend 65
C$_5$H$_6$N$_2$O$_2$ Thymine	ethylene glycol or propylene glycol/H$_2$O	77	3.17, 2.33			Longworth 66

Formula and Substance	Solvent	$T°K$	Transition (μm^{-1}) Abs.	Emis.	τ sec	References
$C_5H_6N_2O_2$ N$_1$-Methyluracil	ethylene glycol or propylene glycol/H_2O	77		3.05 2.28		Longworth 66
$C_5H_7N_3O$ N$_1$-Methylcytosine	ethylene glycol or propylene glycol/H_2O	77		3.13		Longworth 66
C_5H_8O Cyclopentanone	EPA	77		2.27–2.22	$1.1 \cdot 10^{-3}$	LaPaglia 62a
$C_5H_8O_2$ Acetylpropionyl CH_3—CO—CO—CH_2—CH_3	EPA	90		1.86	T	Lewis 45
$C_5H_8O_4$ Glutaric acid HOOC(CH$_2$)$_3$COOH	Solid	90		2.55 S 2.45 T		Ryazanova 59
$C_5H_{10}O$ Diethyl ketone	EPA EPA crystal	83 77 83		2.13	T $1.26 \cdot 10^{-3}$ $0.8 \cdot 10^{-3}$	McClure 49
$C_5H_{10}O$ Methyl isopropyl ketone	EPA	77			$1.7 \cdot 10^{-3}$	McClure 49
$C_6H_2Br_4$ 1,2,4,5-Tetrabromobenzene	EPA	77	2.67		$5.5 \cdot 10^{-4}$	Marchetti 67 McClure 49, 54

Compound	Structure	Medium		Value		Value	References
$C_6H_2Cl_4$ 1,2,4,5-Tetrachlorobenzene		EPA	77	2.68		$1.8 \cdot 10^{-2}$	McClure 49 Marchetti 67
$C_6H_2O_2$ Dihydroxyltriacetylene	$HO-(C\equiv C)_3-OH$	EPA	77			0.2	Beer 56
$C_6H_3Br_3$ 1,3,5-Tribromobenzene		EPA	77	2.76		$7.4 \cdot 10^{-4}$	McClure 49, 54 Marchetti 67
$C_6H_3Cl_3$ 1,3,5-Trichlorobenzene		EPA	77 4.2 77	3.52 2.76		$2.2 \cdot 10^{-2}$	McClure 49 Marchetti 67 Schnepp 59b
$C_6H_4Br_2$ p-Dibromobenzene		glass single crystal	77 77 4.2 4.2	2.77 2.79 3.54	2.79	$2.75 \cdot 10^{-4}$	Castro 66a, 67 Marchetti 67 Mazurenko 62
C_6H_4BrCl 1-Bromo-4-chlorobenzene			77	2.78			Marchetti 67
$C_6H_4Cl_2$ o-Dichlorobenzene		EPA	77			$1.8 \cdot 10^{-2}$	McClure 49

Formula and Substance	Solvent	$T°K$	Transition (μm^{-1}) Abs.	Emis.	τ sec.	References
$C_6H_4Cl_2$ p-Dichlorobenzene	EPA glass single crystal	77 4.2 4.2 77	3.57 2.79 2.80		$1.6\cdot10^{-3}$ $5\cdot10^{-3}$	Castro 66a, 67 McClure 49 Marchetti 67 Mazurenko 62 Moross 66
$C_6H_4I_2$ p-Diiodobenzene	single crystal	4.2	2.72			Castro 66a
$C_6H_4O_2$ p-Quinone	octane crystal hexane	77 77 77 77	1.85 2.00		$2.5\cdot10^{-3}$ 0.1 T S	Kanda 64 Martinez 62
C_6H_5Br Bromobenzene	EPA crystal	77 93		2.29 3.14	10^{-3}	Biswas 55 Gilmore 55 West 56a
C_6H_5Cl Chlorobenzene	EPA	77	3.85		S $4\cdot10^{-3}$ $7\cdot10^{-2}$	Gilmore 55 McClure 49
C_6H_5F Fluorobenzene	EPA	77	3.91		S	Gilmore 55 McClure 49
$C_6H_5N_3$ Benztriazole	ethanol ion in $HClO_3$	93 93	3.42 3.83 4.80 3.30 3.57 4.63	3.35 3.30 2.36	S S S S S T	Schutt 63

C₆H₆ Benzene

Solvent / medium	T			
ethanol	77	3.78	2.95	3.6
ethanol/methanol/isopropanol	106			
EPA	77		2.79	7.68
	90		2.95	8.0
	<100		3.70	
cyclohexane	77		3.78	6.63
	4.2		2.95	
cyclohexane cubic	77		2.94	1.2
monoclinic			3.77	
methylcyclohexane				4.7
glass–site 1	77			6.7
–site 2	77			3.0
crystal	77			2.0
n-pentane	20		3.67	$12 \cdot 10^{-9}$
hexane	20		3.61	
CCl₄	77/90	3.77	2.90	
CCl₄/ethanol		(3.77)	2.94	
petroleum ether				
dioxane	77	3.78	2.94	
3-methylpentane	77		2.95	
methylcyclo-hexane	77			2.98
di-n propylether	83.			4.66
ether	100			6.55
	104			6.67
				7.08
C₆D₆	4.2	3.78	2.96	8.6
C₆D₆/0.2%C₆H₃D₃	4.2			8.51
C₆D₆/0.2%C₆H₅D	4.2			8.51

References:

Bernstein 66, 68b
Broude 62
Ciais 61
Colson 65, 66, 68a, 68b
Coupron 60
Diamant 65
Dikun 49
Gee 67
Kanda 61c, 61b
Kasha 47b
Kembrovskii 68
Maria 63
Martin 68b, 68c, 69
Merrithew 68
Nieman 67
Parker 62
Person 67
P. Pesteil 55c
Pyatnitskii 50
Rabalais 69a, 69b
Spangler 63, 68
Sponer 62
Vatulev 64
West 56a
Wright 60
Zmerli 59a, 59c
Hanson 69
Hatch 68a,b

Formula and Substance	Solvent	$T_{°K}$	Transition (μm^{-1}) Abs.	Emis.	τ sec	References
C_6H_6 Benzene (continued)	crystal	20		3.78		
	crystal	4.2	3.78	3.78– 3.68		
		20	3.69	3.71	T_2	
		20	2.96	2.90	T_1	
		20		3.87	T_2	
		4.2		3.06	T_1	
	C_6HD_5	4.2		3.78		
	$1,3-C_6H_2D_4$	4.2		3.78		
	$1,3,5-C_6H_3D_3$	4.2		3.78		
	$1,4-C_6H_4D_2$	4.2		3.78		
	C_6H_5D	4.2		3.78		
	crystal	77	2.97		3.1	
	crystal/2%O_2	4.2	3.66		T_1	
	crystal/NO	4.2	3.70		T_2	
	argon	4.2/ 20	3.80	2.97	T_2 16	
	CH_4	4.2/ 20			16	
	krypton	4.2/ 20		2.95	1	
	xenon	4.2/ 20		2.95	0.07	
	N_2	4.2/ 20	3.85			
	CO	20				

Compound	Sample		T (K)				Reference
C_6H_5D Benzene-d_1	cyclohexane	cubic	77			1.4	Bernstein 68b
		monoclinic	77			5.2	Broude 62
	C_6H_6		4.2	3.79		8.5	Colson 68b
	C_6D_6		4.2	3.79	2.969	8.62	Martin 68c
	$C_6D_6/0.2\%C_6H_3D_3$		4.2			8.68	Nieman 67
	$C_6D_6/0.2\%C_6H_4D_2$					8.37	
	$C_6D_6/0.2\%C_6H_6$						
1,3-$C_6H_4D_2$ Benzene-d_2	C_6H_6		4.2	3.80			Bernstein 68c
	C_6D_6		4.2		2.972		Broude 62
							Nieman 67
1,4-$C_6H_4D_2$ Benzene-d_2	C_6D_6		4.4	3.79	2.97	8.9	Bernstein 68b
	$C_6D_6/0.2\%C_6H_3D_2$		4.2			8.87	68c
	$C_6D_6/0.2\%C_6H_5D$		4.2			8.08	Broude 62
							Colson 68b
							Nieman 67
1,3,5-$C_6H_3D_3$ Benzene-d_3	C_6D_6		4.2	3.79	2.97	8.4	Bernstein 68b
	cyclohexane	cubic	77			2.4	68c
		monoclinic	77			8.2	Broude 62
	$C_6D_6/0.2\%C_6H_4D_2$		4.2			8.08	Colson 68b
	$C_6D_6/0.2\%C_6H_5D$		4.2			8.30	Martin 68c
	$C_6D_6/0.2\%C_6H_6$		4.2			8.23	Nieman 67

Formula and Substance	Solvent	$T_{°K}$	Transition (μm^{-1}) Abs.	Emis.	τ sec	References
$1,2,4\text{-}C_6H_3D_3$ Benzene-d_3	C_6D_6	4.2		2.975		Broude 62
$1,3\text{-}C_6H_2D_4$ Benzene-d_4	C_6D_6	4.2	3.80	2.98		Broude 62
C_6HD_5 Benzene-d_5	C_6H_6	4.2	3.80			Broude 62 Martin 68c
	cyclohexane					
	cubic	77			3.2	
	monoclinic	77			9.5	
C_6D_6 Benzene-d_6	cyclohexane	77		2.94		
	cubic	77			9.2	
	monoclinic	77			13.9	
	EPA	77			9.85	
	methylcyclo-hexane					
	1-glass	77			5.6	
	2-crystal	77			12.0	
	C_6H_6	4.2	3.80			
	C_6H_5D	4.2	3.80			
	$1,4\text{-}C_6H_4D_2$	4.2	3.80			
	crystal	4.2	2.98			
		4.2	3.71			
		4.2	3.78			
	crystal/2%O_2	4.2	2.98			
		4.2	3.69			
	crystal	20	3.80			
	crystal	4.2	3.80		25.8	

Formula / Name	Medium	Temp				References
C₆H₆N₄O $C_6H_6N_4O$ 6-Methoxypurine	hexane	4	2.57	3.77		Tomlinson 68
	C_6F_{12}	4	2.53	3.80		
	nitrogen	4	2.52			
C_6H_6O Phenol	ethanol	77			$4.7 \cdot 10^{-9}$	Ivanova 61
	EPA	77		2.86	2.1	McClure 51
					2.6	C. Parker 62b
						Pyatnitskii 51
$C_6H_6O_2$ Catechol	pure solid	77			2.22	Pyatnitskii 51
	ethanol	77			2.4	
$C_6H_6O_2$ Hydroquinone	ethanol	77			2.3	Ivanova 61
	acetone	90			$2.0 \cdot 10^{-9}$	Pyatnitskii 51
	crystal	77			2.2	Teplyakov 56a
					3.03	
$C_6H_6O_2$ Resorcinol	ethanol	90			1.8	Ivanova 61
	acetone	90			$2.3 \cdot 10^{-9}$	P. Pesteil 54b
	crystal	90		3.45	2.2	Teplyakov 56a
	single crystal			3.30	1.85	
$C_6H_6O_3$ Phloroglucinol	ethanol	77			2.6	Pyatnitskii 51
	crystal	77			1.39	

Formula and Substance	Solvent	T°K	Transition (μm^{-1}) Abs.	Emis.	τ sec	References
$C_6H_6O_3$ Pyrogallol	ethanol	77			1.88	Pyatnitskii 51
	crystal	77			0.81	
C_6H_7N Aniline	ethanol	77				Ermolaev 61
	ethanol/diethyl- ether	77	2.68	3.05	$2.7 \cdot 10^{-9}$ $2.4 \cdot 10^{-8}$	Ivanova 61
	EPA	77			S	Kasha 47b
	EPA	77				McClure 49, 51
	EPA	90		3.21	4.7	
$C_6H_7N_4$ 9-Methyladenine	C_6F_{12}	4	2.68			Tomlinson 68
	argon	4	2.72			
	nitrogen	4	2.74	3.82	3.1	
	neon	4	2.66	3.80	3.2	
	hexane	4	2.72	3.85	2.5	
	butane	4	2.72			
	CCl_4	4	2.62			
	methanol				2.7	
$C_6H_7NO_3S$ Sulfanilic acid	crystal	93	2.42	1.79	1.2 1.4	Khalupovskii 61
$C_6H_8N_2$ 2,5-Dimethylpyrazine	EPA	77	2.63		T	Goodman 58
$C_6H_8N_2$ m-Phenylenediamine	crystal	93	2.28			Fadeeva 59

Compound	Solvent	Temp	Values	Reference
$C_6H_8N_2O$ 4,6-Dimethyl-2-(1H) pyrimidine	ethylene glycol or propylene glycol/H_2O	77	2.50 3.05	Longworth 66
$C_6H_8N_2O_2$ 2,4-Dimethoxypyrimidine	ethylene glycol or propylene glycol/H_2O	77	2.99 2.57	Longworth 66
$C_6H_8N_2O_2$ N_1,N_3-Dimethyluracil	ethylene glycol or propylene glycol/H_2O	77	3.03	Longworth 66
$C_6H_8N_2O_2$ 4-Ethoxy-2-pyrimidine	ethylene glycol or propylene glycol/H_2O	77	3.08 2.56	Longworth 66
$C_6H_8N_2O_2$ N_1-Methyl thymine	ethylene glycol or propylene glycol/H_2O	77	3.03 2.25	Longworth 66
$C_6H_9N_3$ 6-Amino-4,6-dimethyl-pyrimidine	ethylene glycol or propylene glycol/H_2O	77	3.29 2.44	Longworth 66
$C_6H_9N_3$ Trimethyl-s-triazine	EPA	77	2.20 0.65	Paris 61

Formula and Substance	Solvent	T°K	Transition (μm⁻¹)			References
			Abs.	Emis.	τ sec	
$C_6Cl_4O_2$ Tetrachloro-p-benzoquinone	EPA			2.18		Kasha 47b
C_6Cl_6 Hexachlorobenzene	crystal	77 77 4.2	3.27 2.57	2.43		Kopelman 59 Marchetti 67 Olds 61 Schnepp 59c
C_7H_5BrO p-Bromobenzaldehyde	petroleum ether	78		2.46	T	Ermolaev 56
$C_7H_5BrO_2$ Bromobenzoic acid	CCl₄ acetone ether	90 90 90			1.0 1.7 2.2	Teplyakov 56a
C_7H_5IO m-Iodobenzaldehyde	ethanol/ether petroleum ether	77 77 77	2.63 2.67	2.48 2.47	S $6.5 \cdot 10^{-4}$ S, T	Ermolaev 56, 63
$C_7H_5O_2$ Benzoate ion	EPA	77		2.77	0.7	McClure 49
$C_7H_6Cl_2$ 2,4-Dichlorotoluene	crystal	93		2.46	T	J. Roy 62

Compound	Medium	Temp				Reference
$C_7H_6Cl_2$ 3,4-Dichlorotoluene	crystal	93	2.42		T	J. Roy 62
$C_7H_6N_2$ Benzimidazole	hexane	4	2.78	3.85	5.0	Schutt 63
	neon	4	2.82	3.83	7.6	Tomlinson 68
	nitrogen	4			1.7	
	methanol	4			1.8	
	CCl_4	4	2.79			
	argon	4	2.80			
	ethanol	93	3.58 / 3.98 / 4.85	3.54	S	
	ion/$HClO_3$	93	3.65	2.51 / 3.62 / 2.54	T / S / T	
$C_7H_6N_2$ Indazole	ethanol	93	3.36 / 3.85 / 4.80	3.31	S / S / S	Schutt 63
	ion/$HClO_3$	93	3.29 / 3.82	2.37 / 3.20 / 2.23	T / S / S / T	
C_7H_6O Benzaldehyde	ethanol/ether	77	2.68		S	Ermolaev 63
		77			$1.5 \cdot 10^{-3}$	Kanda 64
	EPA	77		2.52		Teplyakov 56a
	n-hexane	77	2.52	2.53	T	
	petroleum ether	77		2.52	T	

Formula and Substance	Solvent	$T_{°K}$	Transition (μm^{-1})			References
			Abs.	Emis.	τ sec	
$C_7H_6O_2$ Benzoic acid	ethanol	90		2.72	1.9	Kanda 63
	cyclohexane	90		2.71	T	McClure 49
	petroleum ether	90		2.70	T	C. Parker 62b
	benzene	90		2.74	T	Teplyakov 56a
	EPA	77		2.72	2.5	
	crystal	77		2.72	2.2	
$C_7H_6O_3$ Salicylic acid	methanol		3.30	2.21		Teplyakov 56a
	KOH		3.11	2.55		Weller 55
	H_2SO_4		3.04	2.47		
	ethanol	90			1.8	
	crystal	90			1.2	
$C_7H_6O_3$ β-Resorcylaldehyde	ethanol/crystal	77			1.8	Teplyakov 56a
$C_7H_6O_5$ Gallic acid	ethanol	77			1.8	Teplakov 56b
	CCl_4	77			1.6	
	crystal	77			1.5	
$C_7H_6O_5S$ Sulfobenzoic acid	ethanol	77			2.1	Teplyakov 56b
	crystal	77			1.7	
C_7H_7Br m-Bromotoluene	pure solid	93		2.49	T	Biswas 56c

Compound	Structure	Medium		Value		Reference
C₇H₇Br o-Bromotoluene		heptane crystal	93 93	2.52 2.51		Biswas 56b
C₇H₇Br p-Bromotoluene	CH₃—⬡—Br	heptane crystal	93 93	2.46 2.46		Biswas 56b
C₇H₇Cl m-Chlorotoluene	CH₃—⬡ Cl	crystal	93	2.49		Biswas 56c
C₇H₇Cl o-Chlorotoluene		pure solid heptane	93 93	2.41 2.44		Biswas 56b
C₇H₇Cl p-Chlorotoluene	CH₃—⬡—Cl	benzene solid	93 93	2.47 2.47		Sirkar 56
C₇H₇F m-Fluorotoluene		solid	93	2.50		J. Roy 60

Formula and Substance	Solvent	$T_{°K}$	Transition (μm^{-1}) Abs.	Emis.	τ_{sec}	References
C_7H_7NO Benzamide	benzene	90		2.78	2.1	Kanda 63
	ethanol	90		2.76	2.2	
$C_7H_7NO_2$ p-Aminobenzoic acid	ethanol	90			1.2	Teplyakov 56a
	acetone	90			1.1	
	CCl_4	90				
	crystal	90				
$C_7H_7NO_2$ Anthranilic acid	ethanol	77			1.5	Radeeva 65
	benzene	90			0.45	Teplyakov 56a
	acetone	90			1.8	Viktorova 60b
	CCl_4/H_2O	90			1.0	
	pure crystal	90			1.1	
	sugar	77		(2.8)	1.35	
	toluene	77		(2.4)	0.50	
	chloroform	77			0.86	
	H_2O	77				
C_7H_8 Toluene	single crystal	20	3.71		S	Coffman 58
	crystal	77			2.44	Grajcar 61b
	ethanol	77			4.8	Kanda 58
	EPA	77		2.88	8.8	Kasha 47b
	EPA	90		3.70	S	McClure 49
	isopentane			3.72		Pyatnitskii 51
	3-methylpentane/					
	isopentane	77		2.88		

Formula / Name	Structure	Solvent	Temp				Reference
C_7H_8O Anisole	phenyl–O–CH₃	EPA	90		3.55	S	Kasha 47b
		EPA	90		2.82	T	McClure 49
			77		2.82	3	
C_7H_9N p-Toluidine	CH₃–C₆H₄–NH₂	ethanol	90		2.55	T	Fadeeva 59
		ethanol	90			$3 \cdot 10^{-9}$	
$C_7H_9N_5$ 6-(N,N-Dimethylamino) Purine		neon	4	2.83	3.88	2.4	Tomlinson 68
		isopropanol	4	2.90	3.91	1.8	
		hexane	4	2.93	3.93		
		nitrogen	4	2.88	3.90	2.5	
$C_7H_{14}BrNO$ Diisopropylbromonitrosomethane	CH₃–CH–C(NO)(Br)–CH–CH₃ (with CH₃ groups)	EPA	90		>3.00		Kasha 47b
			90		1.36		
$C_7H_{14}O$ Diisopropyl ketone	CH₃–CH–C(=O)–CH–CH₃ (with CH₃ groups)	EPA	77		$3.77 \cdot 10^{-3}$		McClure 49
$C_8H_2O_2$ Dihydroxytetra-acetylene	$HO-(C\equiv C)_4-OH$	EPA	103		0.03		Beer 56

Formula and Substance	Solvent	$T_{°K}$	Transition (μm^{-1}) Abs.	Emis.	τ sec	References
$C_8H_5NO_2$ Phthalimide		93			1.5	Mokeeva 61
$C_8H_6N_2$ Quinoxaline	Durene	1.56 1.56 4.2		(2.10)	0.086 0.26 0.24	van der Waals 67b Vincent 63
$C_8H_6O_4$ Phthalic acid	ethanol CCl_4 crystal	90 90 90			2 1.37 0.99	Teplyakov 56a
C_8H_6S Thianaphthene	EPA	77		2.40	0.5	Heckmann 58
C_8H_7N Indole	ethanol EPA	93 93 93 77 77 77		3.40 3.45 2.47 3.27 2.30 2.47	s s T 6.3 (5)	Ermolaev 61 Heckmann 58 Schutt 63
$(C_8H_8)x$ Polystyrene	toluene pure solid	93		3.23 2.35 2.15		N. Roy 54 Rozman 59

Compound	Solvent	T				Reference
C_8H_8O Acetophenone (⬡—$COCH_3$)	EPA	77		2.59	$8\cdot10^{-3}$	Ermolaev 56, 63
	hexane	77	2.57			Gilmore 55
		77	2.77			Kanda 64
	ethanol/ether	77		2.75	s	C. Parker 62b
		77		2.58	$2.3\cdot10^{-3}$	Vanselov 53
	petroleum ether	78	2.78	2.58	s	
	crystal	80		2.45	T	
$C_8H_8O_2$ Methyl benzoate (⬡—COO—CH_3)	ethanol	90		2.73	T	Kanda 63
	cyclohexane	90		2.72		Naboikin 59
	petroleum ether	90		2.72		
	CCl_4	90		2.72		
	benzene	90	2.7	2.77		
	crystal	93		2.76		
$C_8H_8O_3$ o-Methoxybenzoic acid (⬡—$COOH$, OCH_3)	methanol		3.42	2.83		Naboikin 59
			3.44	2.21		Weller 55
C_8H_9NO Acetanilide (⬡—NH—CO—CH_3)	EPA	77			3.6	C. Parker 62b
C_8H_{10} Ethylbenzene (⬡—C_2H_5)	ethanol	77			4.7	Ivanova 61
	ethanol	77			$11.1\cdot10^{-9}$	Kasha 47b
	hexane				$5.7\cdot10^{-9}$	Pyatnitskii 51
	EPA	90		3.70	s	
		90		2.90	T	
	crystal	77			3.33	

Formula and Substance	Solvent	$T_{°K}$	Transition (μm^{-1}) Abs.	Emis.	τ sec	References
C_8H_{10} m-Xylene	ethanol	77			$12.4 \cdot 10^{-9}$	Blackwell 60
	hexane				$6 \cdot 10^{-9}$	Dikun 51
	EPA			2.81	8.1	Ivanova 61
	crystal	4.2		2.83	T	
				2.81	T	
C_8H_{10} o-Xylene	ethanol	77			5.2	Blackwell 60
	ethanol				$12.2 \cdot 10^{-9}$	Dikun 51
	EPA	77		2.88	$6 \cdot 10^{-9}$	Ivanova 61
	hexane					Pyatnitskii 51
	crystal			2.86	5.6	
	crystal	4.2		2.82		
C_8H_{10} p-Xylene	ethanol	77			6.2	Blackwell 60
	ethanol				$13 \cdot 10^{-9}$	Ivanova 61
	ethanol				$23 \cdot 10^{-9}$	Pyatnitskii 51
	EPA	77		2.81	T	
	crystal	4.2		2.82	T	
	crystal	77			2.86	
$C_8H_{10}N_2O_2$ 4-Nitro-N-ethyl-aniline	EPA	77			0.4	C. Parker 62b
$C_8H_{11}N$ N-Dimethylaniline	ethanol/ether	77		3.00	$15.4 \cdot 10^{-9}$	Ermolaev 61
		77		2.40	2.4	

Compound	Solvent	%				Reference
C$_8$H$_{11}$NO$_2$ 3,4-Dihydroxylphenyl-ethylamine (HO, HO—C$_6$H$_3$—CH$_2$—CH$_2$—NH$_2$)				2.44		Udenfriend 65
C$_9$H$_7$N Isoquinoline	ethanol	93	3.12	3.12	S	Craig 54
	ethanol	93	2.95	2.95	S	Dörr 63
	ethanol	90		2.12	T	Müller 59
	ethanol	90		2.12		Nurmukhametov 67
	EPA	77			1.3	Zimmermann 61a
C$_9$H$_7$N Quinoline	ethanol	90		2.18	1.4	Ermolaev 63
	ethanol/ether	77		2.17		Mamedov 66
	ethanol/ether	77		3.19	S	Nurmukhametov 67a
C$_9$H$_7$NO$_3$ 3-Hydroxy-N-methyl-phthalimide (OH, N—CH$_3$, O=C, C=O)	ethanol	77			0.8	Viktorova 60b
C$_9$H$_7$NO$_3$ 4-Hydroxy-N-methyl-phthalimide (N—CH$_3$)	propyleneace-tate	77			1.1	Viktorova 60b
C$_9$H$_7$N$_3$O$_4$ 3-Amino-6-nitro-N-methylphthalimide (NH$_2$O, N—CH$_3$, NO$_2$)	methanol	77		2.08	0.14	Zelinskii 55
	acetone	77				

Formula and Substance		Solvent	T°K	Transition (μm^{-1})		τ_{sec}	References
				Abs.	Emis.		
C_9H_8 Indene		EPA	77		2.47– 2.06	1	Heckmann 58
$C_9H_8N_2$ 4-Methylquinazoline		ethanol acidic solution		3.10 2.31	1.90	T II* n	Müller 59
$C_9H_8N_2O_2$ 3-Amino-N-methyl-phthalimide			93		2.16		Zelinskii 55
$C_9H_8N_2O_2$ 4-Amino-N-methyl-phthalimide			93		2.17		Zelinskii 55
$C_9H_8O_2$ Cinnamic acid		ethanol or crystal	77			1.8	Teplyakov 56b
C_9H_{10} n-Propylbenzene		ethanol hexane EPA	90 90		3.70 2.90	$10 \cdot 10^{-9}$ $8.2 \cdot 10^{-9}$	Dubois 64 Ivanova 61 Kasha 47b

Compound	Structure	Solvent	Temp.			Reference
$C_9H_{10}O$ Ethylphenylketone		ethanol/ether	77 77	2.80 2.62	$3.8 \cdot 10^{-3}$	Ermolaev 63
$C_9H_{10}O_2$ Ethylbenzoate		ethanol CCl_4 pure solid	93 93 93		2.53 0.68 1.24	Dubinskii 59
$C_9H_{10}O_2$ Hydrocinnamic acid		ethanol acetone crystal	90 90 90		5.3 2.1 3.7	Teplyakov 56a
$C_9H_{11}NO_2$ p-Dimethylaminobenzoic acid		chloroform	77		0.3	Viktorova 60b
$C_9H_{11}NO_2$ Phenylalanine		H_2O H_2O/glucose	77	3.56 2.54	S <0.1	Longin 59 Steele 58
$C_9H_{11}NO_3$ Tyrosine		H_2O Na_2HPO_4 H_2O H_2O/glucose alkaline med. neutral and acid solution	77 77	3.30 2.50	S 0.24 $42 \cdot 10^{-9}$ $8 \cdot 10^{-9}$ 0.9 3	Debye 52 Longin 59 Steele 58 Vladimirov 61 Weber 60

Formula and Substance	Solvent	$T_{°K}$	Transition (μm^{-1})			References
			Abs.	Emis.	τ sec	
C_9H_{12} n-Propylbenzene	EPA	90 / 90	3.70	2.89		Kasha 47b
$C_9H_{12}N_2O_6$ Uridine	ethylene glycol or propylene glycol/H_2O	77	3.14	2.38		Longworth 66
$C_9H_{13}N_2O_9P$ Uridylic acid	polymerized	77		2.17		Douzu 61
$C_9H_{13}N_3O_5$ Cytidine	ethylene glycol or propylene glycol/H_2O	77		3.18		Longworth 66
$C_9H_{18}O$ Di-t-butylketone	EPA	77			$8.6 \cdot 10^{-3}$	McClure 49
$C_{10}H_6Br_2$ 1,4-Dibromonaphthalene		77	2.04		T	Marchetti 67
$C_{10}H_6Br_2$ 1,5-Dibromonaphthalene	petroleum ether	77		2.01		Ferguson 54

Compound	Solvent	T (K)				Reference
$C_{10}H_6Br_2$ 2,6-Dibromonaphthalene	petroleum ether	77		2.01		Ferguson 54
$C_{10}H_6D_2$ 1,5-Dideuteronaphthalene	petroleum ether	77		2.13		Ferguson 54
$C_{10}H_6N_2O_4$ 1,5-Dinitronaphthalene	EPA	77	1.94	1.99	0.11	McClure 49
		77			T	Marchetti 67
$C_{10}H_7Br$ 1-Bromonaphthalene	ether/ethanol	77	2.08	2.07	$1.8 \cdot 10^{-2}$	Ermolaev 63
		77		3.13		Marchetti 67
		77			T	
$C_{10}H_7Br$ 2-Bromonaphthalene	EPA	77	3.11		$2.1 \cdot 10^{-2}$	McClure 49
	EPA	77	2.11		T	Marchetti 67
		77				Sidman 56d
$C_{10}H_7Cl$ 1-Chloronaphthalene	ether/ethanol	77		3.14	0.29	Azumi 63b
		77		2.07	0.23	Ermolaev 63
	EPA	77	2.05	2.07	T	Marchetti 67
		77				
$C_{10}H_7Cl$ 2-Chloronaphthalene	EPA	77	3.11	2.11	0.47	McClure 58
	naphthalene	20	2.11	2.08		Marchetti 67
	pure crystal	20		2.06		Sidman 56d
		77		2.11	T	

Formula and Substance	Solvent	$T°K$	Transition (μm^{-1}) Abs.	Emis.	τ sec.	References
$C_{10}H_7F$ 1-Fluoronaphthalene	ethanol/ether	77	3.16	2.12	$3\cdot10^{-7}$	Azumi 63b
		77			1.5	Ermolaev 59b
	EPA	90	3.19			Kasha 47b
		90		2.11		
	EPA	77			1.4	
$C_{10}H_7F$ 2-Fluoronaphthalene	petroleum ether	77		2.13		Ferguson 54
	naphthalene	20		2.08		Sidman 56d
$C_{10}H_7I$ 1-Iodonaphthalene	ethanol/ether	77	3.10	2.05	$2\cdot10^{-3}$	Ermolaev 63
		77	2.07			Marchetti 67
		77			T	
$C_{10}H_7I$ 2-Iodonaphthalene	EPA	77	3.09	2.10	$2.5\cdot10^{-3}$	McClure 49
		77			2.4	Marchetti 67
	methylcyclohexane/isopentane					
	naphthalene	20	2.09			
	crystal	20	2.05			
		77	2.11		T	
$C_{10}H_7NO_2$ 1-Nitronaphthalene	ethanol/ether	77		1.93	$4.9\cdot10^{-2}$	Ermolaev 59b
	EPA	77		1.92	$4.9\cdot10^{-2}$	McClure 49
$C_{10}H_8$ Azulene	n-hexane	77	2.82	2.82		Beer 55
			1.44			Ruzevich 63
	EPA	77		2.84		Sidman 56a
	EPA	77		2.68		Viswanath 56
	naphthalene	20	2.81	2.81		Hochstrasser 69
			1.47			Robinson 69

$C_{10}H_8$ Naphthalene

Medium	T (°K)				Reference
ethanol	20			$2.7 \cdot 10^{-9}$	Bolotnikova 59b
pentane			3.18–3.17		Ciais 60, 61
pentane	77	2.13		3.3	Colson 68a
isooctane	77			T	Czekalla 59
durene	77			2.31	Ermolaev 63
EPA	77		3.16	2.1	Foerster 64
EPA	77		2.13	2.33	Hadley 63
EPA	77	3.17	2.13	$3.3 \cdot 10^{-5}$	Hochstrasser 64a,e
ether/ethanol	77		3.18	2.8	Hutchison 58
propylether/isopentane	83		2.13	2.15	Ivanova 61
isooctane	77			$3.3 \cdot 10^{-6}$	Kasha 49
isopropanol	77				Keller 69
single crystal	20.4	3.15	3.15	2.5	Lin 68
single crystal	4		2.10	2.45	Marchetti 67
polycrystalline	20		2.13	2.45	Maria 63
$C_{10}D_8$	20		3.16	2.31	Metzger 69
mixed crystal			3.16 / 3.17 / 3.15		McGlynn 62b,63
argon	20/33		(3.15) / 2.12		Olness 63
krypton	20/33		2.11	1.7/1.6	C. Parker 62b
xenon	20		2.12	0.31/0.32	P. Pesteil 60
methane	20/33		(3.15) / 2.12	0.15	Shpak 60a
SF_6	20/33/77		2.12	1.8/1.9	Sidman 56d
benzophenone	77		2.12	1.7/1.8/1.8	Sponer 62
mixed crystal	77				Zmerli 59a
durene	77		2.12	2.6	

Formula and Substance	Solvent	T°K	Transition (μm⁻¹) Abs.	Transition (μm⁻¹) Emis.	τ sec	References
C₁₀H₈ Naphthalene (continued)	butane/iso-pentane	77			2.6	
	methylcyclohexane/pentane	77			2.47	
	3-methyl pentane				2.52	
	ethanol/methanol				2.50	
	EPA				2.52	
	ethanol/methanol/ethyl iodide			(2.18)	1.23	
	ethanol/methanol/propyl chloride			(3.23)	2.27	
	ethanol/methanol/propyl bromide			(2.18)	2.27	
	ethanol/methanol/propyl iodide			(3.23)	1.73	
	ether/isopentane			2.18	1.73	
	propyl chloride			3.23	1.33	
	propyl bromide			2.13	1.33	
	propyl iodide			2.13		
				2.12		
				2.10		
C₁₀D₇H Naphthalene-d₇	durene	20		3.17		McClure 56a
C₁₀D₈ Naphthalene-d₈	ethanol/ether	77		2.14	9.5	Ciais 60, 61
		77		3.19		DeGroot 61
	glass	77		3.19–	18	Ermolaev 63
	pentane	20		3.18		Hadley 63
	durene	77		3.17	16.1	McClure 56a
	durene	20		2.14		Zmerli 59a
	polycrystal	20				
	single crystal	20		3.16		

Compound	Solvent					Reference
$C_{10}H_8N_2O_3$ 3-Acetylamino-phthalimide 	n-octane propylbromide ethanol	77 77	(3.00) (2.35)		1.2 0.15	Bakhshiev 59 Viktorova 60b
$C_{10}H_8N_2O_3$ 4-Acetylamino-phthalimide	methanol benzene	77 77			1.25 0.30	Viktorova 60b
$C_{10}H_8O$ α-Naphthol 	EPA EPA ethanol/ether ethanol/ether NaOH naphthalene solution	90 90 77 77 77 77 20 77	3.14 2.05 2.90 3.07 2.06 2.00 2.39 3.07 3.04		$3 \cdot 10^{-7}$ 1.9	Ermolaev 59b,60a Hercules 59, 60 Kasha 47b Shpak 60b
$C_{10}H_8O$ β-Naphthol 	EPA EPA EPA ethanol chloroform naphthalene 	90 90 77 77 77 77 20 77	3.05 2.11 2.82 2.11 2.99 3.01 2.11		1.3 1.45 0.9 T	Hercules 60 Kasha 47b McClure 49 Marchetti 67 Shpak 60b Viktorova 60b

Formula and Substance	Solvent	$T_{°K}$	Transition (μm^{-1}) Abs.	Emis.	τ sec	References
$C_{10}H_8O_2$ 1,3-Naphthalenediol	EPA ether/ethanol/ ammonia H_2SO_4 H_2O NaOH	77 77		2.69 2.41 2.61 2.21 2.05		Hercules 59,60
$C_{10}H_8O_2$ 1,4-Naphthalenediol	ethanol H_2O EPA	77		2.28 2.17 2.36 2.39		Hercules 59,60
$C_{10}H_8O_2$ 1,5-Naphthalenediol	EPA ether/ethanol/ ammonia	77 77 77	2.02	2.85 2.59	T	Hercules 60 Marchetti 67
$C_{10}H_8O_2$ 1,6-Naphthalenediol	EPA ether/ethanol/ ammonia EPA	77 77 4 77		2.76 2.56 (1.90)	2	Hercules 60
$C_{10}H_8O_2$ 2,3-Naphthalenediol	EPA ether/ethanol/ ammonia	77 77		2.96 2.73		Hercules 60

Formula / Name	Structure	Solvent	Ref.			Author
C₁₀H₈O₂ 2,6-Naphthalenediol		EPA ether/ethanol/ammonia	77 77		2.80 2.55	Hercules 60
C₁₀H₈O₂ 2,7-Naphthalenediol		EPA ether/ethanol/ammonia H₂SO₄	77 77 77	2.13	2.88 2.68 2.88 2.40	Hercules 60 Marchetti 67
C₁₀H₉N α-Naphthylamine		EPA	77		1.90	McClure 49
C₁₀H₉N β-Naphthylamine		ethanol chloroform	77 77		2.60 1.4 1.2	Viktorova 60b Zelinskii 55
C₁₀H₁₀O₂ Triacetylene glycol	CH₃—CHOH—(C≡C)₂—CHOHCH₃		103		2.22	Beer 56
(C₁₀H₁₀N₅NaO₅P)ₙ Sodium polyadenylate		H₂O/glycerin	77		2.3	Bersohn 64

Formula and Substance	Solvent	$T°K$	Transition (μm^{-1}) Abs.	Emis.	τ_{sec}	References
$C_{10}H_{13}N_5O_3$ Deoxyadenosine	H_2O/glycerin	77			2.3	Bersohn 64
$C_{10}H_{13}N_5O_4$ Adenosine	acetate buffer H_2SO_4 ethylene glycol or propylene glycol/H_2O	77 77	3.89	2.56 3.18 3.64		Longworth 66 Stern 37 Udenfriend 65
$C_{10}H_{13}N_5O_5$ Guanosine	ethylene glycol or propylene glycol/H_2O	77		3.08 2.64	1.3	Longworth 66

Formula / Name	Solvent	T				Reference
$C_{10}H_{14}$ n-Butylbenzene	hexane				$6.8\cdot10^{-9}$	Ivanova 61
	ethanol				$10\cdot10^{-9}$	
$C_{10}H_{14}$ Durene	ethanol	77			6.85	Foerster 64
	EPA	77		2.80		Olness 63
	single crystal	20	3.58	3.58		Schnepp 59d
	single crystal	4.5		2.78		Sponer 64
	crystal	77			1.55	
	n-heptane	77			6.40	
	isooctane	77			5.45	
	isopropanol	77			6.30	
$C_{10}H_{14}$ p-Isopropyltoluene	hexane				$6.0\cdot10^{-9}$	Ivanova 61
	ethanol	77			$10.6\cdot10^{-9}$	Pyatnitskii 51
	ethanol	77			5.0	
	pure crystal				1.85	
$C_{10}H_{14}N_2O_5$ Thymidine	ethylene glycol or propylene glycol/H_2O	77		3.14		Longworth 66
				2.30		
$C_{10}H_{14}N_5O_6P$ Deoxyadenosine mono-phosphate	glycerin /water	77		2.60		Bersohn 64
				2.44		
				2.27		
				2.20		

Formula and Substance	Solvent	$T_{°K}$	Transition (μm^{-1}) Abs.	Emis.	τ_{sec}	References
$C_{10}H_{14}N_5O_7P$ Adenosine 5'-mono-phosphate	acetate buffer polymerized	77			2.5	Bersohn 64
		77		2.33	2.3	Douzu 61
		77			2.4	Steele 57
	H_2O/glycerin H_2SO_4	77	3.89	2.56		Udenfriend 65
$C_{10}H_{14}N_5O_7P$ 5'-Adenylic acid	ethylene glycol or propylene glycol/H_2O	77		3.50 2.63	2.5	Longworth 66
$C_{10}H_{14}N_5O_7P$ 5'-Guanylic acid	ethylene glycol or propylene glycol/H_2O	77		3.03 2.63	1.25	Longworth 66
$C_{10}H_{14}N_5O_8P$ Guanylic acid	H_2SO_4	77	3.57	2.56		Udenfriend 65
$C_{10}H_{14}N_6O_3$ Deoxyguanosine	H_2O/glycerin	77			1.2	Bersohn 64

Compound	Structure	Solvent					Reference
$C_{10}H_{15}N$ N N-Diethylaniline	⟨phenyl⟩–$N(C_2H_5)_2$	ethanol/ether	77 77	3.00 2.40	$15\cdot10^{-9}$ 2.0		Ermolaev 61
$C_{10}H_{15}N_2O_8P$ 5-Thymidylic acid		ethylene glycol or propylene glycol/H_2O	77	3.14 2.32			Longworth 66
$C_{10}H_{15}N_5O_{10}P_2$ Adenosine 5'-diphosphate	(structure, X = 3)	acetate buffer H_2SO_2	77	3.89 2.56	2.4		Steele 57 Udenfriend 65
$C_{10}H_{15}N_5O_6P$ Deoxyguanosine monophosphate	(structure)	glycerin /water	77	2.41	1.2		Bersohn 64

Formula and Substance	Solvent	$T_{°K}$	Transition (μm^{-1}) Abs.	Emis.	τ_{sec}	References
$C_{10}H_{16}N_4O_3$ 1,3,6-Trimethyl-7-methoxy-2,4-dioxo-tetrahydropteridine	H_2O		3.15	2.70	s	Lippert 61
$C_{10}H_{16}N_4O_3$ 1,3,6,8-Tetramethyl-2,4,7-trioxohexa-hydropteridine	H_2O		3.03	2.30	s	Lippert 61
$C_{10}H_{16}N_5O_{13}P_3$ Adenosine tri-phosphate	acetate buffer H_2SO_4	77	3.89	2.56	2.4	Steele 57 Udenfriend 65
$C_{11}H_7ClO$ 2-Chloronaphth-aldehyde	ethanol/ether	77		1.93		Ermolaev 60b
$C_{11}H_7N$ β-Naphthonitrile	EPA	90 90		3.00 2.06		Kasha 47b

Formula / Compound	Solvent	T				Reference
$C_{11}H_8O$ 1-Naphthaldehyde	ethanol/ether	77		1.98	0.08	Ermolaev 60b
$C_{11}H_8O$ 2-Naphthaldehyde	ethanol/ether	77	2.68	2.08	0.35	Ermolaev 60b
		77	2.09		T	Marchetti 67
		77				
$C_{11}H_8O_2$ 1-Naphthoic acid	ethanol	77		3.03		Hochstrasser 61d
		77		1.98		Marchetti 67
	methylcyclo-hexane	77		2.97		
		77		1.99		
	ethanol/KOH	77		2.05	T	
$C_{11}H_8O_2$ 2-Naphthoic acid	EPA	77	2.02	2.09	2.5	McClure 49
		77	2.08		T	Marchetti 67
$C_{11}H_9BrN_2O_3$ 3-Acetylamino-6-bromo-N-methyl-phthalimide	methanol	93			$1.4 \cdot 10^{-3}$	Borgman 60
$C_{11}H_9IN_2O_3$ 3-Acetylamino-6-iodo-N-methyl-phthalimide	methanol	93			$1.3 \cdot 10^{-4}$	Borgman 60

Formula and Substance	Solvent	$T_{°K}$	Transition (μm^{-1}) Abs.	Emis.	τ_{sec}	References
$C_{11}H_{10}$ 1-Methylnaphthalene	ethanol/ether	77		3.15	2.1	Ermolaev 63
		77		2.10	2.5	McClure 49
	EPA	77		2.09		Shpak 60b
	naphthalene	20/4		3.13		
				3.09		
$C_{11}H_{10}$ 2-Methylnaphthalene	cyclohexane	77		3.14		Foerster 63
	ethanol	77		3.14		Griessbach 60
	3-methylpentane	77		3.14		McConnell 53
	heptane	77			1.3	Pröpstl 63
	isopropanol	77			1.8	Sponer 62
	naphthalene	4.2		3.11		
	naphthalene	4.2		3.12		
	single crystal	4.2		2.06	1.78	
		77	2.13		T	
$C_{11}H_{10}N_2O_3$ 3-Acetylamino-N-methylphthalimide	solution	77		2.40		Borgman 60
	methanol	93			1.03	Zelinskii 55
$C_{11}H_{10}N_2O_3$ 4-Acetylamino-N-methylphthalimide	methanol	93			1.3	Borgman 60

Compound	Solvent		Value	Reference
C$_{11}$H$_{11}$N$_3$O$_3$ 3-Acetylamino-6-amino-N-methylphthalimide	propyl formate	77	2.05	Zelinskii 55
C$_{11}$H$_{12}$N$_2$O$_2$ 3-Dimethylamino-N-methylphthalimide	ethanol polymethyl methacrylate	93 93	1.95	Zelinskii 55
C$_{11}$H$_{12}$N$_2$O$_2$ Tryptophan	H$_2$O/glucose H$_2$O phosphate buffer	77 77	3.48 3.60 3.08 2.27 2.87 2.74 5.5·10^{-2}	Steele 58
C$_{11}$H$_{13}$N$_3$O$_2$ 3-Dimethylamino-6-amino-N-methylphthalimide	ethanol or butanol	93		Zelinskii 55
C$_{11}$H$_{12}$N$_2$O$_2$ 4-Dimethylamino-N-methylphthalimide	ethanol	93	2.04	Zelinskii 55

Formula and Substance		Solvent	$T_{°K}$	Transition (μm^{-1}) Abs.	Emis.	τ_{sec}	References
$C_{11}H_{14}O_2$ Butylbenzoate		ethanol CCl$_4$ pure solid	93 93 93			2.53 1.3 1.23	Dubinskii 59
$C_{12}H_8Cl_2$ 4,4'-Dichlorobiphenyl			77	2.20		T	Marchetti 67
$C_{12}H_8LiN$ N-Lithium carbazole					2.08		Linschitz 54
$C_{12}H_8N_2$ Benzoquinoxaline		ethanol	100 100		2.75 2.10		Gropper 63
$C_{12}H_8N_2$ 9,10-Diazaphenanthrene		methylcyclo-hexane	110		1.35	T	Lippert 62
$C_{12}H_8N_2$ m-Phenanthroline		ethanol	100 100		2.97 2.22		Gropper 63
$C_{12}H_8N_2$ o-Phenanthroline		ethanol	100 100		2.95 2.22		Gropper 63
$C_{12}H_8N_2$ p-Phenanthroline		ethanol	100 100		2.97 2.22		Gropper 63

Compound	Medium	T		$<10^{-2}$	Reference
$C_{12}H_8N_2$ Phenazine	isopentane	4.2	2.29		Hochstrasser 62a
	single crystal	77	2.30		Kasha 47b
		4.2	2.29		
	single crystal	77	2.34		
		4.2	2.34		
$C_{12}H_8N_2O_2$ 2-Furyl-5-phenyl-1,3,4-oxadiazole	benzene		3.38	2.87	Panov 59
$C_{12}H_8O$ Dibenzofuran	isopropanol	77		5.4	Foerster 63
	n-heptane	77	3.31		Heckmann 58
			2.46		Kanda 61d
	EPA	77	2.45	4.65	Nurmukhametov 65
	cyclohexane	90	2.47–2.45	5	Teplyakov 65
	n-hexane	77	3.30		
	ethanol		2.44		
	n-octane		2.45		
	n-nonane		2.46		
	ether		2.46		
	glutaric acid		2.44		
	azelaic acid		2.45		
			2.44		
$C_{12}H_8S$ Dibenzothiophene	EPA	77	2.43		Heckmann 58

Formula and Substance	Solvent	T °K	Transition (μm⁻¹)			References
			Abs.	Emis.	τ sec	
$C_{12}H_8S_3$ α-Terthienyl	methylcyclohexane/isopentane	77	2.58 2.68	2.50 2.34		Eckert 60
$C_{12}H_9Br$ 2-Bromobiphenyl		77	2.27		T	Marchetti 67
$C_{12}H_9I$ 2-Iodobiphenyl		77	2.20		T	Marchetti 67
$C_{12}H_9N$ Carbazole	ethanol	93	2.95	2.89		Alfimov 67
		93		2.45		Bree 68
	ethanol	77		2.46		El-Bayoumi 61
	ethanol/ether	77	2.95	2.46	7.6	Ermolaev 63
	ether	90		2.49		Heckmann 58
	EPA	77		2.45	14.5	Kasha 47b
	EPA	90		2.91		Kisliak 66
	polystyrene	77				Nurmukhametov 65
	tridecane	77				Pyatnitskii 63
	fluorene	15				Schutt 63
	methylcyclohexane	20				
	n-heptane	77	2.97 (3.0)	2.88 2.46	1.5	
	crystal	90				
$C_{12}H_9NO_2$ p-Nitrobiphenyl	EPA	77	2.05		0.08	McClure 49

Compound	Structure	Solvent	T (K)				References
$C_{12}H_{10}$ Acenaphthene	$H_2C\!-\!CH_2$	pentane	20		3.13		Andreeshchev 60
					2.10		Marchetti 67
		polystyrene	14		3.05	0.42	L. Pesteil 61
		single crystal	14		2.36		P. Pesteil 55b
			77	2.07		T	
$C_{12}H_{10}$ Biphenyl		ethanol/ether	77		2.30	3.1	Clar 56
		EPA	77		3.35		Ermolaev 63
		hexane	77		2.28	5.1	Foerster 63
		cyclohexane	77		2.29		Gobov 63b
						$19.3 \cdot 10^{-9}$	Levshin 59
		heptane	77	3.34	2.29		Marchetti 67
		heptane	77			2.00	C. Parker 62b
		isooctane	77	2.29	3.28	T	Trusov 64
$C_{12}H_{10}$ Diethyltetraacetylene	$H_3C_2\!-\!(C\!\equiv\!C)_4\!-\!C_2H_5$	EPA	103		(1.89)		Beer 56
					(1.67)		
					(1.44)		
$C_{12}H_{10}Hg$ Diphenylmercury			77	2.90		T	Marchetti 67

Formula and Substance		Solvent	$T\,^\circ K$	Transition (μm^{-1})		τ sec	References
				Abs.	Emis.		
$C_{12}H_{10}N_2$ Azobenzene		stilbene single crystal bibenzyl mixed crystal	77/4 77/4 20 20	2.77			Hochstrasser 62d Nurmukhametov 67
$C_{12}H_{10}N_2O_2$ 4-Amino-4-nitro-biphenyl	$H_2N-\bigcirc-\bigcirc-NO_2$	benzene dioxane		2.72 2.68	1.85 1.75		Lippert 57
$C_{12}H_{10}O$ p-Hydroxybiphenyl	$HO-\bigcirc-\bigcirc$	ether/ethanol		3.20	2.24	2.5	Ermolaev 60b
$C_{10}H_{10}O$ 2-Naphthyl methyl ketone	$\bigcirc\bigcirc-C-CH_3$ $=O$	ether/ethanol		2.72	2.08	0.97	Ermolaev 60b
$C_{12}H_{10}O_2$ Tetraacetylene glycol	$CH_3-OHHC(C\equiv C)_4-CHOH-CH_3$	EPA	103		1.88 1.66 1.44		Beer 56
$C_{12}H_{10}S$ Diphenyl sulfide		n-heptane	77		(2.56)		Teplyakov 65
$C_{12}H_{11}N$ Diphenylamine	$\bigcirc-N-\bigcirc$ H	ethanol/ether EPA ethanol n-heptane	77 77 90 90 93 77	3.30	(2.90) (2.50) 2.52 3.17 2.90 3.37 2.51	$1.4\cdot10^{-9}$ 1.9	Ermolaev 61 Kasha 47b Korber 64 Nurmukhametov 66

Compound	Solvent				Reference
$C_{12}H_{11}NO$ α-Acetylaminonaphthalene (CH₃CONH)	ethanol	93			Zelinskii 55
$C_{12}H_{11}NO$ β-Acetylaminonaphthalene	ethanol	93			Borgman 60
	methanol	93			Zelinskii 55
$C_{12}H_{12}$ 1,5-Dimethylnaphthalene (CH₃)	cyclohexane	83	3.12		Griessbach 60
	ethanol	83	3.13		
$C_{12}H_{12}$ 2,3-Dimethylnaphthalene	cyclohexane	83	3.14		Foerster 63
	ethanol	83	3.14		Griessbach 60
	heptane	77		1.65	
$C_{12}H_{12}$ 2,6-Dimethylnaphthalene	ethanol	87	3.10	3.09	Foerster 63
	3-methylpentane	87	3.10	3.08	Griessbach 60
	hexane	20	3.11–	3.11–	Kharitonova 63
			3.09	3.08	McConnell 53
	heptane	77			Wolf 55
	isopropanol	77			Zmerli 60
	cyclohexane	83	3.08	2.0	
	crystal	4		2.8	
		20	3.07		
			3.06		
$C_{12}H_{12}$ 2,7-Dimethylnaphthalene	cyclohexane	83	3.12		Griessbach 60
	ethanol	83	3.12		

Formula and Substance	Solvent	$T_{°K}$	Transition (μm^{-1}) Abs.	Emis.	τ_{sec}	References
$C_{12}H_{12}N_2O_3$ 3-Methylacetylamino-N-methylphthalimide	ethanol	93			0.55	Viktorova 60b
$C_{12}H_{12}N_2O_3$ 4-Methylacetylamino-N-methylphthalimide	ethanol	77			0.71	Viktorova 60b
$C_{12}H_{12}O$ 2-Ethoxynaphthalene		77	2.17		T	Marchetti 67
$C_{12}H_{14}O_2$ Dodecapentenoic acid	ether/ethanol	77	2.33			Hausser 35
$C_{12}H_{14}O_4$ Diethylphthalate	ethanol CCl4 pure solid	93 93 93			0.78 0.65 0.79	Dubinskii 59

Formula / Name	Solvent	Temp			Reference
$C_{12}H_{18}$ Hexamethylbenzene	EPA	77		5.75	Foerster 64
	isooctane	77		2.75	Olness 63
	n-heptane	77		7.55	Schnepp 57
	n-heptane	77		8.55	Sponer 64
	single crystal	4			
	single crystal	20	2.74		
	crystal	4.5	3.51	8.28	
	crystal	77		2.40	
$C_{12}D_{10}$ Decadeutero-acenaphthene	pentane	20	3.14		L. Pesteil 61
		14	2.11		
$C_{13}H_8Cl_2O$ p-p'-Dichloro-benzophenone	ethanol	100	(2.70) (2.40)		Dörr 57
			(2.90) (2.25)		
$C_{13}H_8O$ Fluorenone	crystal	120	2.10–		P. Pesteil 54c
			1.60		
$C_{13}H_8O_2$ Xanthone	ethanol/ether	77	2.70	$2 \cdot 10^{-2}$	Ermolaev 63
		77	2.48		
$C_{13}H_9Br_2N_3$ 2,7-Dibromo-proflavin	base in ethanol	93			Zanker 62
	cation in ethanol	93			

Formula and Substance		Solvent	$T_{°K}$	Transition (μm^{-1}) Abs.	Emis.	τ sec	References
$C_{13}H_9Cl_2N_2$ 2,7-Dichloro-proflavin		base in ethanol cation in ethanol	93 93				Zanker 62
$C_{13}H_9F_2N_3$ 2,7-Difluoro-proflavin		base in ethanol cation in ethanol base in ethanol cation in ethanol	73 73 93 93	2.40 3.90 2.20	2.20 2.10		Körber 64 Zanker 62
$C_{13}H_9N$ Acridine		base in ethanol cation in ethanol	93 93			$14.8 \cdot 10^{-9}$ $36 \cdot 10^{-9}$	Rammensee 60
$C_{13}H_9N$ 5,6-Benzoquinoline		isopentane/methylcyclo-hexane	77 100			1.8	Craig 54 Nurmukhametov 67
$C_{13}H_9N$ 7,8-Benzoquinoline		EPA ethanol isopentane/methylcyclo-hexane	90 100 77	2.18 2.18		1.4	Craig 54 Gropper 63 Kanda 59 Nurmukhametov 67
$C_{13}H_9N$ Phenanthridine		ethanol/H_2O	100 100	(2.85) 2.20			Gropper 63

Formula / Name	Structure	Solvent	Temp.	Value	Value 2	Reference
$C_{13}H_9NO$ Acridone		ethanol	93			Zanker 60
$C_{13}H_9NO_2$ 2-Nitrofluorene		EPA	77	2.06	0.13	McClure 49
$C_{13}H_{10}$ Fluorene		heptane	77	3.32		Benarroche 62a,b
		heptane	77	2.38	5.1	Ciais 61
		EPA	77	2.45	7.1	Dörr 63
		crystal	77	3.12		Ermolaev 61
		single crystal	4	3.12		Foerster 63
		ethanol/ether	77	3.35		Heckmann 58
			77	2.20		Kanda 61d
		isopropanol	77		6.9	Nurmukhametov 62
		pentane	20		5.7	C. Parker 62b
		n-pentane	77	3.34		Trusov 64
		hexane	77	2.37		
		cyclohexane	90	2.36		
				2.39–2.35		
$C_{13}H_{10}N_2$ 1-Amino acridine		ethanol	93			Zanker 60
		cation in ethanol	93			
$C_{13}H_{10}N_2$ 2-Amino acridine		ethanol	93	2.16	$22 \cdot 10^{-9}$	Rammensee 60
		cation in ethanol	93	1.86	$13 \cdot 10^{-9}$	

Formula and Substance		Solvent	$T_{°K}$	Transition (μm^{-1}) Abs.	Emis.	τ sec	References
$C_{13}H_{10}N_2$ 3-Amino acridine		ethanol cation in ethanol	93 93	2.14 2.02		$17.7 \cdot 10^{-9}$ $9.5 \cdot 10^{-9}$	Rammensee 60
$C_{13}H_{10}N_2$ 4-Amino acridine		ethanol	93	2.22		$28.5 \cdot 10^{-9}$	Rammensee 60
$C_{13}H_{10}N_2$ 9-Amino acridine		ethanol cation in ethanol	93 93			$15 \cdot 10^{-9}$ $14.9 \cdot 10^{-9}$	Rammensee 60
$C_{13}H_{10}O$ Benzophenone		ether/ether	78	2.66	2.42	$4.7 \cdot 10^{-3}$	Ermolaev 56,63 Kanda 64 Korsunskii 63 McClure 55b C. Parker 62b Scheibe 54 Terenin 56
		petroleum ether	78		2.40	.005	
		EPA	77		2.42– 1.63		
		n-hexane	77	2.43			
			77	2.64			
		single crystal	20	2.66			
			20		2.38		
		single crystal	90			$(10-15) \cdot 10^{-3}$	
		ethanol/ether	77	2.60	2.42	$4.7 \cdot 10^{-3}$	
		ethanol	100		1.78– 2.50	$6.2 \cdot 10^{-3}$	
		methylcyclo- hexane/isopentane	100		1.75– 2.38	$2.0 \cdot 10^{-3}$	
		methanol/H_2O	100		1.65– 2.50	$8.0 \cdot 10^{-3}$	
		H_2SO_4	100		1.70– 2.34	$<1.2 \cdot 10^{-3}$	

Compound	Solvent	Temp			Reference
$C_{13}H_{10}O$ p-Phenylbenzaldehyde	ether/ethanol	77		2.10	Ermolaev 60b
$C_{13}H_{11}N$ 9,10-Dihydroacridine	ether/ethanol ethanol	77 93	 3.20 3.50	2.90 2.30	3.5	Ermolaev 61 Körber 64
$C_{13}H_{11}N_3$ 3,6-Diaminoacridine	base in ethanol cation in ethanol	93		(2.10) (1.78)	Zanker 57
$C_{13}H_{12}$ Diphenylmethane	single crystal	20	3.67 3.69		Coffman 58
$C_{13}H_{13}N_3O_4$ 3,6-Diacetylamino-N-methylphthalimide	methanol	93		0.61	Borgman 60
$C_{13}H_{13}NO_3$ 3-Methylacetylamino-6-acetylamino-N-phthalimide	ethanol	77		0.50	Viktorova 60b

Formula and Substance	Solvent	T °K	Transition (m⁻¹) Abs.	Emis.	sec	References
$C_{13}H_{14}$ 2,3,6-Trimethyl-naphthalene	cyclohexane ethanol	83 83		3.11 3.10		Griessbach 60
$C_{13}H_{14}$ 2,4,5-Trimethyl-azulene	EPA	77		2.60		Viswanath 56
$C_{13}H_{14}$ 2,4,8-Trimethyl-azulene	EPA	77		2.61		Viswanath 56
$C_{13}H_{15}N_3O_3$ 3-Dimethylamino-6-acetylamino-N-methyl-phthalimide	propyl acetate isopropylformate or chloroform chloroform isopropyl formate	77 77 77 77		1.90 2.55	0.35 0.2	Viktorova 60b Zelinskii 55
$C_{13}H_{21}ClN_2O_4$ 1,5-N,N'-Dipyro-lidylpentameth-ine perchlorate	crystal powder ClO₄⊖	129 77	2.36 2.20	2.27 2.13 2.10 1.96		Baumgartner 56
$C_{14}H_6Cl_2O_2$ 1,5-Dichloroanthra-quinone	paraffin	77		1.92		Shigorin 58

$C_{14}H_6Cl_4$ 1,4,5,8-Tetrachloro-anthracene		EPA	77	1.42	Padhye 56
$C_{14}H_7BrO_2$ β-Bromoanthraquinone		heptane	77	2.18	Shigorin 60
$C_{14}H_7ClO_2$ α-Chloro anthra-quinone		alkanes	77	1.92	Shigorin 59
$C_{14}H_7ClO_2$ β-Chloro anthra-quinone		hexane heptane	77 77	2.18 2.19	Shigorin 59
$C_{14}H_7Cl_3$ 1,5,10-Trichloro-anthracene		EPA	77	1.38	Padhye 56
$C_{14}H_7IO_2$ 2-Iodo anthraquinone		heptane	77	2.17	Shigorin 60

Formula and Substance	Solvent	T °K	Transition (μm^{-1}) Abs.	Emis.	τ_{sec}	References
$C_{14}H_8Cl_2$ 1,5-Dichloro-anthracene	EPA	77		1.46	$3.9 \cdot 10^{-3}$	Padhye 56
$C_{14}C_8Cl$ 1,10-Dichloro-anthracene	EPA	77		1.41		Padhye 56
$C_{14}H_8Cl_2$ 9,10-Dichloro-anthracene	hexane	93		2.48		Bowen 55
$C_{14}H_8O$ Anthraquinone	hexane heptane EPA octane glass crystal	77 77 77		2.18 2.19	$4 \cdot 10^{-3}$ $2.9 \cdot 10^{-3}$ $5 \cdot 10^{-2}$	Martinez 62 C. Parker 62b Shigorin 59
$C_{14}H_8O_3$ 1-Oxyanthraquinone	paraffin	77		(1.80)		Shigorin 58
$C_{14}H_8O_3$ 2-Oxyanthraquinone	paraffin	77		1.94 1.95		Shigorin 58

		Solvent	Temp	Value	Reference
$C_{14}H_8O_4$ 1,4-Dioxyanthra- quinone		paraffin	77	1.91	Shigorin 58
$C_{14}H_8O_4$ 1,5-Dioxyanthra- quinone		paraffin	77	1.76	Shigorin 58
$C_{14}H_8O_4$ 1,8-Dioxyanthra- quinone		paraffin	77	1.85	Shigorin 58
$C_{14}H_9Br$ 9-Bromophenanthrene		isopentane	77		Hilpern 64
$C_{14}H_9Cl$ 1-Chloroanthracene		EPA	77	1.47	Padhye 56
$C_{14}H_9NO_2$ β-Amino anthra- quinone		n-heptane	77	2.01	Shigorin 58

Formula and Substance	Solvent	T°K	Transition (μm^{-1})		τ sec	References
			Abs.	Emis.		
$C_{14}H_{10}$ Anthracene	isopentane	77			0.10	Alexander 61
	EPA	77		1.49	0.09	Borisov 56
	EPA	77	2.66			Brodin 65b
	EPA	77	1.84	1.84		Ciais 61
	naphthalene	4	2.59	2.59		Claxton 61
	p-terphenyl	20		2.59		Hercules 60
	p-quaterphenyl	20		2.58		Hilpern 64
	diphenyl	20		2.60		Hochstrasser 64b, 64e
	9,10-dihydro-anthracene	20		2.59		Galanin 61
	stilbene	14				Jones 68
	phenanthrene	20		2.56		Klimova 66
	phenanthrene	20	2.61			McClure 49
	single crystal	4	2.54–2.83	2.52	$2.4 \cdot 10^{-3}$	McGlynn 60b
	single crystal	14		2.49		C. Parker 62a, 62b
	single crystal	20	2.52–2.83			P. Pesteil 55a
	single crystal	93				Reid 52b
	crystal	77				Sidman 56b,56f
	benzophenone	77	1.84	1.84		Solov'ev 61
	ethanol	78				Vatulov 60
	n-alkanes/naph-thacene					
$C_{14}H_{10}$ Diphenylacetylene	EPA	103		3.31–2.57		Beer 56
	octane	103		2.19–1.76	0.3	Gobov 63b
		77	3.29	3.29		
		77		2.18		

$C_{14}H_{10}$ Phenanthrene

Solvent	T				Reference
pentane	20		2.87		Alfimov 67
ethanol	77	2.89	2.90		Azumi 62
ethanol	90			3.6	Benz 64
pentane	20		2.17		Brinen 67
hexane	77		2.18		Ciais 61
hexane	90			3.7	Clar 56
polymethylmethacrylate	77				Czekalla 59
petroleum ether	90		2.17		Ermolaev 63
heptane	77			3.35	Foerster 64
isooctane	77			3.55	Gropper 63
isopropanol	77			3.65	Kanda 59
EPA	77		2.16	3.50	Kasha 47b
EPA	77		2.88	3.8	Liebson 52
EPA	90		2.17		Marchetti 67
EPA	90		2.89		Melhuish 64
ethanol/ether	77		2.89		Metzger 69
isopentane/methylcyclohexane	77			3.7	Misra 66b
propylether/isopentane	77				Olness 63
single crystal	4	2.10	2.83		C. Parker 62b
single crystal	4.2		2.86		L. Pesteil 62
single crystal	4.5				Pyatnitskii 63
single crystal	90	2.86	2.86	2.81	Reid 52a
crystal				$5.2 \cdot 10^{-4}$	Sponer 62
polystyrene	77				Teplyakov 63
tridecane	77				Wolf 58
nonane	90				Zimmermann 61b
crystal	90			3.0	
octane	90			1.6	
glass	77			3.3	
petroleum ether	90	2.16	2.17	13.1	
	77			T	

Formula and Substance	Solvent	$T_{\circ K}$	Transition (μm^{-1}) Abs.	Emis.	τ sec	References
$C_{14}H_{10}$ Phenanthrene (continued)	argon	20		2.17	2.9	
	argon	33			2.9	
	krypton	20		2.16	0.38	
	krypton				0.49	
	xenon	20		2.17	0.20	
	xenon	77			0.09	
	CH_4	20		2.16	3.0	
	CH_4	33			3.3	
	SF_6	20		2.18	3.3	
	SF_6	39			3.5	
	SF_6	77			3.5	
$C_{14}H_{10}O$ Anthrone	ethanol/ether	77 77	2.70 (2.52)		$1.5 \cdot 10^{-3}$	Ermolaev 63
$C_{14}H_{10}O_2$ Benzil	solid solution crystal	78		1.88	$4.4 \cdot 10^{-3}$	Ermolaev 56 Ganguly 53
$C_{14}H_{10}O_4$ 1,6-Difuryl-hexa-dene-1,5-dione-3,4	ethanol	77			$4.1 \cdot 10^{-9}$	Nepochatykh 58
$C_{14}H_{11}Br$ 4-Bromostilbene	dibenzyl crystal	20		2.90 2.54 2.63		Dyck 62 Malkes 61

	Solvent					References
$C_{14}H_{11}ClN_3$ Trypaflavin	ethanol	90			2.51	Kisliak 58,59
	2-chloroethanol	77	(2.15)	(2.06)	0.25	Martinez 62
				1.72		Mokeeva 60
	alcohol solution	90			$5.3 \cdot 10^{-9}$	Pankeeva 59
	glycerin water	90	2.15			Wrzesinska 35
	glycerin	90			(2.5)	
	H_2O	90			2.55	
	acetic acid	90			2.24	
	formic acid	90			$0.95 \cdot 10^{-9}$	
		93			$6 \cdot 10^{-9}$	
		93			2.5	
$C_{14}H_{12}$ trans-Stilbene	methylpentane	77	3.24	3.04		Dyck 62
	heptane	77	3.00	2.88		Fugol 58
	octane		2.99	3.00		Gobov 63b
				2.99		Malkes 61
	toluene			2.84		Prikhotko 59
	single crystal	20	2.91	2.91		
	toluene	20		2.97–		
				2.95		
	dibenzyl	20.4		2.99		
$C_{14}H_{12}ClN$ N-Methylacri-dinium chloride	ethanol	93				Zanker 60

Formula and Substance	Solvent	$T\,°K$	Transition (μm^{-1}) Abs.	Emis.	τ sec	References
$C_{14}H_{12}O_2$ Benzoin		diethyl ether EPA	78	2.80	2.56	$2.0\cdot10^{-3}$ $1.8\cdot10^{-2}$	Morantz 62
$C_{14}H_{14}$ B Dibenzyl		n-heptane isooctane single crystal	77 77 20	3.73	3.71 3.64		Chizhikova 56 Coffman 58 Gobov 63b Levshin 59
$C_{14}H_{14}O$ Dibenzylether		isooctane	77		2.90		Levshin 59
$C_{14}H_{17}N_3O_3$ 3-Dimethylamino-6-diethyl acetylamino N-methylphthalimide		ethanol or isopropyl formate	77			0.45	Viktorova 60b
$C_{14}H_{21}N_5O_6S$ 5-Hydroxytryptamine creatinine-sulfate		ethanol	77		2.41		Shpolskii 59a
$C_{14}D_{10}$ Decadeutero-phenanthrene		pentane	20		2.90		L. Pesteil 62

$C_{15}H_{10}O_2$ β-Methyl-anthra-quinone		heptane heptane octane	77 77 77		2.18 2.19 2.19	Shigorin 58
$C_{15}H_{12}$ 2-Methylanthracene		ethanol/ether crystal	77 77		2.44– 2.20 2.30– 2.06	Bandow 51
$C_{15}H_{16}$ Diphenylpropane			77			Levshin 59
$C_{15}H_{16}O_9$ Esculin		sugar glycerin solid	93 93	$4.4 \cdot 10^{-9}$ 1.2 $3.7 \cdot 10^{-9}$ $2 \cdot 10^{-9}$		Galanin 50 Mokeeva 61
$C_{15}H_{18}$ 1,4-Dimethyl-7-isopropylazulene		EPA	77		2.57	Viswanath 56
$C_{15}H_{19}IN_2$ 1,1'-Diethyl-2,2'-pyridocyanine iodide		isopropanol/ isopentane	77		1.98– 1.54	Levison 57

Formula and Substance	Solvent	$T_{°K}$	Transition (μm^{-1}) Abs.	Emis.	τ sec	References
$C_{16}H_{10}$ Acepleiadylene	methanol/ethanol	77		1.80		McClure 59
	pyrene	4		1.78		Sidman 56e
	single crystal		1.77 1.96			
$C_{16}H_{10}$ Diphenyldiacetylene	EPA	103		2.03	0.1	Beer 56
$C_{16}H_{10}$ Fluoranthene	heptane	77			0.84	Clar 56
	isopropanol	77			0.87	Foerster 63
	EPA	77		1.85		
$C_{16}H_{10}$ Pyrene	ethanol	77	2.69	2.69		Ciais 61
	pentane	20		2.70		Clar 56
	crystal	4		2.69		Reid 52a
	crystal	100		(2.09)	$1.8 \cdot 10^{-7}$	Zimmermann 61c
	octane	77				
	heptane	77				
	decane	77				
	hexane	77				
	EPA	77		1.68		
$C_{16}H_{10}N_2$ Dibenzoquinoxaline	ethanol	90		2.30	(1)	Dörr 63

Compound	Solvent					Reference
$C_{16}H_{10}N_2O_2$ Indigo	hexane/dioxane alcohol/dioxane xylene aniline	77 77 77 77	1.65 1.65 1.69 1.65	1.69 1.65 1.69 1.64		Nurmukhametov 63
$C_{16}H_{10}O$ Brazan	n-heptane isopropanol	77 77		1.25 1.4		Foerster 63
$C_{16}H_{12}$ 1-Phenylnaphthalene		77	2.06		T	Marchetti 67
$C_{16}H_{12}$ 2-Phenylnaphthalene		77	2.06		T	Marchetti 67
$C_{16}H_{12}$ 4,5-Dihydropyrene		77	2.14		T	Marchetti 67
$C_{16}H_{12}O$ 3-Acetophenanthrene		77	2.06		T	Marchetti 67
$C_{16}H_{12}O$ 9-Acetophenanthrene		77	2.04		T	Marchetti 67

Formula and Substance	Solvent	$T_{°K}$	Transition (μm^{-1}) Abs.	Emis.	τ_{sec}	References
$C_{16}H_{12}N_2O_3$ 4-Acetylamino-N-phenylphthalimide	ethanol ethanol methanol	77 93 93		2.10	0.3	Borgman 60 Zelinskii 55
$C_{16}H_{13}N$ Phenyl-β-naphthylamine	EPA	77			1.3	C. Parker 62b
$C_{16}H_{14}$ 1,4-Diphenyl-(1,3)-butadiene	undecane xylene	77 77	2.80	2.80 2.72		Hausser 35
$C_{16}H_{16}$ 1,2,3,6,7,8-Hexahydropyrene		77	1.99		T	Marchetti 67
$C_{16}H_{16}$ 3,4,5,8,9,10-Hexahydropyrene	isopentane/ methylcyclo-hexane	77		1.98		Moodie 54
$C_{16}H_{18}ClN_3$ Acridine yellow	ethanol boric acid	77 77			2.2 1.7 $8.8 \cdot 10^{-9}$	Baczynski 59 Steele 57

Formula / Name	Structure	Solvent	Temp				Reference
$C_{16}H_{18}O$ Diphenyldiethyl-ether	phenyl-C_2H_4-O-C_2H_4-phenyl	isooctane	77				Levshin 59
$C_{16}H_{18}O$ Diphenyldiethyl-sulfide	phenyl-C_2H_4-S-C_2H_4-phenyl	isooctane	77				Levshin 59
$C_{16}H_{22}O_4$ Dibutylphthalate	COOC$_4$H$_9$ / COOC$_4$H$_9$	ethanol / CCl$_4$ / pure solid	93 / 93 / 93	0.80 / 0.58 / 0.7			Dubinskii 59
$C_{17}H_{12}$ 1,2-Benzofluorene		EPA	77		2.01		Clar 56
$C_{17}H_{12}$ 2,3-Benzofluorene		EPA	77		2.01		Clar 56
$C_{18}H_{12}$ 1,2-Benzanthracene	NH$_2$	hexane	77	$1.59 \cdot 10^{-4}$			Clar 56
		EPA	77		2.61		Czekalla 59
					1.65		Hirschberg 56
		propylether/iso-pentane	83	0.3			McClure 49
				0.4			Moodie 54
		ethanol	93		2.60	2.60	Reid 52a
						2.73	Zimmerman 61b
						3.44	
		isopentane/methylcyclohexane			1.65 / 1.52 / 1.38		

Formula and Substance	Solvent	$T_{°K}$	Transition (μm^{-1})			References
			Abs.	Emis.	τ sec	
$C_{18}H_{12}$ 3,4-Benzphenanthrene	isopentane/cyclohexane	77		1.98		Clar 56
	cyclohexane			1.84		Moodie 54
	EPA	77		2.00		
$C_{18}H_{12}$ chrysene	ethanol	93	2.79	2.79		Clar 56
		90		2.78		Craig 54
				1.98		Dorr 63
	EPA	77		1.98	2.2	Foerster 63
	EPA	90		2.78		Hochstrasser 64c
	n-heptane	77			2.2	Kasha 47b
	n-heptane	77				Melhuish 64
	isopropanol	77		2.01		Nurmukhametov 60
	octane	77			2.65	Olness 63
	polymethylmethacrylate	77		2.77		Sponer 67
	naphthalene	77		1.97		Zimmerman 61b
		77		2.74		
	single crystal	4.2		1.83	1.38	
				2.52		
$C_{18}H_{12}$ Naphthacene (Tetracene)	n-nonane/anthracene	77		2.02		Bolotnikova 59c
	n-heptane/anthracene	77		2.02		Broude 59
	n-hexane/anthracene	77		2.02		Ciais 61
	ethyl ether/methylcyclohexane/isooctane	77	(1.8)	(1.79)		Grzywacz 64
		77		(1.88)		Katul 67
	crystal	77		(1.91)		Klimova 66
						Prikhotko 66
						Reid 52b
						Sidman 56d
						Solov'ev 59

Compound	Medium	Temp			T	References
$C_{18}H_{12}$ Naphthacene (continued) (Tetracene)	polymethylmethacrylate					
	n-alkanes/naphthacene					
	pentane	20		2.12		
	nonane	77		2.12		
	toluene		2.07	2.07		
	tolane	20		2.07		
	dibenzyl	20		2.06		
	diphenyl	20		2.07		
	p-terphenyl	20		2.03		
	anthracene	20	2.02	2.03		
	naphthalene	20	2.03	2.03		
	single crystal	20	1.93	2.03		
$C_{18}H_{12}$ Triphenylene	ethanol	90		2.38		Clar 56
	EPA	77		2.91		Dörr 63
		77		2.38		McClure 49
	polymethylmeth-acrylate	77				Melhuish 64
						C. Parker 62b
$C_{18}H_{14}$ o-Terphenyl		77	2.16		T	Marchetti 67
$C_{18}H_{14}$ m-Terphenyl		77	2.27		T	Marchetti 67
$C_{18}H_{14}$ p-Terphenyl		77	2.04	2.06	T	Clar 56
						Marchetti 67

Formula and Substance	Solvent	$T_{°K}$	Transition (μm^{-1})			References
			Abs.	Emis.	τ sec	
$C_{18}H_{14}O_4$ Difuryl-1,10-decatetrene-1,3,7,9-dione-5,6	ethanol	77			$3.3 \cdot 10^{-9}$	Nepochatykh 58
$C_{18}H_{15}As$ Triphenylarsine	EPA	77 / 77	4.00	2.55	$1.6 \cdot 10^{-3}$	McClure 49
$C_{18}H_{15}N$ Triphenylamine	ethanol/ether	77	2.90	2.45	0.7	Ermolaev 63
$C_{18}H_{15}P$ Triphenylphosphine	EPA	77 / 77	3.80	2.52	0.01	McClure 49
$C_{18}H_{24}$ Dodecahydro-triphenylene	EPA	77		2.64		Clar 56
$C_{19}H_{13}NO$ 9-(p-Hydroxy)-Phenylacridine	solid anion	93		1.89 2.22		Shablya 61

$C_{19}H_{14}$ 1'-Methyl-1,2-benzanthracene		isopentane/ methylcyclo- hexane methanol/ethanol/ ether	77	1.70- 1.42 2.51 S (1.72) T	Hirschberg 56 Moodie 54
$C_{19}H_{14}$ 2'-Methyl-1,2-benzanthracene		isopentane/ methylcyclo- hexane methanol/ethanol/ ether	77	1.66- 1.38 2.44 S (1.68) T	Hirschberg 56 Moodie 54
$C_{19}H_{14}$ 3'-Methyl-1,2-benzanthracene		isopentane/ methylcyclo- hexane methanol/ethanol/ ether	77	1.67- 1.38 2.46 S (1.68) T	Hirschberg 56 Moodie 54
$C_{19}H_{14}$ 4'-Methyl-1,2-benzanthracene		isopentane/ methylcyclo- hexane methanol/ethanol/ ether	77	1.67- 1.38 2.49 S (1.73)	Hirschberg 56 Moodie 54
$C_{19}H_{14}$ 3-Methyl-1,2-benzanthracene		isopentane/ methylcyclo- hexane methanol/ethanol/ ether	77	1.68- 1.40 2.48 S 1.75 T	Hirschberg 56 Moodie 54

Formula and Substance	Solvent	$T \, °K$	Transition (μm^{-1}) Abs.	Emis.	τ sec	References
$C_{19}H_{14}$ 4-Methyl-1,2-benzanthracene	isopentane/ methylcyclo-hexane methanol/ethanol/ether	77	1.70–1.41	2.46 S 1.76 T		Hirschberg 56 Moodie 54
$C_{19}H_{14}$ 5-Methyl-1,2-benzanthracene	isopentane/ methylcyclo-hexane methanol/ethanol/ether	77	1.66–1.41	2.50 S 1.86 T		Hirschberg 56 Moodie 54
$C_{19}H_{14}$ 6-Methyl-1,2-benzanthracene	isopentane/ methylcyclo-hexane methanol/ethanol/ether	77	1.65–1.37	2.45 S (1.66) T		Hirschberg 56 Moodie 54
$C_{19}H_{14}$ 7-Methyl-1,2-benzanthracene	isopentane/ methylcyclo-hexane methanol/ethanol/ether	77	1.68–1.39	2.46 S (1.68) T		Hirschberg 56 Moodie 54
$C_{19}H_{14}$ 8-Methyl-1,2-benzanthracene	isopentane/ methylcyclo-hexane methanol/ethanol/ether	77	1.68–1.41	2.48 S (1.68) T		Hirschberg 56 Moodie 54

Compound	Solvent		Values		Reference
$C_{19}H_{14}$ 9-Methyl-1,2-benzanthracene	isopentane/methylcyclohexane methanol/ethanol/ether	77	1.63–1.32 2.51 1.75	 S T	Hirschberg 56 Moodie 54
$C_{19}H_{14}$ 10-Methyl-1,2-benzanthracene	isopentane/methylcyclohexane methanol/ethanol/ether	77	1.63–1.33 2.48	 S	Hirschberg 56 Moodie 54
$C_{19}H_{14}$ 1-Methyl-3,4-benzphenanthrene	isopentane/methylcyclohexane methanol/ethanol/ether	77	1.97 1.82 2.45		Hirschberg 56 Moodie 54
$C_{19}H_{14}$ 2-Methyl-3,4-benzphenanthrene	isopentane/methylcyclohexane methanol/ethanol/ether	77	1.97 1.83 2.43 1.99	 S T	Hirschberg 56 Moodie
$C_{19}H_{14}$ 3-Methyl-3,4-benzphenanthrene		77	2.44 1.98	S T	Hirschberg 56

458   LOW TEMPERATURE SPECTROSCOPY

Formula and Substance	Solvent	$T_{°K}$	Transition (μm^{-1}) Abs.	Emis.	τ_{sec}	References
$C_{19}H_{14}$ 4-Methyl-3,4-benzphenanthrene	methanol/ ethanol/ ether	77		2.47 1.98	S T	Hirschberg 56
$C_{19}H_{14}$ 5-Methyl-3,4-benzphenanthrene	isopentane/ methylcyclo- hexane methanol/ ethanol/ ether	77		1.89 1.78 2.45 1.98	S T	Hirschberg 56 Moodie 54
$C_{19}H_{14}$ 6-Methyl-3,4-benzphenanthrene	isopentane/ methylcyclo- hexane methanol/ ethanol/ ether	77		1.98 1.84 2.48 1.98		Hirschberg 56 Moodie 54
$C_{19}H_{14}$ 7-Methyl-3,4-benzphenanthrene	isopentane/ methylcyclo- hexane	77		1.98 1.83		Moodie 54
$C_{19}H_{14}$ 8-Methyl-3,4-benzphenanthrene	isopentane/ methylcyclo- hexane	77		1.97 1.83		Moodie 54

Formula / Name	Structure	Conditions	T				References
$C_{19}H_{14}O$ 4-Phenyl benzophenone	(structure)	ethanol/ether	77		2.68	.2	Ermolaev 60b
		MPEG	77		2.12		Ladner 65
$C_{19}H_{15}$ Triphenylmethyl	(structure)	free radical in EPA	90		1.94 / 1.84 / 1.79 / 1.96 / 1.94		Lewis 44a
		triphenylamine	4.2	1.96 / 1.94			Weissman 62
$C_{19}H_{15}N$ 1-Phenyl-4-(2-quinolyl)-buta-diene-(1,3)	(structure)	heptane		2.63	2.33		A. Nikitin 59
		benzene			2.33		
$C_{19}H_{16}$ Triphenylmethane	(structure)	EPA	77	3.88	2.85	5.4	McClure 49
			77				
$C_{20}H_7Br_4NaO_5$ Eosin	(structure)	disodium salt in ethanol	77		1.84		Birks 62
		ethanol	77			$8.9\cdot10^{-3}$	Grzywacz 64
		dianion in ethanol	93				Martinez 62
		cation in ethanol	93				C. Parker 61
		methanol			1.85		Zanker 60
		2-chloroethanol	77			0.5	
		glycerine	77		1.82		
		PMMA	77			$10.7\cdot10^{-3}$	

Formula and Substance		T°K	Transition (μm^{-1}) Abs. Emis. τ_{sec}		References
	Solvent				
$C_{20}H_{10}$ Diphenyltetra- acetylene	EPA	103		2.34– 1.47	Beer 56
$C_{20}H_{10}Br_2O_5$ 2,7-Dibromo fluorescein	dianion in ethanol	93			Zanker 62
$C_{20}H_{10}Br_2O_5$ 4,5-Dibromo fluorescein	dianion in ethanol	93			Zanker 62
$C_{20}H_{10}Cl_2O_5$ 2,7-Dichloro fluorescein	dianion in ethanol	93			Zanker 62
$C_{20}H_{10}I_2O_5$ 4,5-Diiodo fluorescein	dianion in ethanol	93			Zanker 62

Compound	Solvent	T				Reference
C$_{20}$H$_{12}$ 3,4-Benzopyrene 	n-heptane EPA	20 77	2.49		<0.1	Craig 54 Shpolskii 62a
C$_{20}$H$_{12}$ 1,2-Benzopyrene 	EPA	77		1.85		Clar 56
C$_{20}$H$_{12}$ Perylene 	ethanol	93	2.27 2.95 3.43	2.27		Liebson 52 Martinez 62 Shpolskii 60b Val'dman 63 Zimmerman 61b
	hexane polystyrene glass n-hexane dibenzylamino- ether	77 20.4 20.4		2.24 2.26 2.26	0.75	
C$_{20}$H$_{12}$N$_4$Cu Copper porphin	n-octane n-nonane EPAF MPEG	77 77 77 77		1.52 1.52 1.53	(750.155)·10^{-6}	Eastwood 69
C$_{20}$H$_{12}$O$_5$ Fluorescein 	2-chloroethanol EPA acid boric acid/ glycerine PMMA	77 90 90 93 93	2.5	2.10 1.77	2.8 4.9·10^{-9}	Grzywacz 64 Kasha 47b Martinez 62

Formula and Substance	Solvent	$T_{°K}$	Transition (μm^{-1})		τ_{sec}	References
			Abs.	Emis.		
$C_{20}H_{14}$ 2,2'-Dinaphthyl (structure)	EPA	77		1.96		Clar 56
$C_{20}H_{14}N_4$ Porphin	ethanol octane decane	77 77 77	1.62 1.63	1.62 1.63		Sevchenko 63,66
$C_{20}H_{16}$ 7,12-Dimethyl-1,2-benzanthracene	methanol/ ethanol/ ether	77		2.44 1.76	S T	Hirschberg 56
$C_{20}H_{16}$ 9,10-Dimethyl-1,2-benzanthracene	isopentane/ methylcyclo-hexane methanol/ethanol/ ether	77		1.55 1.40 1.27		Moodie 54 Reid 52a
$C_{20}H_{16}$ 10-Ethyl-1,2-benzanthracene	isopentane/ methylcyclo-hexane methanol/ethanol/ ether	77		1.64 1.52 1.39		Moodie 54
$C_{20}H_{16}N_4$ Dihydroporphin	ethanol octane	77 77		1.60 1.58		Sevchenko 63,66

Compound	Structure	Solvent	Temp	Values		Reference
$C_{20}H_{16}O_2$ 4'-Methoxy-4-phenyl benzophenone	CH_3O—〇—CO—〇—〇	ethanol/ether	77	2.14	0.28	Ermolaev 60b
$C_{20}H_{16}O_2$ Phenyl-4-methoxy diphenylketone	〇—C(=O)—〇—OCH_3	ethanol/ether	77	2.06	0.48	Ermolaev 60b
$C_{20}H_{22}$ 9,10-Di-N-propyl anthracene	(C_3H_7 anthracene C_3H_7)	ethanol/ether	77			Ermolaev 63
$C_{20}H_{24}N_2O_2 \cdot H_2SO_4 \cdot 7H_2O$ Quininebisulfate	[quinine structure $\cdot H_2SO_4 \cdot 7H_2O$]	H_2O/glucose crystal	77	1.5	$4.5 \cdot 10^{-9}$	Galanin 50 Steele 57
$C_{20}H_{26}ClN_3$ N-Propyl acridine orange	[acridine orange structure $(CH_3)_2N$ ... $N(CH_3)_2$, C_3H_7]$^+$ $Cl^{\ominus}$	ethanol/ether	90	1.72 1.61 1.82 1.95 1.44		Miethke 58

Formula and Substance	Solvent	$T_{°K}$	Transition (μm^{-1}) Abs.	Emis.	τ sec	References
$C_{21}H_{13}N$ 1,2,3,4-Dibenz-acridine	base in ethanol	93	2.68	2.68		Körber 64
$C_{21}H_{16}$ 8,9-Trimethylene-3,4-benzophenanthrene	EPA	77		1.96		Clar 56
$C_{21}H_{16}$ 11,12-Trimethyl-tetraphene	EPA	77		1.61		Clar 56
$C_{21}H_{16}N_2O_2$ 3-Diphenylamino-N-methylphthalimide	ethanol or iso-propylformate ethanol chloroform	77 93 77 77		1.86	$7 \cdot 10^{-2}$ $6 \cdot 10^{-2}$	Viktorova 60b Zelinskii 55
$C_{22}H_{12}$ 1,12-Benzoperylene	n-hexane EPA	77 77	2.47	1.62		Clar 56 Personov 67
$C_{22}H_{14}$ 1,2,5,6-Dibenz-anthracene	EPA	77 77	2.53	1.83	1.5	McClure 49

$C_{22}H_{14}$ 1,2-Benzochrysene	EPA	77	1.86	Clar 56
$C_{22}H_{14}$ Picene	EPA	77	2.01	Clar 56
$C_{22}H_{14}$ 5,6-Benzochrysene	EPA	77	1.98	Clar 56
$C_{22}H_{14}$ 3,4-5,6-Dibenzo-phenanthrene	EPA	77	1.98	Clar 56
$C_{22}H_{14}$ 1,2-3,4-Dibenz-anthracene	EPA	77	1.78	Clar 56
$C_{22}H_{14}$ 1,2-5,6-Dibenz-anthracene	EPA	77	1.83	Clar 56 Reid 52a
$C_{22}H_{14}$ 1,2-7,8-Dibenz-anthracene	EPA	77	1.85	Clar 56

Formula and Substance	Solvent	$T_{^\circ K}$	Transition (μm^{-1}) Abs.	Emis.	τ sec	References
$C_{22}H_{14}$ Pentaphene	EPA	77		1.69		Clar 56
$C_{22}H_{16}N_2O_2$ 2,2'-Dihydroxy-1,1'-naphthaldazine	solid	80		1.93 1.90 1.79 1.64		Kristianpoller 64
$C_{22}H_{18}$ Distyrylbenzene	hexane heptane hendecane	77		2.60 2.59 2.54		Nurmukhametov 66
$C_{22}H_{20}$ Diphenyldecapentene	xylol	77		1.99		Hausser 35
$C_{23}H_{23}ClN_2$ Pseudoisocyanin-N,N'-diethylchloride	ethanol	93				Zanker 60
$C_{23}H_{23}IN_2$ 1,1'-Diethyl-2,2'-cyanine-(iodide)	EPA solid	77 77				Clementi 57
$C_{23}H_{23}IN_2$ 1,1'-Diethyl-3',4',5,6-dibenzo-2,2'-pyridocyanine-(iodide)	EPA solid	77 77				Clementi 57

Compound	Structure	Solvent	Temp				Reference
$C_{23}H_{24}N_2O$ 4-4'-Bis-dimethyl-aminofuchsone		isopentane/ isopropanol	93	1.70	1.64		Adam 59
$C_{23}H_{26}N_2O$ Hydroxymala-chitegrene		isopentane/ isopropanol	93	(1.61)	1.52		Adam 59
$C_{24}H_{12}$ Coronene		ethanol	90		1.94		Bowen 55
		isopropanol	77			8.6	Clar 56
		hexane	77		2.35		Dörr 63
		n-hexane	77		1.94		Foerster 63
		heptane	93		2.35		McClure 49
		octane	77		2.35		Melhuish 64
		octane	93		1.94		Shpolskii 56b, 59b,60c
		EPA	77		2.36		
			77		1.91	9.4	
		PMMA	77				
$C_{24}H_{14}$ 1,2-6,7-Dibenzo-pyrene		EPA	77		2.04		Clar 56
$C_{24}H_{16}O_2$ 1,5-Dibenzoyl-naphthalene		ethanol/ether	77		1.99	0.56	Ermolaev 60b

Formula and Substance		Solvent	$T_{°K}$	Transition (μm^{-1})			References
				Abs.	Emis.	τ sec	
$C_{24}H_{18}$ Quaterphenyl		heptane	77		2.81		Gobov 63b
$C_{24}H_{18}$ 1,3,5-Triphenylbenzene			77	2.27	2.26	T	Clar 56 Marchetti 67
$C_{24}H_{20}Ge$ Tetraphenylgermane		EPA	77			$3.6 \cdot 10^{-2}$	LaPaglia 62
$C_{24}H_{20}Pb$ Tetraphenyllead		EPA	77 77	>3.85	2.39	0.01 $1 \cdot 10^{-4}$	LaPaglia 62
$C_{24}H_{20}Si$ Tetraphenylsilane		EPA	77 77	3.81	2.82	1.24 1.1	LaPaglia 62 McClure 49
$C_{24}H_{20}Sn$ Tetraphenyltin		EPA	77 77	3.89 2.92	2.84	0.003 $1 \cdot 10^{-4}$	LaPaglia 62 McClure 49 Marchetti 67
$C_{25}H_{19}$ Diphenyl p-biphenyl carbonium		solid	77		1.72 1.64		Chu 54

$C_{25}H_{19}$ Diphenyl p-biphenyl methyl (free radical)	toluene triethylamine	77	1.67 1.54 1.41	Chu 54
$C_{25}H_{29}IN_2$ 1,3,1',3',- Hexamethylindo- carbocyanine- (iodide)	EPA solid	77 77		Clementi 57
$C_{26}H_{16}$ 1,2-7,8-Dibenzo- chrysene	EPA	77	1.73	Clar 56
$C_{26}H_{16}$ 1,2-3,4-5,6-Tribenz- anthracene	EPA	77	1.94	Clar 56
$C_{26}H_{32}O_4$ Isomethylbixin	xylene	77	1.89 1.75	Hausser 35

Structure for 1,2-3,4-5,6-Tribenzanthracene:

Isomethylbixin:

$$H_3C \cdot OOC-C=C-C=C-C=C-C=C-C=C-C=C-C=C-C=C-C \cdot COOCH_3$$
with CH_3 groups as indicated

Formula and Substance		Solvent	T°K	Transition (μm^{-1}) Abs.	Emis.	τ_{sec}	References
$C_{27}H_{16}$ 3,4,5,6,7-Tri-benzopyrene		octane ethanol	77 77		2.53 2.53		Khesina 60
$C_{27}H_{18}$ 3'-Methyl-4',5-ethylene-3,4,6,7-dibenzopyrene		ethanol octane	77 77		2.50 2.51		Khesina 60
$C_{28}H_{16}$ 3,4-Naptho-6,7-benzopyrene		hexane	77 77		2.40–2.38 1.69		Khesina 61
$C_{28}H_{22}$ 1,1',4,4'-Tetra-phenyl-1,3-buta-diene		single crystal	14		2.18 2.26 2.31 2.42 2.48		P. Pesteil 54a
$C_{28}H_{22}$ 1,4-Dimethyl-9,10-diphenylanthracene		ethanol	90				Cherkasov 59a

Compound	Structure	Solvent		Value	Reference
$C_{28}H_{22}$ 2,3-Dimethyl-9,10-diphenylanthracene		ethanol	90		Cherkasov 59a
$C_{28}H_{22}Br_2N_2$ Lucigenin bromide		H_2O/alkali/H_2O	77	2.08 1.94	Ermolaev 56
$C_{28}H_{22}N_2$ N,N'-Dimethyl-biacridine		H_2O/H_2O_2	77	1.91	Ermolaev 56
$C_{28}H_{22}N_2O$ N,N'-Dimethyl-biacridinoxide		H_2O/H_2O_2	77	1.82	Ermolaev 56

Formula and Substance	Solvent	$T \, {}^\circ K$	Transition (μm^{-1}) Abs.	Emis. τ_{sec}	References
$C_{30}H_{18}$ 1,2-3,4-5,6-7,8-Tetrabenzanthracene	EPA	77		2.06	Clar 56
$C_{30}H_{18}$ 3,4-9,10-Dibenzopentaphene	EPA	77		1.76	Clar 56
$C_{30}H_{22}$ 1,4-Bis(1-naphthyl-vinylbenzene)	hexane heptadecane	77 77		2.41 2.28	Nurmukhametov 66
$C_{30}H_{22}$ 1,4-Bis(2-naphthyl-vinylbenzene)	hexane octane heptadecane	77 77 77		2.47 2.47 2.44	Nurmukhametov 66
$C_{31}H_{23}$ Phenyldi-p-bi-phenylcarbonium	H_3PO_4	77		1.56 1.72	Chu 54

Compound	Solvent	T	Values		Reference
C$_{31}$H$_{27}$ClN$_3$ 1,1'-Diethyl-5,6,5',6'-dibenzo-2,2'-cyanine chloride 	EPA solid solid	77 77 77			Clementi 57
C$_{32}$H$_{16}$MgN$_8$ Magnesium-phthalocyanine 	n-octane	77	1.50 1.49 1.48 1.47	1.50 1.49 1.48 1.47 1.42 1.41 1.40 1.35 1.34 1.33	Becker 55b Gurinovich 63 Litvin 61 Personov 63
		77			
	octane EPA	77 77	1.50	1.50 1.49	7.6·10^{-9}
C$_{32}$H$_{16}$N$_8$O$_2$U Uranylphthalocyanine	octane nonane	77 77		1.47 1.46 1.45 1.43 1.38 1.33 1.30 1.29	Lyalin 63
	dioxane	77	1.51 1.58 1.67	1.48 1.41 1.34	

Formula and Substance	Solvent	$T_{°K}$	Transition (μm^{-1}) Abs.	Emis.	τ sec	References
$C_{32}H_{16}N_8Zn$ Zinc^{2+}-Phthalocyanine	EPA	77		1.49		Allison 60
	argon	20	1.50– 1.54	1.45– 1.53		Bajema 68
	xenon	20	1.48– 1.51	1.46– 1.51		
	krypton	20	1.49– 1.53	1.47– 1.52		
	N_2	20	1.50– 1.55	1.40– 1.53		
	SF_6	20	1.52– 1.54	1.53		
	CO	20	1.50– 1.53	1.47– 1.53		
	CH_4	20	1.49– 1.53	1.46– 1.53		
$C_{32}H_{18}N_8$ Phthalocyanine	octane	77	1.45	1.45 1.44 1.38 1.37 1.33 1.31 1.30 1.29		Akimov 60 Bajema 68 R. Becker 55b Litvin 61 Lyalin 63 Personov 63
	n-octane	77	1.53			
	nonane	77	1.45			
	n-decane	77	1.45			
	dioxane		1.41			
			1.37			
			1.30			
	EPA	77	1.45			

					Gradyushko 69
C$_{32}$H$_{18}$N$_8$ Phthalocyanine (continued)	argon	20	1.46–1.49 1.53–1.58	1.46–1.48	
	xenon	20	1.44–1.46 1.52–1.56	1.42–1.46	
	krypton	20	1.45–1.48 1.54–1.57	1.44–1.48	
	CH$_4$	20	1.44–1.48 1.54–1.58	1.44–1.48	
	N$_2$	20	1.46–1.49 1.54–1.58	1.45–1.49	
	SF$_6$	20	1.46–1.49 1.56–1.58	1.43–1.50	
C$_{32}$H$_{36}$AlN$_4$ Al-Etioporphyrin	EPA	77		11.5	

Formula and Substance	Solvent	T °K	Transition (μm^{-1}) Abs.	Emis.	τ sec	References
$C_{32}H_{36}CuN_4$ Copper-Etio-porphyrin I	EPA	77	2.53	1.47	0.012	Becker 55
	EPAF	(83)	1.79		$80 \cdot 10^{-6}$	Eastwood 69
	n-alkanes	(83)	1.48	1.47		Gradyushko 69
			2.53–1.79			B. Smith 68
	triethylamine		2.49	1.45		
			1.79			
	MPEG	80	1.45	1.45	$95 \cdot 10^{-6}$	
	PMMA		1.47	1.47	$80 \cdot 10^{-6}$	
$C_{32}H_{36}MgN_4$ Magnesium^{2+}-etioporphyrin II	EPA	77	1.70	1.70	$>5 \cdot 10^{-4}$	Allison 60
			1.34	1.34	1.3	Glaskow 66
						Gradyushko 69
$C_{32}H_{36}N_4Pd$ Pd-Etioporphyrin	EPAF	83			$1.93 \cdot 10^{-6}$	Eastwood 69
		83			$1.21 \cdot 10^{-4}$	Gradyushko 69
					0.18	
$C_{32}H_{36}N_4Pt$ Pt-Etioporphyrin	MPEG	78			$1.27 \cdot 10^{-4}$	Eastwood 69
$C_{32}H_{36}N_4Sn$ Sn-Etioporphyrin	EPA	77			3.3	Seybold 65

Molecule	Matrix	Temp			References
$C_{32}H_{36}N_4Zn$ Zinc^{2+}-Etioporphyrin II	EPA	77	1.75	4.5	Becker 55
	PMMA	80	1.43	7.5	Gradyushko 69
				$10.6 \cdot 10^{-3}$	Seybold 65
					B.Smith 68
$C_{32}H_{38}N_4$ Etioporphyrin II	EPA	77	1.60	$.10^{-2}$	Becker 55b
	ethanol	77	1.24		Glaskow 66
	isobutanol		0.03		Gradyushko 69
$C_{34}H_{32}O_4N_4Zn$ Zinc-Protoporphyrin	ethanol isobutanol EPA	90		0.05	Glaskow 66
$C_{34}H_{34}N_4O_4$ Protoporphyrin dimethylester	cation in n-octane	77	1.58	$12.8 \cdot 10^{-9}$ $2.6 \cdot 10^{-9}$ 0.03	Glaskow 66 Gurinovich 63
	octane	77	1.58	1.58	Litvin 61 Personov 63
$C_{34}H_{36}CuO_4N_4$ Copper-Mesoporphyrin	ethanol isobutanol EPA	90		$2 \cdot 10^{-4}$	Glaskow 66

Formula and Substance	Solvent	$T_{°K}$	Transition (μm^{-1}) Abs.	Emis.	τ sec	References
$C_{34}H_{36}N_4O_4Zn$ Zn-Mesoporphyrin	ethanol isobutanol EPA	90			0.05	Glaskow 66
$C_{36}H_{20}CdN_4$ Cd-Tetrabenzo-porphyrin					0.75	Gradyushko 69
$C_{36}H_{20}MgN_4$ Mg-Tetrabenzo-porphyrin					12.0	Gradyushko 69
$C_{36}H_{20}N_4Zn$ Zn-Tetrabenzo-porphyrin					4.2	Gradyushko 69
$C_{36}H_{20}N_4Zn$ Zn-Tetraphenyl-porphyrin					2.0	Gradyushko 69
$C_{36}H_{42}N_4O_4$ Mesoporphyrin-IX dimethylester Cu²⁺- Co²⁺- Cd²⁺- Cd	EPA EPA EPA EPA	77 77 77 77 77		1.62 1.33 1.47 1.49 1.72 1.38	$5 \cdot 10^{-4}$ $<5 \cdot 10^{-4}$ $5 \cdot 10^{-4}$ $5 \cdot 10^{-4}$	Allison 60 Ladner 65

Compound		Solvent	Temp			Reference
$C_{36}H_{42}N_4O_4$ Mesoporphyrin-IX-dimethylester (continued)						
	Pd^{2+}	EPA	77		1.52	$5\cdot10^{-4}$
		MPEG	77			$1.80\cdot10^{-3}$
	Ni^{2+}	EPA	77		1.47	$5\cdot10^{-4}$
	Zn^{2+}	EPA	77		1.75	
	Ba^{2+}	EPA	77		1.43	$5\cdot10^{-4}$
		EPA	77		1.68	
		EPA	77		1.33	$5\cdot10^{-4}$
$C_{36}H_{44}CuN_4$ Copper Octaethyl-porphyrin		nonane	(83)	1.48	1.46	
		EPAF	(83)		1.47	$80\cdot10^{-6}$
$C_{37}H_{38}CuN_4O_5$ Copper-ethyl-chlorophyllid (a) chlorophyll		EPA	77		1.16	Fernandez 59

Compound	Solvent	Temp	Value	Reference
$C_{37}H_{27}$ Tri-p-biphenyl-carbonium	H_3PO_4	77	1.67	Chu 54

Formula and Substance	Solvent	T°K	Transition (μm^{-1}) Abs.	Emis.	τ sec	References
$C_{40}H_{36}CuN_4O_{16}$ Copper-Uroporphyrin	EG-A-caff	83	2.48 / 1.77			Eastwood 69
	EG-A	83	1.48	1.46 / 1.46	$60 \cdot 10^{-6}$	
	pyridine	83	1.48	1.47		
$C_{44}H_{28}N_4Zn$ Zinc-Tetraphenylporphin	isobutanol	90		1.64	.025	Dorough 50
	ethanol			1.52		Glaskow 66
	EPA			1.52		Gurinovich 63
$C_{44}H_{28}CuN_4$ Copper-Tetraphenylporphin	isobutanol	90			$2 \cdot 10^{-4}$	Eastwood 69
	ethanol					Glaskow 66
	1-chloronaphthalene			1.34		B. Smith 68
	EPAF	80				
	PMMA	80		1.32	$300 \cdot 10^{-6}$	
	MPEG	78			$(610,145,25) \cdot 10^{-6}$	
$C_{44}H_{30}N_4$ Tetraphenylporphin	EPA	77	1.94	1.40	0.85	Dorough 50
	isobutanol	77	1.69	1.55		Glaskow 66
	oil			1.54		B. Smith 68
	ethanol			1.40		Weigl 57

$C_{44}H_{30}N_4Zn$ Zn-Tetraphenylchlorin	EPA	77	1.11 1.25	Dorough 52
$C_{44}H_{32}N_4$ Tetraphenylchlorin	EPA	77	1.11 1.25	Dorough 52
$C_{55}H_{70}CuN_4O_6$ Copperchlorophyll b	methylpentane	77	1.14	Fernandez 59
$C_{55}H_{70}MgN_4O_6$ Chlorophyll b	EPA	77 77	1.52 1.16	Beer 55
$C_{55}H_{72}MgN_4O_5$ Chlorophyll a	3-methylpentane ethanol isobutanol EPA	77 90	1.32 $5 \cdot 10^{-4}$ 0.004	Fernandez 59 Glaskow 66

F. Organic Radicals

The listing is entirely analogous to that of organic molecules in Table 10E. Molecules are arranged according to the number of carbon atoms. For a given number of carbon atoms, the order follows the number of hydrogen atoms. All molecules with CH come first, followed by those with other atoms, in alphabetical sequence of the symbol of the third type of atom.

Radical and Formula	Solvent	$T_{°K}$	Transition Abs.	Emis.	Remarks	Preparation	References
C_2H_5O Ethoxy	ethanol	77		1.94	broad band	photolysis of photochemically active compounds in ethanol, i.e., H_2O_2, ClO_2	Symons 56
C_6H_5O Phenoxy	EPA	77		3.48		photolysis of phenol, anisole, phenetole	Norman 55 Porter 58 Roebber 62
	N_2	4.2		3.39	1st bands		
C_6H_5O 6-Oxo-1,3,5-hexa-trienyl-1-radical	N_2	4.2		3.84			Roebber 62
$C_6H_5O_2$ p-Hydroxy phenoxy	EPA	77		2.42		photolysis of p-hydroxphenol	Porter 58
C_6H_6 Hexatriene	EPA isopentane N_2, Ar	77 77 20		3.60 3.61 3.10 3.88	other bands at 267 and 256 biradical 4 bands 6 bands	irradiation in rigid media of benzene	Leach 58 Norman 55
C_6H_6N Anilino	EPA	77		3.23		photolysis of aniline	Norman 55 Porter 58
$C_6H_7^{\oplus}$ Benzene carbonium ion	$HF-BF_3$	90		1.85 1.67			Reid 54

	Medium	T				Method	References
$C_6H_7N^{\oplus}$ Aniline radical cation	EPA	77	2.33			photolysis of aniline	Norman 55
$C_7H_5D_2$ Benzyl-d_2	cyclohexane methylpentane	77 77		2.16 2.16	$^2A_2 - {^2}B_2$ 70 sharp bands		Grajcar 63 Leach 62
$C_7H_5Cl_2$ Dichlorophenyl methyl	EPA	77	3.09			photolysis of trichlorophenyl-methane	Porter 58
C_7H_6Cl Chloro-phenyl methyl	EPA	77	3.10			photolysis of dichloro phenyl-methane	Porter 58
C_7H_7 Benzyl	EPA	77	3.14	2.16	sharp bands	1) photolysis of benzyl compounds 2) discharge through benzyl compounds	Angell 67 Grajcar 61a,b 63 Leach 62 Norman 55 Porter 58, 58c Ripoche 67 Vacher 59
	methylpentane	77	3.28 3.14	2.16	series of bands in luminescence $^2A_2 \rightarrow {^2}B_2$		
	isopentane	77		2.16			
	cyclohexane	77		2.17			
	Ne	4	2.20 3.28 4.08	2.20 3.28 4.08	70 sharp bands $1^2A_2 \leftrightarrow 1^2B_2$ $2^2A_2 \leftrightarrow 1^2B_2$ $3^2B_2 \leftrightarrow 1^2B_2$		
	solid parent molecule	77	3.11	2.01			

Radical and Formula	Solvent	$T_{°K}$	Transition Abs.	Transition Emis.	Remarks	Preparation	References
	methylcyclohexane	4.2		2.18	sharp bands	3) photolysis of toluene	
	cyclopentane	4.2		2.18			
	methylcyclopentane	4.2		2.17			
C_7D_7 Benzyl-d_7	cyclohexane	77		2.18	70 sharp bands		Grajcar 63
	methylpentane	77		2.17	$^2A_2 - {}^2B_2$		Leach 62b
	cyclopentane	4.2		2.17	sharp bands		Riproche 67
	methylcyclopentane	4.2		2.18			
C_7H_8 Methyl hexatriene	EPA	77	3.52		diffuse	photolysis of	Grajcar 61b
	methylpentane	77	3.47	3.38	2 bands	toluene	Norman 55
	isopentane		3.57		may not be a radical		
C_7H_8N N-methyl anilino	EPA	77	3.16			photolysis of N-methylaniline or N-dimethylaniline	Porter 58
C_7H_8N o-Toluidino	EPA	77	3.11			photolysis of o-toluidine	Norman 55
			3.20				
$C_7H_9^{\oplus}$ Toluene carbonium ion	HF-BF$_3$	90		1.85			Reid 54
				1.67			

Species	Matrix	Temp.	value	Bands	Method	References
C_8H_8 Bicyclo-octatriene	N_2, Ar	20	3.32	biradical	photolysis of cyclo-octatetraene	Leach 58
C_8H_9 m-methyl benzyl or m-xylyl	EPA	77	3.10		photolysis of m-xylene	Leach **67d** Porter 58
	single crystal	77	2.11	8 broad bands		
C_8H_9 o-methyl benzyl o-xylyl	EPA	77	3.10		photolysis of o-xylene	Porter 58 Leach **67d**
	single crystal	77	2.10	S; 42 bands, 2 systems		
C_8H_9 p-methyl benzyl p-xylyl	isopentane/methylcyclo-hexane	77	3.10	band center	photolysis of p-xylene or p-methylbenzyl chloride	Leach 67d Norman 55 Porter 58
	EPA single crystal	77 77	3.10	25 bands		
C_8H_9 Phenyl ethyl	EPA isopentane/methylcyclo-hexane	77 77	3.10 3.12		photolysis of phenyl ethane and derivatives	Norman 55 Porter 58

Radical and Formula	Solvent	$T_{°K}$	Transition Abs.	Emis.	Remarks	Preparation	References
$C_{10}H_9^{\oplus}$ Naphthalene carbonium ion	$HF-BF_3$	193 / 90	2.50	1.85 / 1.64			Reid 54
C_9H_{11} Mesityl	EPA	77	3.08			photolysis of mesitylene	Porter 58
C_9H_{11} Dimethylphenyl methyl	EPA	77	3.08			photolysis of dimethylphenyl-methane or trimethyl-phenylmethane	Porter 58
$C_9H_{13}^{\oplus}$ Mesitylene carbonium ion	$HF-BF_3$	193 / 90	2.50	1.76			Reid 54
$C_{10}H_{13}$ Duryl	polycrystal methylcyclohexane	77 / 77	2.04 / 3.01	2.04	S; analogous to $1^2A_2 \to 1^2B_2$ of benzyl; 27 narrow bands. Absorption: $2^2A_2 \leftarrow 1^2B_2$	photolysis of durene	Migirdicyan 68b

$C_{10}H_{13}$ Isoduryl	methylcyclohexane	77	2.09 2.04 1.95 3.00 3.14	S; 3 radical species formed	photolysis of isodurene	Migirdicyan 68b
	methylpentane	77				
$C_{10}H_{13}$ Prehnityl	methylcyclohexane	77	2.04	isomers formed	photolysis of prehnitene	Migirdicyan 68b
	methylpentane	77	3.00 3.01			
$C_{10}H_{13}O_2$ Durosemi quinone	EPA	77	2.37		photolysis of durohydroquinone	Porter 58
$C_{10}H_{16}N_2$ Wurster's blue	EPA	90	1.63 3.08	broad bands	photo-oxidation of N,N,N',N'-tetra-methyl paraphenyl-enediamine	Cadogan 65 Dolan 62, 63 Johnson 65 Lewis 42b,43a McClain 65 W. Meyer 62
	3-methylpentane		2.59 2.11 1.74 1.58	$\tau = 3 \cdot 10^{-6}$ sec $\tau = 2.3$ sec recombination luminescence		
$C_{11}H_9$ α-Naphthyl methyl	methylcyclohexane/isopentane	77	2.70		photolysis of α-methyl naph-thalene	Porter 58
$C_{11}H_9$ β-Naphthyl methyl	methylcyclohexane/isopentane	77	2.60		phototlysis of β-methyl naph-thalene	Porter 58

Radical and Formula	Solvent	$T_{°K}$	Transition Abs.	Emis.	Remarks	Preparation	References
$C_{12}H_8N$ Carbazole radical	EPTM	78	1.64			photolysis of N-lithium carbazole	Linschitz 54
$C_{12}H_{10}N$ Diphenyl nitrogen	EPA	90	1.33		band center	photolysis of tetraphenylhydrazine, lithium di-phenylamide, tri-phenylmethylidi-phenylamine; irradiation Li diphenylamide	Lewis 42b Linschitz 54
	EPTM	78	1.33				
$C_{13}H_9$ Fluorenyl	methylcyclo-hexane/iso-pentane	77	2.90			photolysis of fluorene	Norman 55
$C_{13}H_{11}$ Diphenyl methyl	methylcyclo-hexane/iso-pentane	77	2.98		band center	photolysis	Chilton 59 Leach 62b Norman 55 Porter 58
	EPA	77	2.98				
	methylpentane KCl (disk)	163	2.96				
$C_{13}H_{12}N$ Benzylaniline	EPA	77	2.67		$\Phi CH_2 N\Phi$ or $\Phi CHNH\Phi$	photolysis of $\Phi-CH_2-NH\Phi$	Porter 58
$C_{13}H_{13}N^{\oplus}$ Methyl diphenyl-amine ion	EPA	90	1.52			photo-oxidation	Lewis 42b

$C_{14}H_9O_2$	EPA	77	1.96		photolysis of 9:10 anthra-quinone	Porter 58
$C_{14}H_{11}^{\oplus}$ Anthracene carbonium ion	HF-BF$_3$	193 90	2.50 1.82			Reid 54
$C_{14}H_{11}^{\oplus}$ Phenanthrene carbonium ion	HF-BF$_3$	193 90	1.96 1.82			Reid 54
$C_{14}H_{13}$ Dibenzyl radical	EPA	77	2.76	band center	photolysis of 1,2-diphenyl ethane	Norman 55 Porter 58
$C_{16}H_{11}^{\oplus}$ Pyrene carbonium ion	HF-BF$_3$	193 90	2.13 1.56			Reid 54
$C_{16}H_{13}^{\oplus}$ Naphthacene carbonium ion	HF-BF$_3$	193 90	2.09 1.34			Reid 54
$C_{16}H_{20}N_2^{\oplus}$ Tetramethyl-benzidine ion	EPA	90	1.25		photo oxidation	Lewis 42b
$C_{19}H_{12}N_3O_6$ Tris-(p-nitro-phenyl) methyl	EPA	90	1.50		reduction of halide or with Hg or Ag	Lewis 44a

Radical and Formula	Solvent	$T\,°K$	Transition Abs.	Emis.	Remarks	Preparation	References
$C_{19}H_{15}$ Triphenyl methyl	EPA	77	2.93	1.95	10 bands	photolysis of triphenyl methane	Chilton 59
	EPA	90	1.96	1.94	7 max. for abs.		Chu 54
	EPA methylpentane	4.2	1.96	1.96	9 max. for fluor.		Leach 62b
	KCl (disks)	163	2.92				Lewis 44a
	toluene/tri-ethylamine	77	1.94		$A_1'' \leftarrow A_2''$	from triphenyl-chloromethane	Linschitz 54
			2.90		$E'' \leftarrow A_2''$	photolysis of potassium triphenyl methide	Porter 58
	EPTM	78	2.88				Vorob'ev 65
	single crystal	20		1.92	5 centers		Weissman 62
$C_{19}H_{15}$ Triphenyl methyl carbonium ion	H_3PO_4	77	1.52	1.82			Chu 54
$C_{21}H_{21}N^{\oplus}$ Tri-p-tolyl-amine ion	EPA	90				photo oxidation	Lewis 44a
$C_{23}H_{23}$ Diphenyl p-t-butylphenyl methyl	EPA	90	1.94		5 maxima	chemical reduction of halide with Hg or Ag	Lewis 44a

		Temp	g-values		Transition	Preparation	Reference
C$_{25}$H$_{19}$ Biphenyl p-xenyl methyl	toluene/tri-ethylamine	77	1.67 2.67 2.90	1.67	A$_2$ ↔ B$_1$ A$_2$ ↔ B$_1$ B$_1$ ← B$_1$	reduction of di-phenyl-p-xenyl-carbinol	Chu 54
C$_{25}$H$_{19}$ Biphenyl p-xenyl methyl carbonium ion	H$_3$PO$_4$			1.72	A$_1$ ← A$_1$		Chu 54
C$_{27}$H$_{31}$ Bis-(p-t-butyl-phenyl) phenyl methyl	EPA	90	1.92			reduction of halide by Hg or Ag	Lewis 44a
C$_{31}$H$_{23}$ Phenyl di-p-xenyl methyl	toluene/tri-ethylamine	77	1.64 2.44 2.78	1.63	A$_2$ ↔ B$_1$ A$_2$ ← B$_1$ B$_1$ ← B$_1$	from phenyl-di-p-xenyl carbinol chemical reduction	Chu 54
C$_{31}$H$_{23}$ Phenyl di-p-xenyl methyl carbonium ion	H$_3$PO$_4$	77		1.72	A$_1$ → A$_1$		Chu 54
C$_{31}$H$_{39}$ Tris-(p-t-butyl-phenyl) methyl	EPA	90	1.92			chemical reduction of halide by Hg,Ag	Lewis 44a
C$_{37}$H$_{27}$ Tri-p-xenyl methyl carbonium ion	toluene/triethyl-amine	77	1.64 2.38	1.61	A$_1$" ↔ A$_2$" E" ← A$_2$"	from tri-p xenyl carbinol chemical reduction	Chu 54

Bibliography

INTRODUCTION

This chapter contains the references to all earlier chapters. In addition, it lists other articles in the field of low temperature optical and infrared spectroscopy of molecules and atoms at low temperature, generally only below 77°K. The bibliography covers the period from 1885 to June 1969. Newer references were included when easily available; some older references, especially to Russian papers not yet translated, may be missing.

References are listed alphabetically according to the name of the first author. When one author has published several papers, the listing is chronological, with the oldest paper first. If an author published several papers in the same year, the references are identified with a letter following the year.

A

Abramowitz, S., and H. P. Broida, *J. Chem. Phys.* **39**, 2383 (1963). "Vibration of Methane in Condensed Oxygen, Nitrogen, and Argon."

Ackermann, F., and E. Miescher, *Chem. Phys. Lett.* **2**, 351 (1968). "Spin-orbit Coupling in Molecular Rydberg States of the Nitric Oxide Molecule."

Acquista, N., L. J. Schoen, and D. R. Lide, Jr., *J. Chem. Phys.* **48**, 1534 (1968a). "Infrared Spectrum of the Matrix Isolated OH Radical."

Acquista, N., S. Abramowitz, and D. R. Lide, *J. Chem. Phys.* **49**, 780 (1968b). "Structure of the Alkali Hydroxides. II. The Infrared Spectra of Matrix-Isolated CsOH and CsOD."

Acquista, N., and L. J. Schoen, *J. Chem. Phys.* **53**, 1290 (1970). "Matrix Isolation Spectrum of the SH Radical."

Adam, F. C., and W. T. Simpson, *J. Mol. Spectrosc.* **3**, 363 (1959). "Electronic Spectrum of 4,4'-bis-Dimethylamino Fuchsone and Related Triphenylmethane Dyes."

Adamov, M. N., *Zh. Eksp. Teor. Fiz.* **22**, 120 (1952). "Remarks on the Scheme of Temperature Damping of the Luminescence of Crystalline Phosphors Proposed by E. I. Adirovich."

Adelman, A. H., and G. Oster, *J. Amer. Chem. Soc.* **78**, 3977 (1956). "Long-lived States in Photochemical Reactions. II. Photoreduction of Fluorescein and its Halogenated Derivatives."

495

Adrian, F. J., E. L. Cochran, and V. A. Bowers, *J. Chem. Phys.* **36**, 1661 (1962). "ESR Spectrum and Structure of the Formyl Radical."

Adrian, F. J., E. L. Cochran, and V. A. Bowers, *J. Chem. Phys.* **47**, 5441 (1967). "ESR Spectrum of HO_2 in Argon at 4.2°K."

Agee, F. J., Jr., R. J. Manning, J. S. Vinson, and F. L. Hereford, *Phys. Rev.* **153**, 255 (1967). "Inhibition of the Scintillation of Stationary and Rotating He."

Agranovich, V. M., *Opt. Spectrosc.* (USSR) (English Transl.) **9**, 113 (1960a). "The Transfer of Electronic Excitation Energy with the Aid of a Virtual Exciton Mechanism."

Agranovich, V. M., *Opt. Spectrosc.* (USSR) (English Transl.) **9**, 421 (1960b). "Letter to the Editor."

Agranovich, V. M., and V. L. Ginzburg, Interscience Monographs and Texts in Physics and Astronomy, Vol. 18. "Spatial Dispersion in Crystal Optics and the Theory of Excitons." Interscience (Wiley), New York, 1966.

Akasaka, K., *J. Chem. Phys.* **45**, 90 (1966). "Spin-Lattice Relaxation in Organo-Sulfur Radicals."

Akimoto, H., and J. N. Pitts, Jr., *J. Chem. Phys.* **53**, 1312 (1970). "Emission Spectra of $O_2(^1\Delta_g)$ Trapped in Solid Oxygen at 4.2°K."

Akimov, I. A., and G. A. Korsunovskii, *Opt. Spectrosc.* (USSR) (English Transl.) **8**, 223 (1960). "Influence of Some Electronic Compounds on the Absorption and Luminescence Spectra of Magnesium Phthalocyanin Solutions."

Albrecht, A. C., and W. T. Simpson, *J. Chem. Phys.* **23**, 1480 (1955). "Low Resolution Electronic Spectrum of Crystalline *para*-Dimethoxybenzene with Application to Benzene."

Alcock, W. G., and G. C. Pimentel, *J. Chem. Phys.* **48**, 2373 (1968). "Infrared Spectrum of Dichlorine Dioxide, $(ClO)_2$."

Aleksandrov, A. N., A. N. Sidorov, and N. G. Yaroslavskii, *Opt. Spectrosc.* (USSR) (English Transl.) **22**, 307 (1967). "Long-Wavelength Infrared Absorption Spectra of Phthalocyanines."

Alexander, P. W., A. R. Lacey, and L. E. Lyons, *J. Chem. Phys.* **34**, 2200 (1961). "Absorption and Luminescence Origins in Anthracene Crystals."

Alfimov, M. V., and Y. B. Shekk, *Khim. Vys. Energ.* **1**, 235 (1967). "Comparative Study of the Radio- and Photoluminescence of Solid Organic Solutions."

Allavena, M., R. Rysnik, D. White, V. Calder, and D. E. Mann, *J. Chem. Phys.* **50**, 3399 (1969). "Infrared Spectra and Geometry of SO_2 Isotopes in Solid Krypton Matrices."

Allin, E. J., W. F. J. Hare, and R. E. MacDonald, *Phys. Rev.* **98**, 554 (1955). "Infrared Absorption of Liquid and Solid Hydrogen."

Allin, E. J., T. Feldman, and H. L. Welsh, *J. Chem. Phys.* **24**, 1116 (1956). "Raman Spectra of Liquid and Solid Hydrogen."

Allison, J. B., and R. S. Becker, *J. Chem. Phys.* **32**, 1410 (1960). "Effect of Metal Atom Perturbations on the Luminescence Spectra of Porphyrins."

Aluker, E. D., and I. P. Mezina, *Opt. Spectrosc.* (USSR) (English Transl.) **22**, 428 (1967). "The Mechanism of the Low-Temperature Decrease of Radioluminescence Yield."

Ames, L. L., D. White, and D. E. Mann, *J. Chem. Phys.* **38**, 910 (1963). "Infrared Absorption Spectra of Carbon Suboxide and Malononitrile in Solid Argon Matrices."

Anderson, A., and G. E. Leroi, *J. Chem. Phys.* **45**, 4359 (1966). "Far-Infrared Spectra of Crystalline Nitrogen and Carbon Monoxide."

Anderson, J. S., and J. S. Ogden, *J. Chem. Phys.* **51**, 4189 (1969). "Matrix Isolation

Studies of Group-IV Oxides. I. Infrared Spectra and Structures of SiO, Si_2O_2, and Si_3O_3."

Andreeshchev, E. A., and I. M. Rozman, *Opt. Spectrosc.* (USSR) (English Transl.) **8**, 435 (1960). "Fluorescence Quantum Yield of Certain Substances in Polystyrene."

Andreeshchev, E. A., S. F. Kilin, I. M. Rozman, and V. I. Shirokov, *Bull. Acad. Sci. USSR Phys. Ser.* (English Transl.) **27**, 530 (1963). "Electronic Excitation Energy Transfer in Solid Solutions of Organic Substances."

Andrews, L., and G. C. Pimentel, *J. Chem. Phys.* **47**, 2905 (1967a). "Visible Spectra of Lithium in Inert-Gas Matrices."

Andrews, L., and G. C. Pimentel, *J. Chem. Phys.* **47**, 3637 (1967b). "Infrared Spectrum of the Methyl Radical in Solid Argon."

Andrews, L., *see also* Andrews, W. L. S.

Andrews, L., *J. Chem. Phys.* **47**, 4834 (1967c). "Infrared Spectrum of Methyl Lithium Monomer in Solid Argon."

Andrews, L., *J. Chem. Phys.* **48**, 972 (1968a). "Infrared Spectrum of the Trichloromethyl Radical in Solid Argon."

Andrews, L., *J. Chem. Phys.* **48**, 979 (1968b). "Infrared Spectrum of Dichlorocarbene in Solid Argon."

Andrews, L., *Tetrahedron Lett.* **12**, 1423 (1968c). "On the Infrared Spectra of Dichlorocarbene and the Trichloromethyl Radical in Solid Argon."

Andrews, L., and T. G. Carver, *J. Phys. Chem.* **72**, 1743 (1968d). "Infrared Spectral Evidence for Trihalomethyllithium and -sodium Compounds in Solid Argon."

Andrews, L., and T. G. Carver, *J. Chem. Phys.* **49**, 896 (1968e). "Reactions of Alkali-Metal Atoms with Carbon Tetrabromide. Infrared Spectra and Bonding in the Tribromomethyl Radical and Dibromocarbene in Solid Argon."

Andrews, W. L. S., *see also* Andrews, L.

Andrews, W. L. S., Ph. D. Thesis, University of California, Berkeley, 1963. "Spectroscopic Studies of Reactions of Lithium Atoms in Inert Gas Matrices."

Andrews, W. L. S., and G. C. Pimentel, *J. Chem. Phys.* **44**, 2361 (1966a). "Infrared Spectrum, Structure, and Bonding of Lithium Nitroxide, LiON."

Andrews, W. L. S., and G. C. Pimentel, *J. Chem. Phys.* **44**, 2527 (1966b). "Infrared Detection of Methyl Radical in Solid Argon."

Andrews, W. L. S., *J. Phys. Chem.* **71**, 2761 (1967). "Infrared Detection of Trichloromethyl Radical in Solid Argon."

Angell, C. L., E. Hedaya, and D. McLeod, Jr., *J. Amer. Chem. Soc.* **89**, 4214 (1967). "The Electronic, Vibrational, and Electron Spin Resonance Spectra of the Benzyl Radical."

Antonov-Romanovskii, V. V., *Bull. Acad. Sci. USSR Phys. Ser.* (English Transl.) **21**, 483 (1957). "New Results in the Field of Phosphorescence Research."

Anufrieva, E. V., *Opt. Spectrosc.* (USSR) (English Transl.) **9**, 547 (1960). "Effect of Glassing on the Polarization of the Long-Lasting Luminescence of Organic Substances."

Aristov, A. V., and B. Y. Sveshnikov, *Bull. Acad. Sci. USSR Phys. Ser.* (English Transl.) **27**, 639 (1963). "Effect of Temperature on the Probability for Transition of Molecules to the Phosphorescent State."

Aristov, A. V., and E. V. Viktorova, *Opt. Spectrosc.* (USSR) (English Transl.) **22**, 340 (1967). "Determination of Certain Luminescent and Spectral Characteristics of Organic Phosphors in Binary Solvents."

Aristov, A. V., and E. N. Viktorova, *Opt. Spectrosc.* (USSR) (English Transl.) **24**, 283

(1968). "Phosphorescence and Fluorescence of Two-Component and Multicomponent Solutions of Biphenyl Derivatives."

Arkell, A., R. R. Reinhard, and L. P. Larson, *J. Amer. Chem. Soc.* **87**, 1016 (1965a). "Matrix Infrared Studies of OF Compounds."

Arkell, A., *J. Amer. Chem. Soc.* **87**, 4057 (1965b). "Matrix Isolated Studies of OF Compounds. II. The O_2F Radical."

Arkell, A., and I. Schwager, *J. Am. Chem. Soc.* **89**, 5999 (1967). "Matrix Infrared Study of the ClOO Radical."

Armstrong, R. L., *J. Chem. Phys.* **44**, 530 (1966). "Repulsive Interactions and Molecular Rotation in Inert-Gas Lattices."

Arndt, R. A., and A. C. Damask, *J. Chem. Phys.* **45**, 4627 (1966). "Conductivity and Polarization Phenomena in Phenanthrene Crystals."

Arnold, G. M., and R. Heastie, *Chem. Phys. Lett.* **1**, 51 (1967). "Far Infra-red Absorption in Each Solid Phase of HCl and DBr."

Arnold, L. B., Jr., and G. B. Kistiakowsky, *J. Amer. Chem. Soc.* **54**, 1713 (1932). "Absorption Spectra in Solution at Low Temperatures."

Atkins, P. W., and M. C. R. Symons, *The Structure of Inorganic Radicals: An Application of Electron Spin Resonance to the Study of Molecular Structure*, American Elsevier, New York and Amsterdam, 1967.

Atwood, M. R., M. Jean-Louis, and H. Vu, *J. Phys.* (Paris) **28**, 31 (1967). "Agrégation pour des Solutions de HCl et de HBr dans l'Argon Solide à − 196°C et Spectres Infrarouges d'Absorption des Polymères et des Copolymères de ces Molécules."

Austin, A., and H. Pelzer, *Nature* **157**, 693 (1946). "Linear 'Curves of Best Fit'."

Austin, I. G., B. D. Clay, C. E. Turner, and A. J. Springthorpe, *Solid State Commun.* **6**, 53 (1968). "Near and Far Infrared Absorption by Small Polarons in Semiconducting Nickelous Oxide and Cobaltous Oxide."

Azarraga, L., T. N. Misra, and S. P. McGlynn, *J. Chem. Phys.* **42**, 3720 (1965). "Delayed Fluorescence of Mixed Crystals."

Azumi, T., and S. P. McGlynn, *J. Chem. Phys.* **37**, 2413 (1962). "Polarization of the Luminescence of Phenanthrene."

Azumi, T., and S. P. McGlynn, *J. Chem. Phys.* **38**, 2773 (1963a). "Delayed Fluorescence of Solid Solutions of Polyacenes."

Azumi, T., and S. P. McGlynn, *J. Chem. Phys.* **39**, 1186 (1963b). "Delayed Fluorescence of Solid Solutions of Polyacenes. II. Kinetic Considerations."

Azumi, T., and S. P. McGlynn, *J. Chem. Phys.* **39**, 3533 (1963c). "Delayed Fluorescence of Solid Solutions of Polyacenes. IV. The Origin of Excimer Fluorescence."

Azumi, T., and H. Azumi, *Bull. Chem. Soc. Jap.* **39**, 1829 (1966a). "The Energy of Excimer Luminescence of Naphthalene under a Variety of Geometrical Configurations."

Azumi, T., and H. Azumi, *Bull. Chem. Soc. Jap.* **39**, 2317 (1966b). "Lifetime of Excimer Fluorescence of Naphthalene."

Azumi, T., and H. Azumi, *Bull. Chem. Soc. Jap.* **40**, 279 (1967a). "A Simple Hueckel Treatment of the Energy of Excimer Luminescence."

Azumi, T., Y. Udagawa, M. Ito, and S. Nagakura, *J. Chem. Phys.* **47**, 4850 (1967b). "Zeeman Splitting of the Phosphorescence of Pyrazine Crystal."

Azumi, T., M. Ito, and S. Nagakura, *Tech. Rep. Inst. Solid State Phys., Univ. Tokyo, Ser. A*, **290** (1967c). "Zeeman Effect of Phosphorescence. II. Intensity Considerations on Pyrazine Crystal."

Azumi, T., and S. Nagakura, *Tech. Rep. Inst. Solid State Phys., Univ. Tokyo, Ser. A,*

309 (1968). "Zeeman Effect of Phosphorescence. III. Theory of Photoselection for Zeeman Split Phosphorescence."

Azumi, T., and Y. Nakano, *J. Chem. Phys.* **50**, 539 (1969a). "Spin Polarization as a Probe to Measurements of Radiative and Radiationless Decay Constants for Each of the Three Triplet Subcomponents; Quinoxaline."

Azumi, T., and Y. Nakano, *J. Chem. Phys.* **51**, 2515 (1969b). "Defect Phosphorescence of Pyrazine Crystal."

B

Baczynski, A., and M. Czajkowski, *Bull. Acad. Pol. Sci., Ser. Sci. Math., Astron., Phys.* **7**, 357 (1959). "The Metastable State of Dye Molecules."

Bagdasar'yan, K. S., R. I. Milyutinskaya, and Y. V. Kovalek, *Khim. Vys. Energ.* **1**, 127 (1967). "Luminescence at Low Temperatures of γ-Irradiated Organic Glasses."

Bajema, L., M. Gouterman, and B. Meyer, *J. Mol. Spectrosc.* **27**, 225 (1968). "Spectra of Porphyrins. XI. Absorption and Fluorescence Spectra of Matrix Isolated Phthalocyanines."

Bajema, L., Ph. D. thesis, University of Washington, Seattle, 1970. "Spectra of Matrix Isolated Species."

Bakhshiev, N. G., *Opt. Spectrosc.* (USSR) (English Transl.) **7**, 29 (1959). "The Internal Field and the Position of the Electronic Absorption and Emission Bands of Polyatomic Organic Molecules in Solution."

Bakhshiev, N. G., *Bull. Acad. Sci. USSR, Phys. Ser.* (English Transl.) **26**, 1252 (1963). "Influence of the Solvent on the Intensity and Position of the Bands in the Electronic Spectra of Molecules."

Bakhshiev, N. G., and I. V. Piterskaya, *Opt. Spectrosc.* (USSR) (English Transl.) **20**, 437 (1966). "Universal Intermolecular Interactions and Their Effect on the Positions of the Electron Spectra of Molecules in Two-Component Solutions. XII. The Dependence of the Absorption and Fluorescence Spectra of Phthalimide Derivatives on the Temperature and Aggregation State of the Solvent (+ 20 to − 196°C)."

Bakhshiev, N. G., and V. N. Korovina, *Opt. Spectrosc.* (USSR) (English Transl.) **22**, 17 (1967a). "Relationship between the Observed and True Absorption Spectra of Molecules in Condensed Media. VI. Electronic Absorption Spectra of Certain Organic Dyes in Various States of Aggregation."

Bakhshiev, N. G., O. P. Girin, and V. S. Libov, *Opt. Spectrosc.* (USSR) (English Transl,) **22**, 124 (1967b). "Relationship between the Optical Characteristics of Condensed Media and the Spectroscopic Parameters of Their Component Molecules."

Baldeschwieler, J. D., and G. C. Pimentel, *J. Chem. Phys.* **33**, 1008 (1960). "Light-Induced *cis-trans* Isomerization of Nitrous Acid Formed by Photolysis of Hydrazoic Acid and Oxygen in Solid Nitrogen."

Baldini, G., *Phys. Rev.* **128**, 1562 (1962). "Ultraviolet Absorption of Solid Argon, Krypton, and Xenon."

Baldini, G., *Phys. Rev.* **136A**, 248 (1964). "Is-2p Transition of H and D in Solid Argon."

Baldwin, B. A., and H. W. Offen, *J. Chem. Phys.* **46**, 4509 (1967). "Effects of High Pressures on the Phosphorescence of Aromatic Hydrocarbons."

Baldwin, B. A., and H. W. Offen, *J. Chem. Phys.* **48**, 5358 (1968a). "Environmental Effects on Phosphorescence. II. 'Activation Volumes' for Triplet Decay of Aromatic Hydrocarbons."

Baldwin, B. A., and H. W. Offen, *J. Chem. Phys.* **49**, 2933 (1968b). "Environmental Effects on Phosphorescence. III. Oxygen Quenching of Naphthalene Triplets in Compressed Polymethylmethacrylate."

Baldwin, B. A., and H. W. Offen, *J. Chem. Phys.* **49**, 2937 (1968c). "Environmental Effects on Phosphorescence. IV. Triplet Decay of Halonaphthalenes in Compressed PMMA."

Baldwin, B. A., *J. Chem. Phys.* **50**, 1038 (1969). "Temperature Effect on Triplet Decay of Organic Molecules."

Ballik, E. A., and D. A. Ramsay, *Astrophys. J.* **137**, 83 (1963). "The Electronic Spectrum of C_2."

Bandow, F., *Z. Phys. Chem.* (Leipzig) **196**, 329 (1951). "Untersuchungen über die Spektren einiger polyzyklischer Kohlenwasserstoffe."

Barger, R. L., and H. P. Broida, *J. Chem. Phys.* **37**, 1152 (1962). "Absorption Spectrum of Carbon Vapor in Solid Argon at 4° and 20°K."

Barger, R. L., and H. P. Broida, *Nat. Bur. Std. (U.S.) Rep.* 8200 (1963). "Absorption Spectrum and Intensity Effects of Barium in Solid Argon at 4°K."

Barger, R. L., Ph. D. Thesis, University of Colorado, Boulder, Colorado, 1964; and *Nat. Bur. Std. Rep.* 8290 (1964). "Spectra of C_2 and C_3 in Frozen Gases at 4°K and 20°K."

Barger, R. L., and H. P. Broida, *J. Chem. Phys.* **43**, 2364 (1965). "Spectra of C_3 in Solidified Gases at 4° and 20°K."

Barrett, C. S., L. Meyer, and J. Wasserman, *J. Chem. Phys.* **44**, 998 (1966a). "Argon-Oxygen Phase Diagram."

Barrett, C. S., L. Meyer, and J. Wasserman, *J. Chem. Phys.* **45**, 834 (1966b). "Crystal Structure of Solid Hydrogen and Deuterium, and of Neon-Hydrogen and Neon-Deuterium Mixtures."

Barrow, R. F., G. G. Chandler, and B. Meyer, *Phil. Trans. Roy. Soc. London Ser. A* **260**, 395 (1966). "The $B\,^3\Sigma_u^- - X\,^3\Sigma_u^-$ Band System of the Se_2 Molecule."

Basco, N., and K. K. Yee, *Chem. Commun.* **21**, 1146 (1961). "Spectrum of the PCl Free-Radical."

Basco, N., and K. K. Yee, *Chem. Commun.* **24**, 1255 (1967). "Spectrum of the AsCl Free-Radical."

Bass, A. M., and H. P. Broida, *Phys. Rev.* **101**, 1740 (1956). "Spectra Emitted from Solid Nitrogen Condensed at 4°K from a Gas Discharge."

Bass, A. M., and H. P. Broida, *J. Mol. Spectrosc.* **2**, 42 (1958). "Absorption Spectra of Solids Condensed at Low Temperatures from Electric Discharges."

Bass, A. M., and H. P. Broida, eds., *The Formation and Trapping of Free Radicals.* Academic Press, New York, 1960a.

Bass, A. M., and H. P. Broida, *Nat. Bur. Std. (U.S.) Monograph* 12 (1960b). "Stabilization of Free Radicals at Low Temperatures."

Bass, A. M., and D. E. Mann, *J. Chem. Phys.* **36**, 3501 (1962). "Absorption Spectrum of CF_2 Trapped in an Argon Matrix."

Bass, A. M., and H. P. Broida, *J. Mol. Spectrosc.* **12**, 221 (1964). "Vacuum Ultraviolet Absorption Spectra of Oxygen in Liquid and Crystalline Argon and Nitrogen."

Bass, A. M., and J. Shirk, *J. Chem. Phys.* **52**, 1894 (1970). "Absorption and Fluorescence of Matrix Isolated CuO."

Bass, C. D., and G. C. Pimentel, *J. Amer. Chem. Soc.* **83**, 3754 (1961). "Hydrogen Abstraction from Hydrocarbons by Methyl Radicals from the Photolysis of Methyl Iodide in Solid Nitrogen."

Bassler, J. M., P. L. Timms, and J. L. Margrave, *Inorg. Chem.* **5**, 729 (1966a). "Silicon-Fluorine Chemistry. III. Infrared Studies of SiF_2 and Its Reactions in Low-Temperature Matrices."

Bassler, J. M., P. L. Timms, and J. L. Margrave, *J. Chem. Phys.* **45**, 2704 (1966b). "Evidence for the Existence of BF_3 Dimers in Argon and Krypton Matrices."

Batley, M., and D. R. Kearns, *Chem. Phys. Lett.* **2**, 423 (1968). "The Second Triplet State of Benzophenone."

Batscha, B., *Deut. Chem. Ges., Ber.* **58**, 187 (1925). "Über die Phosphoreszenz-Fähigkeit des Fluoresceins."

Baumgartner, F., E. Gunther, and G. Scheibe, *Z. Elektrochem.* **60**, 570 (1956). "Über Stereoisomerie und angeregte Zustände einfacher Polymethinfarbstoffe."

Baur, E., *Z. Phys. Chem.* **B16**, 465 (1932). "Desensikilatoren, Antioxygene und Antifluoreszenz."

Bayliss, N. S., *J. Chem. Phys.* **18**, 292 (1950). "The Effect of Electrostatic Polarization of the Solvent on the Electronic Absorption Spectra in Solution."

Becker, E. D., and G. C. Pimentel, *J. Chem. Phys.* **25**, 224 (1956). "Spectroscopic Studies of Reactive Molecules by the Matrix Isolation Method."

Becker, E. D., G. C. Pimentel, and M. Van Thiel, *J. Chem. Phys.* **26**, 145 (1957). "Matrix Isolation Studies: Infrared Spectra of Intermediate Species in the Photolysis of Hydrazoic Acid."

Becker, R. S., and M. Kasha, *J. Amer. Chem. Soc.* **77**, 3669 (1955). "Luminescence Spectroscopy of Porphyrin-like Molecules Including the Chlorophylls."

Becker, R. S., and J. B. Allison, *J. Phys. Chem.* **67**, 2662, 2669 (1963). "Metalloporphyrins. Electronic Spectra and Nature of Perturbations. I. Transition Metal Ion Derivatives. II. Group IIA, IIB, and IVA Derivatives."

Becker, R. S., *Theory and Interpretation of Fluorescence and Phosphorescence*, Interscience (Wiley), New York, 1969.

Becquerel, J., *C. R. Acad. Sci.* (Paris) **144**, 132 (1907). "The Changes Produced in the Absorption Bands of Tysonite Crystals by a Magnetic Field."

Beens, H., and A. Weller, *Chem. Phys. Lett.* **2**, 140 (1968). "Triplet Complex Formation in the Excited State."

Beer, M., and H. C. Longuet-Higgins, *J. Chem. Phys.* **23**, 1390 (1955). "Anomalous Light Emission of Azulene."

Beer, M., *J. Chem. Phys.* **25**, 745 (1956). "Electronic Spectra of Polyacetylenes."

Belford, R. L., and J. W. Carmichael, Jr., *J. Chem. Phys.* **46**, 4515 (1967). "Bis(3-Phenyl-2,4-Pentanedionato)Copper. II. Polarized Crystal Spectra."

Belyaeva, A. A., Y. B. Predtechenskii, and L. D. Shcherba, *Opt. Spectrosc.* (USSR) (English Transl.) **24**, 233 (1968). "Absorption Spectra of Lithium Atoms Stabilized in Noble-Gas Matrices."

Belyi, M. U., and B. A. Okhrimenko, *Ukr. Fiz. Zh.* **9**(10), 1059 (1964a). "Effect of Temperature on the Luminescence and Absorption Spectra of Heavy Metal Salt Solutions. II. Investigations of Tin-Salt Solutions."

Belyi, M. U., and B. A. Okhrimenko, *Ukr. Fiz. Zh.* **9**(10), 1063 (1964b). "Effect of Temperature on the Luminescence and Absorption Spectra of Heavy Metal Salt Solutions. III. Interpretation of the Spectra of Solutions Containing Tl^+, Pb^{2+}, Sn^{2+}, Sn^{4+} Ions."

Benarroche, M. M., *C. R. Acad. Sci.* (Paris) **254**, 1406 (1962a). "Spectre d'Absorption du 2,6-Diméthylnaphtalène à Basse Température."

Benarroche, M. M., *C. R. Acad. Sci.* (Paris) **254**, 3520 (1962b). "Spectres d'Absorption et de Fluorescence du Fluorène Cristallisé pur à 4°K."

Bender, C. F., and E. R. Davidson, *J. Chem. Phys.* **70**, 2675 (1966). "A Natural Orbital Based Energy Calculation for Helium Hydride and Lithium Hydride."

Bennet, R. G., and F. W. Dalby, *J. Chem. Phys.* **40**, 1414 (1964). "Experimental Detection of the Oscillator Strength of the Violet System of OH."

Bennett, J. E., B. Mile, and A. Thomas, *Symp. Combustion* **11**, 853 (1966), Reinhold, New York. "Studies of the Formation, Structure and Reactivity of Peroxyl Radicals at Low Temperatures with a Rotating Cryostat."

Bennett, R. G., *Rev. Sci. Instrum.* **31**, 1275 (1960). "Instrument to Measure Fluorescence Lifetimes in the Millimicrosecond Region."

Benson, S. W., and J. H. Buss, *J. Chem. Phys.* **27**, 1382 (1957). "Halogen-Catalyzed Decomposition of N_2O and the Role of the Hypohalite Radical."

Benson, S. W., and K. H. Anderson, *J. Chem. Phys.* **31**, 1082 (1959). "On the Trapping of Free Radicals of Oxygen and Chlorine."

Benz, K. W., and H. C. Wolf, *Z. Naturforsch.* **19a**, 181 (1964). "Fluoreszenz und Energie-übertragung in Phenanthren-Kristallen."

Berdowski, W., *Bull. Acad. Pol. Sci. Ser. Sci. Chim.* **11**, 227 (1963). "Vibrational Levels and Eigenfunction of the HgA van der Waals Molecule."

Berend, G. C., and S. W. Benson, *J. Chem. Phys.* **48**, 4743 (1968). "Vibrational Relaxation Times of Br_2 in Ar."

Berlman, I. B., in *Luminescence of Organic and Inorganic Materials (Int. Conf., N. Y. Univ.,* p. 62) Wiley, New York, 1962.

Berlman, I. B., *Handbook of Fluorescence Spectra of Aromatic Molecules,* Academic Press, New York, 1965.

Berne, A., G. Boato, and M. De Paz, *Nuovo Cimento* **24**, 1179 (1962). "Self-Diffusion Coefficient in Solid Argon."

Bernstein, E. R., and S. D. Colson, *J. Chem. Phys.* **45**, 3873 (1966). "Observation of the Second Triplet of Solid Benzene Using NO Perturbation."

Bernstein, E. R., S. D. Colson, D. S. Tinti, and G. W. Robinson, *J. Chem. Phys.* **48**, 4632 (1968a). "Static Crystal Effects on the Vibronic Structure of the Phosphorescence, Fluorescence, and Absorption Spectra of Benzene Isotopic Mixed Crystals."

Bernstein, E. R., S. D. Colson, R. Kopelman, and G. W. Robinson, *J. Chem. Phys.* **48**, 5596 (1968b). "Electronic and Vibrational Exciton Structure in Crystalline Benzene."

Bernstein, E. R., and G. W. Robinson, *J. Chem. Phys.* **49**, 4962 (1968c). "Vibrational Exciton Structure in Crystals of Isotopic Benzenes."

Bersohn, R., and J. Isenberg, *J. Chem. Phys.* **40**, 3175 (1964). "Phosphorescence in Nucleotides and Nucleic Acids."

Bertie, J. E., and E. Whalley, *J. Chem. Phys.* **46**, 1271 (1967). "Optical Spectra of Orientationally Disordered Crystals. II. Infrared Spectrum of Ice Ih and Ice Ic from 360 to 50 cm^{-1}."

Bhaumik, M. L., H. Lyons, and P. C. Fletcher, *J. Chem. Phys.* **38**, 568 (1963). "Fluorescence Decay Times of Rare Earth Chelates."

Bhaumik, M. L., and C. L. Telk, *J. Opt. Soc. Amer.* **54**, 1211 (1964). "Fluorescence Quantum Efficiency of Rare Earth Chelates."

Bhaumik, M. L., and M. A. El-Sayed, *J. Chem. Phys.* **42**, 787 (1965a). "Mechanism and Rate of the Intramolecular Energy Transfer Process in Rare-Earth Chelates."

Bhaumik, M. L., and M. A. El-Sayed, *Appl. Opt.*, Suppl. 2, Chemical Lasers, p. 214 (1965b). "Mechanism of Energy Transfer in Some Rare-Earth Chelates."

Bhaumik, M. L., and M. A. El-Sayed, *J. Phys. Chem.* **69**, 275 (1965c). "Studies on the Triplet-Triplet Energy Transfer to Rare Earth Chelates."

Binet, D., E. L. Goldberg, and L. S. Forster, *J. Phys. Chem.* **72**, 3017 (1968). "Energy Transfer and Quenching of Triplet States by Chromium(III) Complexes."

Binsch, G., E. Heilbronner, R. Jankow, and D. Schmidt, *Chem. Phys. Lett.* **1**, 135 (1967). "On the Fluorescence Anomaly of Azulene."

Birks, J. B., and W. A. Little, *Proc. Phys. Soc.* (London) **A66**, 921 (1953). "Photo-Fluorescence Decay Times of Organic Phosphors."

Birks, J. B., *Proc. Phys. Soc.* (London) **79**, 494 (1962). "The Fluorescence and Scintillation Decay Times of Crystalline Anthracene."

Birks, J. B., and L. G. Christophorou, *Proc. Roy. Soc.* (London) *Ser. A* **277**, 571 (1964). "'Excimer' Fluorescence. IV. Solution Spectra of Polycyclic Hydrocarbons."

Birks, J. B., and J. Grzywacz, *Chem. Phys. Lett.* **1**, 187 (1967a). "Prompt and Delayed Fluorescence of Dyes in Solid Solution."

Birks, J. B., *Chem. Phys. Lett.* **1**, 304 (1967b). "Exciton Resonance States of Aromatic Excimers."

Birks, J. B., and A. A. Kazzaz, *Chem. Phys. Lett.* **1**, 307 (1967c). "Experimental Determination of the Pyrene Crystal Excimer Interaction Potential."

Birks, J. B., and I. H. Munro, *Progr. Reaction Kinetics* **4**, 239 (1967d). "The Fluorescence Lifetimes of Aromatic Molecules."

Birks, J. B., *Chem. Phys. Lett.* **1**, 625 (1968). "Higher Excited States of Benzene and Toluene Excimers."

Bischoe, G., *Chem. News* **53**, 205 (1886). "Dr. Koch's Gelatin-Peptone Water-Test."

Biswas, D. C., *Indian J. Phys.* **29**, 503b (1955). "Raman Spectra of a Few Monosubstituted Benzene Compounds in the Solid State at Different Low Temperatures."

Biswas, D. C., *Indian J. Phys.* **30**, 143 (1956a). "Fluorescence of *p*-chlorotoluene in the Solid State at Low Temperature."

Biswas, D. C., *Indian J. Phys.* **30**, 407 (1956b). "On the Fluorescence of Para-bromo-toluene, Ortho-bromo and Ortho-chlorotoluene in the Solid State at Low Temperature."

Biswas, D. C., *Indian J. Phys.* **30**, 565 (1956c). "Fluorescence Spectra of Methyl Benzoate *m*-Chlorotoluene and *m*-Bromotoluene."

Bixon, M., and J. Jortner, *J. Chem. Phys.* **48**, 715 (1968). "Intramolecular Radiationless Transitions."

Bixon, M., and J. Jortner, *J. Chem. Phys.* **50**, 3284 (1969a). "Long Radiative Lifetimes of Small Molecules."

Bixon, M., and J. Jortner, *J. Chem. Phys.* **51**, 4061 (1969b). "Electronic Relaxation in Large Molecules."

Björklund, S., N. Filipescu, N. McAvoy, and J. Degnan, *J. Phys. Chem.* **72**, 970 (1968). "Correlation of Molecular Structure with Fluorescence Spectra in Rare Earth Chelates. I. Internal Stark Splitting in Tetraethylammonium Tetrakis (Dibenzoylmethido) Europate (III)."

Black, G., *Org. Finishing* **7**, 9 (1946). "Luminescence–Fluorescence–Phosphorescence."

Blackman, M., A. Egerton, and E. V. Truter, *Proc. Roy. Soc.* (London) **194**, 147 (1948). "Heat Transfer by Radiation to Surfaces at Low Temperatures."

Blackwell, L. A., Y. Kanda, and H. Sponer, *J. Chem. Phys.* **32**, 1465 (1960). "Triplet-

Singlet Emission Spectra of Xylenes in Crystalline State at 4.2° and 77°K, and in EPA at 77°K."

Blagoi, Y. P., A. E. Butko, S. A. Mikhailenko, and V. V. Yakuba, *Russ. J. Phys. Chem.* **41**, 908 (1967). "Velocity of Sound in Liquid Krypton, Xenon and Methane."

Blake, N. W., D. S. McClure, and H. Winston, *Phys. Rev.* **85**, 754 (1952). "Electronic States of Molecular Crystals."

Blake, N. W., and D. S. McClure, *J. Chem. Phys.* **29**, 722 (1958). "Delayed Singlet-Singlet Emission from Molecular Crystals."

Blandamer, M. J., T. A. Claxton, and M. F. Fox, *Chem. Phys. Lett.* **1**, 203 (1967). "Thermal Anomalies in the Temperature Dependence of the Energy of the First Absorption Band Maximum of Iodide in Water."

Blickensderfer, R. P., and G. E. Ewing, *J. Chem. Phys.* **51**, 873 (1969). "Collision-Induced Absorption Spectrum of Gaseous Oxygen at Low Temperatures and Pressures. I. The $^1\Delta_g \leftarrow {}^3\Sigma_g{}^-$ System."

Blukis, U., and R. J. Myers, *J. Phys. Chem.* **69**, 1154 (1965). "Disulfur Monoxide. III. Its Infrared Spectrum and Thermodynamic Function."

Boato, G., *Cryogenics* **4**, 65 (1964). "The Solidified Inert Gases."

Boesman, E., and D. Schoemaker, *J. Chem. Phys.* **37**, 671 (1962). "Paramagnetic Resonance of the I_2-Center in KCl Doped with KI."

Bojarski, C., *Acta Phys. Pol.* **30**, 169 (1966). "Resonance Quenching of Solid Solution Luminescence."

Bolotnikova, T. N., *Izv. Akad. Nauk SSSR, Ser. Fiz.* **23**, 29 (1959a). "Fluorescence Spectra of Frozen Crystalline Solutions of Simple Aromatic Hydrocarbons."

Bolotnikova, T. N., *Opt. Spectrosc.* (USSR) (English Transl.) **7**, 24 (1959b). "On the Question of Interpretation of the Fluorescence Spectrum of Naphthalene."

Bolotnikova, T. N., *Opt. Spectrosc.* (USSR) (English Transl.) **7**, 138 (1959c). "Spectroscopy of Certain Simple Aromatic Hydrocarbons in Frozen Crystalline Solutions."

Bolotnikova, T. N., L. A. Klimova, G. N. Nersesova, and L. F. Utkina, *Opt. Spectrosc.* (USSR) (English Transl.) **21**, 237 (1966). "A Study of the Quasiline Fluorescence and Absorption Spectra of Anthracene at 77.3 and 4.3°K."

Bolotnikova, T. N., T. M. Naumova, F. I. Gurov, and V. G. Kazachkov, *Opt. Spectrosc.* (USSR) (English Transl.) **24**, 291 (1968). "Concentration Effect on the Decay Time of the Naphthalene and Phenanthrene Phosphorescence."

Bolz, L. A., H. P. Broida, and H. S. Peiser, *Acta Cryst.* **15**, 810 (1962). "Some Observations on Growing Crystals of Argon."

Bonch-Bruevich, A. M., and A. V. Burlakov, *Sov. Phys.-Solid State* (English Transl.) **8**, 1034 (1966). "Electroluminescence Due to Unipolar Voltage Pulses and Mechanism of Luminescence Excitation."

Bondi, A., *Physical Properties of Molecular Crystals, Liquids and Glasses*, Wiley, New York, 1968.

Bonn, R., R. Metselaar, and J. Van der Elsken, *J. Chem. Phys.* **46**, 1988 (1967). "Infra-red-Absorption Spectra of Solid Solutions: The Rotatory Motions of Nitrate and Nitrite Ions in Alkali Halides."

Bonneau, R., J. Faure, and J. Joussot-Dubien, *Chem. Phys. Lett.* **2**, 65 (1968). "Singlet-Singlet Absorption and Intersystem Crossing from the $^1B_{3u-}$ State of Naphthalene."

Borgman, V. A., I. A. Zhmyreva, V. V. Zelinskii, and V. P. Kolobkov, *Sov. Phys. Dokl.* (English Transl.) **5**, 324 (1960). "The Influence of Heavy Halogens on the

Probability of Transition to a Metastable State and the Probabilities of Disactivation of This State."

Borisov, M. D., and V. N. Vishnevski, *Bull. Acad. Sci. USSR, Phys. Ser.* (English Transl.) **20**, 459 (1956). "Absolute Photoluminescence Efficiency of Anthracene and Naphthalene Crystals."

Borkman, R. F., and D. R. Kearns, *Chem. Commun.* **48**, 446 (1966). "Investigation of Singlet-Triplet Transitions by the Phosphorescence Excitation Method. Spectroscopic Determination of Intersystem Crossing Quantum Yields and Extinction Coefficients of Singlet-Triplet Transitions."

Borkman, R. F., and D. R. Kearns, *J. Chem. Phys.* **46**, 2333 (1967). "Heavy-Atom and Substituent Effects on S-T Transitions of Halogenated Carbonyl Compounds."

Bostanjoglo, O., and L. Schmidt, *Phys. Lett.* **22**, 130 (1966). "Excitons in Solid Argon."

Boudin, S., *J. Chim. Phys.* **27**, 285 (1930). "Phosphorescence des Solutions Glycériques d'Eosine. Influence des Iodures."

Bovey, L. F. H., and G. B. B. M. Sutherland, *J. Chem. Phys.* **17**, 843 (1949). "Infrared Evidence for Free Rotation in the Solid State."

Bowen, E. J., and A. H. Williams, *Trans. Faraday Soc.* **35**, 765 (1939). "The Photo-Oxidation of Hydrocarbon Solutions."

Bowen, E. J., *The Chemical Aspects of Light*, Oxford Univ. Press (Clarendon), Oxford, 1946.

Bowen, E. J., and E. Coates, *J. Chem. Soc.* (London) **1947**, 105 (1947). "Solvent Quenching of Fluorescence."

Bowen, E. J., and B. Brocklehurst, *J. Chem. Soc.* (London) **1954**, 3875 (1954). "The Fluorescence Spectra of Coronene and 1 : 12-Benzoperylene at Low Temperatures."

Bowen, E. J., and B. Brocklehurst, *J. Chem. Soc.* (London) **1955**, 4320 (1955). "The Emission Spectra of Aromatic Hydrocarbons in Crystalline Paraffins at − 180°."

Bowen, E. J., *Ciba Rev.* **12**, 2 (1960). "Luminescence."

Bowen, E. J., *Advan. Photochem.* **1**, 23 (1963). "The Photochemistry of Aromatic Hydrocarbon Solutions."

Bowers, M. T., and W. H. Flygare, *J. Chem. Phys.* **44**, 1389 (1966a). "Vibration-Rotation Spectra of Monomeric HCl, DCl, HBr, DBr, and HI in the Rare-Gas Lattices and N_2 Doping Experiments in the Rare-Gas Lattices."

Bowers, M. T., G. I. Kerley, and W. H. Flygare, *J. Chem. Phys.* **45**, 3399 (1966b). "Vibration-Rotation Spectra of Monomeric HCl in the Rare-Gas Lattices. II."

Brabson, G. D., unpublished results (1965a). "Perturbation of the Equilibrium Internuclear Distance of S_2 by Frozen Inert Gas Matrices."

Brabson, G. D., Ph. D. Thesis, University of California, Berkeley (1965b) and UCLRL-11976. "Spectroscopic Investigation of High Temperature Species Isolated in Inert Gas Matrices."

Brabson, G. D., and A. M. Bass, unpublished NBS report, 1970. "Spectra of Matrix Isolated Species."

Bradley, H., Jr., and A. D. King, Jr., *J. Chem. Phys.* **47**, 1189 (1967). "Solubilities of Benzene, Naphthalene, and Anthracene in Compressed Argon and Oxygen: Evidence for Zero Stabilization of Aromatic-Oxygen Charge-Transfer Complexes."

Brasch, J. W., and R. J. Jakobsen, *Spectrochim. Acta* **20**, 1644 (1964). "The Use of a Polyethylene Matrix for Studying Dilution and Low-Temperature Effects in the Far-Infrared."

Brasch, J. W., *Spectrochim. Acta* **21**, 1183 (1965). "High-Pressure Effects on Organic Liquids. Production and Infrared Spectra of Single Crystals."

Bree, A., and R. Zwarich, *J. Chem. Phys.* **49**, 3344 (1968a). "Vibrational Assignment of Carbazole from Infrared, Raman and Fluorescence Spectra."

Bree, A., and R. Zwarich, *J. Chem. Phys.* **49**, 3355 (1968b). "Absorption Spectrum of Carbazole in a Fluorene Matrix."

Breene, R. G., Jr., *The Shift and Shape of Spectral Lines*, Pergamon, New York, 1961.

Brewer, L., D. Bromley, P. Gilles, and D. Lofgren, UCRL-CT (1944). "A High Temperature-High Vacuum Furnace."

Brewer, L., G. D. Brabson, and B. Meyer, *J. Chem. Phys.* **42**, 1385 (1965a). "UV Absorption Spectrum of Trapped S_2."

Brewer, L., B. Meyer, and G. D. Brabson, *J. Chem. Phys.* **43**, 3973 (1965b). "Ultraviolet Absorption Spectrum of Mercury in Low-Temperature Matrices."

Brewer, L., and G. D. Brabson, *J. Chem. Phys.* **44**, 3274 (1966). "Fluorescent and Absorption Spectra of S_2 Isolated in Inert-Gas Matrices."

Brewer, L., *Nat. Acad. Sci.—Nat. Res. Council Publ.* **1470**, 3 (1967). "Future Developments in the Spectroscopy of High-Temperature Molecules."

Brewer, L., B. A. King, J. L. Wang, B. Meyer, and G. F. Moore, *J. Chem. Phys.* **49**, 5209 (1968). "Absorption Spectrum of Silver Atoms in Solid Argon, Krypton and Xenon."

Brewer, L., C. A. Chang, and B. King, *Inorg. Chem.*, **9**, 814 (1970). "Reaction of Ammoniated Electrons with Sulfur Hexafluoride and Its Use as a Matrix Gas."

Briegleb, G., J. Trencseni, and W. Herre, *Chem. Phys. Lett.* **3**, 146 (1969). "Unusually Large Stoke's Shifts and Fluorescence Decay Times of the Charge Transfer Fluorescence."

Bril, A., and W. L. Wanmaker, *Phillips Tech. Rev.* **27**, 22 (1966). "New Phosphors for Colour Television."

Brinen, J. S., and W. G. Hodgson, *J. Chem. Phys.* **47**, 2946 (1967a). "Application of Electron Spin Resonance in the Study of Triplet States. II. Effect of Triplet-Triplet Reabsorption of Quantitative Phosphorescence Measurements."

Brinen, J. S., and M. K. Orloff, *Chem. Phys. Lett.* **1**, 276 (1967b). "Zero-Field Splitting in Phosphorescent Triplet States of Aromatic Hydrocarbons. III. Correlation between D and the Triplet State Energy."

Brinen, J. S., and J. G. Koren, *Chem. Phys. Lett.* **2**, 671 (1968). "The Lowest Triplet State of 9,10-Diphenylanthracene."

Brith, M., and O. Schnepp, *J. Chem. Phys.* **39**, 2714 (1963). "Removal of Orbital Degeneracy in an Asymmetric Molecular Environment."

Brith, M., and D. White, *Phys. Lett.* **11**, 203 (1964). "The Crystal Structure of Solid Deuterium."

Brith, M., and O. Schnepp, *Mol. Phys.* **9**, 473 (1965). "The Absorption Spectra of Solid CO and N_2."

Brith, M., and A. Ron, *J. Chem. Phys.* **50**, 3045 (1969). "Far-Ultraviolet Spectra of Xe and CO Adsorbed on Cooled LiF Films."

Brobeck, W. M., and D. T. Scalise, University of California, Lawrence Radiation Laboratory, Berkeley, UCRL-3687 (1957). "UCRL Design Data of General Interest."

Brocklehurst, B., and G. C. Pimentel, *J. Chem. Phys.* **36**, 2040 (1962). "Thermoluminescence of Solid Nitrogen after Electron Bombardment at 4.2°K."

Brocklehurst, B., W. A. Gibbons, F. T. Lang, G. Porter, and M. I. Savadatti, *Trans.*

Faraday Soc. **62**, 1793 (1966a). "Primary Photochemical Processes in Aromatic Molecules."

Brocklehurst, B., R. D. Russell, and M. I. Savadatti, *Trans. Faraday Soc.* **62**, 1129 (1966b). "Thermoluminescence of λ-Irradiated Solutions of Aromatic Compounds in Rigid Organic Glasses."

Brodin, M. S., V. N. Vatuly'ov, and S. V. Zakrevskyi, *Ukr. Fiz. Zh.* **9**, 1150 (1965a). "The Luminescence Appearing under the Acid of a Ruby Laser Beam on Sodium-Uranyl-Acetate Crystals."

Brodin, M. S., and S. V. Marisova, *Opt. Spectrosc.* (USSR) (English Transl.) **19/2, 132** (1965b). "The Oscillator Strength of the First Electronic Transition of Crystalline Anthracene."

Brody, M., and H. Linschitz, *Science* **133**, 705 (1961). "Fluorescence of Photosynthetic Organisms at Room and Liquid Nitrogen Temperatures."

Broida, H. P., and J. R. Pellam, *Phys. Rev.* **95**, 845 (1954). "Phosphorescence of Atoms and Molecules of Solid Nitrogen at $4°K$."

Broida, H. P., and O. S. Lutes, *J. Chem. Phys.* **24**, 484 (1956). "Abundance of Free Atoms in Solid Nitrogen Condensed at $4°K$ from a Gas Discharge."

Broida, H. P., *Ann. N. Y. Acad. Sci.* **67**, 530 (1957a). "Stabilization of Free Radicals at Low Temperature."

Broida, H. P., in *The Threshold of Space* (M. Zelikoff, ed.), p. 194, Pergamon, New York, 1957b. "Spectroscopic Studies of Solids Condensed at $4.2°K$ from Electric Discharge through Nitrogen, Oxygen, Hydrogen, Water and Ammonia."

Broida, H. P., and M. Peyron, *J. Chem. Phys.* **28**, 725 (1958a). "Evaporation of Active Species Trapped in a Solid Condensed from 'Discharged' Nitrogen."

Broida, H. P., *Endeavour* **17**, 208 (1958b). "Trapped Radicals."

Broida, H. P., and M. Peyron, *J. Chem. Phys.* **32**, 1068 (1960a). "Emission Spectra of N_2, O_2 and NO Molecules Trapped in Solid Matrices."

Broida, H. P., and R. W. Nicholls, *J. Chem. Phys.* **32**, 623 (1960b). "Phosphorescence of Nitrogen and Nitrogen-Argon Deposited Films at $4.2°K$."

Broida, H. P., and R. W. Nicholls, *J. Chem. Phys.* **32**, 623 (1960c). "Phosphorescence of Nitrogen and Nitrogen-Argon Deposited Films at $4°K$."

Broida, H. P., and S. Abramowitz, *J. Res. Nat. Bur. Std.* **68A**, 331 (1964a). "The 0-2 Transition of CO in Condensed Oxygen, Nitrogen and Argon."

Broida, H. P., and F. C. Fehsenfeld, *Nat. Bur. Std.* (*U.S.*) *Rep.* 8701 (1964b). "Microwave Discharge Cavities Operating at 2450 MHz."

Brongersma, H. H., and L. J. Oosterhoff, *Chem. Phys. Lett.* **1**, 169 (1967). "High Resolution Singlet-Triplet Excitation Spectra by Low Energy Electron Impact Spectroscopy."

Broude, V. L., V. S. Medvedev, and A. F. Prikhot'ko, *Fiz. Sb.* **1**, 14 (1957). "Spectral Study of Benzene Crystals at $20.4°K$."

Broude, V. L., A. V. Prikhot'ko, and E. I. Rashba, *Sov. Phys.-Usp.* (English Transl.) **2**, 38 (1959). "Some Problems of Crystal Luminescence."

Broude, V. L., *Sov. Phys.-Usp.* (English Transl.) **4**, 584 (1962). "Spectroscopic Studies of Benzene."

Broude, V. L., E. F. Sheka, and M. T. Shpak, *Bull. Acad. Sci. USSR Phys. Ser.* **27**, 597 (1963). "Exciton Luminescence of Molecular Crystals."

Brown, D. M., and F. S. Dainton, *Trans. Faraday Soc.* **62**, 1139 (1966). "Matrix Isolation of Unstable Lower Valency States of Metal Cations."

Brown, F. H., M. Furst, and H. P. Kallmann, *J. Chim. Phys.* **55**, 688 (1958). "Energy Transfer in Liquid and Rigid Organic Systems."

Brown, H. W., and G. C. Pimentel, *J. Chem. Phys.* **29**, 883 (1958). "Photolysis of Nitromethane and of Methyl Nitrite in an Argon Matrix; Infrared Detection of Nitroxyl, HNO."

Brown, I. M., D. J. Sloop, and D. P. Ames, *Chem. Phys. Lett.* **1**, 167 (1967). "Spin-Lattice Relaxation of the Biphenyl Anion Radical in a Rigid Matrix."

Brown, I. M., and D. J. Sloop, *Chem. Phys. Lett.* **1**, 579 (1968). "The Direct Process in the Spin-Lattice Relaxation of DPPH in a Rigid Matrix."

Brown, M. R., H. Thomas, and J. S. S. Whiting, *J. Chem. Phys.* **50**, 881 (1969a). "Experiments on Er^{3+} in SrF_2. I. Fluorescence Quantum Efficiencies and Lifetimes."

Brown, M. R., K. G. Roots, and J. M. Williams, *J. Chem. Phys.* **50**, 891 (1969b). "Experiments on Er^{3+} in SrF_2. II. Concentration Dependence of Site Symmetry."

Broyde, S. B., and S. S. Brody, *J. Chem. Phys.* **46**, 3334 (1967). "Emission Spectra of Chlorophyll-α in Polar and Nonpolar Solvents."

Brunel, L. C., and M. Peyron, *C. R. Acad. Sci.* (Paris) Ser. C **262**, 1297 (1966). "Infrared Absorption of HCl Trapped in Solid Matrices."

Brynestad, J., H. L. Yakel, and G. Pedro Smith, *J. Chem. Phys.* **45**, 4652 (1966). "Temperature Dependence of the Absorption Spectrum of Nickel(II)-Doped $KMgCl_3$ and the Crystal Structure of $KMgCl_3$."

Buchler, A. B., and W. Klemperer, *J. Chem. Phys.* **29**, 121 (1961). "Infrared Spectra of the Alkaline-Earth Halides. I. Beryllium Fluoride, Beryllium Chloride, and Magnesium Chloride."

Buckingham, A. D., *Proc. Roy. Soc.* (London) Ser. A **248**, 169 (1958). "Solvent Effects in Infra-Red Spectroscopy."

Buckingham, A. D., *Proc. Roy. Soc.* (London) Ser. A **255**, 32 (1960). "A Theory of Frequency, Intensity, and Band-Width Changes Due to Solvents in Infra-Red Spectroscopy."

Budininkas, P., *Diss. Abstr. B* **28**(4), 1442 (1967). "Dissociation Energies of Gaseous Diatomic Sulfur, Selenium and Tellurium."

Bulanin, M. O., and N. D. Orlova, *Opt. Spectrosc.* (USSR) (English Transl.) **15**, 112 (1963). "Shapes of Infrared Absorption Bands and the Rotational Motion of Molecules in Liquids. Carbon Monoxide Solutions."

Bulanin, M. O., M. G. Melnik, and M. V. Tonkov, *Opt. Spectrosc.* (USSR) (English Transl.) **22**, 389 (1967). "Induced Absorption Spectra of Condensed Systems: Theory of the Translation-Vibrational Branches in the Spectra of Liquid Hydrogen and Its Solutions."

Bullot, J., A. Deroulede, and F. Kieffer, *Int. Symp. Luminescence, Munich, 1965*, p. 173, Thiemig, Munich, 1966. "Thermoluminescence Spectra of Some Gamma-Irradiated Molecular Solids at 77°K."

Bullot, J., and A. C. Albrecht, *J. Chem. Phys.* **51**, 2220 (1969). "Coupling of Matrix-Trapped Electrons with an External Electric Field: Electrophotoluminescence in a Rigid Organic Solution at 77°K."

Burkov, V. I., V. A. Kizel, Y. I. Krasilov, and V. N. Shamraev, *Opt. Spectrosc.* (USSR) (English Transl.) **22**, 127 (1967). "Luminescence of Crystals and Solid Solutions of Benzyl."

Burshtein, E. A., and Y. A. Vladimirov, *Biophysics* (USSR) (English Transl.) **9**, 193 (1964). "Measurement of the Absorption Spectra and the Spectra of Excitation of Luminescence of Biological Specimens in the Shortwave Ultraviolet Region."

Burtsey, V. T., R. A. Karasev, and A. M. Samarin, *Eksp. Tekh. Metody Vysokotemp. Izmer., Akad. Nauk SSSR, Inst. Met.* **1966**, 73 (1966) (in Russian). "Evaporation of Sulfur from Iron-Carbon-Sulfur Melts."

Butlar, V. A., and D. M. Grebenshchikov, *Opt. Spectrosc.* (USSR) (English Transl.) **22**, 413 (1967). "Phosphorescence Spectra of Coronene and Triphenylene in Carbon Tetrachloride."

Bylina, A., *Chem. Phys. Lett.* **1**, 509 (1968). "Triplet-Triplet Energy Transfer and the Overlap of Singlet-Triplet Bands of Sensitizer and Acceptor. Remarks on the Phantom Triplet of Stilbene."

Byrne, J. P., E. F. McCoy, and I. G. Ross, *Austr. J. Chem.* **18**, 1589 (1965). "Internal Conversion in Aromatic and N-Heteroaromatic Molecules."

C

Cabana, A., G. B. Savitsky, and D. F. Hornig, *J. Chem. Phys.* **39**, 2942 (1963). "Vibration-Rotation Spectra of CH_4 Impurities in Xenon, Krypton and Argon Crystals."

Cadogan, K. D., and A. C. Albrecht, *J. Chem. Phys.* **43**, 2550 (1965). "Two-Photon Ionizations in Rigid Organic Solutions and the Triplet-State Intermediate."

Cadogan, K. D., and A. C. Albrecht, *J. Phys. Chem.* **72**, 929 (1968). "Detailed Studies of a One-Electron, Two-Photon Ionization in a Rigid Organic Solution at 77°K."

Cadogan, K. D., and A. C. Albrecht, *J. Chem. Phys.* **51**, 2710 (1969). "Photoconductivity in Rigid Organic Solutions. III. The Triplet Intermediate and a Kinetic Model Involving Secondary Matrix Trap Photoionization."

Cahill, J. E., and G. E. Leroi, *J. Chem. Phys.* **51**, 1324 (1969). "Raman Spectra of Solid CO_2, N_2O, N_2, and CO."

Cairns, B. R., and G. C. Pimentel, *J. Chem. Phys.* **43**, 3432 (1965). "Infrared Spectra of Solid α- and β-Oxygen."

Calder, V., D. E. Mann, K. S. Seshadri, M. Allavena, and D. White, Dept. of Navy, Contract ONR N00014-67-A-0216-0001, *Tech. Rep.* No. 3 (1960). "Geometry and Vibrational Spectra of Alkaline-Earth Dihalides. II. CaF_2, SrF_2, and BaF_2."

Calvert, J. G., and J. N. Pitts, Jr., *Photochemistry*, Wiley, New York, 1966.

Calvin, M., and G. D. Dorough, *Science* **105**, 433 (1947). "The Phosphorescence of Chlorophyll and Some Chlorin Derivatives."

Carelli, A., and P. Pringsheim, *Z. Phys.* **18**, 317 (1923). "Über die Photolumineszenz von Farbstoffen in zähen Lösungsmitteln."

Carlson, G. A., and G. C. Pimentel, *J. Chem. Phys.* **44**, 4053 (1966). "Infrared Detection of Gaseous Trifluoromethyl Radical."

Carver, T. G., and L. Andrews, *J. Chem. Phys.* **51**, 5100 (1969). "Infrared Spectrum of the Difluoromethyl Radical in Solid Argon."

Castellucci, E., G. Sbrana, and F. D. Verderame, *J. Chem. Phys.* **51**, 3762 (1969). "Infrared Spectra of Crystalline and Matrix Isolated Pyridine and Pyridine-D_5."

Castro, G., and R. M. Hochstrasser, *J. Chem. Phys.* **44**, 412 (1966a). "Singlet-Triplet Absorption Spectra of Single Crystals of the ρ-Dihalogenated Benzenes."

Castro, G., and R. M. Hochstrasser, *J. Chem. Phys.* **45**, 4352 (1966b). "Triplet State Excimers."

Castro, G., and R. M. Hochstrasser, *J. Chem. Phys.* **46**, 3617 (1967). "Singlet-Triplet Transitions in ρ-Dihalogenated Benzenes."

Castro, G., and R. M. Hochstrasser, *J. Chem. Phys.* **48**, 637 (1968). "Electronic Zeeman Measurements on 1,4-Dibromonaphthalene."

Castro, G., and G. W. Robinson, *J. Chem. Phys.* **50**, 1159 (1969). "Singlet-Triplet Absorption of Crystalline Naphthalene by High-Resolution Photoexcitation Spectroscopy."

Catalano, E., and D. E. Milligan, *J. Chem. Phys.* **30**, 45 (1959). "Infrared Spectra of H_2O, D_2O, and HDO in Solid Argon, Krypton, and Xenon."

Catalano, E., R. H. Sanborn, and J. W. Frazer, *J. Chem. Phys.* **38**, 2265 (1963a). "On the Infrared Spectrum of Hydrazine Matrix—Isolation Studies of the System $NH_2NH_2 : N_2$. I."

Catalano, E., and R. H. Sanborn, *J. Chem. Phys.* **38**, 2273 (1963b). "On the Infrared Spectrum of Hydrogen Peroxide Matrix—Isolation Studies of the System $H_2O_2 : N_2$. II."

Chaiken, R. F., and D. R. Kearns, *J. Chem. Phys.* **45**, 3966 (1966). "Intrinsic Photoconduction in Anthracene Crystals."

Chandross, E. A., and J. Ferguson, *J. Chem. Phys.* **45**, 3564 (1966). "Photodimerization of Crystalline Anthracene. The Photolytic Dissociation of Crystalline Dianthracene."

Chang, C. A., Ph. D. Thesis, University of California, Berkeley, 1970. "Optical Spectroscopic Studies of Atoms and Molecules in the Low Temperature Matrices."

Charles, S. W., and K. O. Lee, *Trans. Faraday Soc.* **61**, 2081 (1965). "Interpretation of the Matrix-Induced Shifts of Vibration and Band Frequencies."

Charles, S. W., P. H. H. Fischer, and C. A. McDowell, *Chem. Phys. Lett.* **1**, 451 (1967). "Electron Spin Resonance Study of the Photolytic Decomposition of CF_3I in Inert Matrices between $4.2°K$ and $35°K$."

Charlesby, A., and R. H. Partridge, *Proc. Roy. Soc.* (London) *Ser. A* **271**, 170 (1963a). "The Thermoluminescence of Irradiated Polyethylene and Other Polymers."

Charlesby, A., and R. H. Partridge, *Proc. Roy. Soc.* (London) *Ser. A* **271**, 188 (1963b). "The Effect of Oxygen on the Thermoluminescence of Irradiated Polyethylene."

Charlesby, A., and R. H. Partridge, *Proc. Roy. Soc.* (London) *Ser. A* **283**, 312 (1965a). "The Identification of Luminescence Centres in Polyethylene and Other Polymers."

Charlesby, A., and R. H. Partridge, *Proc. Roy. Soc.* (London) *Ser. A* **283**, 329 (1965b). "Thermoluminescence and Phosphorescence in Polyethylene under Ultra Violet Irradiation."

Chaudhuri, J. N., and S. Basu, *Trans. Faraday Soc.* **54**, 1605 (1958). "Magnetic Perturbation of Triplet Transitions."

Chaudhuri, N. K., and S. C. Ganguly, *Proc. Roy. Soc.* (London) *Ser. A* **259**, 419 (1960). "The Absorption and Fluorescence Spectra of Naphthalene Molecules in Anthracene Crystals."

Chaudhuri, N. K., and M. A. El-Sayed, *J. Chem. Phys.* **42**, 1947 (1965a). "Concentration Depolarization of the Phosphorescence Emission."

Chaudhuri, N. K., and M. A. El-Sayed, *J. Chem. Phys.* **43**, 1423 (1965b). "Host-Crystal Effects on the Mechanism of the Phosphorescence Process of Aromatic Hydrocarbons."

Chaudhuri, N. K., and M. A. El-Sayed, *J. Chem. Phys.* **43**, 1424 (1965c). "Out-of-Plane Polarization in the Fluorescence Emission of Naphthalene-d_8 in Durene."

Chaudhuri, N. K., and M. A. El-Sayed, *J. Chem. Phys.* **44**, 3728 (1966a). "Host-Crystal Effects on the Mechanism of the π, π^* Phosphorescence. II. N-Heterocyclics."

Chaudhuri, N. K., and M. A. El-Sayed, *J. Chem. Phys.* **45**, 1358 (1966b). "Induced Intramolecular Heavy-Atom Effect on the Phosphorescence Process by Host-Guest Crystal Interactions."

Cheng-Tsai, S., and G. W. Robinson, *J. Chem. Phys.* **49**, 3184 (1968). "Phosphorescence and the True Lifetime of Triplet States in Fluid Solutions."

Chen-Hanson Ting, *Chem. Phys. Lett.* **1**, 335 (1967). "Electronic Structure and Intersystem Crossing in 9,10-Diphenylanthracene."

Cherkasov, A. S., *Bull. Acad. Sci. USSR, Phys. Ser.* **20** (1956). "Absorption and Fluorescence Spectra and the Quantum Efficiency of Fluorescence of Certain Meso-Derivatives of Anthracene."

Cherkasov, A. S., *Opt. Spectrosc.* (USSR) (English Transl.) **7**, 211 (1959a). "Absorption Spectra, Fluorescence Spectra and Quantum Yields of Fluorescence of Some Methyl- and Methyl-meso-arylanthracenes."

Cherkasov, A. S., and T. M. Vember, *Opt. Spectrosc.* (USSR) (English Transl.) **4**, 319 (1959b). "The Influence of Oxygen on Photochemical Transformations and the Concentration Quenching of Fluorescence of some Anthracene Derivatives."

Chilton, H. T. J., and G. Porter, 4th *Int. Symp. Free Radical Stabilization*, C-I-1 (1959). "Studies of Some New Matrices for Radical Stabilization."

Chilton, H. T. J., *Spectrochim. Acta* **16**, 979 (1960). "Dewar Vessel for the Infrared Spectroscopy of Solids at Low Temperature."

Chisholm, D. A., and H. L. Welsh, *Can. J. Phys.* **32**, 291 (1954). "Induced Infrared Absorption in Hydrogen and Hydrogen-Foreign Gas Mixtures at Pressures up to 1500 Atmospheres."

Chisler, E. V., *Opt. Spectrosc.* (USSR) (English Transl.) **22**, 313 (1967). "Temperature Dependence of the Intensity of Raman Spectra of Crystals. Second-Order Spectra."

Chizhikova, Z. A., and M. D. Galanin, *Sov. Phys. JETP* (English Transl.) **3**, 115 (1956). "Gamma and Photoluminescence Yields in Organic Crystals."

Cho, C. W., E. J. Allin, and H. L. Welsh, *J. Chem. Phys.* **25**, 371 (1956). "Structure of the Infrared 'Atmospheric' Bands in Liquid Oxygen."

Chock, D. P., J. Jortner, and S. A. Rice, *J. Chem. Phys.* **49**, 610 (1968a). "Theory of Radiationless Transitions in an Isolated Molecule."

Chock, D. P., and S. A. Rice, *J. Chem. Phys.* **49**, 4345 (1968b). "Cooperative Excitons in a Crystal with Two Molecules per Unit Cell."

Chomse, H., *Z. Anorg. Allg. Chem.* **233**, 140 (1937a). "Über Organo-Phosphore mit Anorganischem Grundmaterial. I. Phosphore auf der Basis von Mono-Erdalkali-phosphaten und Freien Phosphorsäuren."

Chomse, H., *Z. Anorg. Allg. Chem.* **233**, 145 (1937b). "Über Organo-Phosphore mit Anorganischem Grundmaterial. II. Sauerstoffempfindliche Borsäure-Phosphore."

Chomse, H., and W. Lutzenberger, *Z. Anorg. Allg. Chem.* **238**, 236 (1938). "Über Organo-Phosphore mit Anorganischem Grundmaterial. III. Lumineszenzfähige Erdalkali-karbonate."

Chowdhury, M., and L. Goodman, *J. Chem. Phys.* **38**, 2979 (1963). "Nature of S-Tetrazine Emission Spectra."

Chu, T. L., and S. I. Weissman, *J. Chem. Phys.* **22**, 21 (1954). "Symmetry Classification of the Energy Levels of Some Triarylmethyl Free Radicals and Their Cations."

Chu-Cheng, I., and G. M. Barrow, *J. Chem. Phys.* **43**, 1430 (1965). "Trapping of Neutral Molecules in Ionic Matrices."

Ciais, A., *C. R. Acad. Sci.* (Paris) **250**, 1243 (1960). "Un Modèle Classique Simple de l'Exciton Organique."

Ciais, A., *J. Chim. Phys.* **58**, 190 (1961). "Structure Fine des Spectres de Luminescence de Molécules Organiques en Solutions Cristallisées."

Claassen, H. H., *The Noble Gases*, Heath, Boston, Massachusetts, 1966.

Clar, E., and M. Zander, *Chem. Ber.* **89**, 749 (1956). "Aromatische Kohlenwasserstoffe. LXXII. Mitt.: Die Zusammenhänge zwischen chemischer Reaktivität, Phosphoreszenz und Para-Absorptionsbanden und die 'Wasserstoffähnlichkeit' des oberen Niveaus der *p*-Banden in den Absorptionsspektren aromatischer Kohlenwasserstoffe."

Clarke, A. G., and E. B. Smith, *J. Chem. Phys.* **48**, 3988 (1968). "Low Temperature Viscosities of Argon, Krypton and Xenon."

Clarke, R. H., and R. M. Hochstrasser, *J. Chem. Phys.* **46**, 4532 (1967). "Electronic Zeeman Effect in Anthracene."

Clarke, R. H., and R. M. Hochstrasser, *J. Chem. Phys.* **49**, 3313 (1968). "Electronic Zeeman Effect in the Naphthalene Crystal."

Claxton, T. A., D. P. Craig, and T. Thirimamachandran, *J. Chem. Phys.* **35**, 1525 (1961). "Crystal Splitting of the Anthracene 3800 Å System."

Clementi, E., and M. Kasha, *J. Chem. Phys.* **26**, 956 (1957). "Spin-Orbital Perturbation in Cyanine Dyes Absorbed on Surfaces Containing High-Z Atoms."

Clementi, E., and M. Kasha, *J. Mol. Spectrosc.* **2**, 297 (1958). "Spin-Orbital Interaction in N-Heterocyclic Molecules. General Results in a Cylindrical Potential Approximation."

Clifton, J. R., and D. M. Gruen, *20th Ann. Mid-Amer. Symp. Spectroscopy, Chicago, Illinois, 1969*a, paper No. 179.

Clifton, J. R., D. M. Gruen, and A. Ron, *J. Chem. Phys.* **51**, 224 (1969b). "Electronic Absorption Spectra of Matrix-Isolated Uranium Tetrachloride and Uranium Tetrabromide Molecules."

Clouter, M., and G. P. Gush, *Phys. Rev. Lett.* **15**, 200 (1965). "Change in the Crystal Structure of Solid Normal Hydrogen Near 1.5°K."

Cochran, E. L., F. J. Adrian, and V. A. Bowers, *J. Chem. Phys.* **36**, 1938 (1962). "ESR Detection of the Cyanogen and Methylene Imino Free Radicals."

Cochran, E. L., F. J. Adrian, and V. A. Bowers, *J. Chem. Phys.* **40**, 213 (1964). "ESR Study of Ethynyl and Vinyl Free Radicals."

Coffman, R., and D. S. McClure, *Can. J. Chem.* **36**, 48 (1958). "The Electronic Spectra of Crystalline Toluene, Dibenzyl, Diphenylmethane, and Biphenyl in the Near Ultraviolet."

Cohen, B. J., and L. Goodman, *J. Chem. Phys.* **46**, 713 (1967). "Radiationless Paths in the Diazines."

Coker, E. H., and D. E. Hofer, *J. Chem. Phys.* **48**, 2713 (1968). "Infrared Spectra of Borohydride Ions in Alkali Halide Single Crystals."

Cole, T., H. O. Pritchard, N. R. Davidson, and H. M. McConnell, *Mol. Phys.* **1**, 406 (1958). "Structure of the Methyl Radical."

Colson, S. D., and E. R. Bernstein, *J. Chem. Phys.* **43**, 2661 (1965). "First and Second Triplets of Solid Benzene."

Colson, S. D., *J. Chem. Phys.* **45**, 4746 (1966). "Absorption Spectra of Strained Benzene Crystals at Low Temperature."

Colson, S. D., R. Kopelman, and G. W. Robinson, *J. Chem. Phys.* **47**, 27 (1967). "Frenkel Exciton Selection Rules for $k \neq 0$ Transitions in Molecular Crystals."

Colson, S. D., D. M. Hanson, R. Kopelman, and G. W. Robinson, *J. Chem. Phys.* **48**, 2215 (1968a). "Direct Observation of the Entire Exciton Band of the First Excited Singlet States of Crystalline Benzene and Naphthalene."

Colson, S. D., and G. W. Robinson, *J. Chem. Phys.* **48**, 2550 (1968b). "Trap-Trap

Triplet Energy Transfer in Isotopic Mixed Benzene Crystals."

Colson, S. D., *J. Chem. Phys.* **48**, 3324 (1968c). "Location of the Fourth, Forbidden Factor Group Component of the $^1B_{2u}$ State of Crystalline Benzene."

Comeford, J. J., Ph. D. Thesis, Georgetown University, Washington, D.C., 1966. "Low Temperature Molecular Spectroscopy of Matrix Isolated Systems."

Conway, J. G., *J. Inorg. Nucl. Chem.* **14**, 303 (1960a). "Absorption Spectrum of Pm^{+3} in D_2O, DCl."

Conway, J. G., and J. B. Gruber, *J. Chem. Phys.* **32**, 1586 (1960b). "Luminescence Spectrum of $PmCl_3$."

Conway, J. G., B. Meyer, J. J. Smith, and L. J. Williamson, *J. Chem. Phys.* **51**, 1671 (1969). "Zeeman Effect on Phosphorescent Lifetime of Matrix-Isolated SO_2."

Cook, G. A., ed., *Argon, Helium and the Rare Gases*, Vols. I and II, Interscience (Wiley), New York, 1961.

Cooper, D. H., *Rev. Sci. Instr.* **37**, 1407 (1966). "Estimation of Fluorescent Decay Times."

Cotterill, R. M. J., and M. Doyama, *Phys. Lett.* **25A**, 35 (1967). "Formation Energies of Vacancies and Interstitials in Solid Krypton."

Coupron, C., R. Lochet, J. Meyer, and A. Rousset, *C. R. Acad. Sci.* (Paris) **250**, 3095 (1960). "Luminescence Moléculaire du Benzène en Solution Etendue dans le Cyclohexane à la Température de l'Azote Liquide."

Cozzens, R. F., and R. B. Fox, *J. Chem. Phys.* **50**, 1532 (1969). Intramolecular Triplet Energy Transfer in Poly (1-vinylnaphthalene)."

Craig, D. P., and I. G. Ross, *J. Chem. Soc.* **1954**, 1589 (1954). "The Triplet-Triplet Absorption Spectra of Some Aromatic Hydrocarbons and Related Substances."

Craig, D. P., and S. H. Walmsley, *Excitons in Molecular Crystals*, Benjamin, New York, 1968a.

Craig, D. P., and S. H. Walmsley, *Physics and Chemistry of the Solid State*, Vol. 2, Interscience (Wiley), New York, 1968b.

Crane, A., and H. P. Gush, *Can. J. Phys.* **44**, 373 (1966). "The Induced Infrared Absorption Spectrum of Solid Deuterium and Solid Hydrogen Deuteride."

Crosby, G. A., and M. Kasha, *Spectrochim. Acta* **10**, 377 (1958). "Intramolecular Energy Transfer in Ytterbium Organic Chelates."

Crosby, G. A., R. E. Whan, and R. M. Alire, *J. Chem. Phys.* **34**, 743 (1961). "Intramolecular Energy Transfer in Rare Earth Chelates. Role of the Triplet State."

Crosby, G. A., *Am. Chem. Soc. 24th Northwest Regional Meeting, Salt Lake City, 1969.* "Charge Transfer Luminescence."

Crosley, D. R., and R. Bersohn, *J. Chem. Phys.* **45**, 4353 (1966). "Detection of Hydrogen Atoms and Free Radicals during the Photolysis of Ethane."

Cubicciotti, D., *Nat. Acad. Sci.—Nat. Res. Counc., Publ.* **1470**, 53 (1967). "Problem Areas in High-Temperature Chemistry."

Cullen, W. R., and R. M. Hochstrasser, *J. Mol. Spectrosc.* **5**, 118 (1960). "The Electronic Spectra of the Arylarsines. I. The Nature of the Transitions in the Phenylarsines and the Relative Influence of $- CH_3$ and $- CF_3$ Groups."

Cullen, W. R., B. R. Green, and R. M. Hochstrasser, *J. Inorg. Nucl. Chem.* **27**, 641 (1965). "Spectra of Arylarsines. II. Spectral Manifestations of Charge Transfer Character."

Curie, M., *Fluorescence and Phosphorescence*, Hermann, Paris, 1946.

Currie, S., A. Morelle, and B. Meyer, unpublished, 1970. "Temperature Dependence of Atomic Spectra."

Czarnecki, S., and M. Kryszewski, *J. Polymer Sci.*, *Part A* **1**, 3067 (1963). "Some Applications of Afterglow Studies of Luminescent Compounds in Solid Polymers."

Czekalla, J., G. Briegleb, W. Herre, and H. J. Vahlensieck, *Z. Elektrochem.* **63**, 715 (1959). "Phosphoreszenzspektren und -abklingzeiten aromatischer Kohlenwasserstoffe und ihrer Donator-Akzeptor-Komplexe."

D

Dalby, F. W., *Can. J. Phys.* **36**, 1336 (1958). "The Spectrum and Structure of the HNO Molecule."

Dauben, W. G., G. C. Pimentel, and C. W. Vaughan, Jr., *J. Amer. Chem. Soc.* **77**, 2886 (1955). "The Infrared Intensity of the C-D Stretching Vibration in Deuterobenzene, *m*-Deuteronitrobenzene and *m*-Deuteroaniline."

Davydov, A. S., *Zh. Esks. Teor. Fiz.* **18**, 210 (1948). "Theory of Absorption Spectra of Molecular Crystals."

Davydov, A. S., *Izv. Akad. Nauk SSSR, Ser. Fiz.* **15**, 605 (1951). "Theory of Luminescence of Molecular Crystals."

Davydov, A. S., *Theory of Molecular Excitons* (translated from the Russian text by M. Oppenheimer, Jr., and M. Kasha), McGraw-Hill, New York, 1962.

Dawson, W. R., J. L. Kropp, and M. W. Windsor, *J. Chem. Phys.* **45**, 2410 (1966). "Internal-Energy-Transfer Efficiencies in Eu^{3+} and Tb^{3+} Chelates Using Excitation to Selected Ion Levels."

Dawson, W. R., and M. W. Windsor, *J. Phys. Chem.* **72**, 3251 (1968). "Fluorescence Yields of Aromatic Compounds."

Dawson, W. R., and J. L. Kropp, *J. Phys. Chem.* **73**, 693 (1969). "Radiative and Radiationless Processes in Aromatic Molecules (77°K up)."

Day, P., and C. K. Jorgensen, *Chem. Phys. Lett.* **1**, 507 (1968). "Electron Transfer Bands of Hexachloro-Iridate(IV) at 20°K."

Debye, P., and J. O. Edwards, *Science* **116**, 143 (1952a). "A Note on the Phosphorescence of Proteins."

Debye, P., and J. O. Edwards, *J. Chem. Phys.* **20**, 236 (1952b). "Long-Lifetime Phosphorescence and the Diffusion Process."

De Groot, M. S., and J. H. van der Waals, *Mol. Phys.* **3**, 190 (1960). "Paramagnetic Resonance in Phosphorescent Aromatic Hydrocarbons. II. Determination of Zero-Field Splitting from Solution Spectra."

De Groot, M. S., and J. H. van der Waals, *Mol. Phys.* **4**, 189 (1961). "The Effect of Deuterium and Chlorine Substitution on Triplet → Singlet Transition Probabilities in Naphthalene."

De Groot, M. S., I. A. M. Hesselmann, and J. H. van der Waals, *Mol. Phys.* **10**, 91 (1965). "Electron Resonance of Phosphorescent Mesitylene."

De Groot, M. S., I. A. M. Hesselmann, and J. H. van der Waals, Int. Coll. No. 164, "La Structure Hyperfine Magnétique des Atomes et des Molécules," p. 385. CNRS, Paris, 1966. (1967a).

De Groot, M. S., I. A. M. Hesselmann, and J. H. van der Waals, *Mol. Phys.* **12**, 259 (1967b). "Phosphorescence and Spin Polarization. A Preliminary Report."

De Groot, M. S., I. A. M. Hesselmann, and J. H. van der Waals, *Mol. Phys.* **13**, 583 (1967c). "Electron Resonance of Phosphorescent Benzene in a Single Crystal."

De Groot, M. S., *Mol. Phys.* **16**, 45 (1969a). "Paramagnetic Resonance and Phosphorescent Aromatic Hydrocarbons. V. Benzene in Perdeutero Benzene."

De Groot, M. S., I. A. M. Hesselmann, and J. H. van der Waals, *Mol. Phys.* **16**, 61 (1969b). "ESR in Phosphorescent Aromatic Hydrocarbons. VI. Mesitylene in B-Trimethylborazole."

De Groot, R. L., and G. J. Hoijtink, *J. Chem. Phys.* **46**, 4523 (1967). "Triplet-Triplet Transitions in Naphthalene."

De Groot, S. R., and C. A. Ten Seldam, *Physica* **12**, 669 (1946). "On the Energy Levels of a Model of the Compressed Hydrogen Atom."

DeKock, C. W., and D. M. Gruen, *J. Chem. Phys.* **44**, 4387 (1966). "Electronic Absorption Spectra of the Gaseous 3d Transition-Metal Dichlorides."

DeKock, C. W., and D. M. Gruen, *J. Chem. Phys.* **49**, 4521 (1968). "Charge-Transfer Spectra of Matrix-Isolated 3d Transition-Metal Dichlorides."

Deloupy, C., J. Barcelo, and G. Volat, *J. Phys.* (Paris), Suppl., **5-6**, 49 (1966). "Adaptation of an Infrared Spectrometer to Obtain Reflection Spectra at Low Temperature."

DeMore, W. B., Ph. D. Thesis, California Institute of Technology, Pasadena, California, 1958. "Chemical Processes in Rigid Media at Low Temperatures."

DeMore, W. B., and N. Davidson, *J. Am. Chem. Soc.* **81**, 5869 (1959a). "Photochemical Experiments in Rigid Media at Low Temperatures. I. Nitrogen Oxides and Ozone."

DeMore, W. B., H. O. Pritchard, and N. Davidson, *J. Am. Chem. Soc.* **81**, 5874 (1959b). "Photochemical Experiments in Rigid Media at Low Temperatures. II. The Reactions of Methylene, Cyclopentadienylene and Diphenylmethylene."

Denariez, M., *J. Chim. Phys.* **62**, 323 (1965). "Etude par Spectroscopie IR des Bandes de Vibration CH du Chloroforme et du Chloroforme Deutéré à l'Etat Solide."

De Shazer, L. G., and L. G. Komai, *J. Amer. Opt. Soc.* **55**, 940 (1965). "Fluorescence Conversion Efficiency of Neodymium Glass."

Detry, D., J. Drowart, P. Goldfinger, H. Keller, and H. Rickert, *Z. Phys. Chem.* **55**, 314 (1967). "Zur Thermodynamik von Schwefeldampf. Massenspektrometrische Untersuchungen mit der elektrochemischen Knudsen-Zelle."

DeVoe, H., *J. Chem. Phys.* **41**, 393 (1964). "Optical Properties of Molecular Aggregates. I. Classical Model of Electronic Absorption and Refraction."

De Voss, J., Ph. D. thesis, University of Amsterdam, 1956. "Computation of Radiant Energy Emitted from Black Bodies."

Dewar, J., *Proc. Roy. Soc.* **55**, 340 (1894). "Oral Communication to the Royal Society."

Dexter, D. L., *J. Chem. Phys.* **21**, 836 (1953). "A Theory of Sensitized Luminescence in Solids."

Dexter, D. L., and J. H. Schulman, *J. Chem. Phys.* **22**, 1063 (1954). "Theory of Concentration Quenching in Inorganic Phosphors."

Dexter, D. L., *Solid State Phys.* **6**, 355 (1958). "Theory of Optical Properties of Imperfections in Nonmetals."

Dexter, D. L., *Radiat. Res.* **20**, 118 (1963). "Optical Absorption by a Pair of Ions."

Dexter, D. L., and R. S. Knox, *Excitons*, Interscience (Wiley), New York, 1965.

Diamant, Y., R. M. Hexter, and O. Schnepp, *J. Mol. Spectrosc.* **18**, 158 (1965). "The Near Ultraviolet Spectra of Benzene in Inert Solid Solutions."

Dieke, G. H., in *Phonons in Perfect Lattices and in Lattices with Perfect Imperfections* (R. Stevenson, ed.), Chapter 12, Oliver & Boyd, London, 1966. "Experimental Spectroscopy."

DiGiorgio, V. E., and G. W. Robinson, *J. Chem. Phys.* **31**, 1678 (1959). "Rotational Fine Structure in the $^3A_2 \leftarrow {}^1A_1 \Pi^* \leftarrow \eta$ Transition of Formaldehyde."

Dijkgraaf, C., and G. J. Hoijtink, *Tetrahedron Lett.*, Suppl. **2**, 179 (1963). "Environmental

Effects on Singlet-Triplet Transitions in Aromatic Molecules."

Dikun, P. P., and B. Y. Sveshnikov, *Zh. Eksp. Teor. Fiz.* **19**, 1000 (1949). "Phosphorescence Spectra of Benzene and Its Methyl Derivatives."

Dikun, P. P., A. A. Petrov, and B. Y. Sveshnikov, *Zh. Eksp. Teor. Fiz.* **21**, 150 (1951). "Duration of the Phosphorescence of Benzene and Its Derivatives."

Dixon, R. N., *Can. J. Phys.* **38**, 10 (1960a). "A $^2\pi$-$^2\pi$ Electronic Band System of the Free NCO Radical."

Dixon, R. N., *Phil. Trans. Roy. Soc. London Ser. A* **252**, 165 (1960b). "The Absorption Spectra of the Free NCO Radical."

Dobbs, E. R., and B. F. Figgins, *Nature* **178**, 483 (1956). "Density and Expansivity of Solid Argon."

Dobbs, E. R., and G. O. Jones, *Rep. Progr. Phys.* **20**, 516 (1957). "Theory and Properties of Solid Argon."

Dolan, E., and A. C. Albrecht, *J. Chem. Phys.* **37**, 1149 (1962a). "Stimulated Emission in Photosensitized Rigid-Glass Solutions."

Dolan, E., *J. Chem. Phys.* **37**, 2508 (1962b). "ESR Signals Observed in Ultraviolet Irradiated Glasses of Organic Solutions."

Dolan, E., and A. C. Albrecht, *J. Chem. Phys.* **38**, 567 (1963). "On the Lifetime of Infrared Stimulated Emission in Photosensitized Rigid Glass Solutions."

Dorough, G. D., and K. T. Shen, *J. Am. Chem. Soc.* **72**, 3939 (1950). "A Spectroscopic Study of N-H Isomerism in Porphyrin Free Bases."

Dorough, G. D., and F. M. Haennekens, *J. Amer. Chem. Soc.* **74**, 3974 (1952). "The Spectra of $\alpha, \beta, \gamma, \delta$-Tetraphenylchlorin and Its Metallo-derivatives."

Dörr, F., *Z. Elektrochem.* **61**, 950 (1957). "Absorptions- und Lumineszenzspektren von Ketonen."

Dörr, F., and H. Gropper, *Z. Elektrochem.* **67**, 193 (1963). "Die Polarisation der Triplett-Singulett-Phosphoreszenz einiger Aromaten und Heterozyklen."

Douglas, A. E., *Astrophys. J.* **114**, 466 (1951). "Laboratory Studies of the λ 4050 Group of Cometary Spectra."

Douglas, A. E., *J. Chem. Phys.* **45**, 1007 (1966). "Anomalously Long Radiative Lifetimes of Molecular Excited States."

Douzu, P., J. C. Franco, M. Haus, and M. Ptak, *J. Chim. Phys.* **58**, 926 (1961). "Les Approches Expérimentales du Comportement Supra-moléculaire des Acides Nucléiques: Leur Luminescence de Longue Durée."

Dows, D. A., E. Whittle, and G. C. Pimentel, *J. Chem. Phys.* **23**, 1475 (1955a). "Infrared Spectrum of Solid Ammonium Azide: A Vibrational Assignment."

Dows, D. A., G. C. Pimentel, and E. Whittle, *J. Chem. Phys.* **23**, 1606 (1955b). "Infrared Spectra of Intermediate Species in the Formation of Ammonium Azide from Hydrazoic Acid."

Dreeskamp, H., and M. Burton, *Phys. Rev. Lett.* **2**, 45 (1959). "Measurement of Fast Luminescence Decay Times."

Dressler, K., and D. A. Ramsay, *Phil. Trans. Roy. Soc. London Ser. A* **251**, 553 (1959). "The Electronic Absorption Spectra of NH_2 and ND_2."

Dressler, K., and O. Schnepp, *J. Chem. Phys.* **33**, 270 (1960). "Absorption Spectra of Solid Methane, Ammonia, and Ice in the Vacuum Ultraviolet."

Dressler, K., *J. Chem. Phys.* **35**, 165 (1961). "Ultraviolet Absorption Spectrum of Ammonia in Solid Argon at $4.2°K$."

Dressler, K., *J. Quant. Spectrosc. Radiat. Transfer* **2**, 683 (1962). "Absorption Spectroscopy of Condensed Gases at Low Temperatures."

Drowart, J., and P. Goldfinger, *J. Chim. Phys.* **55**, 721 (1958). "Thermodynamic Study of Group III-V and Group II-VI Compounds by Mass Spectroscopy."

Druger, S. D., and R. S. Knox, *J. Chem. Phys.* **50**, 3143 (1969). "Theory of Trapped-Hole Centers in Rare-Gas Solids."

Dubinskii, I. B., *Bull. Acad. Sci. USSR, Phys. Ser.* (English Transl.) **23**, 111 (1959). "Photoluminescence of Phthalic Acid and Benzoic Acid Esters."

Dubois, J. T., and R. L. van Hemert, *J. Chem. Phys.* **40**, 923 (1964). "Lifetime of Excited States in Solution by the Quenching Method."

Duley, W. W., *Phys. Lett.* **19**, 361 (1965). "Vacuum-Ultraviolet Absorption Spectra of Mercury Atoms Trapped in Inert-Gas Matrices at Low Temperatures."

Duley, W. W., *Nature* **210**, 624 (1966a). "Absorption Spectra of Cadmium and Zinc Atoms Trapped in Noble Gas Matrices."

Duley, W. W., *Proc. Phys. Soc.* **88**, 1049 (1966b). "Crystal Field Parameters from the Ultra-Violet Absorption Spectra of Mercury-Doped Inert-Gas Matrices."

Duley, W. W., *Proc. Phys. Soc.* **90**, 263 (1967a). "The Spectroscopy of Metal Atoms Trapped in Low-Temperature Matrices of the Inert Gases: Mercury."

Duley, W. W., *Proc. Phys. Soc.* **91**, 976 (1967b). "The Spectroscopy of Metal Atoms Trapped in Low-Temperature Matrices of the Inert Gases: Cadmium and Zinc."

Duley, W. W., and W. R. S. Garton, *Proc. Phys. Soc.* **92**, 830 (1967c). "The Spectroscopy of Metal Atoms Trapped in Low-Temperature Matrices of the Inert Gases: Indium."

Duncan, A. B. F., in *Chemical Applications of Spectroscopy* (W. West, ed.), p. 581, Interscience (Wiley), New York, 1956. "Electronic Spectra in the Visible and Ultra-violet Regions."

Dunn, T. M., in *Modern Coordination Chemistry: Principles and Methods* (J. Lewis, ed.), p. 229, Interscience (Wiley), New York, 1960. "The Visible and Ultra-Violet Spectra of Complex Compounds."

DuPre, F., and A. Daniels, *Signal* (September, 1965). "Miniature Refrigerator Opens New Possibilities for Cryo-Electronics."

Durig, J. R., and D. W. Wertz, *J. Chem. Phys.* **46**, 3069 (1967). "On the Infrared Spectra of HNCS and DNCS."

Durig, J. R., S. F. Bush, and F. G. Baglin, *J. Chem. Phys.* **49**, 2106 (1968). "Infrared and Raman Investigation of Condensed Phases of Methylamine and Its Deuterium Derivatives."

Durocher, G., and D. F. Williams, *J. Chem. Phys.* **51**, 1675 (1969). "Temperature Dependence of Triplet Diffusion in Anthracene."

Dyck, R. H., and D. S. McClure, *J. Chem. Phys.* **36**, 2326 (1962). "Ultraviolet Spectra of Stilbene, *p*-Monohalogen Stilbenes, and Azobenzene and the *trans* to *cis* Photo-isomerization Process."

Dym, S., R. M. Hochstrasser, and M. Schafer, *J. Chem. Phys.* **48**, 646 (1968). "Assignment of the Lowest Triplet State of the Carbonyl Group."

E

Easley, W. C., and W. Weltner, Jr., *J. Chem. Phys.* **52**, 197 (1970). "ESR of the CN Radical in Inert Matrices."

Eastman, J. W., *J. Chem. Phys.* **49**, 4617 (1968). "Fluorescence of Benzene. The Effects of Solvent and Temperature on the Quantum Yield."

Eastwood, D., and M. Gouterman, *J. Mol. Spectrosc.* in press. "Luminescence of Copper Complexes at Liquid Nitrogen Temperature."

Eaton, W. A., and R. M. Hochstrasser, *J. Chem. Phys.* **46**, 2533 (1967). "Electronic Spectrum of Single Crystals of Ferricytochrome-c."

Eaton, W. A., and R. M. Hochstrasser, *J. Chem. Phys.* **49**, 985 (1968). "Single-Crystal Spectra of Ferrimyoglobin Complexes in Polarized Light."

Eatwell, A. J., and B. L. Smith, *Phil. Mag.* **6**, 461 (1961). "Density and Expansivity of Solid Xenon."

Eckert, R., and H. Kuhn, *Z. Elektrochem.* **64**, 356 (1960). "Richtungen der Übergangs-momente der Absorptionsbanden von Polyenen, Cyaninen und Vitamin B_{12} aus Dichroismus und Fluoreszenzpolarisation."

Edgell, W. F., in *Argon, Helium and the Rare Gases* (G. A. Cook, ed.), Vol. 1, p. 97. Interscience (Wiley), 1961. "Atomic Structure and Spectra."

Ehret, P., Ph. D. Thesis, University of Stuttgart, 1968a. "Elektron-Kern-Doppel-resonanz-Untersuchung am metastabilen Triplett-Zustand des Naphthalin-Moleküls."

Ehret, P., G. Jesse, and H. C. Wolf, *Z. Naturforsch.* **23a**, 195 (1968b). "ENDOR-Unter-suchungen am metastabilen Triplett-Zustand des Naphthalin-Moleküls."

Eisenthal, K. B., and M. A. El-Sayed, *J. Chem. Phys.* **42**, 794 (1965). "Heavy-Atom Effects on Radiative and Radiationless Processes in Charge-Transfer Complexes."

Eisenthal, K. B., *J. Chem. Phys.* **50**, 3120 (1969). "Relative Orientation of Molecules Involved in Triplet-Triplet Energy Transfer."

Eisinger, J., and G. Navon, *J. Chem. Phys.* **50**, 2069 (1969). "Fluorescence Quenching and Isotope Effect of Tryptophan."

El-Bayoumi, M. A., and M. Kasha, *J. Chem. Phys.* **34**, 2181 (1961). "Energy Transfer in Hydrogen-Bonded N-Heterocyclic Complexes and Their Possible Role as Energy Sinks."

Elkana, Y., J. Feitelson, and E. Katchalski, *J. Chem. Phys.* **48**, 2399 (1968). "Effect of Diffusion on Transfer of Electronic Excitation Energy."

El-Kareh, T. B., and H. C. Wolf, *Z. Naturforsch.* **22a**, 1242 (1967). "Die Abklingdauer der Fluoreszenz von Naphthalin-Kristallen."

El-Sayed, M. A., and M. Kasha, *J. Chem. Phys.* **34**, 334 (1961a). "Ionization Potentials of Benzene, Hexadeuterobenzene, and Pyridine from Their Observed Rydberg Series in the Region 600–2000 Å."

El-Sayed, M. A., and G. W. Robinson, *J. Chem. Phys.* **34**, 1840 (1961b). "Excitation Transfer Splitting in the $\eta \rightarrow \pi$ Transitions of the Diazines."

El-Sayed, M. A., and G. W. Robinson, *Mol. Phys.* **4**, 273 (1961c). "Intramolecular Excitation Transfer. The Lowest $\eta \rightarrow \pi$ Transitions in Pyrazine."

El-Sayed, M. A., *Bull. Am. Phys. Soc.* **7**, 499 (1962a). "S → T Radiationless Process and the Emission Properties of Nitrogen Heterocyclics."

El-Sayed, M. A., *J. Chem. Phys.* **36**, 573 (1962b). "The Radiationless Processes Involving Change of Multiplicity in the Diazenes."

El-Sayed, M. A., *J. Chem. Phys.* **37**, 1568 (1962c). "Proposed Effect of High Pressures on the Radiationless Processes."

El-Sayed, M. A., M. T. Wauk, and G. W. Robinson, *Mol. Phys.* **5**, 205 (1962d). "Retarda-tion of Singlet and Triplet Excitation Migration in Organic Crystals by Isotopic Dilution."

El-Sayed, M. A., *J. Chem. Phys.* **38**, 2834 (1963a). "Spin-Orbit Coupling and the Radia-tionless Processes in Nitrogen Heterocyclics."

El-Sayed, M. A., *J. Chem. Phys.* **38**, 3032 (1963b). "Comments on Contaminating the Ground State with Triplet Character."

El-Sayed, M. A., and R. G. Brewer, *J. Chem. Phys.* **39**, 1623 (1963c). "Polarization of the $\pi^* \rightarrow \pi$ and $\pi^* \rightarrow n$ Phosphorescence Spectra of N-Heterocyclics."

El-Sayed, M. A., and T. Pavlopoulos, *J. Chem. Phys.* **39**, 1899 (1963d). "Intramolecular Heavy-Atom Effect on the Polarization of Naphthalene Phosphorescence."

El-Sayed, M. A., and M. L. Bhaumik, *J. Chem. Phys.* **39**, 2391 (1963e). "Inter-Intra-(Intera) Molecular Energy Transfer to Rare-Earth Ions in Chelates."

El-Sayed, M. A., *Nature* **197**, 481 (1963f). "Origin of the Phosphorescence Radiation in Aromatic Hydrocarbons."

El-Sayed, M. A., *J. Phys. Chem.* **68**, 433 (1964a). "A New Class of Photochromic Substances: Metal Carbonyls."

El-Sayed, M. A., *J. Chem. Phys.* **41**, 2462 (1964b). "Vanishing First- and Second-Order Intramolecular Heavy-Atom Effects on the $(\pi^* \rightarrow n)$ Phosphorescence in Carbonyls."

El-Sayed, M. A., *J. Chem. Phys.* **43**, 2864 (1965). "Theoretical Considerations Concerning the Intramolecular Heavy-Atom Effect on the Phosphorescence Process: C_{2v} Symmetric Dihalonaphthalene."

El-Sayed, M. A., and S. Siegel, *J. Chem. Phys.* **44**, 1416 (1966). "Method of 'Magneto-photoselection' of the Lowest Excited Triplet State of Aromatic Molecules."

El-Sayed, M. A., *J. Chem. Phys.* **47**, 2200 (1967). "Medium Effects on the Phosphorescence Mechanism of Aromatic Hydrocarbons."

El-Sayed, M. A., and W. R. Moomaw, in *Excitons, Magnons, and Phonons in Molecular Crystals* (A. B. Zahlan, ed.), p. 103, Cambridge University Press, London and New York, 1968a. "The Effect of Phonons on the Pyrazine Phosphorescence."

El-Sayed, M. A., *Acta Phys. Pol.* **34** (1968b). "Recent Studies on Triplet-Singlet Transitions in Aromatic Molecules."

El-Sayed, M. A., *Accounts Chem. Res.* **1**, 8 (1968d). "The Triplet State: Its Radiative and Nonradiative Properties."

El-Sayed, M. A., *Proc. Int. Conf. Luminescence, Budapest, 1966*, p. 373, Publishing House of the Hungarian Academy of Sciences, Budapest, 1968e. "Theoretical Considerations concerning the Intramolecular Heavy-Atom Effect on the Phosphorescence Process."

El-Sayed, M. A., W. R. Moomaw, and D. S. Tinti, *J. Chem. Phys.* **50**, 1888 (1969a). "Time-Resolved Polarization Measurements of the Phosphorescence from the Different Zero-Field Multiplets of the Lowest Triplet State."

El-Sayed, M. A., and L. Hall, *J. Chem. Phys.* **50**, 3113 (1969b). "Determination of the Rate Constants of the Intersystem Crossing Processes to the Individual Zero-Field Levels of the Lowest Triplet State."

Engel, C. E., ed., *Photography for Scientists*, Academic Press, New York, 1968.

Erlitz, M. D., and G. C. Nieman, *J. Chem. Phys.* **50**, 1479 (1969). "Temperature Dependence of the Phosphorescence Lifetime of Mesitylene."

Ermolaev, V. L., *Opt. Spectrosc.* (USSR) (English Transl.) **1**, 523 (1956). "Luminescence of Aromatic Aldehydes and Ketones."

Ermolaev, V. L., and A. Terenin, *J. Chim. Phys.* **55**, 698 (1958). "Transfert d'Energie entre Niveaux de Triplets."

Ermolaev, V. L., *Opt. Spectrosc.* (USSR) (English Transl.) **6**, 417 (1959a). "Dependence of the Probability of Energy Transport in Sensitized Phosphorescence on the Oscillator Strength of a Triplet-Singlet Transition in an Energy Acceptor Molecule."

Ermolaev, V. L., and K. K. Svitashev, *Opt. Spectrosc.* (USSR) (English Transl.) **7**, 399 (1959b). "Quantum Yields of Phosphorescence and Fluorescence of some *l*-Derivatives of Naphthalene in Solutions at − 196°C."

Ermolaev, V. L., I. P. Kotlyar, and K. K. Svitashev, *Bull. Acad. Sci. USSR, Phys. Ser.* (English Transl.) **24**, 499 (1960a). "Internal Conversion from the Fluorescence to the Phosphorescence Level in Naphthalene Derivatives."

Ermolaev, V. L., and A. N. Terenin, *Sov. Phys.-Usp.* (English Transl.) **3**, 423 (1960b). "Intramolecular Energy Transfer between Triplet Levels."

Ermolaev, V. L., *Opt. Spectrosc.* (USSR) (English Transl.) **11**, 266 (1961). "The Luminescence of Simple Derivatives of Benzene. I. The Aromatic Amines."

Ermolaev, V. L., *Opt. Spectrosc.* (USSR) (English Transl.) **13**, 49 (1962a). "Measurement of the Quantum Yields of Sensitized Phosphorescence as a Method of Investigating the Quenching Processes at the Triplet Level of Organic Molecules."

Ermolaev, V. L., and E. B. Sveshnikova, *Bull. Acad. Sci. USSR* **26**, 29 (1962b). "Nonradiative Energy Transfer between the Triplet and Singlet Levels of Organic Molecules."

Ermolaev, V. L., *Sov. Phys.-Dokl.* (English Transl.) **6**, 600 (1962c). "Spheres of Quenching in Case of Energy Transfer between Triplet Levels."

Ermolaev, V. L., *Sov. Phys.-Usp.* **6**, 333 (1963). "Energy Transfer in Organic Systems Involving the Triplet State. III. Rigid Solutions and Crystals."

Ermolaev, V. L., and E. B. Sveshnikova, *Opt. Spectrosc.* (USSR) (English Transl.) **21**, 78 (1966). "Radiationless Transitions in Perfluorinated and Perchlorinated Aromatic Compounds."

Ermolaev, V. L., E. A. Saenko, G. A. Domrachev, Y. K. Khudenskii, and V. G. Aleshin, *Opt. Spectrosc.* (USSR) (English Transl.) **22**, 466 (1967). "Study of the Mechanism of Intermolecular Energy Transfer in Rare-Earth-Chelates."

Esposito, J. N., L. E. Sutton, and M. E. Kenney, *Inorg. Chem.* **6**, 1116 (1967). "Infrared and Nuclear Magnetic Resonance Studies of Some Germanium Phthalocyanines and Hemiporphyrazines."

Evans, D. F., *J. Chem. Phys.* **23**, 1429 (1955). "Perfluoroheptane as a Spectroscopic Solvent."

Evans, D. F., *Nature* **178**, 534 (1956). "Magnetic Perturbation of the Lowest Triplet States of Aromatic Molecules by Dissolved Oxygen."

Evans, D. F., *J. Chem. Soc.* **1957**, 3885 (1957). "Magnetic Perturbation of Singlet-Triplet Transitions."

Evans, D. F., *Proc. Chem. Soc.* (London) **1963**, 378 (1963a). "Effect of Nitrogen under Pressure on the Rydberg Spectra of Polyatomic Molecules; the Nature of the Long-wavelength Olefin Bands."

Evans, D. F., *J. Chem. Soc.* **1963**, 5575 (1963b). "Solvent Shifts of Nuclear Spin Coupling Constants due to Hydrogen Bonding."

Evans, J. C., and G. Y. Lo, *J. Phys. Chem.* **73**, 448 (1969). "Vibrational Spectra of the Hydrogen Dihalide Ions. V. $BrHBr^{\theta}$ at 20°K."

Ewing, G. E., W. E. Thompson, and G. C. Pimentel, *J. Chem. Phys.* **32**, 927 (1960). "Infrared Detection of the Formyl Radical HCO."

Ewing, G. E., and G. C. Pimentel, *J. Chem. Phys.* **35**, 925 (1961). "Infrared Spectrum of Solid Carbon Monoxide."

Ewing, G. E., and S. Trajmar, *J. Chem. Phys.* **41**, 814 (1964). "Infrared Induced Absorption of Dilute Solutions of H_2 and D_2 in Liquid Argon."

Ewing, G. E., and S. Trajmar, *J. Chem. Phys.* **42**, 4038 (1965). "Induced Infrared

Absorption of Solutions of H_2 and D_2 in Liquid Neon."

Ezhik, I. I., G. D. Mokhov, and V. A. Bazakutsa, *Opt. Spectrosc.* (USSR) (English Transl.) **21**, 288 (1966). "The Visible and Near Infrared Luminescence of Selenium Treated with Mercury Vapor."

F

Fadeeva, M. S., *Bull. Acad. Sci. USSR, Phys. Ser.* (English Transl.) **23**, 139 (1959). "Phosphorescence Spectra of Some Aromatic Hydrocarbons at Different Temperatures."

Fadeeva, M. S., *Bull. Acad. Sci. USSR* (English Transl.) **29**, 1441 (1965). "Phosphorescence of Organic Phosphors and the Influence of Temperature on the Afterglow."

Faidysh, A. N., and O. P. Kharitonova, *Dopov. Akad. Nauk Ukr. RSR* **1951**, 324 (1951). "Excitation of Luminescence of Naphthacene in Solutions."

Faidysh, A. N., and I. Y. Kucherov, *Ukr. Fiz. Zh.* **2**, 68 (1957). "The Quantum Yields of the Luminescences of Solid Solutions of Condensed Hydrocarbons as a Function of the Temperatures."

Falk, J. E., *Porphyrins and Metalloporphyrins*, Elsevier, Amsterdam and New York, 1964.

Fallon, R. J., J. T. Vanderslice, and E. A. Mason, *J. Chem. Phys.* **32**, 1453 (1960). "Potential Energy Curves for Lithium Hydride."

Farmer, J. B., C. L. Gardner, and C. A. McDowell, *J. Chem. Phys.* **34**, 1058 (1961). "Energy Transfer between Triplet States Detected by Electron Spin Resonance Spectroscopy."

Farmer, V. M., and D. P. Forse, *Infrared Phys.* **8**, 37 (1968). "Improved Cooling Techniques for Detectors."

Fateley, W. G., H. A. Bent, and B. Crawford, Jr., *J. Chem. Phys.* **31**, 204 (1959). "Infrared Spectra of the Frozen Oxides of Nitrogen."

Faure, E., F. Valadier, R. Bergeon, and J. Janin, *J. Phys.* (Paris) **28**, C 3-143 (1967). "Luminescence du Benzène Excité dans des Matrices d'Azote et d'Argon Solides."

Fedosov, V. N., and A. P. Nadol'skii, *Tr. Irkutsk. Politekh. Inst.* **27**, 80 (1966). "Dependence of the Vapor Pressure of Scandium Oxide on Temperature."

Feldman, C., and M. L. Klein, *Phil. Mag.* **17**, 145 (1968). "On the Elastic Constants of Polycrystalline Argon."

Fenina, N. A., *Opt. Spectrosc.* (USSR) (English Transl.) **20**, 428 (1966). "A Study of the Quasi-Line Spectra of 1,2-Benzanthracene and Its Methyl Derivatives. I. The Quasi-Line Luminescence and Absorption Spectra of 1,2-Benzanthracene at 77°K."

Ferguson, J., T. Iredale, and J. A. Taylor, *J. Chem. Soc.* **1954**, 3160 (1954). "The Phosphorescence Spectra of Naphthalene and Some Simple Derivatives."

Ferguson, E. E., and H. P. Broida, *J. Chem. Phys.* **40**, 3715 (1964). "Charge Transfer Absorption Spectra of NO in Kr and Methanol Solutions."

Fernandez, J., and R. S. Becker, *J. Chem. Phys.* **31**, 467 (1959). "Unique Luminescences of Dry Chlorophylls."

Fessenden, R. W., and R. H. Schuler, *J. Chem. Phys.* **45**, 1845 (1966). "Isotropic ESR Spectra of Fluorine-Containing Radicals in SF_6 Matrices."

Figgins, B. F., and B. L. Smith, *Phil. Mag.* **5**, 186 (1960). "Density and Expansivity of Solid Krypton."

Fischer, P. H. H., S. W. Charles, and C. A. McDowell, *J. Chem. Phys.* **46**, 2162 (1967).

"Electron Spin Resonance Study of the Photolytic Decomposition of HN_3 in Inert Matrices at 4.2°K."

Fiutak, J., and M. Frackowiak, *Bull. Acad. Pol. Sci.* **11**, 175 (1963). "The HgA van der Waals Molecule."

Fletcher, A. N., *J. Phys. Chem.* **72**, 2742 (1968). "Fluorescence Emission Band Shift with Wavelength of Excitation."

Flygare, W. F., *J. Chem. Phys.* **39**, 2263 (1963). "Molecular Rotation in the Solid State. Theory of Rotation of Trapped Molecules in Rare-Gas Lattices."

Foerster, G. v., *Z. Naturforsch.* **18a**, 620 (1963). "Triplett-Phosphoreszenz und Elektronenspinresonanz-Absorption einiger organischer Moleküle in glasigen Lösungen."

Foerster, G. v., *J. Chem. Phys.* **40**, 2059 (1964). "Studies of the Phosphorescence of Organic Substances in Crystalline Form or in Frozen Solutions."

Foley, W. T., and P. A. Giguere, *Science* **113**, 754 (1951). "Radioactive Tracers in Solid Solution Investigations."

Fonda, G. R., *J. Electrochem. Soc.* **98**, 35c (1951). "Review of Articles on Luminescence for 1950."

Fonda, G. R., *J. Electrochem. Soc.* **102**, 129c (1955). "Review of Articles on Luminescence for 1953–1954."

Fonda, G. R., *J. Electrochem. Soc.* **104**, 525 (1957). "Review of Articles on Luminescence for 1955–1956."

Foner, S. N., E. L. Cochran, V. A. Bowers, and C. K. Jen, *J. Chem. Phys.* **32**, 963 (1960). "Multiple Trapping Sites for Hydrogen Atoms in Rare Gas Matrices."

Forster, L. S., S. A. Greenberg, R. I. Lym, and M. E. Smith, *Spectrochim. Acta* **16**, 128 (1960). "Luminescence and Internal Conversion in Biacetyl Solutions."

Forster, L. S., and D. Dudley, *J. Phys. Chem.* **66**, 838 (1962). "The Luminescence of Fluorescein Dyes."

Förster, T., *Ann. Phys.* **2**, 55 (1948). "Zwischenmolekulare Energiewanderung und Fluoreszenz."

Förster, T., *Z. Naturforsch.* **4a**, 322 (1949a). "Experimentelle und theoretische Untersuchung des zwischenmolekularen Übergangs von Elektronenanregungsenergie."

Förster, T., *Naturwissenschaften* **36**, 240 (1949b). "Neuere Untersuchungen über die Phosphoreszenz organischer Stoffe in festen Lösungen."

Förster, T., *Fluoreszenz organischer Verbindungen*, Vandenhoeck & Ruprecht, Göttingen, 1951.

Förster, T., and K. Kasper, *Z. Elektrochem.* **59**, 976 (1955). "Ein Konzentrationsumschlag der Fluoreszenz des Pyrens."

Förster, T., *Disc. Faraday Soc.* **22**, 7 (1959). "Transfer Mechanisms of Electronic Excitation."

Förster, T., *Radiat. Rev.*, Suppl. 2, 326 (1960a). "Transfer Mechanisms of Electronic Excitation Energy."

Förster, T., *Z. Elektrochem.* **64**, 157 (1960b). "Zwischenmolekularer Übergang von Elektronenanregungsenergie."

Förster, T., and K. Rokos, *Chem. Phys. Lett.* **1**, 279 (1967a). "A Deuterium Isotope Solvent Effect on Fluorescence."

Förster, T., in *Comprehensive Biochemistry* (M. Florkin and E. H. Stotz, eds.), Vol. 22, p. 61. Elsevier, Amsterdam and New York, 1967b. "Mechanisms of Energy Transfer."

Fox, D., and O. Schnepp, *Phys. Rev.* **96**, 1196 (1954). "Exciton Bands in Crystalline Benzene."

Fox, D., and R. M. Hexter, *J. Chem. Phys.* **41**, 1125 (1964). "Crystal Shape Dependence of Exciton States in Molecular Crystals."

Frackowiak, M., *Acta Phys. Pol.* **16**, 63 (1957a). "Decay of Phosphorescence of Rigid Solutions."

Frackowiak, M., *Bull. Acad. Pol. Sci.* **5**, 809 (1957b). "Further Investigations on the Decay of Phosphorescence of Rigid Solutions."

Franck, H. S., *Int. Symp. Luminescence, Munich, 1965*, p. 155, Thiemig, Munich, 1966. "Triplet-Singlet Luminescence from Methylated Benzenes in the Crystalline State and in Rigid Glass Solutions."

Franklin, J. L., and H. P. Broida, *Amer. Rev. Phys. Chem.* **10**, 145 (1959). "Trapped Energetic Radicals."

Frayer, F. H., and G. E. Ewing, *J. Chem. Phys.* **46**, 1994 (1967). "Spectroscopic Observation of Nuclear Spin Conversion in Methane."

Frayer, F. H., and G. E. Ewing, *J. Chem. Phys.* **48**, 781 (1968). "Nuclear-Spin Conversion and Vibration-Rotation Spectra of Methane in Solid Argon."

Freed, K. F., and J. Jortner, *J. Chem. Phys.* **50**, 2916 (1969). "Radiative Decay of Polyatomic Molecules."

Freed, S., J. H. Turnbull, and W. Salmre, *Nature* **181**, 1731 (1958). "Proteins in Solutions at Low Temperatures."

Freed, S., and M. H. Vise, *Anal. Biochem.* **5**, 338 (1963). "On Phosphorimetry as Quantitative Microanalysis with Application to Some Substances of Biochemical Interest."

Freed, S., *Science* **150**, 576 (1965). "Chemical-Biochemical Signal and Noise."

Freedhoff, H. S., *Proc. Phys. Soc.* **92**, 505 (1967). "Molecular Features in the Spectra of Atoms Trapped in Inert Gas Matrices."

Freiberg, M., A. Ron, and O. Schnepp, *J. Phys. Chem.* **72**, 3526 (1968). "The Low Frequency Spectra of Lithium Halide Molecular Species."

Frenkel, J., *Phys. Rev.* **37**, 17 (1931). "On the Transformation of Light into Heat in Solids. II."

Friedmann, H., and S. Kimel, *J. Chem. Phys.* **41**, 2552 (1964). "Interpretation of the Spectra of HCl and DCl in an Argon Matrix."

Friedmann, H., and S. Kimel, *J. Chem. Phys.* **43**, 3925 (1965). "Theory of Shifts of Vibration-Rotation Lines of Diatomic Molecules in Noble-Gas Matrices. Intermolecular Forces in Crystals."

Friedmann, H., and S. Kimel, *J. Chem. Phys.* **44**, 4359 (1966). "Rotation-Translation Coupling Spectrum of Matrix-Isolated Diatomic Molecules in the Near and Far Infrared."

Friedmann, H., and S. Kimel, *J. Chem. Phys.* **47**, 3589 (1967). "Rotation-Translation Coupling Effect in Noble-Gas Crystals Containing Molecular Impurities."

Frosch, R. P., and G. W. Robinson, *J. Chem. Phys.* **41**, 367 (1964). "Emission Spectrum of NO in Solid Rare Gases: The Lifetime of the a $^4\pi$-State and the Spectrum of the a $^4\pi \rightarrow X\,^2\pi$ and B $^2\pi \rightarrow X\,^2\pi$ Transitions."

Frosch, R. P., *Diss. Abstr.* **26**, 3646 (1966). "I. The Emission and Absorption Spectra of Some Simple Molecules Trapped in Solid Rare Gases. II. Theory of Electronic Relaxation in the Solid Phase," Ph. D. Thesis, 1965.

Fruwert, J., E. Kowasch, and G. Geiseler, *Z. Phys. Chem.* **232**, 415 (1966). "Temperature Dependence of Infrared Band Intensity."

Fugol, I. Y., *Ukr. Fiz. Zh.* **3**, Suppl. 1, 40 (1958). "Absorption and Luminescence of Crystalline Solutions of Stilbene in Toluene."

Fukuda, A., *Oyo Butsuri* **36**, 223 (1967). "Spectroscopic Measurement at Low Temperatures."

Furst, M., E. Levin, and H. Kallman, *Int. Symp. Luminescence, Munich, 1965*, p. 24, Thiemig, Munich, 1966. "Fluorescence and Energy Transfer from 300°K to 550°K."

G

Gadzhiev, A. Z., *Opt. Spectrosc.* (USSR) **23**, 722 (1967). "Dependence of the Infrared Absorption Band Frequency on the Local Intermolecular Interaction."

Gaevskii, A. S., V. G. Roskolodko, and A. N. Faidysh, *Opt. Spectrosc.* (USSR) (English Transl.) **22**, 124 (1967). "The Effect of the Phase State on the Phosphorescence of Benzophenone and the Transfer of Electron Excitation Energy in Solid Solutions."

Gaevskii, A. S., V. G. Roskolodko, and A. N. Faidysh, *Opt. Spectrosc.* (USSR) (English Transl.) **24**, 113 (1968). "Transfer of Triplet Level Energy in Benzophenone Crystals Containing Phenanthrene and Phenazine."

Gaines, J. R., E. M. de Castro, and D. White, *Phys. Rev. Lett.* **13**, 425 (1964). "Observation of the λ Anomaly in Solid D_2 by Nuclear Magnetic Resonance."

Galanin, M. D., *Tr. Fiz. Inst. Akad. Nauk SSSR* **5**, 341 (1950). "Duration of the Excited State of a Molecule and the Properties of Fluorescent Solutions."

Galanin, M. D., *Sov. Phys. JETP* (English Transl.) **1**, 317 (1955). "The Problem of the Effect of Concentration on the Luminescence of Solutions."

Galanin, M. D., and Z. A. Chizikova, *Opt. Spectrosc.* (USSR) (English Transl.) **11**, 143 (1961). "Duration of the Photo- and Radioluminescence of Anthracene and Naphthalene Crystals."

Gallivan, J. B., and J. S. Brinen, *J. Chem. Phys.* **50**, 1590 (1969). "Polarization of Electronic Transitions of Aromatic Hydrocarbons."

Gallus, G., and H. C. Wolf, *Z. Naturforsch.* **23a**, 1333 (1968a). "Excitonendiffusion in Naphthalin-Aufdampfschichten."

Gallus, G., Ph. D. Thesis, University of Stuttgart, 1968b. "Naphthalinaufdampfschichten Lumineszenz und Exzitonendiffusion."

Gandrud, W. B., and H. W. Moos, *J. Chem. Phys.* **49**, 2170 (1968). "Rare-Earth Infrared Lifetimes and Exciton Migration Rates in Trichloride Crystals."

Ganguly, S. C., and N. K. Chaudhury, *J. Chem. Phys.* **21**, 554 (1953). "Polarized Fluorescence of Molecules of Some Single Organic Crystals."

Garlick, G. F., *Endeavour* **15**, 144 (1956). "Some Aspects of Luminescence."

Gausset, L., G. Herzberg, A. Lagerqvist, and B. Rosen, *Disc. Faraday Soc.* **35**, 113 (1963). "Spectrum of the C_3 Molecule."

Gausset, L., G. Herzberg, A. Lagerqvist, and B. Rosen, *Astrophys. J.* **142**, 45 (1965). "Analysis of the 4050 Å Group of the C_3 Molecule."

Gavrilov, M. Z., and I. N. Ermolenko, *Zh. Prikl. Spektrosk.* (USSR) **5**, 762 (1966). "Investigation of Cellulose Luminescence."

Geacintov, N., G. Oster, and T. Cassen, *J. Opt. Soc. Amer.* **9**, 1217 (1968). "Polymeric Matrices for Organic Phosphors."

Geacintov, N., M. Pope, and F. Vogel, *Phys. Rev. Lett.* **22**, 593 (1969). "Effect of Magnetic Field on the Fluorescence of Tetracene Crystals: Exciton Fission."

Gee, A. R., and G. W. Robinson, *J. Chem. Phys.* **46**, 4847 (1967). "Raman Spectrum of Crystalline Benzene."

Geisler, H. F., and K. H. Hellwege, *Z. Phys.* **136**, 293 (1953). "Spektrum und Leuchtprozess von kristallinem Terbiumbromat."

Gerding, H., and J. W. Ypenburg, *Rec. Trav. Chim. Pays-Bas* **86**, 458 (1967). "The Vibrational Spectra of Liquid and Solid Sulfur Dioxide."

Gerkin, R. E., and A. M. Winer, *J. Chem. Phys.* **50**, 3114 (1969). "Deuterium Isotope Effect in Zero-field Splittings of Phosphorescent Phenanthrene Oriented in Biphenyl."

Gerlovin, Y. I., *Opt. Spectrosc.* (USSR) (English Transl.) **9**, 349 (1960). "A Method for Determination of the Radiation Probability of Gases and Vapors."

Gerö, L., G. Herzberg, and R. Schmid, *Phys. Rev.* **52**, 467 (1937). "On the Cameron Bands $(^3\Pi - {}^1\Sigma)$ of Carbon Monoxide."

Geschwind, S., R. J. Collins, and A. L. Schawlow, *Phys. Rev. Lett.* **3**, 545 (1959). "Optical Detection of Paramagnetic Resonance in an Excited State of Cr^{3+} in Al_2O_3."

Gibbons, W. A., G. Porter, and M. J. Savadatti, *Nature* **206**, 1355 (1965). "Photoionization of Aromatic Compounds in Hydrocarbon Glass at 77°K."

Gierke, T. D., R. J. Watts, and S. J. Strickler, *J. Chem. Phys.* **50**, 5425 (1969). "Phosphorescence Lifetimes of Dideuteronaphthalenes."

Giguère, P. A., *J. Chem. Phys.* **22**, 2085 (1954). "Spectroscopic Evidence for Stabilized HO_2 Radicals."

Giguère, P. A., and K. B. Harvey, *J. Chem. Phys.* **25**, 373 (1956). "On the Presumed Spectroscopic Evidence for Trapped HO_2 Radicals."

Gilles, P. W., *Nat. Acad. Sci.—Nat. Res. Council*, Publ. No. **1470**, 82 (1967). "Future Investigations in High-Temperature Chemistry Suggested by Vaporization Studies."

Gilmore, E. H., G. E. Gibson, and D. S. McClure, *J. Chem. Phys.* **20**, 829 (1952). "Absolute Quantum Efficiencies of Luminescence of Organic Molecules in Solid Solution."

Gilmore, E. H., G. E. Gibson, and D. S. McClure, *J. Chem. Phys.* **23**, 399 (1955). "Errata: Absolute Quantum Efficiencies of Luminescence of Organic Molecules in Solid Solution."

Gilmore, E. H., and E. C. Lim, *J. Phys. Chem.* **63**, 15 (1959). "A Method for Evaluating Rate Constants in the Jablonski Model of Excited Species in Rigid Glasses."

Gissler, W., and H. Stiller, *Naturwissenschaften* **52**, 512 (1965). "Zur Kristallstruktur des Methans."

Glascow, J., G. Gourinowitch, and A. Patsko, *Abh. Deut. Akad. Wiss. Berlin, Kl. Med.* **1966**, 339 (1966). "Some Features of Triplet States of Porphyrins."

Glasel, J. A., *J. Chem. Phys.* **34**, 1649 (1961). "Near-Infrared Absorption Spectrum of Solid Methane at the λ Point."

Glaser, P. E., *Cryogenic Eng. News* **4**, 16 (1969). "Effective Thermal Insulation: Multilayer System."

Glowacki, L., and R. Pohoski, *Bull. Acad. Pol. Sci.* **7**, 301 (1959). "Quenching of Photoluminescence of Liquid and Solid Solutions."

Glyadovskii, V. I., L. A. Klimova, and G. N. Nersesova, *Opt. Spectrosc.* (USSR) (English Transl.) **23**, 219 (1967). "Spectroscopy of Aromatic Hydrocarbon Mixtures in Frozen Crystalline Solutions. II."

Gobov, G. V., *Bull. Acad. Sci. USSR, Phys. Ser.* **27**, 13 (1963a). "Absorption and Luminescence Spectra of Stilbene and Diphenyl Acetylene in Frozen Solutions at 77°K."

Gobov, G. V., *Opt. Spectrosc.* (USSR) (English Transl.) **15**, 194 (1963b). "Spectroscopy of Frozen Crystalline Solutions of Diphenylpolyenes and Polyphenyls. II."

Gobrecht, H., and D. Hahn, *Z. Phys.* **135**, 523 (1953). "Die Lumineszenz der Erdalkalipolysulfide."

Godfrey, T. S., J. W. Hilpern, and G. Porter, *Chem. Phys. Lett.* **1**, 490 (1967). "Triplet-

Triplet Absorption Spectra of Benzophenone and Its Derivatives."

Godlove, T. F., *J. Appl. Phys.* **32**, 1589 (1961). "Nanosecond Triggering of Air Gaps with Intense Ultraviolet Light."

Gold, A., *Phys. Rev.* **124**, 1740 (1961). "Calculation of Excitation Energies in 'Tightly-Bound' Solids."

Gold, A., and R. S. Knox, *J. Chem. Phys.* **36**, 2805 (1962). "Line Shape of Ultraviolet Absorption in Crystalline Rare Gases."

Goldfarb, T. D., and G. C. Pimentel, *J. Chem. Phys.* **33**, 105 (1960a). "Chemiluminescence of Ethylene Formed Probably from Methylene in an Inert Matrix."

Goldfarb, T. D., and G. C. Pimentel, *J. Amer. Chem. Soc.* **82**, 1865 (1960b). "Spectroscopic Study of the Photolysis of Diazomethane in Solid Nitrogen."

Goldfarb, T. D., and B. N. Khare, *J. Chem. Phys.* **46**, 3379 (1967a). "Infrared Spectra of Solid and Matrix-Isolated $(CH_3)_3N$, $(CD_3)_3N$, and $(SiH_3)_3N$."

Goldfarb, T. D., and B. N. Khare, *J. Chem. Phys.* **46**, 3384 (1967b). "Infrared Studies of Dimethylsilylamine and Methyldisilylamine by the Matrix-Isolation Technique."

Goldring, H., J. Kwok, and G. W. Robinson, *J. Chem. Phys.* **43**, 3220 (1965). "Infrared Spectra and Intensity Enhancements in Solutions of Hydrogen Halides in Liquid Xenon."

Goldstein, E., *Phys. Z.* **12**, 614 (1911). "Über die Untersuchung der Emissionsspektra fester aromatischer Substanzen mit dem Ultraviolettfilter."

Goldstein, E., *Phys. Z.* **13**, 188 (1912). "Über die Emissionsspektra aromatischer Verbindungen in ultraviolettem Licht, in Kathodenstrahlen, Radiumstrahlen und Kanalstrahlen."

Goldstein, H. W., E. F. Neilson, P. N. Walsh, and D. White, *J. Phys. Chem.* **63**, 1445 (1959). "The Heat Capacities of Yttrium Oxide (Y_2O_3), Lanthanum Oxide (La_2O_3) and Neodymium Oxide (Nd_2O_3) from 16 to 300°K."

Goldstein, H. W., P. Walsh, D. White, *J. Phys. Chem.* **64**, 1087 (1960). "On the Use of Tantalum Knudsen Cells in High Temperature Thermodynamic Studies of Oxides."

Goldstein, H. W., P. N. Walsh, and D. White, *J. Phys. Chem.* **65**, 1400 (1961). "Rare Earths. I. Vaporization of La_2O_2 and Nd_2O_3: Dissociation Energies of Gaseous LaO and NdO."

Gonzalez, O. D., D. White, and H. L. Johnston, *J. Phys. Chem.* **61**, 773 (1957). "The Heat Capacity of Solid Deuterium between 0.3 and 13°K."

Goode, D. H., and F. R. Lipsett, *J. Chem. Phys.* **51**, 1222 (1969). "Delayed Fluorescence of Anthracene at Low Temperatures. Failure of Square Dependence on Exciting Light."

Goodman, L., and M. Kasha, *J. Mol. Spectrosc.* **2**, 58 (1958). "The Observation and Assignment of the Lowest Multiplicity-Forbidden Transition in Pyrazine."

Gordon, R. G., *J. Chem. Phys.* **39**, 2788 (1963). "Molecular Motion and the Moment Analysis of Molecular Spectra in Condensed Phases. I. Dipole-Allowed Spectra."

Gorshkov, V. K., and N. D. Zhevandrov, *Zh. Prikl. Spektrosk.* **6**, 267 (1967). "Changes of Luminescence Spectra of Anthracene Single Crystals with the Naphthacene Admixture under Cooling to Liquid Helium Temperatures."

Gosavi, R. K., and C. N. R. Rao, *Indian J. Chem.* **5**, 126 (1967). "Rotation of Guest Molecules in Host Lattices of Clathrates and Inclusion Compounds."

Goto, T., M. Ueta, and T. Yashiro, *J. Phys. Soc. Jap.* **20**, 870 (1964). "An Emission Spectrum of CuBr at 4°K."

Goudmand, P., and O. Dessaux, *J. Chim. Phys.* **64**, 135 (1967). "Formation de Molécules

NS et NSe Electroniquement Excitées dans les Réactions de l'Azote Actif sur les Chlorures de Soufre et de Sélénium."

Gouterman, M., *J. Chem. Phys.* **30**, 1369 (1959). "Calculations on the Zero-Field Splittings in Triplet States of Various Aromatic Hydrocarbons. II."

Gouterman, M., *J. Chem. Phys.* **36**, 2846 (1962). "Radiationless Transitions: A Semi-classical Model."

Grabowska, A., *Spectrochim. Acta* **19**, 307 (1963). "Enhancement of the Singlet-Triplet Absorption Band of α-Chloronaphthalene in the Presence of Xenon under High Pressure."

Grabowska, A., *Chem. Phys. Lett.* **1**, 113 (1967a). "Triplet-States of Six-Membered N-heterocycles. Spin Orbit Coupling in Diazines."

Grabowska, A., and B. Pakula, *Chem. Phys. Lett.* **1**, 369 (1967b). "Triplet States of Six-Membered N-heterocycles. Phosphorescence of Pyrazine and Its Two Conjugate Acids."

Gradyushko, A. T., V. A. Mashenkov, A. N. Sevchenko, K. N. Solov'ev, and M. P. Tsvirko, *Sov. Phys. Dokl.* **13**, 869 (1969). "Effect of Heavy Atoms on Intercombination Transitions in Porphyrin Molecules."

Graham, G. M., J. S. M. Harvey, and H. Kiefte, *J. Chem. Phys.* **52**, 2235 (1970). "EPR of O_2 Impurity in Solid N_2."

Graham, R., R. A. Howald, E. M. Layton, Jr., *Amer. Chem. Soc. 24th Northwest Regional Meeting Phys. Chem., Salt Lake City, 1969.* "Singlet-Triplet Absorption Spectra of Charge Transfer Complexes of Naphthalene."

Graham-Bryce, I. J., and J. M. Corkhill, *Nature* **186**, 965 (1960). "Use of Solvents Containing Ethyl Iodide in the Investigation of Phosphorescence Spectra of Organic Compounds."

Grajcar, L., and S. Leach, *C. R. Acad. Sci.* (Paris) **252**, 1014 (1961a). "Sur les Spectres d'Emission et d'Absorption vers 4600 Å du Radical Benzyle à 77°K."

Grajcar, L., and S. Leach, *C. R. Acad. Sci.* (Paris) **252**, 3577 (1961b). "Etude Spectroscopique de la Photolyse du Toluène en Solution Rigide à 77°K."

Grajcar, L., and S. Leach, *6th Int. Symp. Free Radicals, Cambridge Univ., 1963.* "The Fluorescence Spectra of Benzyl Type Radicals in Cyclohexane. Crystalline Phase Studies Using a Trapped Radical Probe."

Grajcar, L., and S. Leach, *J. Chim. Phys.* **61**, 1523 (1964). "Analyse du Spectre d'Emission du Radical Benzyle et de Certains de ses Isotopes Deutérés."

Granier-Mayence, J., and J. Romand, *J. Phys. Radium* **14**, 428 (1953). "Complément a l'Etude du Spectre d'Absorption de l'Oxyde Azoteux Solide dans la Région de Schumann."

Grebenshchikov, D. M., V. A. Butlar, and V. V. Solodunov, *Opt. Spectrosc.* (USSR) (English Transl.) **21**, 147 (1966). "On the Phosphorescence of Two Types of Luminescent Centers of Coronene in Paraffin Solutions."

Green, W. H., and A. B. Harvey, *J. Chem. Phys.* **49**, 3586 (1968). "Vibrational Spectra and Structure of Dimethyl Diselenide and Dimethyl Diselenide-d_6."

Greene, R. L., and D. D. Sell, *Phys. Rev.* **171**, 600 (1968). "Impurity-Induced Optical Fluorescence in MnF_2."

Greenspan, H., and E. Fischer, *J. Phys. Chem.* **69**, 2466 (1965). "Viscosity of Glass-Forming Solvent Mixtures at Low Temperatures."

Greer, W. L., S. A. Rice, J. Jortner, and R. Silbey, *J. Chem. Phys.* **48**, 5667 (1968). "Re-Examination of the Theoretical Interpretations of the Spectra of Crystalline

Benzene and Naphthalene."

Grenier, G., and D. White, *J. Phys. Chem.* **61**, 1681 (1957). "The Heat of Solution of Sodium Metaborate at 0°."

Grenier, G., and D. White, *J. Chem. Phys.* **37**, 1563 (1962). "λ Anomaly in the Heat Capacity of Para Enriched Solid Deuterium."

Grenier, G., and D. White, *J. Chem. Phys.* **40**, 345 (1964a). "Heat Capacity of Solid HD."

Grenier, G., and D. White, *J. Chem. Phys.* **40**, 3015 (1964b). "Heat Capacities of Solid Deuterium (33.1%–87.2% *Para*) from 1.5°K to the Triple Points. Heats of Fusion and Heat Capacity of Liquid."

Gribkov, V. I., N. D. Zhevandrov, and E. I. Chebotareva, *Bull. Acad. Sci. USSR, Phys. Ser.* **27**, 513 (1963). "Variation of the Polarization of the Luminescence of Stilbene Single Crystals as a Function of the Wavelength at Liquid Nitrogen Temperature."

Griessbach, D., *Z. Naturforsch.* **15a**, 296 (1960). "Fluoreszenzmessungen an Cyclohexan-Mischkristallen."

Grimison, A., and G. A. Simpson, *J. Phys. Chem.* **72**, 1776 (1968). "Spectroscopic Identification of γ-Radiolytic Intermediates in New Halogenic Glassy Matrix."

Groenewegen, P. P. M., and R. H. Cole, *J. Chem. Phys.* **46**, 1069 (1967). "Dielectric Properties of Hydrogen Halides. III. High-Frequency Dispersion in Solid Phases of HI and HBr."

Gropper, H., and F. Dörr, *Z. Elektrochem.* **67**, 46 (1963). "Die Orientierung der optischen Übergangsmomente in Phenanthren und seinen Azaderivaten."

Gross, E. F., and L. G. Suslina, *Sov. Phys. Solid State* (English Transl.) **6**, 2949 (1965). "Mirror Symmetry of Absorption and Luminescence Spectra of ZnTe Crystals."

Gross, E. F., S. A. Permogorov, and B. S. Razbirin, *Sov. Phys. Solid State* (English Transl.) **8**, 1180 (1966). "Motion of Free Excitons and Their Interaction with Phonons."

Gruber, J. B., and J. G. Conway, *J. Chem. Phys.* **36**, 191 (1962). "Absorption Spectrum and Zeeman Effect of Am^{3+} in $LaCl_3$."

Gruen, D. M., J. R. Clifton, and C. W. DeKock, *J. Chem. Phys.* **48**, 1394 (1968). "Fluorescence Spectrum of Matrix-Isolated $NiCl_2$."

Gryglewicz, S., *Acta Phys. Pol.* **6**, 210 (1936). "Über den Einfluß der Temperatur auf die Fluoreszenzausbeute einer Anthrazenlösung in Paraffinöl."

Grzywacz, J., and R. Pohoski, *Acta Phys. Pol.* **26**, 393 (1964). "The Phosphorescence of Plexiglassphosphors in Liquid Air."

Gualtieri, J. G., and T. R. AuCoin, *J. Chem. Phys.* **45**, 4348 (1966). "Crystal-Field Term Symbols for Nd^{3+} in $CaWo_4$."

Guarino, J. P., and W. H. Hornill, *J. Amer. Chem. Soc.* **86**, 777 (1964). "Ionic Intermediates in γ-Irradiated Organic Glasses at $-196°$."

Guilbault, G. G., ed., *Fluorescence: Theory, Instrumentation, and Practice*, Marcel Dekker, New York, 1967.

Guillory, W. A., and C. E. Hunter, *J. Chem. Phys.* **50**, 3516 (1969). "Infrared Spectrum of Matrix-Isolated $(NO)_2$."

Gurinovich, G. P., A. N. Sevchenko, and K. N. Solovev, *Sov. Phys. Usp.* (USSR) (English Transl.) **6**, 67 (1963). "The Spectroscopy of the Porphyrins."

Gurinovich, G. P., E. K. Kruglik, and A. N. Sevchenko, *Sov. Phys. Dokl.* (English Transl.) **11**, 338 (1966). "The Fluorescence Quantum Yield in Solutions of Polyatomic Molecules under Long-Wave Excitation."

Gurvich, L. V., and E. A. Shenyavskaya, *Opt. Spectrosc.* (USSR) (English Transl.) **14**, 161 (1962). "The Electronic Spectrum of Scandium Monofluoride."

Gush, H. P., W. F. J. Hare, E. J. Allin, and H. L. Welsh, *Phys. Rev.* **106**, 1101 (1957). "Double Transitions in the Infrared Spectrum of Solid Hydrogen."

Guy, M., J.-Y. Roncin, and N. Damany, *C. R. Acad. Sci.* (Paris) **263**, 546 (1966). "Perturbation de la Raie de Résonance du Zinc et du Cadmium Piégés en Matrices de Gaz Rares à Basse Température."

H

Haarer, D., D. Schmid, and H. C. Wolf, *Phys. Status Solidi* **23**, 633 (1967). "Elektronen-spin-Resonanz von Triplett-Exzitonen in Anthrazen."

Hadley, S. G., H. E. Rast, Jr., and R. A. Keller, *J. Chem. Phys.* **39**, 705 (1963). "Radiationless Triplet-Singlet Transitions in Naphthalene."

Hadley, W. B., S. Polick, R. G. Kaufman, and H. N. Hersh, *J. Chem. Phys.* **45**, 2040 (1966). "Energy Storage and Luminescence in KI: Tl at Low Temperatures."

Hadni, A., B. Wyncke, G. Morlot, and X. Gerbaux, *J. Chem. Phys.* **51**, 3514 (1969). "Transitional Frequencies of Molecules in Naphthalene, Durene, and Anthracene Single Crystals at Low Temperatures."

Hagan, L. G., Ph. D. Thesis, University of California, Berkeley, 1963, UCRL-10620. "The Absolute Intensity of C_2 Swan Bands."

Hagenbach, G. F., in *Argon, Helium and the Rare Gases* (G. A. Cook, ed.), Vol. 2, p. 413, Interscience (Wiley), New York, 1961. "Gases from the Air."

Hainer, R. M., and G. W. King, *Nature* **166**, 1029 (1950). "Effect of Low Temperatures on Infrared Spectra."

Hall, H. T., *Nat. Acad. Sci. — Nat. Res. Council, Publ.* No. **1740**, 65 (1967). "High Temperatures, High Pressures, and Periodic Compounds."

Hall, L., A. Armstrong, W. Moomaw, and M. A. El-Sayed, *J. Chem. Phys.* **48**, 1395 (1968). "Spin-Lattice Relaxation and the Decay of Pyrazine Phosphorescence at Low Temperatures."

Hall, R. T., and G. C. Pimentel, *J. Chem. Phys.* **38**, 1889 (1963). "Isomerization of Nitrous Acid: An Infrared Photochemical Reaction."

Hallam, H. E., *Mol. Spectrosc.* (The Institute of Petroleum) **22**, 329 (1968). "Recent Advances in the Infrared Spectroscopy of Matrix-Isolated Species."

Haller, I., Ph. D. Thesis, University of California, Berkeley, California, 1961. "Matrix Isolation Studies Using Far Ultraviolet Photolysis and the Structure of Some Unstable Molecules."

Haller, I., and G. C. Pimentel, *J. Amer. Chem. Soc.* **84**, 2855 (1962). "Reaction of Oxygen Atoms with Acetylene to Form Ketene."

Haller, W., G. Jura, and G. C. Pimentel, *J. Chem. Phys.* **22**, 720 (1954). "Infrared Studies of Solutions Involving Aromatics and Halogens."

Hallett, A. C. H., in *Argon, Helium and the Rare Gases*, (G. A. Cook, ed.), Vol. 1, p. 313, Interscience (Wiley), New York, 1961a. "Liquid and Solid-State Properties."

Hallett, A. C. H., and G. A. Cook, in *Argon, Helium and the Rare Gases*, (G. A. Cook, ed.), Vol. 2, p. 543, Interscience (Wiley), New York, 1961b. "Cryogenic Applications."

Hameka, H. F., and L. J. Oosterhoff, *Mol. Phys.* **1**, 358 (1958). "The Probabilities of Triplet-Singlet Transitions in Aromatic Hydrocarbons and Ketones."

Hamilton, T. D. S., and K. R. Naqvi, *Chem. Phys. Lett.* **2**, 374 (1968). "Isobestic Points in Emission Spectra."

Hannay, N. B., *Solid State Chemistry*, Prentice-Hall, Englewood Cliffs, New Jersey, 1967.

Hanson, D. M., and G. W. Robinson, *J. Chem. Phys.* **43**, 4174 (1965). "Exciton Structure in Two Triplet States of Crystalline Naphthalene."

Hanson, D. M., *J. Chem. Phys.* **51**, 653 (1969). "Optical Transitions in $^{13}CC_5H_6 - C_6H_6$ Mixed Crystals in the Region of the Factor-Group Components of Crystalline Benzene."

Harada, I., and T. Shimanouchi, *J. Chem. Phys.* **46**, 2708 (1967). "Far-Infrared Spectra of Crystalline Benzene at 138°K and Intermolecular Forces."

Haranath, P. B. V., and V. Sivaramamurty, *Indian J. Phys.* **35**, 599 (1961). "Emission Band Spectrum of SeO_2 Molecule."

Hardy, W. N., and J. R. Gaines, *Phys. Rev. Lett.* **19**, 1417 (1967). "Crystal-Field Splitting of Orthohydrogen in Solid Parahydrogen."

Hare, W. F. J., E: J. Allin, and H. L. Welsh, *Phys. Rev.* **99**, 1887 (1955). "Infrared Absorption of Liquid and Solid Hydrogen with Various Ortho-Para Ratios."

Harmony, M. D., R. J. Myers, L. J. Schoen, D. R. Lide, Jr., and D. E. Mann, *J. Chem. Phys.* **35**, 1129 (1961). "Infrared Spectrum and Structure of the NF_2 Radical."

Harrigan, E. T., and N. Hirota, *Chem. Phys. Lett.* **1**, 281 (1967). "Direct Observation of Triplet State Energy Transfer from Guest to Host in Mixed Organic Crystals."

Harrigan, E. T., and N. Hirota, *J. Chem. Phys.* **49**, 2301 (1968). "Experimental Investigations of Temperature and Host Effects on the Phosphorescent Triplet State in Mixed Organic Crystals."

Harris, R. A., *J. Chem. Phys.* **39**, 978 (1963). "Predissociation."

Hartman, K. O., and I. C. Hisatsune, *J. Chem. Phys.* **44**, 1913 (1966). "Infrared Spectrum of Carbon Dioxide Anion Radical."

Hartmann, W. M., and R. J. Elliott, *Proc. Phys. Soc.* **91**, 187 (1967). "Theory of One-Phonon Impurity-Induced Infrared Absorption in Rare-Gas Solids."

Harvey, E. N., *A History of Luminescence*, American Philosophical Society, Philadelphia, Pennsylvania, 1957.

Harvey, K. B., and H. W. Brown, *J. Chim. Phys.* **56**, 745 (1959). "Etude aux Infrarouges de Certains Solides Condensés à Partir de Décharges en Phase Gazeuse."

Harvey, K. B., and J. F. Ogilvie, *Can. J. Chem.* **40**, 85 (1962). "Infrared Absorption of HCHO at Low Temperatures — Evidence for Multiple Trapping Sites in an Argon Matrix."

Harvey, K. B., and H. F. Shurvell, *Chem. Commun.* **1967**, 490 (1967a). "Evidence for the Rotation of HCl in Solid Nitrogen Matrix."

Harvey, K. B., and H. F. Shurvell, *Can. J. Chem.* **45**, 2689 (1967b). "Infrared Absorption of HCl and HBr in Solid Nitrogen. Evidence for Rotation in a Nitrogen Matrix."

Harvey, K. B., and H. F. Shurvell, *J. Mol. Spectrosc.* **25**, 120 (1968). "Infrared Absorption of D_2O in Solid Nitrogen."

Hastie, J. W., R. Hauge, and J. L. Margrave, *J. Phys. Chem.* **72**, 4492 (1968). "Infrared Vibrational Properties of GeF_2."

Hastie, J. W., R. H. Hauge, and J. L. Margrave, *J. Chem. Phys.* **51**, 2648 (1969). "Infrared Spectra and Geometry of TiF_2 and TiF_3 in Rare-Gas Matrices."

Hatch, G. F., and G. C. Nieman, *J. Chem. Phys.* **48**, 4116 (1968a). "Triplet-Triplet Annihilation and Delayed Fluorescence in Isotopic Mixed Crystals of Benzene."

Hatch, G. F., M. D. Erlitz, and G. C. Nieman, *J. Chem. Phys.* **49**, 3723 (1968b). "Environmental Effects on the Phosphorescent Lifetime of Benzene."

Haubach, W. J., and D. White, *J. Chim. Phys.* **60**, 97 (1963). "Chromatographic Separation of the Isotopic and Nuclear Spin Species of the Hydrogens at Low Temperatures."

Haubach, W. J., C. M. Knobler, A. Katorski, and D. White, *J. Phys. Chem.* **71**, 1398

(1967). "The Low-Temperature Chromatographic Separation of the Isotopic Hydrogens at 27 and 55°K."

Hauer, F. v., and J. v. Kowalski, *Phys. Z.* **15**, 322 (1914). "Zur Photometrie der Lumineszenzerscheinungen."

Haug, A., *Phys. Rev.* **147**, 612 (1966). "Damping of Molecular Excitons Interacting with Phonons and Impurities in Thin Crystals."

Haug, A., *Nuovo Cimento* **A48**, 80 (1967). "Green's Function Approach to Electrical Conductivity of an Excess Charge Carrier Interacting with Phonons in Molecular Crystals."

Hausser, K. W., R. Kuhn, and E. Kuhn, *Z. Phys. Chem.* (Leipzig) **B29**, 417 (1935). "Lichtabsorption und Doppelbindung. VI. Über die Fluoreszenz der Diphenylpolyene."

Heber, J., *Z. Angew. Phys.* **20**, 278 (1966). "Eine gegengekoppelte Torstufe in der Sampling-Technik für den Mikro- und Millisekundenbereich."

Hecht, H. G., *J. Chem. Phys.* **46**, 23 (1967). "Study of the Structure of Vanadium in Soda-Boric Oxide Glasses."

Heckmann, R. C., *J. Mol. Spectrosc.* **2**, 27 (1958). "Phosphorescence Studies of Some Heterocyclic and Related Organic Compounds."

Hedberg, K., and R. M. Badger, *J. Chem. Phys.* **19**, 508 (1951). "The Infrared Spectra of HOCl and DOCl."

Hein, D. E., and H. W. Offen, *Mol. Cryst.* **5**, 217 (1969). "Fluorescence Spectra in Frozen Heptane at High Pressures."

Held, A. M., and J. C. Declus, *Amer. Chem. Soc. 24th Northwest Regional Meeting, Salt Lake City, 1969.* "The Infrared and Far Infrared Spectra of Films of Formaldehyde."

Heller, W. R., *Phys. Lett.* **26A**, 54 (1967). "The Cohesion of Ionic Crystals of Alkali Metal and Noble Gas Atoms."

Henderson, J. R., M. Muramoto, and J. B. Gruber, *J. Chem. Phys.* **46**, 2515 (1967). "Spectrum of Nd^{3+} in Lanthanide Oxide Crystals."

Henri, V., and M. C. Teves, *Nature* **114**, 894 (1924). "Absorption Spectrum and Constitution of Sulphur Vapour. Predissociation of Molecules."

Henry, B. R., and M. Kasha, *J. Chem. Phys.* **47**, 3319 (1967). "Triplet-Triplet Absorption Studies on Aromatic and Heterocyclic Molecules at 77°K."

Henry, B. R., and M. Kasha, *J. Mol. Spectrosc.* **26**, 536 (1968a). "Criteria for Maximizing Steady-State Population of the Lowest Excited Triplet State."

Henry, B. R., and M. Kasha, *Ann. Rev. Phys. Chem.* **19**, 161 (1968b). "Radiationless Molecular Electronic Transitions."

Henry, B. R., and W. Siebrand, *Chem. Phys. Lett.* **3**, 90 (1969a). "Spin-Orbit Coupling in Aromatic Hydrocarbons. The Radiative Triplet Lifetime of Naphthalene."

Henry, B. R., and W. Siebrand, *J. Chem. Phys.* **51**, 2396 (1969b). "Spin-Orbit Coupling in Aromatic Hydrocarbons. Calculation of the Radiative Triplet Lifetimes of Naphthalene, Anthracene, and Phenanthrene."

Hercules, D. M., and L. B. Rogers, *Spectrochim. Acta* **15**, 393 (1959). "Absorption and Fluorescence Spectra of Some Mono- and Di-Hydroxy-Naphthalenes."

Hercules, D. M., and L. B. Rogers, *J. Phys. Chem.* **64**, 397 (1960). "Luminescence Spectra of Naphthols and Naphthalenediols: Low-Temperature Phenomena."

Hercules, D. M., ed., *Fluorescence and Phosphorescence Analysis*, Interscience (Wiley), New York, 1966.

Herington, E. F. G., *Zone Melting of Organic Compounds*, Wiley, New York, 1963.

Hermann, T. S., *Appl. Opt.* **23**, 435 (1969a). "Infrared Spectroscopy at Sub-Ambient Temperatures: I. Literature Review."

Hermann, T. S., *Appl. Opt.* **23**, 451 (1969b). "Infrared Spectroscopy at Sub-Ambient Temperatures: II. Pure Molecules."

Hermann, T. S., *Appl. Opt.* **23**, 461 (1969c). "Infrared Spectroscopy at Sub-Ambient Temperatures: III. Molecules and Molecular Fragments within Matrices."

Hermann, T. S., *Appl. Opt.* **23**, 473 (1969d). "Infrared Spectroscopy at Sub-Ambient Temperatures: IV." "Bibliography."

Hermann, T. S., *Rev. Sci. Instrum.* **40**, 1062 (1969e). "Infrared Cell for Low Temperature Studies."

Hernandez, J. P., and S. Choi, *J. Chem. Phys.* **50**, 1524 (1969). "Optical Absorption by Charge-Transfer Excitons in Linear Molecular Crystals."

Herr, K. C., and G. C. Pimentel, *Appl. Opt.* **4**, 25 (1965). "A Rapid-Scan Infrared Spectrometer; Flash Photolytic Detection of Chloroformic Acid and of CF_2."

Hersh, C. K., *Molecular Sieves*, Reinhold, New York, 1961.

Herzberg, G., *Infrared and Raman Spectra of Polyatomic Molecules*, Van Nostrand, Princeton, New Jersey, 1945.

Herzberg, G., and D. A. Ramsay, *Proc. Roy. Soc.* (London), *Ser. A* **233**, 34 (1955). "The 7500 to 4500 Å Absorption System of the Free HCO Radical."

Herzberg, G., and A. Lagerqvist, *Can. J. Phys.* **46**, 2363 (1960). "The Spectrum of C_2^-."

Herzberg, G., *Spectra of Diatomic Molecules*, 2nd ed., Van Nostrand, Princeton, New Jersey, 1961.

Herzberg, G., and D. N. Travis, *Can. J. Phys.* **42**, 1658 (1964). "The Spectrum and Structure of the Free NCN Radical."

Herzberg, G., *Electronic Spectra and Electronic Structure of Polyatomic Molecules*, Van Nostrand, Princeton, New Jersey, 1967.

Herzberg, G., *The Spectra and Structures of Simple Free Radicals*, Cornell University Press, New York, 1971.

Herzfeld, C. M., and H. P. Broida, *Phys. Rev.* **101**, 606 (1956). "Interpretation of Spectra of Atoms and Molecules in Solid Nitrogen Condensed at $4°K$."

Herzfeld, C. M., *Phys. Rev.* **107**, 1239 (1957). "Theory of the Forbidden Transitions of Nitrogen Atoms Trapped in Solids."

Hesser, J. E., *J. Chem. Phys.* **48**, 2518 (1968). "Absolute Transition Probabilities in Ultraviolet Molecular Spectra."

Hestermans, P., and D. White, *J. Phys. Chem.* **65**, 362 (1961). "The Vapor Pressure, Heat of Vaporization and Heat Capacity of Methane from the Boiling Point to the Critical Temperature."

Hexter, R. M., and D. A. Dows, *J. Chem. Phys.* **25**, 504 (1956a). "Low-Frequency Librations and the Vibrational Spectra of Molecular Crystals."

Hexter, R. M., *J. Chem. Phys.* **25**, 1286 (1956b). "Relative Magnitude of Crystalline Fields; Crystal Structure of Methyl Iodide."

Hexter, R. M., and T. D. Goldfarb, *J. Inorg. Nucl. Chem.* **4**, 171 (1956c). "Infra-red Spectra of Quinol Clathrate Compounds."

Hexter, R. M., *J. Opt. Soc. Amer.* **48**, 770 (1958). "On the Infrared Absorption Spectra Crystalline Brucite $\{Mg\ (OH)_2\}$ and Portlandite $\{Ca\ (OH)_2\}$."

Hexter, R. M., *J. Mol. Spectrosc.* **3**, 67 (1959a). "Low-Frequency Librations and the

Vibrational Spectra of Molecular Crystals. Part II."

Hexter, R. M., *Amer. Rev. Phys. Chem.* **10** (1959b). "Vibration-Rotation Spectroscopy."

Hexter, R. M., *J. Chem. Phys.* **33**, 1833 (1960). "Intermolecular Coupling of Vibrations in Molecular Crystals: A Vibrational Exciton Approach."

Hexter, R. M., *J. Chem. Phys.* **34**, 941 (1961). "Infrared Spectrum of Single Crystals of LiOH, LiOD, and LiOH-LiOD."

Hexter, R. M., *J. Chem. Phys.* **36**, 2285 (1962a). "Vibrational Excitons. II. Degenerate Vibrations."

Hexter, R. M., *J. Chem. Phys.* **37**, 1347 (1962b). "Evaluation of Lattice Sums in the Calculation of Crystal Spectra."

Hexter, R. M., *J. Chem. Phys.* **38**, 1024 (1963a). "Comment on 'Infrared Absorption Spectra of LiOH and LiOD'."

Hexter, R. M., *J. Chem. Phys.* **39**, 1608 (1963b). "Erratum and Further Comments: Vibrational Excitons. II. Degenerate Vibrations."

Hexter, R. M., *J. Opt. Soc. Amer.* **53**, 703 (1963c). "Excitation-Modulation Spectroscopy: A Technique for Obtaining Vibrational Spectra of Excited Electronic States."

Hexter, R. M., *J. Chem. Phys.* **46**, 2300 (1967). "Forbidden Transitions in Molecular Crystals: The Cameron System of Solid α-CO."

Hildenbrand, D. L., *J. Chem. Phys.* **40**, 3438 (1964). "Entropies of Some Gaseous Metal Dihalides."

Hilland, C. G. A., and H. A. Klasens, *J. Electrochem. Soc.* **96**, 275 (1949). "Influence of Temperature on the Efficiencies of Zinc Sulfide Phosphors Containing Silver and Cobalt."

Hillier, I. H., and S. A. Rice, *J. Chem. Phys.* **46**, 3881 (1967). "Comments on the Influence of Intermediate Excitons and Exchange Forces on the Interaction in Molecular Crystals: The Crystal Structure of Chlorine."

Hilpern, J. W., G. Porter, and L. J. Stief, *Proc. Roy. Soc.* (London) *Ser. A* **277**, 437 (1964). "Decay of the Triplet State. I. First-Order Processes in Solution."

Hingsammer, J., and E. Lüscher, *Helv. Phys. Acta* **41**, 657 (1968). "Edelgaskristalle, eine Übersicht."

Hirayama, F., *J. Chem. Phys.* **42**, 3726 (1965). "Concentration Dependence of Benzene Emission in Frozen Solutions."

Hirota, N., and C. A. Hutchison, Jr., *J. Chem. Phys.* **46**, 1561 (1967). "Effect of Deuteration of Durene on the Lifetime of the Phosphorescent Triplet State of Naphthalene in a Durene Host Crystal."

Hirschberg, Y., *Anal. Chem.* **28**, 1954 (1956). "Full Luminescence at Liquid-Air Temperature of Methyl-1,2 Benzanthracenes and Methylbenzo[c]phenanthrenes."

Hiza, M. J., *Chem. Eng. Progr.* **56**, 68 (1960). "Cryogenic Impurity Adsorption from Hydrogen."

Hochstrasser, R. M., *Can. J. Chem.* **37**, 1123 (1959a). "Note on the Photooxidation of Tetramethylrubrene."

Hochstrasser, R. M., *Can. J. Chem.* **37**, 1367 (1959b). "The Luminescence of Complex Molecules in Relation to the Internal Conversion of Excitation Energy. II."

Hochstrasser, R. M., *Spectrochim. Acta* **16**, 497 (1960a). "On the Problem of Radiative Combinations between Upper Singlet States and the Ground State in Aromatic Molecules."

Hochstrasser, R. M., *J. Chem. Phys.* **33**, 459 (1960b). "Polarization of the First Two Electronic Transitions of Pyrene."

Hochstrasser, R. M., *J. Chem. Phys.* **33**, 950 (1960c). "Electronic Absorption Spectrum of Diphenylene in Substitutional Solid-Solid Solution."

Hochstrasser, R. M., *Can. J. Chem.* **38**, 233 (1960d). "The Luminescence of Complex Molecules in Relation to the Internal Conversion of Excitation Energy. II. N-Heteroaromatics."

Hochstrasser, R. M., *Can. J. Chem.* **39**, 451 (1961a). "The Crystal Spectrum of Perylene."

Hochstrasser, R. M., *Can. J. Chem.* **39**, 459 (1961b). "The Effect of Intramolecular Twisting on the Emission Spectra of Hindered Aromatic Molecules. I. 1,1'-Binaphthyl."

Hochstrasser, R. M., *Can. J. Chem.* **39**, 765 (1961c). "The Absorption Spectrum of Diphenylene in the Near-Ultraviolet."

Hochstrasser, R. M., *Can. J. Chem.* **39**, 1776 (1961d). "The Luminescence of Complex Molecules in Relation to the Internal Conversion of Excitation Energy. III. The Total Emission Spectra of 1-Naphthoic Acid."

Hochstrasser, R. M., *Can. J. Chem.* **39**, 1853 (1961e). "The Polarization of the Fluorescence of 1- and 2-Naphthoic Acid."

Hochstrasser, R. M., *J. Chem. Phys.* **36**, 1808 (1962a). "Absorption Spectrum of Phenazine Single Crystals at 77°K and 4.2°K in the Region of the $\eta \rightarrow \pi^*$ Transition."

Hochstrasser, R. M., *J. Mol. Spectrosc.* **8**, 485 (1962b). "The Influence of Temperature on the Emission Spectra of Stilbene Monocrystals and Mixed Crystals with Tetracene."

Hochstrasser, R. M., *Rev. Mod. Phys.* **34**, 531 (1962c). "The Luminescence of Organic Molecular Crystals."

Hochstrasser, R. M., *J. Chem. Phys.* **36**, 3505 (1962d). "Polarization of the Spectra of Crystalline Azobenzene and Mixed Crystals of Azobenzene in Stilbene at 77°K and 4.2°K in the Region of the Lowest $\eta \rightarrow \pi^*$ Transition."

Hochstrasser, R. M., *Radiat. Res.* **20**, 107 (1963). "The Problem of Defects in Relation to the Optical Properties of Organic Molecular Crystals."

Hochstrasser, R. M., *J. Chem. Phys.* **40**, 1038 (1964a). "Determination of the Efficiency of Triplet Energy Migration in Benzophenone Crystals."

Hochstrasser, R. M., and S. K. Lower, *J. Chem. Phys.* **40**, 1041 (1964b). "Polarized Emission and Triplet-Triplet Absorption Spectra of Aromatic Hydrocarbons in Benzophenone Crystals."

Hochstrasser, R. M., *J. Chem. Phys.* **40**, 2559 (1964c). "Spectral Effects of Strong Exciton Coupling in the Lowest Electronic Transition of Perylene."

Hochstrasser, R. M., *J. Chem. Phys.* **40**, 2737 (1964d). "Photoprocesses Involving Triplet States of Organic Crystals."

Hochstrasser, R. M., *J. Chem. Phys.* **41**, 1073 (1964e). "Experimental Evidence for Localized Excitons in the Spectra of Charge-Transfer Complex Molecular Crystals."

Hochstrasser, R. M., S. K. Lower, and C. Reid, *J. Mol. Spectrosc.* **15**, 257 (1965a). "Absolute Ultraviolet Absorption Intensities of the Anthracene-Trinitrobenzene Crystal."

Hochstrasser, R. M., and G. J. Small, *Chem. Commun.* **5**, 87 (1965b). "Multiplet Structure in the Absorption, Fluorescence, and Phosphorescence of Mixed Molecular Crystals."

Hochstrasser, R. M., and G. J. Small, *J. Chem. Phys.* **45**, 2270 (1966a). "Electronic Spectra of Phenanthrene in Mixed Crystals."

Hochstrasser, R. M., and C. Marzzacco, *J. Chem. Phys.* **45**, 4681 (1966b). "Electronic States of 9,10-Diazaphenanthrene."

Hochstrasser, R. M., and C. Marzzacco, *J. Chem. Phys.* **46**, 4155 (1967). "Singlet-Triplet Transitions in o-Diazines: Pyridazine."

Hochstrasser, R. M., and L. J. Noe, *J. Chem. Phys.* **48**, 514 (1968a). "Stark Splitting in Molecular Crystals."

Hochstrasser, R. M., and G. J. Small, *J. Chem. Phys.* **48**, 3612 (1968b). "Spectra and Structure of Mixed Organic Crystals."

Hochstrasser, R. M., and C. Marzzacco, *J. Chem. Phys.* **48**, 4079 (1968c). "$n \to \pi^*$ Transitions in Diazine: Phthalazine."

Hochstrasser, R. M., and C. Marzzacco, *J. Chem. Phys.* **49**, 971 (1968d). "Perturbations between Electronic States in Aromatic and Heteroaromatic Molecules."

Hochstrasser, R. M., and G. J. Small, *J. Chem. Phys.* **49**, 4730 (1968e). "Erratum: Spectra and Structure of Mixed Organic Crystals."

Hochstrasser, R. M., and A. P. Marchetti, *Chem. Phys. Lett.* **1**, 597 (1968f). "The Polarization of the Allowed Triplet-Triplet Absorption in Anthracene."

Hochstrasser, R. M., and L. J. Noe, *J. Chem. Phys.* **50**, 1684 (1969a). "Dipole Moments of the Excited States of Azulene."

Hochstrasser, R. M., and A. P. Marchetti, *J. Chem. Phys.* **50**, 1727 (1969b). "Electronic, Vibrational, and Zeeman Spectra of Triplet NO_2^-."

Hoffman, R. E., and D. F. Hornig, *J. Chem. Phys.* **17**, 1163 (1949). "The Infra-Red Spectrum of Solid Hydrogen Cyanide."

Hoijtink, G. J., *Mol. Phys.* **3**, 67 (1960). "The Influence of Paramagnetic Molecules on Singlet-Triplet Transitions."

Holden, R. B., W. J. Taylor, and H. L. Johnston, *J. Opt. Soc. Amer.* **40**, 757 (1950). "A Variable Thickness Low Temperature Infrared Cell."

Holland, R., D. W. G. Style, R. N. Dixon, and D. A. Ramsay, *Nature* **182**, 336 (1958). "Emission and Absorption Spectra of NCO and NCS."

Hollas, J. M., E. Gregorek, and L. Goodman, *J. Chem. Phys.* **49**, 1745 (1968). "Allowed and Forbidden Character in the 3715 Å $\pi^* \leftarrow n$ System of Benzaldehyde."

Holzrichter, J. F., and J. L. Emmett, *Appl. Opt.* in press. "A High Brightness Axial Flashlamp."

Honig, R. E., *Vapor Pressure of Elements and Some of the Most Common Gases*, Radio Corporation of America, Princeton, 1962. (Unpublished report.)

Hopfield, J. J., and R. T. Birge, *Phys. Rev.* **29**, 922 (1927). "CO Cameron Bands."

Hopkins, H. P., Jr., J. V. V. Kasper, and K. S. Pitzer, *J. Chem. Phys.* **46**, 218 (1967). "Restricted Rotation in Solid Deuteromethanes."

Hopkins, H. P., Jr., R. F. Curl, Jr., and K. S. Pitzer, *J. Chem. Phys.* **48**, 2959 (1968). "Infrared Matrix-Isolation Studies of Nuclear-Spin-Species Conversion."

Horrocks, A. R., T. Medinger, and F. Wilkinson, *Int. Symp. Luminescence, Munich, 1965*, p. 16, Thiemig, Munich, 1966. "Fluorescence Quenching by Compounds Containing Heavy Atoms."

Horrocks, A. R., and F. Wilkinson, *Proc. Roy. Soc.* (London) *Ser. A* **306**, 257 (1968). "Triplet State Formation Efficiencies of Aromatic Hydrocarbons in Solution."

Hrostowski, H. J., and G. C. Pimentel, *J. Amer. Chem. Soc.* **76**, 998 (1954). "The Infrared Spectra of Stable Pentaborane and Deuterated Pentaborane."

Huggins, C. M., G. C. Pimentel, and J. N. Shoolery, *J. Phys. Chem.* **60**, 1311 (1956a). "Proton Magnetic Resonance Studies of the Hydrogen Bonding of Phenol, Substituted Phenols and Acetic Acid."

Huggins, C. M., and G. C. Pimentel, *J. Phys. Chem.* **60**, 1615 (1956b). "Systematics of the Infrared Spectral Properties of Hydrogen Bonding Systems: Frequency Shift, Half Width and Intensity."

Hunt, G. R., E. F. McCoy, and I. G. Ross, *Aust. J. Chem.* **15**, 591 (1962). "Excited States of Aromatic Hydrocarbons: Pathways of Internal Conversion."

Hunter, T. F., R. D. McAlpine, and R. M. Hochstrasser, *J. Chem. Phys.* **50**, 1140 (1969). "Triplet-Triplet Energy Transfer in Ordered and Random Media."

Hutchison, C. A., Jr., and B. W. Mangum, *J. Chem. Phys.* **29**, 952 (1958). "Paramagnetic Resonance Absorption in Naphthalene in Its Phosphorescent State."

Hutchison, C. A., Jr., and B. W. Mangum, *J. Chem. Phys.* **32**, 1261 (1960). "Effect of Deuterium Substitution on the Lifetime of the Phosphorescent Triplet State of Naphthalene."

Hutchison, C. A., Jr., and B. W. Mangum, *J. Chem. Phys.* **34**, 908 (1961). "Paramagnetic Resonance Absorption in Naphthalene in Its Phosphorescent State."

I

Ikenberry, D., and T. P. Das, *J. Chem. Phys.* **45**, 1361 (1966). "Chemical-Shift Calculations in Alkali Halides."

Il'ina, A. A., and E. V. Shpol'skii, *Izv. Akad. Nauk SSSR, Ser. Fiz.* **15**, 585 (1951). "Fluorescence and Phosphorescence Spectra of Pyrene-type Carbohydrates in Frozen Solutions."

Imakubo, K., T. Higashimura, and T. Sidei, *J. Phys. Soc. Jap.* **22**, 339 (1967). "Phosphorescence of Nucleotides and DNA at 77°K."

Imbusch, G. F., W. M. Yen, A. L. Schawlow, D. E. McCumber, and M. D. Sturge, *Phys. Rev.* **133**, A1029 (1964). "Temperature Dependence of the Width and Position of the $^2E \rightarrow {}^4A_2$ Fluorescence Lines of Cr^{3+} and V^{2+} in MgO."

Imbusch, G. F., A. L. Schawlow, A. D. May, and S. Sugano, *Phys. Rev.* **140**, A830 (1965). "Fluorescence of $MgO:Cr^{3+}$ Ions in Noncubic Sites."

Irie, M., K. Hayashi, S. Okamura, and H. Yoshida, *J. Chem. Phys.* **48**, 922 (1968). "Behavior of Trapped Electrons in Irradiated 3-Methylpentane Glass at 77°K."

Ito, M., *Chem. Phys. Lett.* **2**, 371 (1968). "Exciton Splitting of Absorption Spectra in Radical Dimers."

Ivanova, T. V., P. I. Kudriashov, and V. Y. Sveshnikov, *Dokl. Akad. Nauk SSSR* **138**, 572 (1961). "Lifetime of Ultraviolet Fluorescence of Some Aromatic Compounds."

Iwai, T., M. I. Savadatti, and H. P. Broida, *J. Chem. Phys.* **47**, 3861 (1967). "Mechanism of Populating Electronically Excited CN in an Active Nitrogen Flame."

J

Jablonski, A., *Z. Phys.* **94**, 38 (1935a). "Über den Mechanismus der Photolumineszenz von Farbstoffphosphoren."

Jablonski, A., *Acta Phys. Pol.* **4**, 311 (1935b). "Weitere Versuche über die negative Polarisation der Phosphoreszenz."

Jablonski, A., *Acta Phys. Pol.* **5**, 371 (1936). "Über einige optische Eigenschaften der in festen und flüssigen Medien eingebetteten Moleküle."

Jablonski, A., *Acta Phys. Pol.* **13**, 175 (1954). "Quenching of Photoluminescence of Solutions."

Jacox, M. E., and D. E. Milligan, *Spectrochim. Acta* **17**, 1196 (1961). "The Infrared Spectra of Thick Films of CO_2 and $CO_2 + H_2O$ at Low Temperatures."

Jacox, M. E., and D. E. Milligan, *Spectrochim. Acta* **19**, 1173 (1963a). "The Infrared Spectra of Dilute Solid Solutions of Ammonia in Carbon Dioxide."

Jacox, M. E., and D. E. Milligan, *J. Amer. Chem. Soc.* **85**, 278 (1963b). "Infrared Study of the Reactions of CH_2 and NH with C_2H_2 and C_2H_4 in Solid Argon."

Jacox, M. E., and D. E. Milligan, *J. Chem. Phys.* **40**, 2457 (1964a). "Low-Temperature Infrared Study of Intermediates in the Photolysis of HNCO and DNCO."

Jacox, M. E., and D. E. Milligan, *Appl. Opt.* **3**, 873 (1964b). "Low-Temperature Infrared Studies of the Chemistry of Free Radicals."

Jacox, M. E., and D. E. Milligan, *J. Chem. Phys.* **43**, 866 (1965a). "Matrix Isolation Study of the Reaction of Cl Atoms with CO. The Infrared Spectrum of the Free Radical ClCO."

Jacox, M. E., D. E. Milligan, N. G. Moll, and W. E. Thompson, *J. Chem. Phys.* **43**, 3734 (1965b). "Matrix-Isolation Infrared Spectrum of the Free Radical CCO."

Jacox, M. E., and D. E. Milligan, *J. Chem. Phys.* **46**, 184 (1967a). "Production and Reaction of Atomic Fluorine in Solids. Vibrational and Electronic Spectra of the Free Radical HNF."

Jacox, M. E., and D. E. Milligan, *J. Chem. Phys.* **47**, 1626 (1967b). "Matrix-Isolation Study of the Reaction of Carbon Atoms with CHCl. The Infrared Spectrum of the Free Radical HCCl."

Jacox, M. E., and D. E. Milligan, *J. Chem. Phys.* **48**, 4040 (1968a). "Matrix Isolation Study of the Infrared Spectrum of the Free Radical F_2CN."

Jacox, M. E., and D. E. Milligan, *J. Chem. Phys.* **49**, 3130 (1968b). "Matrix Isolation Study of the Vacuum-Ultraviolet Photolysis of Trichlorosilane."

Jacox, M. E., and D. E. Milligan, *J. Chem. Phys.* **50**, 3252 (1969a). "Matrix-Isolation Study of the Vacuum-Ultraviolet Photolysis of Methyl Fluoride. The Infrared Spectra of the Free Radicals CF, HCF, and H_2CF."

Jacox, M. E., and D. E. Milligan, *J. Chem. Phys.* **51**, 4143 (1969b). "Matrix-Isolation Study of the Infrared and Ultraviolet Spectra of Several First-Series Transition-Metal Chlorides."

Jakobsson, L. R., *Ark. Fys.* **34**, 19 (1967). "The Infrared Spectrum of the Neutral Sulphur Atom."

James, T. C., W. G. Norris, and W. Klemperer, *J. Chem. Phys.* **32**, 728 (1960). "Infrared Spectrum and Dipole Moment Function of Lithium Hydride."

Jansen, L., *Phys. Lett.* **4**, 91 (1963). "Absolute Stability of Cubic Crystal Structures of Heavy Rare Gas Atoms. I."

Jansen, L., *Phys. Rev.* **135A**, 1292 (1964). "Stability of Crystals of Rare-Gas Atoms and Alkali Halides in Terms of Three-Body Interactions. I. Rare-Gas Crystals."

Jansen, L., and E. Lombardi, *Chem. Phys. Lett.* **1**, 33 (1967). "Three-Body Exchange Forces in Rare-Gas Crystals."

Janssen, O., and K. Funabashi, *J. Chem. Phys.* **46**, 101 (1967). "Luminescence Phenomena in Gamma-Irradiated Pure Alkanes at 77°K."

Japar, S. M., M. Pomerantz, and E. W. Abrahamson, *Chem. Phys. Lett.* **2**, 137 (1968). "Common Intermediates in the Transfer of Triplet Excitation Energy and Molecular Exchange Reactions."

Jen, C. K., L. C. Aamodt, and A. H. Piksis, in *The Triplet State, Proc. Int. Symp., Beirut, 1967* (A. B. Zahlan, ed.), p. 143, Cambridge University Press, London and New York, 1967. "Changes Induced in the Phosphorescent Radiation of Aromatic Molecules by Paramagnetic Resonance in Their Metastable Triplet States."

Jenkins, A. C., in *Argon, Helium and the Rare Gases* (G. A. Cook, ed.), Vol. 1, p. 391, Interscience (Wiley), New York, 1961. "Summary of Physical Properties."

Johns, J. W. C., *Can. J. Phys.* **39**, 1738 (1961). "The Absorption Spectrum of BO_2."

Johns, J. W. C., S. H. Pirddle, and D. A. Ramsay, *Disc. Faraday Soc.* **35**, 90 (1963). "Electronic Absorption Spectra of HCO and DCO Radicals."

Johnson, G. E., W. M. McClain, and A. C. Albrecht, *J. Chem. Phys.* **43**, 2911 (1965). "Electric Stimulation of Recombination Luminescence in a Rigid Organic Solution."

Johnson, N. M., and F. Daniels, *J. Chem. Phys.* **34**, 1434 (1961). "Luminescence during Annealing and Phase Change in Crystals."

Johnson, P. D., *Proc. Nat. Electronics Conf.* **11**, 152 (1955). "Luminescence and Luminescent Devices."

Johnson, S. A., H. G. Freie, A. L. Schawlow, and W. M. Yen, *J. Opt. Soc. Amer.* **57**, 734 (1967). "Thermal Shifts in the Energy Levels of LaF_3: Nd^{3+}."

Jolly, W. L., *Synthetic Inorganic Chemistry*, Prentice-Hall, Englewood Cliffs, New Jersey, 1960.

Jones, P. F., and S. Siegel, *J. Chem. Phys.* **45**, 4757 (1966). "High Pressure Effects on the Triplet-Singlet Transition Probability of Naphthalene."

Jones, P. F., and M. Nicol, *J. Chem. Phys.* **48**, 5440 (1968a). "Excimer Emission of Naphthalene, Anthracene, and Phenanthrene Crystals Produced by Very High Pressures."

Jones, P. F., *J. Chem. Phys.* **48**, 5448 (1968b). "Spectral Shifts and Broadening of the Fluorescence of Anthracene and Tetracene in Several Host Crystals at High Pressures."

Jones, P. F., and M. Nicol, *J. Chem. Phys.* **48**, 5457 (1968c). "Fluorescence of Doped Crystals of Anthracene, Naphthalene and Phenanthrene under High Pressures: the Role of Excimers in Energy Transfer to the Guest Molecules."

Jones, P. F., *J. Chem. Phys.* **49**, 3730 (1968d). "Growth and Decay of Phosphorescence."

Jones, P. F., and S. Siegel, *Chem. Phys. Lett.* **2**, 486 (1968e). "Intersystem Crossing in Pyrene-h_{10} and pyrene-d_{10}."

Jones, P. F., and S. Siegel, *J. Chem. Phys.* **50**, 1134 (1969a). "Temperature Effects on the Phosphorescence of Aromatic Hydrocarbons in Poly(methylmethacrylate)."

Jones, P. F., and A. R. Calloway, *J. Chem. Phys.* **51**, 1661 (1969b). "Temperature and Matrix Effects on the Phosphorescence Lifetime of Naphthalene-d_8."

Jones, T. H., and R. Livingston, *Trans. Faraday Soc.* **60**, 2168 (1964). "Temperature Dependence of the Lifetime of Phosphorescence of Some Polynuclear Hydrocarbons in Viscous Solution."

Jortner, J., L. Meyer, S. A. Rice, and E. G. Wilson, *Low Temp. Phys.* **1**, 356 (1965). "Localized Excitations in Condensed Neon, Argon, Krypton, and Xenon."

Jortner, J., and R. S. Berry, *J. Chem. Phys.* **48**, 2757 (1968). "Radiationless Transitions and Molecular Quantum Beats."

K

Kabler, M. N., and D. A. Patterson, *Phys. Rev. Lett.* **19**, 652 (1967). "Evidence for a Triplet State of the Self-Trapped Exciton in Alkali-Halide Crystals."

Kadhim, A. H., and H. W. Offen, *J. Chem. Phys.* **48**, 749 (1968). "Spectroscopy of EDA Complexes at High Pressures. VI. Absorption and Fluorescence of Crystalline TNB and TNF Complexes."

Kalantar, A. H., and A. C. Albrecht, *J. Phys. Chem.* **66**, 2279 (1962). "Concerning the Primary Absorption Act in a One-Electron Photo-Oxidation in a Rigid Medium."

Kalantar, A. H., *J. Chem. Phys.* **48**, 4992 (1968). "Consequences of Photoselection on the Intensity and Polarization of Luminescent Molecules."

Kallmann, H. P., and G. M. Spruch, eds., *Luminescence of Organic and Inorganic Materials* (*Int. Conf., N. Y. Univ.*), Wiley, New York, 1962.

Kanda, Y., and H. Sponer, *J. Chem. Phys.* **28**, 798 (1958). "Triplet-Singlet Emission Spectra of Solid Toluene at 4°K and 77°K and in EPA Solution at 77°K."

Kanda, Y., and R. Shimada, *Spectrochim. Acta* **15**, 211 (1959). "The Triplet-Singlet Emission Spectra of Phenanthrene and Related Compounds in EPA and in Petroleum Ether at 90°K."

Kanda, Y., R. Shimada, and Y. Sakai, *Spectrochim. Acta* **17**, 1 (1961a). "Phosphorescence Spectrum of Biphenyl at 90°K."

Kanda, Y., and R. Shimada, *Spectrochim. Acta* **17**, 7 (1961b). "The Triplet-Singlet Emission Spectra of Benzene in Carbon Tetrachloride and Dioxane Matrices at 90°."

Kanda, Y., Y. Gondo, and R. Shimada, *Spectrochim. Acta* **17**, 424 (1961c). "Absorption Spectrum of Benzene in Carbon Tetrachloride at 77°K."

Kanda, Y., R. Shimada, K. Hanada, and S. Kajigaeshi, *Spectrochim. Acta* **17**, 1268 (1961d). "Phosphorescence Spectra of Polycrylic Compounds. I. Fluorene and Dibenzofuran."

Kanda, Y., R. Shimada, and Y. Takenoshita, *Spectrochim. Acta* **19**, 1249 (1963). "The Phosphorescence Spectrum of Benzoic Acid, Methyl Benzoate and Benzamide at 90°K."

Kanda, Y., H. Kaseda, and T. Matumura, *Spectrochim. Acta* **20**, 1387 (1964). "Singlet-Triplet Absorption Spectra of Several Carbonyl Compounds."

Kapany, N. S., *Fiber Optics*, Academic Press, 1967.

Karo, A. M., *J. Chem. Phys.* **32**, 907 (1960). "Electron-Population Analysis and the Dipole Moment of the LiH $^1\Sigma^+$ Excited State."

Kasai, P. H., W. Weltner, Jr., and E. B. Whipple, *J. Chem. Phys.* **42**, 1120 (1965a). "Orientation of NO_2 and Other Molecules in Neon Matrices at 4°K."

Kasai, P. H., and W. Weltner, Jr., *J. Chem. Phys.* **43**, 2553 (1965b). "Ground States and Hyperfine-Structure Separations of ScO, YO, and LaO from ESR Spectra at 4°K."

Kasai, P. H., E. B. Whipple, and W. Weltner, Jr., *J. Chem. Phys.* **44**, 2581 (1966). "ESR of $Cu(NO_3)_2$ and CuF_2 Molecules Oriented in Neon and Argon Matrices at 4°K."

Kasai, P. H., and D. McLeod, Jr., *J. Chem. Phys.* **51**, 1250 (1969). "Electron Spin Resonance Study of Molecular Anions Generated in Argon Matrix at 4°K: ESR Spectrum of $B_2H_6^-$."

Kasha, L., and M. Kasha, *Molecular Electronic Bibliography*, Vol. 1: Molecular Quantum Mechanics and Molecular Electronic Spectroscopy. Early Workers. Publishers Press, Tallahassee, Florida, 1958.

Kasha, M., and R. E. Powell, *J. Amer. Chem. Soc.* **69**, 2909 (1947a). "On the Correlation of the Spectroscopic and Thermal Energy Differences between the Fluorescence and Phosphorescence Levels of Dye Molecules."

Kasha, M., *Chem. Rev.* **41**, 401 (1947b). "Phosphorescence and the Role of the Triplet State in the Electronic Excitation of Complex Molecules."

Kasha, M., *Science* **107**, 556 (1948a). "On the Properties of Gelatin-Dye Phosphors and the Continuum Theory of Szent-Györgyi."

Kasha, M., *J. Opt. Soc. Amer.* **38**, 929 (1948b). "Transmission Filters for the Ultraviolet."

Kasha, M., *J. Opt. Soc. Amer.* **38**, 1068 (1948c). "Fabrication of Boric Acid Glass for Luminescence Studies."

Kasha, M., and R. V. Nauman, *J. Chem. Phys.* **17**, 516 (1949). "The Metastability of the Lowest Excited Singlet Level of Naphthalene."

Kasha, M., *Disc. Faraday Soc.* **9**, 14 (1950). "Characterization of Electronic Transitions in Complex Molecules."

Kasha, M., *J. Chem. Phys.* **20**, 71 (1952). "Collisional Perturbation of Spin-Orbital Coupling and the Mechanism of Fluorescence Quenching. A Visual Demonstration of the Perturbation."

Kasha, M., and S. P. McGlynn, *Ann. Rev. Phys. Chem.* **7**, 403 (1956). "Molecular Electronic Spectroscopy."

Kasha, M., *Rev. Mod. Phys.* **31**, 162 (1959). "Relation between Exciton Bands and Conduction Bands in Molecular Lamellar Systems."

Kasha, M., *Radiat. Res.* **2**, 243 (1960). "Paths of Molecular Excitation."

Kasha, M., M. Ashraf El-Bayoumi, and W. Rhodes, *J. Chim. Phys.* **58**, 916 (1961a). "Excited States of Nitrogen Base-Pairs and Polynucleotides."

Kasha, M., *J. Mol. Spectrosc.* **6**, 111 (1961b). "Introductory Remarks of Dr. M. Kasha to the Symposium on Molecular Electronic Spectra."

Kasha, M., *Radiat. Res.* **20**, 53 (1963a). "Introductory Remarks to the Exciton Symposium."

Kasha, M., *Radiat. Res.* **20**, 55 (1963b). "Energy Transfer Mechanisms and the Molecular Exciton Model for Molecular Aggregates."

Kasha, M., in *Physical Processes in Radiation Biology* (L. G. Augenstein, B. Rosenberg, and R. Mason, eds.), p. 17, Academic Press, New York, 1964. "Classification of Excitons."

Kasha, M., H. R. Rawls, and M. Ashraf El-Bayoumi, *Pure Appl. Chem.* **2**, 371 (1965). "The Exciton Model in Molecular Spectroscopy."

Kasha, M., *Proc. Int. Conf. Luminescence, Budapest, 1966*, p. 166, Publishing House of the Hungarian Acad. Sci., Budapest, 1968a. "Theory of Molecular Luminescence."

Kasha, M., *Proc. Ann. Sci. Conf., Yeshiva Univ., N. Y.* **2**, 1 (1968b). "Theory of Molecular Luminescence (Luminescence and Intramolecular Energy Transfer)."

Katorski, A., and D. White, *J. Chim. Phys.* **60**, 29 (1963). "Theory of Isotope Separation of Homo- and Heteronuclear Diatomic Molecules by Adsorption at Low Temperatures."

Katorski, A., and D. White, *J. Chem. Phys.* **40**, 3183 (1964). "Theory of Adsorption of the Isotopic Hydrogen Molecules at Low Temperatures."

Kats, M. L., K. E. Gyunsburg, and L. I. Golubentseva, *Izv. Akad. Nauk SSSR, Ser. Fiz.* **25**, 43 (1961). "Exciton Excitation of Luminescence in Activated Alkali-Iodides at Low Temperature."

Katul, J. A., *J. Chem. Phys.* **47**, 1012 (1967). "Tetracene Dimer."

Katz, B., A. Ron, and O. Schnepp, *J. Chem. Phys.* **46**, 1926 (1967a). "Far-Infrared Spectra of HCl and HBr in Solid Solutions."

Katz, B., A. Ron, and O. Schnepp, *J. Chem. Phys.* **47**, 5303 (1967b). "Far-Infrared Spectrum of HCl Dimers."

Katz, B., and J. Jortner, *Chem. Phys. Lett.* **2**, 437 (1968a). "Observation of Molecular Rydberg States in Rare Gas Solids."

Katz, B., M. Brith, A. Ron, B. Sharf, and J. Jortner, *Chem. Phys. Lett.* **2**, 189 (1968b). "An Experimental Study of the Higher Excited States of Benzene in Rare-Gas Matrix."

Katz, B., M. Brith, B. Sharf, and J. Jortner, *J. Chem. Phys.* **50**, 5195 (1969). "Rydberg States of Benzene in Rare-Gas Matrices."

Kautsky, H., *Nature* **19**, 1043 (1931). "Die Aufklärung der Photolumineszenztilgung fluoreszierender Systeme durch Sauerstoff: Die Bildung aktiver, diffusionsfähiger

Sauerstoffmoleküle durch Sensibilisierung."

Kautsky, H., and A. Hirsch, *Deut. Chem. Ges. Ber.* **65**, 401 (1932). "Phosphoreszenz adsorbierter fluoreszierender Farbstoffe und ihre Beziehung zu reversiblen und irreversiblen Struktur-Änderungen der Gele."

Kawaoka, K., A. U. Khan, and D. R. Kearns, *J. Chem. Phys.* **46**, 1842 (1967). "Role of Singlet Excited States of Molecular Oxygen in the Quenching of Organic Triplet States."

Kawski, A., *Bull. Acad. Pol. Sci.* **6**, 533 (1958). "Effect of Concentration on the Polarization of the Fluorescence of Rigid Solutions."

Kazzaz, A. A., and A. B. Zahlan, *J. Chem. Phys.* **48**, 1242 (1968). "Temperature Dependence of Crystalline Tetracene Fluorescence."

Kearns, D. R., G. Marsh, and K. Schaffner, *J. Chem. Phys.* **49**, 3316 (1968). "Excited Singlet and Triplet States of a Cyclic Conjugated Enone."

Keil, T. H., *J. Chem. Phys.* **46**, 4404 (1967). "Polarizability of an Argon Atom in Solid Argon."

Keller, R. A., *Chem. Phys. Lett.* **3**, 27 (1969). "Excited Triplet-Singlet Intersystem Crossing."

Kelliher, J. M., Jr., Ph. D. Thesis, University of Connecticut, Storrs, Connecticut, 1966. "The Effect of Temperature on Infrared Spectra."

Kellogg, R. E., and R. P. Schwenker, *J. Chem. Phys.* **41**, 2860 (1964). "'Temperature Effect' on Triplet State Lifetimes in Solid Solutions."

Kellogg, R. E., and N. C. Wyeth, *J. Chem. Phys.* **45**, 3156 (1966). "Evidence of Franck-Condon Factors in Radiationless Transitions."

Kembrovskii, G. S., V. P. Bobrovich, and A. N. Sevchenko, *Opt. Spectrosc.* (USSR) (English Transl.) **24**, 213 (1968). "Quasiline Luminescence Spectra of Benzene."

Kerley, G. I., *Diss. Abstr. B*, **27**, 3888 (1967). "Theoretical Study of the Rotation and Vibration of Matrix-Isolated Molecules."

Kern, J., F. Dörr, and G. Scheibe, *Z. Electrochem.* **66**, 462 (1962). "Verzögerte Fluoreszenz bei Cyaninfarbstoffen."

Kestner, N. R., and O. Sinanoglu, *J. Chem. Phys.* **45**, 194 (1966a). "Intermolecular-Potential-Energy Curves—Theory and Calculations on the Helium-Helium Potential."

Kestner, N. R., *J. Chem. Phys.* **45**, 208 (1966b). "Long-Range Interaction of Helium Atoms. A. Calculations."

Kestner, N. R., *J. Chem. Phys.* **45**, 213 (1966c). "Long-Range Interaction of Helium Atoms. B. Study of Approximations."

Kestner, N. R., *J. Chem. Phys.* **45**, 3121 (1966d). "Effect of Intra-Atomic Correlation on Long-Range Intermolecular Forces: An Exactly Soluble Model."

Keyser, L. F., and G. W. Robinson, *J. Amer. Chem. Soc.* **82**, 5245 (1960). "Frozen NH Radicals from the Photodecomposition of Hydrozoic Acid."

Keyser, L. F., Ph. D. Thesis, California Institute of Technology, 1965. "Spectra of Matrix Isolated Molecules."

Keyser, L. F., and G. W. Robinson, *J. Chem. Phys.* **44**, 3225 (1966a). "Infrared Spectra of HCl and DCl in Solid Rare Gases. I. Monomers."

Keyser, L. F., and G. W. Robinson, *J. Chem. Phys.* **45**, 1694 (1966b). "Infrared Spectra of HCl and DCl in Solid Rare Gases. II. Polymers."

Khalupovskii, M. D., *Opt. Spectrosc.* (USSR) (English Transl.) **11**, 352 (1961). "On the Phosphorescence of Organic Molecules with Two Metastable Levels."

Khanna, V. M., G. Besenbruch, and J. L. Margrave, *J. Chem. Phys.* **46**, 2310 (1967).

"Ultraviolet Absorption Spectrum of SiF₂."

Kharitonova, O. P., *Opt. Spectrosc.* (USSR) (English Transl.) **15**, 9 (1963). "Electronic Spectra of 2,6-Dimethylnaphthalene in Solution."

Khesina, A. Y., *Bull. Acad. Sci. USSR. Phys. Ser.* (English Transl.) **24**, 629 (1960). "Spectroscopy of Some Pyrene Derivatives in Frozen Solutions."

Khesina, A. Y., *Opt. Spectrosc.* (USSR) (English Transl.) **10**, 319 (1961). "Emission and Absorption Spectra of Frozen Crystalline Solutions of Certain Pyrene Derivatives."

Kim, J. J., R. A. Beardslee, D. T. Phillips, and H. W. Offen, *J. Chem. Phys.* **51**, 2761 (1969). "Fluorescence Lifetimes of Pyrene Monomer and Excimer at High Pressures."

King, B. A., Ph. D. Thesis, University of California, Berkeley, California, 1968, and UCRL-18618. "Optical Absorption Spectra of Matrix-Isolated Copper, Silver, and Gold."

King, C. M., and E. R. Nixon, *J. Chem. Phys.* **48**, 1685 (1968). "Matrix-Isolation Study of the Hydrogen Cyanide Dimer."

King, S. T., *J. Chem. Phys.* **49**, 1321 (1968). "Infrared Study of Matrix-Isolated Chlorinated Tetrahedral Molecules."

Kinoshita, M., T. N. Misra, and S. P. McGlynn, *J. Chem. Phys.* **45**, 817 (1966). "Delayed Luminescence of Organic Mixed Crystals. III. Decay Characteristics."

Kinoshita, M., and S. P. McGlynn, *Mol. Cryst.* **3**, 163 (1967). "Delayed Luminescence of Organic Mixed Crystals."

Kinoshita, M., K. Stolzle, and S. P. McGlynn, *J. Chem. Phys.* **48**, 1191 (1968). "Delayed Luminescence of Organic Mixed Crystals. VII. Intermolecular Triplet Decay Processes."

Kirk, R. D., *J. Electrochem. Soc.* **101**, 461 (1954). "Role of Sulfur in the Luminescence and Coloration of Some Aluminosilicates."

Kisliak, G. M., *Opt. Spectrosc.* (USSR) (English Transl.) **5**, 297 (1958). "On the Dependence of the Excited State Duration of Organoluminophors on the Wavelength of the Exciting Light."

Kisliak, G. M., *Opt. Spectrosc.* (USSR) (English Transl.) **6**, 144 (1959). "The Law of Phosphorescence Decay for Trypaflavine in Formic Acid."

Kisliak, G. M., G. M. Lysenko, and V. I. Ponochovny, *Ukr. Fiz. Zh.* **11**, 1350 (1966). "Carbazol Phosphorescence."

Kittelberger, J. S., and D. F. Hornig, *J. Chem. Phys.* **46**, 3099 (1967). "Vibrational Spectrum of Crystalline HF and DF."

Kiyanskaya, L. A., *Bull. Acad. Sci. USSR Phys. Ser.* **29**, 1363 (1965). "Concerning the Kinetics of Quenching of the Luminescence of Organic Substances in Solutions."

Klasens, H. A., *Phys. Chem. Solids* **9**, 185 (1959). "The Temperature Dependence of the Fluorescence of Photoconductors."

Klein, M. L., and R. J. Munn, *J. Chem. Phys.* **47**, 1035 (1967). "Interaction Potential of the Inert Gases."

Klemperer, W., and G. C. Pimentel, *J. Chem. Phys.* **22**, 1399 (1954). "Hydrogen Bonding in Sodium Trifluoroacetate-Trifluoroacetic Acid Compounds."

Klick, C. C., *J. Phys. Chem.* **57**, 776 (1953). "Emission and Absorption in Luminescent Centers at Low Temperatures."

Klick, C. C., and J. H. Schulman, *Solid State Phys.* **5**, 97 (1957). "Luminescence in Solids."

Kliger, D. S., J. D. Laposa, and A. C. Albrecht, *J. Chem. Phys.* **48**, 4326 (1968). "Recombination Lifetime of Laser Stimulated Recombination Luminescence in a Rigid Organic Solution."

Klimova, L. A., and G. N. Nersesova, *Opt. Spectrosc.* (USSR) (English Transl.) **21**, 167 (1966). "Spectroscopy of Aromatic Hydrocarbon Mixtures in Frozen Crystalline Solutions. I. Study of a Binary Mixture of Anthracene and Naphthacene in *n*-Paraffin Solutions at 77°K."

Klochkov, V. P., and S. M. Korotkov, *Bull. Acad. Sci. USSR Phys. Ser.* **29**, 1359 (1965). "Temperature Dependence of Change of the Equilibrium Separations in Aromatic Compounds."

Klöpffer, W., *J. Chem. Phys.* **50**, 1689 (1969a). "Transfer of Electronic Excitation Energy in Solid Solutions of Perylene in N-Isopropylcarbazole."

Klöpffer, W., *J. Chem. Phys.* **50**, 2337 (1969b). "Transfer of Electronic Excitation Energy in Polyvinyl Carbazole."

Kloss, H. G., and G. Wendel, *Z. Naturforsch.* **16a**, 61 (1961). "Ein neues Phasenfluorometer."

Knox, R. S., *J. Chem. Phys.* **9**, 238 (1959). "Exciton States in Rare-Gas Crystals."

Knox, R. S., *Radiat. Res.* **20**, 77 (1963). "Wannier Excitons in Simple van der Waals Crystals."

Knox, R. S., and M. H. Reilly, *Phys. Rev.* **135A**, 166 (1964). "Atomic Multipole Interactions in Rare-Gas Crystals."

Koehler, T. R., *Phys. Rev. Lett.* **22**, 777 (1969). "Theoretical Temperature-Dependent Phonon Spectra of Solid Neon."

Kölbel, H., *Naturwissenschaften* **41**, 550 (1954). "Light-Filter Combination for Observation of Fluorescence in Entire Spectral Range."

Kondo, M., M. R. Romayne, J. P. Guarino, and W. H. Hamill, *J. Amer. Chem. Soc.* **86**, 1297 (1964). "Photoionization and γ-Induced Oxidation of Aromatic Amines in Rigid Organic Glasses."

Konstantinova-Shlesinger, M. A., *Lyuminestsentsii Analiz*, Izdatelstvo Akademia Nauk SSSR, Moscow and Leningrad, 1948.

Kopelman, R., and O. Schnepp, *J. Chem. Phys.* **30**, 597 (1959). "Infrared Spectrum of Hexachlorobenzene."

Kopelman, R., *J. Chem. Phys.* **44**, 3547 (1966). "Vibrational Exciton Splitting, Fermi Resonance, and Crystal Structure of Methyl Iodide."

Kopelman, R., *J. Chem. Phys.* **47**, 2631 (1967a). "Interchange Symmetry. I. Molecules, Crystals, and Excitons."

Kopelman, R., *J. Chem. Phys.* **47**, 3227 (1967b). "Benzene Vibrational Exciton Spectrum."

Körber, W., and V. Zanker, *Z. Angew. Phys.* **17**, 398 (1964). "Zuordnung von π-Elektronenabsorptionsbanden mit Hilfe der Methode der Fluoreszenzpolarisation."

Korsunskii, V. M., and A. N. Faidysh, *Sov. Phys. Dokl.* (English Transl.) **8**, 564 (1963). "Triplet-Level Energy Migration in Benzophenone Crystals."

Kortüm, G., *Z. Phys. Chem.* **40**, 431 (1938). "Das optische Verhalten gelöster Ionen und seine Bedeutung für die Struktur elektrolytischer Lösungen. VII. Fluoreszenzauslöschung und Solvatation."

Kortüm, G., and B. Finckh, *Z. Phys. Chem.* **52**, 263 (1942). "Über die Fluoreszenz vielatomiger Moleküle."

Kovac, I., *Rotational Structure in Spectra of Diatomic Molecules*, American Elsevier, New York and Amsterdam, 1969.

Kowalski, J. von, *Phys. Z.* **12**, 956 (1911). "Untersuchungen über Phosphoreszenz organischer Verbindungen bei tiefen Temperaturen."

Kozyreva, E. B., and P. V. Meiklar, *Opt. Spectrosc.* (USSR) (English Transl.) **23**, 226 (1967). "Luminescence Spectra of Silver Halides at 4.2°K."

Krasnovskii, A. A., Y. E. Erokhin, and B. A. Gulyaev, *Sov. Phys. Dokl.* (English Transl.) **8**, 1020 (1964). "Temperature Dependence of Luminescence of Bacterioviridin and State of This Pigment in Photosynthetic Bacteria."

Kriegler, R. J., and H. L. Welsh, *Can. J. Phys.* **46**, 1181 (1968). "Induced Infrared Fundamental Band of Hydrogen Dissolved in Solid Argon."

Krishna, V. G., and L. Goodman, *J. Amer. Chem. Soc.* **83**, 2042 (1961). "Protonation Effects on $n \rightarrow \pi$ Transitions in Pyrimidine."

Krishna, V. G., and L. Goodman, *J. Chem. Phys.* **36**, 2217 (1962). "Polarization of $T \rightarrow S$ Emission Spectra of Azines."

Kristianpoller, N., and D. Dutton, *Appl. Opt.* **3**, 287 (1964). "Optical Properties of 'Linmogen': A Phosphor for Wavelength Conversion."

Kroenke, W. J., and M. E. Kenney, *Inorg. Chem.* **3**, 696 (1964). "The Infrared Spectra of Some Tin and Lead Phthalocyanines."

Krongauz, V. G., *Opt. Spectrosc.* (USSR) (English Transl.) **22**, 502 (1967). "On the Parallelism between the Temperature Dependence of the Brightness of X-Ray Luminescence and Optical Flash in Alkali-Halide Phosphors."

Kropp, J. L., and W. R. Dawson, *J. Chem. Phys.* **45**, 2419 (1966). "Temperature-Dependent Quenching of Fluorescence of Europic-Ion Solutions."

Kropp, J. L., and W. R. Dawson, *Int. Conf. Molecular Luminescence, Loyola Univ., Chicago, 1968.* "Fluorescence and Phosphorescence of Aromatic Hydrocarbons in Poly(Methylmethacrylate) as a Function of Temperature."

Krupskii, I. N., and V. G. Manzhely, *Phys. Status Solidi* **24**, K53 (1967). "Thermal Conductivity of Solid Argon."

Kuan, T. S., A. Warshel, and O. Schnepp, *J. Chem. Phys.* **52**, 3012 (1970). "Intermolecular Potentials for N_2 Molecules and the Lattice Vibrations of Solid α-N_2."

Kudryashov, P. I., and B. Y. Sveshnikov, *Opt. Spectrosc.* **8**, 344 (1960). "On the Concentration Depolarization of the Phosphorescence of Organoluminophors."

Kulyupin, Y. A., and A. F. Yatsenko, *Bull. Acad. Sci. USSR Phys. Ser.* (English Transl.) **29**, 1417 (1965). "On Mirror Similarity of Luminescence and Absorption Spectra."

Kupferman, S. L., and F. M. Pipkin, *Phys. Rev.* **66**, 207 (1968). "Properties of Rubidium Atoms Trapped in a Solid Argon Matrix."

Kuzmin, M. G., and L. N. Guseva, *Chem. Phys. Lett.* **3**, 71 (1969). "Donor-Acceptor Complexes of Singlet Excited States of Aromatic Hydrocarbons with Aliphatic Amines."

Kuznetsova, L. A., and B. Y. Sveshnikov, *Bull. Acad. Sci. USSR, Phys. Ser.* (English Transl.) **20**, 394 (1956). "The Influence of Concentration on the Luminescence of Alcohol Solutions of Acridine Orange at $-180°C$."

Kwiram, A. L., *Chem. Phys. Lett.* **1**, 272 (1967). "Optical Detection of Paramagnetic Resonance in Phosphorescent Triplet States."

Kwok, J., and G. W. Robinson, *J. Chem. Phys.* **36**, 3137 (1962). "Spectroscopy in Liquid-Rare-Gas Solvents. Infrared Spectra of CH_4 in Argon and of HCl in Xenon."

L

Ladner, S. J., and R. S. Becker, *J. Chem. Phys.* **43**, 3344 (1965). "Effect of Environment on the Unimolecular Decay of the Triplet State."

Laffitte, E., *C. R. Acad. Sci.* (Paris) **232**, 812 (1951). "Luminescence of Coloring Materials in Solid Solution in Plexiglass."

Laffitte, E., *Ann. Phys.* (Paris) **10**, 71 (1955). "Contribution à l'Etude de la Luminescence des Matières Colorantes."

Lalos, G. T., R. J. Corruccini, and H. P. Broida, *Rev. Sci. Instrum.* **29**, 505 (1958). "Design and Construction of a Blackbody and Its Use in the Calibration of a Grating Spectroradiometer."

Lami, H., G. Pfeffer, and G. Laustriat, *J. Phys.* (Paris) **27**, 398 (1966). "Rendements Quantiques de Fluorescence et Durées de Vie Radiative de Quelques Solutés Utilisés dans les Scintillateurs Liquides."

Landolt-Börnstein, *Zahlenwerte und Funktionen aus Naturwissenschaften und Technik* (K.-H. Hellwege and A. M. Hellwege, eds.), Gruppe II, Band 3: Luminescence of Organic Substances (by A. Schmillen and R. Legler), Springer, Berlin, 1967.

Langouet, L., and A. T'kint de Roodenbeke, *J. Phys.* (Paris) **27**, 237 (1966). "Saturation de l'Emission des Substances Fluorescentes."

La Paglia, S. R., and B. C. Roquitte, *J. Phys. Chem.* **66**, 1739 (1962a). "The Luminescence of Cyclopentane."

La Paglia, S. R., *Spectrochim. Acta* **18**, 1295 (1962b). "Singlet-Triplet Transitions in the Tetraphenyls."

Lascombe, J., P. Van Huong, and M.-L. Josien, *Soc. Chim.* (Paris) **5**, 76 (1959). "Structure de Vibration-Rotation dans les Spectres de Quelques Molécules Simples en Solution."

Lashkov, G. I., and V. L. Ermolaev, *Opt. Spectrosc.* (USSR) (English Transl.) **22**, 462 (1967). "Triplet-Triplet Energy Transfer along the Chains of Aromatic Polymers. Triplet Excitons in Polymers."

Lavalette, D., *Chem. Phys. Lett.* **3**, 67 (1969). "Polarized Excitation Spectrum of the Triplet-Triplet Absorption of Aromatic Hydrocarbons."

Lawson, C. W., F. Hirayama, and S. Lipsky, *J. Chem. Phys.* **51**, 1590 (1969). "Effect of Solvent Perturbation on the $S_3 \rightarrow S_1$ Internal Conversion Efficiency of Benzene, Toluene, and p-Xylene."

Leach, S., *J. Chim. Phys.* **55**, 714 (1958). "Méthode des Radicaux Piégés. Spectres d'Absorption et Photolyse de Quelques Molécules à 20°K."

Leach, S., R. Lopez-Delgado, and F. Delmas, *J. Mol. Spectrosc.* **7**, 304 (1961a). "On the $^3E_{1u} - {}^1A_{1g}$ Transition of Benzene and the Attribution of Weak Bands Near 2600 Å to the $^1B_{2u} - {}^1A_{1g}$ Transition."

Leach, S., and L. Grajcar, *5th Int. Symp. Free Radicals, Pure Appl. Chem.* **36**, 24, *Uppsala, 1961.* (1961b). "The Photolysis of Toluene, Dibenzyl and Benzyl Chloride in Rigid Media: Studies by Absorption and Luminescence Spectroscopy."

Leach, S., and R. Lopez-Delgado, *Advan. Mol. Spectrosc.* 419 (1962a). "Effets de Milieux Rigides sur les Spectres Electroniques du Benzène."

Leach, S., in *Luminescence of Organic and Inorganic Materials* (H. P. Kallmann and G. N. Spruch, eds.), Wiley, New York, (1962b). "The Luminescence Spectra of Some Trapped Organic Radicals."

Leach, S., and R. Lopez-Delgado, *J. Chim. Phys.* 723 (1963a). "Influence de l'Oxygène et du Tétrachlorure de Carbone sur les Spectres Electroniques du Benzène. I. Effet d'Oxygène."

Leach, S., and R. Lopez-Delgado, *C. R. Acad. Sci.* (Paris) **256**, 1299 (1963b). "Photo-ionisation, par Irradiation Ultraviolette en Milieu Rigide à 77°K, de Dérivés du Benzène Formant des Complexes Moléculaires avec le Tétrachlorure de Carbone. Piégeage d'Anions CCl_4^-."

Leach, S., *J. Chim. Phys.* 1493 (1964a). "Structure des Radicaux par Spectroscopie Electronique."

Leach, S., and R. Lopez-Delgado, *J. Chim. Phys.* 1636 (1964b). "Le Premier Etat Triplet du Benzène."

Leach, S., A. Lopez-Campillo, R. Lopez-Delgado, and M. Tomas-Magos, *C. R. Acad. Sci.* (Paris) *Ser. B* **263**, 1230 (1966a). "Spectroscopie Moléculaire—Effets de Gaz Occlus et de l'Histoire Thermique entre le Benzène et le Toluène à 80°K. Etude par Spectroscopie de Fluorescence."

Leach, S., R. Lopez-Delgado, and L. Grajcar, *J. Chim. Phys.* **63**, 194 (1966b). "Effets de Température sur les Spectres Electroniques de Benzène dans le Cyclohexane. Etudes sur le Polymorphisme Cristallin du Cyclohexane par la Méthode de la Sonde Electronique."

Leach, S., and R. Lopez-Delgado, *J. Chim. Phys.* **64**, 1247 (1967a). "Etude, par Spectroscopie de Luminescence, de l'Etat de Dispersion du Benzène dans le Cyclohexane et dans des Hydrocarbures Paraffiniques Linéaires, à 77°K."

Leach, S., *J. Phys.* (Paris) **28**, C3–134 (1967b). "Spectres Electroniques de Molécules et Radicaux Organiques en Solution Solide."

Leach, S., A. Lopez-Campillo, R. Lopez-Delgado, and M. C. Tomas-Magos, *J. Phys.* (Paris) **28**, C3–147 (1967c). "Spectres Electroniques, en Matrice Rigide, des Produits Radicalaires de la Photolyse des Diméthylbenzènes."

Leach, S., and R. Lopez-Delgado, *J. Phys.* (Paris) **28**, C3–150 (1967d). "Effets de Matrice sur les Spectres Electroniques de Benzène."

Leach, S., and E. Migirdicyan, *C. R. Acad. Sci.* (Paris) *Ser. B* **264**, 156 (1967e). "Spectroscopie Moléculaire—Le Spectre d'Emission du Radical Duryle en Phase Solide."

Leach, S., and E. Migirdicyan, *Chem. Phys. Lett.* **1**, 21 (1967f). "On the Electronic Spectra of the Duryl Radical and the Origin of the Green Emission of Durene."

Lee, E. L., *J. Phys. Chem.* **23**, 1823 (1962). "The Absorption Spectrum of Manganese Atoms in Solid Argon at 4°K."

Leech, J. W., and C. J. Peachey, *Chem. Phys. Lett.* **1**, 643 (1968). "Frequency Distribution of Phonons in Low Temperature Phase of Solid HCl."

Lefebvre-Brion, H., and F. Guérin, *J. Chem. Phys.* **49**, 1446 (1968). "Calculation of the Radiative Lifetime of the $a^4\pi$ State of NO."

Lehovec, K., *J. Opt. Soc. Amer.* **45**, 219 (1955). "Decay of Phosphorescence with Activators and Traps Arising from the Same Impurity in Different Valence States."

Leroi, G. E., G. E. Ewing, and G. C. Pimentel, *J. Chem. Phys.* **40**, 2298 (1964). "Infrared Spectra of Carbon Monoxide in an Argon Matrix."

LeRoy, A., and P. Jouvé, *C. R. Acad. Sci.* (Paris) *Ser. B* **264**, 1656 (1967). "Analyse du Spectre d'Absorption Infrarouge de N_2O Solide à 80°K."

Levenson, L. L., *Nuovo Cimento*, Suppl. **5**, 321 (1967). "Condensation Coefficients of Argon, Krypton and Xenon Measured with a Quartz Crystal Microbalance at 4.2°K."

Leverenz, H. W., *Colloid Chem.* **7**, 125 (1950). "Luminescent Solids (Phosphors)."

Levine, M., J. Jortner, and A. Szöke, *J. Chem. Phys.* **45**, 1591 (1966). "Diffusion of Triplet Excitons in Crystalline Anthracene."

Levison, G. S., W. T. Simpson, and W. Curtis, *J. Amer. Chem. Soc.* **79**, 4314 (1957). "Electronic Spectra of Pyridocyanine Dyes with Assignments of Transitions."

Levshin, V. L., *Z. Phys.* **43**, 230 (1927). "Die Auslöschung der Fluoreszenz in festen und flüssigen Farbstofflösungen."

Levshin, V. L., *Z. Phys.* **72**, 368 (1931). "Das Gesetz der Spiegelkorrespondenz der

Absorptions- und Fluoreszenzspektren. I."

Levshin, V. L., *Izv. Akad. Nauk SSSR, Ser. Fiz.* 12, 217 (1948). "The Emission Processes of Crystal Phosphors."

Levshin, V. L., *Bull. Acad. Sci. USSR, Phys. Ser.* (English Transl.) 20, 362 (1956). "Effect of Association and Other Physico-Chemical Factors on the Luminescence and Absorption of Complex Molecules in Solutions."

Levshin, V. L., and E. G. Baranova, *Izv. Akad. Nauk SSSR, Ser. Fiz.* 22, 1038 (1958a). "Different Types of Concentration Quenching and Possibility of Separating Them."

Levshin, V. L., *Advan. Phys. Sci.* 64, 62 (1958b). "The Study of Luminescence Phenomena and Development of Their Applications in the Soviet Union."

Levshin, V. L., and K. I. Mamedov, *Izv. Akad. Nauk SSSR, Ser. Khim.* 9, 1571 (1959). "Fluorescence Spectra of Aromatic Hydrocarbons of the Biphenyl Series and Their Oxygen and Sulphur-containing Analogs."

Levshin, V. L., and K. I. Mamedov, *Izv. Akad. Nauk SSSR, Ser. Fiz.* 27, 606 (1963). "Fluorescence and Phosphorescence Spectra of α- and β-Methylnaphthalenes in Normal and Isoparaffinic Solvents at 77°K."

Lewis, G. N., D. Lipkin, and T. T. Magel, *J. Amer. Chem. Soc.* 63, 3005 (1941). "Reversible Photochemical Processes in Rigid Media. A Study of the Phosphorescent State."

Lewis, G. N., T. T. Magel, and D. Lipkin, *J. Amer. Chem. Soc.* 64, 1774 (1942a). "Isomers of Crystal Violet Ion. Their Absorption and Re-emission of Light."

Lewis, G. N., and D. Lipkin, *J. Amer. Chem. Soc.* 64, 2801 (1942b). "Reversible Photochemical Processes in Rigid Media: The Dissociation of Organic Molecules into Radicals and Ions."

Lewis, G. N., and J. Bigeleisen, *J. Amer. Chem. Soc.* 65, 520 (1943a). "The Orientation of Molecules Produced Photochemically in Rigid Solvents."

Lewis, G. N., and J. Bigeleisen, *J. Amer. Chem. Soc.* 65, 2419 (1943b). "Photochemical Reactions of Leuco Dyes in Rigid Solvents. Quantum Efficiency of Photo-oxidation."

Lewis, G. N., and J. Bigeleisen, *J. Amer. Chem. Soc.* 65, 2424 (1943c). "Further Photo-oxidations in Rigid Media."

Lewis, G. N., D. Lipkin, and T. T. Magel, *J. Amer. Chem. Soc.* 66, 1579 (1944a). "The Light Absorption and Fluorescence of Triarylmethyl Free Radicals."

Lewis, G. N., and M. Kasha, *J. Amer. Chem. Soc.* 66, 2100 (1944b). "Phosphorescence and the Triplet State."

Lewis, G. N., and M. Kasha, *J. Amer. Chem. Soc.* 67, 994 (1945a). "Phosphorescence in Fluid Media and the Reverse Process of Singlet-Triplet Absorption."

Lewis, G. N., and M. Calvin, *J. Amer. Chem. Soc.* 67, 1232 (1945b). "Paramagnetism of the Phosphorescent State."

Lewis, G. N., M. Calvin, and M. Kasha, *J. Chem. Phys.* 17, 804 (1949). "Photomagnetism. Determination of the Paramagnetic Susceptibility of a Dye in Its Phosphorescent State."

Libby, W. F., *Amer. Chem. Soc. Meeting, Minneapolis, April 1969*, unpublished. "Polymers from Carbon Vapor and Benzene."

Lider, K. F., and B. V. Novikov, *Opt. Spectrosc.* (USSR) (English Transl.) 22, 328 (1967). "Effect of Ionic Bombardment on the Low-Temperature Luminescence Spectrum of CdS Crystals."

Liebson, S. H., *Nucleonics* 10, 41 (1952). "Temperature Effects in Organic Fluors."

Lim, E. C., and G. W. Swenson, *J. Chem. Phys.* 36, 118 (1962). "Delayed Fluorescence of Acriflavine in Rigid Media."

Lim, E. C., and W.-Y. Wen, *J. Chem. Phys.* **39**, 847 (1963a). "Delayed Fluorescence and Possible One-Electron Photo-Ionization of Dyes in Rigid Media."

Lim, E. C., and G. W. Swenson, *J. Chem. Phys.* **39**, 2768 (1963b). "One-Electron Photo-Ionization of Acridine Dyes in Rigid Media: Evidence for the Formation of Transient Radical Ion."

Lim, E. C., C. P. Lazzarce, M. Y. Young, and G. W. Swenson, *J. Chem. Phys.* **43**, 970 (1965). "Photoionization and Delayed Fluorescence of Dyes in Rigid Organic Matrices. I. A Proposed Model."

Lim, E. C., and S. K. Chakrabarti, *Chem. Phys. Lett.* **1**, 28 (1967a). "Intramolecular Charge-Transfer Transition and Spin Orbit Coupling in Heteroaromatic Molecules."

Lim, E. C., and S. K. Chakrabarti, *Mol. Phys.* **13**, 293 (1967b). "Excimer Phosphorescence of Halogenated Benzenes in Organic Glasses."

Lin, S. H., and R. Bersohn, *J. Chem. Phys.* **48**, 2732 (1968). "Effect of Partial Deuteration and Temperature on Triplet-State Lifetimes."

Linevsky, M. J., *J. Chem. Phys.* **34**, 587 (1961). "Infrared Spectrum of Lithium Fluoride Monomer by Matrix Isolation."

Linevsky, M. J., *J. Chem. Phys.* **38**, 658 (1963). "Infrared Absorption Spectra of LiF and Li_2F_2 in Solid Argon, Krypton, and Xenon Matrices."

Ling, H. C., and J. E. Willard, *J. Phys. Chem.* **72**, 1918 (1968a). "Viscosities of Some Organic Glasses Used as Trapping Matrices."

Ling, H. C., and J. E. Willard, *J. Phys. Chem.* **72**, 3349 (1968b). "Viscosities of Some Organic Glasses Used as Trapping Matrices. II."

Linschitz, H., M. G. Berry, and D. Schweitzer, *J. Amer. Chem. Soc.* **76**, 5833 (1954a). "The Identification of Solvated Electrons and Radicals in Rigid Solutions of Photo-oxidized Organic Molecules; Recombination Luminescence in Organic Phosphors."

Linschitz, H., J. Rennert, and J. M. Korn, *J. Amer. Chem. Soc.* **76**, 5839 (1954b). "Symmetrical Semiquinone Formation by Reversible Photo-oxidation and Photo-reduction."

Lippert, E., *Z. Elektrochem.* **61**, 962 (1957). "Spektroskopische Bestimmung des Dipol-momentes aromatischer Verbindungen im ersten angeregten Singulettzustand."

Lippert, E., W. Luder, F. Moll, W. Nagele, H. Boos, H. Prigge, and I. Seibold, *Z. Angew. Chem.* **73**, 695 (1961). "Umwandlung von Elektronenanregungsenergie."

Lippert, E., and W. Voss, *Z. Phys. Chem.* (Frankfurt) **31**, 321 (1962). "Die Elektronen-Spektren des 3,4-Benzcinnolins. Beobachtung einer $\pi^* \to n$-Fluoreszenz."

Lipsett, R. F., and D. H. Goode, in *The Triplet State* (*Proc. Int. Symp. Amer. Univ., Beirut*) (A. B. Zahlan, ed.), p. 425, Cambridge University Press, London and New York, 1967. "Decay Time of Delayed Fluorescence of Anthracene as a Function of Temperature."

Lisovskaya, I. A., M. D. Zakharova, and I. G. Kaplan, *Opt. Spectrosc.* **22**, 348 (1967). "On Triplet-Triplet Energy Transfer from Benzene and Toluene to Diacetyl in the Liquid Phase."

Litvin, F. F., and R. I. Personov, *Sov. Phys. Dokl.* (English Transl.) **6**, 134 (1961). "Fine Structure of the Absorption and Fluorescence Spectra of Some Pigments at 77°K."

Loewenschuss, A., A. Ron, and O. Schnepp, *J. Chem. Phys.* **49**, 272 (1968). "The Vibrational Spectra and Thermodynamics of the Zinc Halides."

Loewenschuss, A., A. Ron, and O. Schnepp, *J. Chem. Phys.* **50**, 2502 (1969). "Vibrational Spectra of Group IIB Halides. II. The Halides of Cadmium and Mercury."

Loewenthal, E., *J. Chem. Phys.* **48**, 2819 (1968a). "Delayed Fluorescence of Solid Solutions of Cyclohexane."

Loewenthal, E., Y. Tomkiewicz, and A. Weinrib, *Chem. Phys. Lett.* **2**, 29 (1968b). "An Effect of Concentration and Excitation Wavelength on the Emission Spectrum of Pyrene Monomer."

Lombardi, J. R., and G. A. Daffron, *J. Chem. Phys.* **44**, 3882 (1966). "Anisotropic Rotational Relaxation in Rigid Media by Polarized Photoselection."

Lombos, B. A., P. Sauvageau, and C. Sandorfy, *Chem. Phys. Lett.* **1**, 382 (1967a). "Far Ultraviolet Spectra of Solid Films of Methane, Ethane and Propane."

Lombos, B. A., P. Sauvageau, and C. Sandorfy, *Chem. Phys. Lett.* **1**, 39 (1967b). "The Electronic Spectra of Normal Paraffin Hydrocarbons."

Longin, P., *C. R. Acad. Sci.* (Paris) **248**, 1971 (1959). "Contribution à l'Etude de la Fluorescence des Acides Aminés en Solutions Aqueuses."

Longin, P., *C. R. Acad. Sci.* (Paris) **251**, 2499 (1960). "Luminescence en Phase Vapeur en Solution Etendue. Cristallisée à 77°K de Quelques Aldehydes et Cétones Aliphatiques."

Longuet-Higgins, H. C., and J. A. Pople, *J. Chem. Phys.* **27**, 192 (1957). "Electronic Spectral Shifts of Nonpolar Molecules in Nonpolar Solvents."

Longworth, J. W., R. O. Rahn, and R. G. Shulman, *J. Chem. Phys.* **45**, 2930 (1966). "Luminescence of Pyrimidines, Purines, Nucleosides, and Nucleotides at 77°K. The Effect of Ionization and Tautomerization."

Lord, R. C., R. S. McDonald, and F. A. Miller, *J. Opt. Soc. Amer.* **42**, 149 (1952). "Notes on the Practice of Infrared Spectroscopy."

Low, W., in *Quantum Electronics*, a symposium (C. H. Towns, ed.), p. 40. Columbia University Press, New York, 1960. "Optical Properties of Paramagnetic Solids."

Lower, S. K., R. M. Hochstrasser, and C. Reid, *Mol. Phys.* **4**, 161 (1961). "The Polarized Charge-Transfer Spectrum of Crystalline Anthracene-TNB Complex."

Lower, S. K., and M. A. El-Sayed, *Chem. Rev.* **66**, 199 (1966). "The Triplet State and Molecular Electronic Processes in Organic Molecules."

Lushchik, C. B., *Bull. Acad. Sci. USSR Phys. Ser.* (English Transl.) **29**, 11 (1965). "Physical Processes in Luminescent Ionic Crystals."

Lyalin, G. N., and G. I. Kobyshev, *Opt. Spectrosc.* (USSR) (English Transl.) **15**, 135 (1963). "Luminescence and Intracomplex Energy Transfer of Uranyl Phthalocyanine."

M

McCarty, M., Jr., and G. W. Robinson, *Mol. Phys.* **2**, 415 (1959a). "Environmental Perturbations on Foreign Atoms and Molecules in Solid Argon, Krypton and Xenon."

McCarty, M., Jr., and G. W. Robinson, *J. Amer. Chem. Soc.* **81**, 4472 (1959b). "Imine and Imine-d Radicals Trapped in Argon, Krypton and Xenon Matrices at 4.2°K."

McCarty, M., Jr., and G. W. Robinson, *J. Chim. Phys.* **56**, 723 (1959c). "Les Spectres d'Absorption Electroniques des Radicaux Libres de Petite Dimension dans les Milieux Rigides Constitués par des Gaz Rares."

McCarty, M., *J. Chem. Phys.* **52**, 4973 (1970). "Mercury $^3P_1 \leftarrow {}^1S_0$ Transition in Solid Rare Gases."

McClain, W. M., and A. C. Albrecht, *J. Chem. Phys.* **43**, 465 (1965). "On the Nature of Stimulated Emission in Rigid Organic Solutions."

McClellan, A. L., and G. C. Pimentel, *J. Chem. Phys.* **23**, 245 (1955). "Vibrational Assignment and Thermodynamic Properties of Naphthalene."

McClure, D. S., *J. Chem. Phys.* **17**, 905 (1949). "Triplet-Singlet Transitions in Organic Molecules. Lifetime Measurements of the Triplet State."

McClure, D. S., *J. Chem. Phys.* **19**, 670 (1951). "Excited Triplet States of Some Polyatomic Molecules. I."

McClure, D. S., N. W. Blake, and P. L. Hanst, *J. Chem. Phys.* **22**, 255 (1954). "Singlet-Triplet Absorption Bands in Some Halogen Substituted Aromatic Compounds."

McClure, D. S., *J. Chem. Phys.* **23**, 1575 (1955a). "Electronic States of the Naphthalene Crystal."

McClure, D. S., and P. L. Hanst, *J. Chem. Phys.* **23**, 1772 (1955b). "Excited Triplet States of Polyatomic Molecules. II. Flash-Lamp Studies on Aromatic Ketones."

McClure, D. S., *J. Chem. Phys.* **24**, 1 (1956a). "Excited States of the Naphthalene Molecule. II. Further Studies on the First Singlet-Triplet Transition."

McClure, D. S., *J. Chem. Phys.* **25**, 481 (1956b). "First Singlet-Singlet Electronic Transition in the Phenanthrene Molecule and the Band Structure of the Phenanthrene Crystal."

McClure, D. S., *Solid State Phys.* **8**, 1 (1959). "Electronic Spectra of Molecules and Ions in Crystals. I. Molecular Crystals."

McClure, D. S., *Radiat. Res.*, Suppl. **2**, 218 (1960). "Electronic Structure of Transition-Metal Complex Ions."

McClure, D. S., *Proc. Conf. on Electrical Conductivity in Organic Solids* (H. Kallmann, ed.), p. 219, Interscience (Wiley), New York, 1961a. "Dispersion Forces in Molecular Crystals."

McClure, D. S., *Proc. 6th Int. Conf. on Coordination Chemistry*, p. 498, Macmillan, New York, 1961b. "Energy Level Splittings in Non-Cubic Ions and the Two-Dimensional Spectrochemical Series."

McClure, D. S., *J. Chem. Phys.* **36**, 2757 (1962). "Optical Spectra of Transition-Metal Ions in Corundum."

McClure, D. S., in *Phonons in Perfect Lattices and in Lattices with Perfect Imperfections* (R. Stevenson, ed.), Oliver & Boyd, Edinburgh and London, 1966. "The Electronic States and Spectra of Ions and Imperfections in Solids."

McConnell, H., and D. S. McClure, *J. Chem. Phys.* **21**, 1296 (1953). "Even-Odd Character of the 2900–3200 Å Absorption Transition in Naphthalene."

Macfarlane, R. M., *Phys. Rev.* **158**, 252 (1967). "Stress-Induced Trigonal Crystal-Field Parameters in Some Oxide Lattices."

Macfarlane, R. M., and J. Y. Wong, *Phys. Rev.* **166**, 250 (1968). "Dynamic Jahn-Teller Effect in Octahedrally Coordinated d^1 Impurity Systems."

McGlynn, S. P., *Chem. Rev.* **58**, 1113 (1958). "Energetics of Molecular Complexes."

McGlynn, S. P., *Radiat. Res.*, Suppl. **2**, 300 (1960a). "Donor-Acceptor Interaction."

McGlynn, S. P., J. D. Boggus, and E. Elder, *J. Chem. Phys.* **32**, 357 (1960b). "Energy Transfer in Molecular Complexes. II. The Anthracene-*sym*-Trinitrobenzene Complex."

McGlynn, S. P., R. Sunseri, and N. Christodouleas, *J. Chem. Phys.* **37**, 1818 (1962a). "External Heavy-Atom Spin-Orbital Coupling Effect. I. The Nature of the Interaction."

McGlynn, S. P., M. J. Reynolds, G. W. Daigre, and N. D. Christodouleas, *J. Phys. Chem.* **66**, 2499 (1962b). "The External Heavy-Atom Spin-Orbital Coupling Effect. III. Phosphorescence Spectra and Lifetimes of Externally Perturbed Naphthalenes."

McGlynn, S. P., J. Daigre, and N. Christodouleas, *Org. Cryst. Symp.*, *Proc. Nat. Res. Council Can.* p. 33 (1962c). "Intersystem Crossing and Donor-Acceptor Interaction."

McGlynn, S. P., and T. Azumi, *J. Chem. Phys.* **37**, 2413 (1962d). "The Polarization of the Luminescence of Phenanthrene."

McGlynn, S. P., J. Daigre, and F. J. Smith, *J. Chem. Phys.* **39**, 675 (1963). "External Heavy-Atom Spin-Orbital Coupling Effect. IV. Intersystem Crossing."

McGlynn, S. P., and N. Christodouleas, *J. Chem. Phys.* **40**, 166 (1964a). "Energy Transfer in Charge Transfer Complexes. III. Intersystem Crossing."

McGlynn, S. P., and T. Azumi, *J. Chem. Phys.* **40**, 507 (1964b). "External Heavy-Atom Spin-Orbital Coupling Effect. V. Absorption Studies of Triplet States."

McGlynn, S. P., and F. J. Smith, *J. Chem. Phys.* **42**, 4308 (1965a). "Delayed Excimer Fluorescence of Pyrene."

McGlynn, S. P., A. T. Armstrong, and T. Azumi, in *Modern Quantum Chemistry* (O. Sinanoğlu, ed.), Part III, Chapter 6, Academic Press, New York, 1965b. "Interaction of Molecular Exciton, Charge Resonance States and Excimer Luminescence."

McGlynn, S. P., L. Azarraga, and F. Watson, in *Modern Quantum Chemistry* (O. Sinanoğlu, ed.), Part III, Chapter 9, Academic Press, New York, 1965c. "Temperature Dependence of Photoconductivity in Organic Molecular Crystals."

McGlynn, S. P., T. N. Misra, and E. F. McCoy, *Proc. Int. Symp. Luminescence Munich, 1965*, p. 320, Thiemig, Munich, 1966. "A Mechanistic Model of the Origin of Delayed Fluorescence of Organic Mixed Crystals."

McGlynn, S. P., M. Kinoshita, M. McCarville, B. N. Srinivasan, and J. W. Rabalais, *Photochem. Photobiol.* **8**, 349 (1968). "Delayed Luminescence of Organic Mixed Crystals. VIII. The Luminescence of Impure Crystals."

McGlynn, S. P., T. Azumi, and M. Kinoshita, *Molecular Spectroscopy of the Triplet State*, Prentice-Hall, Englewood Cliffs, New Jersey, 1969.

McIntosh, J. S. E., and G. B. Porter, *J. Chem. Phys.* **48**, 5475 (1968). "Kinetics of Excited Molecules. VI. Energy Transfer from Hexafluoroacetone Hexafluorobiacetyl."

McKean, D. C., *Spectrochim. Acta* **23A**, 2403 (1967). "Infra-red Spectra of Crystals. IV. Matrix Shifts and the Contribution from Classical Electrostatic Forces."

McLennan, J. C., and G. M. Shrum, *Proc. Roy. Soc.* (London) *Ser. A* **106**, 138 (1924). "On the Luminescence of Nitrogen, Argon, and Other Condensed Gases at Very Low Temperatures."

McLennan, J. C., H. J. C. Ireton, and E. W. Samson, *Proc. Roy. Soc.* (London) *Ser. A* **120**, 303 (1928). "On the Luminescence of Solid Nitrogen under Cathode Ray Bombardment."

McLennan, J. C., and J. H. McLeod, *Nature* **123**, 160 (1929). "The Raman Effect with Liquid Oxygen, Nitrogen and Hydrogen."

McLeod, D., Jr., and W. Weltner, Jr., *J. Phys. Chem.* **70**, 3293 (1966). "Spectroscopy and Franck-Condon Factors of Scandium Fluoride in Neon Matrices at 4°K."

Macleod, H. A., *Thin Film Optical Filters*, American Elsevier, New York and Amsterdam, 1969.

McMahon, D. H., and M. Kestigian, *J. Chem. Phys.* **46**, 137 (1967). "Triplet-Triplet Annihilation in Anthracene at Low-Excitation Intensities: Wavelength and Temperature Dependence."

McMurry, H. L., *J. Chem. Phys.* **9**, 241 (1941). "The Long Wave-Length Spectra of Aldehydes and Ketones. Part II. Conjugated Aldehydes and Ketones."

McNamee, R. W., Jr., Ph. D. Thesis, University of California, Berkeley, California (1962) and U.S. Atomic Energy Comm., UCLRL 10451 (1962). "Matrix Isolation Studies of High-Temperature Species. Group II Chlorides."

McRae, E. G., and M. Kasha, *J. Chem. Phys.* **28**, 721 (1958). "Enhancement of Phosphorescence Ability upon Aggregation of Dye Molecules."

Macnab, R. M., and K. Sauer, *J. Chem. Phys.* **53**, 2805 (1970). "Absorption and Fluorescence of Anthracene in *n*-Alkane Matrices at 4°K."

Mador, I. L., and R. S. Quinn, *J. Chem. Phys.* **20**, 1837 (1952). "The Influence of Temperature and State on Infrared Absorption Spectra: Methyl Iodide."

Mador, I. L., and M. C. Williams, *J. Chem. Phys.* **22**, 1627 (1954). "Stabilization of Free Radicals from the Decomposition of Hydrazoic Acid."

Magee, J. L., *Radiat. Res.* **20**, 71 (1963). "Energy Transfer Phenomena and Dissociation Processes in Electronically Excited Molecules."

Mahbub'ul Alam, A. S. M., and B. Di Bartolo, *J. Chem.* **47**, 3790 (1967). "Thermal Dependence of Fluorescence and Lifetimes of Sm^{2+} in Several Host Lattices."

Maier, G., U. Haeberlen, and H. C. Wolf, *Phys. Lett.* **25A**, 323 (1967a). "Kernspin-Relaxation durch Triplett-Excitonen in Anthracen."

Maier, G., U. Haeberlen, H. C. Wolf, and K. H. Hausser, *Phys. Lett.* **25A**, 384 (1967b). "Optische Kernspin-Polarisation in Anthracen-Kristallen."

Maier, G., and H. C. Wolf, *Z. Naturforsch.* **23a**, 1068 (1968). "Relaxation und optische Kernspinpolarisation der Protonen in optisch angeregten Anthracen-Kristallen."

Majernikova, L., *Czech. J. Phys.* **17**, 717 (1967). "A Contribution to the Theory of the Faraday Effect of Excitons in Rare-Gas Crystals."

Makarevich, L. A., E. S. Sokolova, and G. A. Sorina, *Russ. J. Phys. Chem.* (English Transl.) **42** (1968). "Critical Parameters of Sulphur Hexafluoride."

Maki, A., and J. C. Decius, *J. Chem. Phys.* **28**, 1003 (1958). "Infrared Spectrum of Cyanate Ion as a Solid Solution in a Potassium Iodide Lattice."

Malkes, L. Y., L. L. Nagornaya, and A. I. Timchenko, *Opt. Spectrosc.* (USSR) (English Transl.) **10**, 291 (1961). "The Luminescence Spectra and Scintillation Properties of Para-Monohalogen Substituted Trans-Stilbene."

Mamedov, K. I., *Bull. Acad. Sci., USSR, Phys. Ser.* (English Transl.) **29**, 1413 (1965). "Absorption, Fluorescence and Phosphorescence Spectra of Acenaphthene in Alkane Solvents at 77°K."

Mamedov, K. I., and R. Z. Laipanov, *Opt. Spectrosc.* (USSR) (English Transl.) **20**, 280 (1966). "On the Manifestation of Lines and Background in the Quasi-Line Phosphorescence Spectrum of Quinoline in Paraffins at 77°K."

Mann, D. E., N. Acquista, and D. White, *J. Chem. Phys.* **44**, 3453 (1966). "Infrared Spectra of HCl, DCl, HBr, and DBr in Solid Rare-Gas Matrices."

Mann, D. E., G. V. Calder, K. S. Seshadri, D. White, and M. J. Linevsky, *J. Chem. Phys.* **46**, 1138 (1967). "Geometry and Vibrational Spectra of the Alkaline-Earth Dihalides. I. MgF_2."

Mann, D. M., and H. P. Broida, Arpa Report #125; Ph. D. Thesis, University of California, Santa Barbara, 1970. "UV Absorption Spectra of Transition Metal Atoms in Rare Gas Matrices."

Mansour, S., and A. Weinreib, *Chem. Phys. Lett.* **2**, 653 (1968). "On the Decay Pattern of Solid Solutions of Anthracene and Naphthalene."

Maradudin, A. A., *Ann. Rev. Phys. Chem.* **14**, 90 (1963). "Equilibrium Thermodynamic Properties of Harmonic Crystals."

March, N. H., and J. C. Stoddart, *Rep. Progr. Phys.* **31**, 534 (1968). "Localization of Electrons in Condensed Matter."

Marchetti, A. P., and D. R. Kearns, *J. Amer. Chem. Soc.* **89**, 768 (1967). "Investigation of Singlet-Triplet Transitions by the Phosphorescence Excitation Method. IV. The Singlet-Triplet Absorption Spectra of Aromatic Hydrocarbons."

Marcus, R. A., *J. Chem. Phys.* **43**, 1261 (1965). "On the Theory of Shifts and Broadening of Electronic Spectra of Polar Solutes in Polar Media."

Margolis, J. S., and D. Bass, *J. Chem. Phys.* **45**, 3162 (1966). "Spectrum of I_2 Trapped in Benzene Matrix."

Margrave, J. L., *Amer. Chem. Soc. Meeting, Minneapolis, April 1969*, unpublished. "Reactions of SiF_2 with BF_2, Olefines and Acetylenes."

Maria, H., and A. Zahlan, *J. Chem. Phys.* **38**, 941 (1963). "Exciton-Phonon Interaction in Crystalline Benzene."

Maria, H. J., and A. B. Zahlan, *J. Chem. Phys.* **46**, 4329 (1967). "Phonon Effects in the uv Spectrum of Crystalline Hexamethylbenzene."

Maria, H. J., A. T. Armstrong, and S. P. McGlynn, *J. Chem. Phys.* **48**, 4694 (1968). "Luminescence of Inorganic Nitrite Salts."

Maria, H. J., A. T. Armstrong, and S. P. McGlynn, *J. Chem. Phys.* **50**, 2777 (1969). "Spin Polarization in the Triplet State of Silver Nitrate."

Marisova, S. V., *Opt. Spectrosc.* (USSR) (English Transl.) **22**, 310 (1967). "Reflection Spectra of the Anthracene Crystal and the Structure of Exciton Zones."

Marsh, F. D., and M. E. Harvey, *J. Amer. Chem. Soc.* **86**, 4506 (1964). "Cyanogen Azide."

Martin, T. E., and A. H. Kalantar, *J. Chem. Phys.* **48**, 4996 (1968a). "Nonradiative Decay Processes of the Triplet State of Aromatic Compounds: Benzene."

Martin, T. E., and A. H. Kalantar, *J. Chem. Phys.* **49**, 235 (1968b). "CH and CD Stretching Anharmonicities and Radiationless Decay of Triplet Benzene."

Martin, T. E., and A. H. Kalantar, *J. Chem. Phys.* **49**, 244 (1968c). "Nonexponential Phosphorescence Decay of Benzene."

Martin, T. E., and A. H. Kalantar, *J. Phys. Chem.* **72**, 2265 (1968d). "Observed Phosphorescence Lifetimes and Glass Relaxation at 77°K."

Martin, T. E., and A. H. Kalantar, *Chem. Phys. Lett.* **1**, 623 (1968e). "Radiationless Decay Processes in Some Alkyl Aromatics."

Martin, T. E., and A. H. Kalantar, *J. Chem. Phys.* **50**, 1485 (1969). "Relative Phosphorescence Radiative Rate Constants: Benzene in Two Cyclohexane Sites at 77°K."

Martinez, A., *C. R. Acad. Sci.* (Paris) **255**, 491 (1962). "Mesure de la Durée de Vie dans l'Etat Triplet."

Martinez, A., *J. Phys.* (Paris) Suppl. **24**, 117 A (1963). "Apparatus for Studying Decrease in T → S Luminescence."

Marx, R., S. Leach, and M. Horani, *J. Chim. Phys.* **60**, 726 (1963). "Excitation Electronique d'un Jet de Molécules d'Eau et de ses Isotopes Deutérés: Etude par Résonance Paramagnétique Electronique des Produits Condensés à 77°K."

Marzocchi, M. P., V. Schettino, and S. Califano, *J. Chem. Phys.* **45**, 1400 (1966). "Infrared Spectrum of Crystalline CH_2I_2 Crystal Structure and Phase Transition."

Mason, M. G., W. G. von Holle, and D. W. Robinson, *J. Chem. Phys.* in press. "IR Spectra of HF and DF in Rare Gas Matrices."

Mason, S. F., *J. Chem. Soc.* **1958**, 976 (1958). "The Infrared Spectra of N-Heteroaromatic Systems. I. The Porphins."

Masunaga, S., I. Morita, and M. Ishiguro, *J. Phys. Soc. Jap.* **21**, 638 (1966). "Optical Properties of CsI: Tl and CsBr: Tl."

Mataga, N., and S. Tsuno, *Bull. Chem. Soc. Jap.* **30**, 368 (1957). "Hydrogen Bonding Effect on the Fluorescence of Some Nitrogen Heterocycles. I."

Mataga, N., *Bull. Chem. Soc. Jap.* **31**, 459 (1958). "Electronic Spectra of Quinoline and Isoquinoline and the Mechanism of Fluorescence Quenching in These Molecules."

Mataga, N., H. Obashi, and T. Okada, *Chem. Phys. Lett.* **1**, 133 (1967a). "Electronic Excitation Transfer from Pyrene to Perylene by Very Weak Interaction. An Accurate Experimental Verification of Forster's Mechanism."

Mataga, N., Y. Torihashi, and Y. Ota, *Chem. Phys. Lett.* **1**, 385 (1967b). "Studies on the Fluorescence Decay Times of Anthracene and Perylene Excimers in Rigid Matrices at Low Temperatures in Relation to the Structures of Excimers."

Mataga, N., T. Okada, and N. Yamamoto, *Chem. Phys. Lett.* **1**, 119 (1968). "Electronic Processes in Hetero-Excimers and the Mechanism of Fluorescence Quenching."

Mataga, N., H. Obashi, and T. Okada, *J. Phys. Chem.* **73**, 370 (1969). "Electronic Excitation Transfer from Pyrene to Perylene by a Very Weak Interaction Mechanism."

Matheson, M. S., and B. Smaller, *J. Chem. Phys.* **23**, 521 (1955). "Paramagnetic Species in Gamma-Irradiated Ice."

Mauer, F. A., in *The Formation and Trapping of Free Radicals* (A. M. Bass and H. P. Broida, eds.), Chapter 5, Academic Press, New York, 1960. "Low Temperature Equipment and Techniques."

Mazurenko, Y. T., *Opt. Spectrosc.* (USSR) (English Transl.) **13**, 486 (1962). "Separation of Active and Non-Active Absorption in the Long-Wavelength Region of Excitation of Luminescence."

Mead, C. A., *Radiat. Res.* **20**, 101 (1963). "Absorption of Light by a Rigid Crystal."

Mees, C. E. K. and T. H. James, *The Theory of the Photographic Process*, Macmillan, New York, 1966.

Meinert, H., *Z. Chem.* **6**, 71 (1966). "Über die Bildung von Xenondichlorid."

Melhuish, W. H., *J. Opt. Soc. Amer.* **54**, 183 (1964). "Measurement of Quantum Efficiencies of Fluorescence and Phosphorescence and Some Suggested Luminescence Standards."

Melhuish, W. H., *J. Chem. Phys.* **50**, 2779 (1969). "Low-Energy Triplet-Triplet Transitions in Naphthalene and Some Monosubstituted Derivatives."

Merer, A. J., and D. N. Travis, *Can. J. Phys.* **44**, 525 (1966a). "Absorption Spectra of HCCl and DCCl."

Merer, A. J., and D. N. Travis, *Can. J. Phys.* **44**, 1541 (1966b). "Rotational Analysis of Bands of the HCF Molecule."

Merrifield, R. E., *Radiat. Res.* **20**, 154 (1963). "Vibronic States of Dimers."

Merrifield, R. E., *J. Chem. Phys.* **48**, 4318 (1968). "Theory of Magnetic Field Effects on the Mutual Annihilation of Triplet Excitons."

Merrifield, R. E., P. Avakian, and R. P. Groff, *Chem. Phys. Lett.* **3**, 155 (1969). "Fission of Singlet Excitons into Pairs of Triplet Excitons in Tetracene Crystals."

Merrithew, R. B., G. V. Marusak, and C. E. Blount, *J. Mol. Spectrosc.* **25**, 269 (1968). "Temperature Dependence of the Matrix Isolation Spectrum of Benzene."

Merrithew, R. B., G. V. Marusak, and C. E. Blount, *J. Mol. Spectrosc.* **29**, 54 (1969). "Absorption Spectra of Metal Atoms in Solid Xenon."

Meschi, D., and A. Searcy, *J. Chem. Phys.* **51**, 5134 (1969). "Investigation of the Magnetic Moments of S_2, Se_2, Te_2, Se_6, and Se_5."

Metlay, M., *J. Chem. Phys.* **39**, 491 (1963). "Fluorescence Lifetime of the Europium Dibenzoylmethides."

Metzger, J. L., B. Smith, and B. Meyer, *Spectrochim. Acta* **25A**, 1177 (1969). "Phosphorescence of Matrix Isolated Naphthalene and Phenanthrene."

Meyer, B., Ph. D. Thesis, University of Zürich (1960a). "Zur Allotropie des Schwefels."

Meyer, B., and E. Schumacher, *Helv. Chim. Acta* **43**, 1333 (1960b). "Isolation and Identification of S_2."

Meyer, B., *J. Chem. Phys.* **37**, 1577 (1962). "Vibration Spectrum of Trapped S_2."

Meyer, B., *J. Chem. Phys.* **43**, 2986 (1965). "Absorption Spectrum of Na and K in Rare-Gas Matrices."

Meyer, B., L. F. Phillips, and J. J. Smith, *Proc. Nat. Acad. Sci. U.S.* **67**, 7 (1968). "Temperature Dependence of Intersystem Crossing: Lifetime and Intensity of SO_2 Phosphorescence in Low-Temperature Solids."

Meyer, B., *Science* **168**, 783 (1970a). "Optical Spectra of Molecules at Low Temperature."

Meyer, B., unpublished work, 1970b. "Temperature Dependence of SO_2 Fluorescence."

Meyer, B., J. J. Smith, and K. Spitzer, *J. Chem. Phys.* **53**, 3616 (1970c). "Phosphorescent Decay Time of Matrix-Isolated GeO, GeS, SnO, and SnS, and the Lifetime of the Cameron Bands of CO-Type Diatomics."

Meyer, B., Y. Jones, J. J. Smith, and K. Spitzer, *J. Mol. Spectrosc.* **37**, 100 (1971a). "The Spectrum of Matrix-Isolated GeO and GeS."

Meyer, B., T. V. Oommen, and D. Jensen, *J. Chem. Phys.* **75**, 912 (1971b). "The Color of Liquid Sulfur; S_3 and S_4."

Meyer, L., L. S. Barrett, and P. Haasen, *J. Chem. Phys.* **40**, 2744 (1964). "New Crystalline Phase in Solid Argon and Its Solid Solutions."

Meyer, W. C., and A. C. Albrecht, *J. Phys. Chem.* **66**, 1168 (1962). "A Quantitative Study of a One-Electron Photooxidation in a Rigid Medium."

Michel, P., *Colloq. Diffusion Solids, Saclay (July 1958)* (M. Chandron, ed.), North-Holland Publ., Amsterdam, 1959. "Surface Diffusion in Vapor Deposited Films."

Miethke, E., and V. Zanker, *Z. Phys. Chem. (Frankfurt)* **18**, 375 (1958). "Die Reaktion des Chlordioxyds mit Nitrosylchlorid in der Gasphase."

Migirdicyan, E., and S. Leach, *Bull. Soc. Chim. Belges* **71**, 845 (1962). "La Photolyse de Quelques Composés Cycliques en Milieu Rigide."

Migirdicyan, E., *J. Chim. Phys.* **4**, 520 (1966a). "Photolyse et Radiolyse du Benzène en Milieu Rigide. I. Détection des Produits de Photodécomposition Primaire et Secondaire."

Migirdicyan, E., *J. Chim. Phys.* **4**, 535 (1966b). "Photolyse et Radiolyse du Benzène en Milieu Rigide. II. Mécanisme de la Photodécomposition."

Migirdicyan, E., *J. Chim. Phys.* **4**, 543 (1966c). "Photolyse et Radiolyse du Benzène en Milieu Rigide. III. Détection par R.P.E."

Migirdicyan, E., *C. R. Acad. Sci.* (Paris) *Ser. B* **266**, 756 (1968a). "Photochimie-Photolyse en Milieu Rigide des Dérivés Méthyles du Benzène: Détection d'Espèces Piégées Nouvelles."

Migirdicyan, E., *Ber. Bunsenges. Phys. Chem.* **72**, 344 (1968b). "Solid State Photolysis of the Tetramethylbenzenes."

Mikhailenko, V. I., P. A. Teplyakov, V. V. Trusov, and V. M. Martynchenko, *Opt. Spectrosc.* (USSR) (English Transl.) **20**, 29 (1966). "Vibrational Structure of the Luminescence Spectra of Frozen Solutions of Naphthalene and Tolan."

Mile, B., *Angew. Chem.* **80**, 519 (1968). "Die Untersuchung freier Radikale bei tiefer Temperatur."

Milligan, D. E., H. W. Brown, and G. C. Pimentel, *J. Chem. Phys.* **25**, 1080 (1956). "Infrared Absorption by the N_3 Radical."

Milligan, D. E., and G. C. Pimentel, *J. Chem. Phys.* **29**, 1405 (1958). "Matrix Isolation Studies: Possible Infrared Spectra of Isomeric Forms of Diazomethane and of Methylene, CH_2."

Milligan, D. E., and R. M. Hexter, Technical Report to the Air Force Office of Scientific Research (ARDC), Contract No. Af 49(638)542; AFOSR TN-59-1327 (December 18, 1959). "Infrared Spectroscopic Evidence for the Rotation of Ammonia Molecule in Solid Argon and Nitrogen."

Milligan, D. E., R. M. Hexter, and K. Dressler, *J. Chem. Phys.* **34**, 1009 (1961a). "Infrared Spectroscopic Evidence for the Rotation of the Ammonia Molecule in Solid Argon and Nitrogen."

Milligan, D. E., *J. Chem. Phys.* **35**, 372 (1961b). "Infrared Spectroscopic Study of the Photolysis of Chlorine Azide in Solid Argon at 4.2°K."

Milligan, D. E., *J. Chem. Phys.* **35**, 1491 (1961c). "Infrared Spectroscopic Study of the Photolysis of Methyl Azide and Methyl-d_3 Azide in Solid Argon and Carbon Dioxide."

Milligan, D. E., and M. E. Jacox, *J. Chem. Phys.* **36**, 2911 (1962a). "Infrared Study of the Reaction of CH_2 with CO_2 in the Solid State."

Milligan, D. E., and M. E. Jacox, *J. Mol. Spectrosc.* **8**, 126 (1962b). "Solid-State Vibrational Spectra of Methyl and Methyl-d_2 Cyanide."

Milligan, D. E., M. E. Jacox, S. W. Charles, and G. C. Pimentel, *J. Chem. Phys.* **37**, 2302 (1962c). "Infrared Spectroscopic Study of the Photolysis of HN_2 in Solid CO_2."

Milligan, D. E., and M. E. Jacox, *J. Chem. Phys.* **38**, 2627 (1963a). "Infrared Spectroscopic Evidence for the Species HO_2."

Milligan, D. E., and M. E. Jacox, *J. Chem. Phys.* **39**, 712 (1963b). "Infrared Spectroscopic Evidence for the Species HNC."

Milligan, D. E., *J. Amer. Chem. Soc.* **85**, 823 (1963c). "A Synthesis of Xenon Difluoride Not Involving Use of Elemental Fluorine."

Milligan, D. E., and M. E. Jacox, *J. Chem. Phys.* **40**, 605 (1964a). "Infrared Spectroscopic Evidence for the Species HO_2."

Milligan, D. E., and M. E. Jacox, *J. Chem. Phys.* **40**, 2461 (1964b). "Infrared Spectra of NF, NCl, and NBr."

Milligan, D. E., D. E. Mann, M. E. Jacox, and R. A. Mitsch, *J. Chem. Phys.* **41**, 1199 (1964c). "Infrared Spectrum of CF_2."

Milligan, D. E., and M. E. Jacox, *J. Chem. Phys.* **41**, 2838 (1964d). "Infrared Studies of the Photolysis of HN_3 in Inert and Reactive Matrices. The Infrared Spectrum of NH."

Milligan, D. E., and M. E. Jacox, *J. Chem. Phys.* **41**, 3032 (1964e). "Infrared Spectrum of HCO."

Milligan, D. E., M. E. Jacox, and J. D. McKinley, *J. Chem. Phys.* **42**, 902 (1965a). "Spectra of Matrix-Isolated NiF_2 and $NiCl_2$."

Milligan, D. E., M. E. Jacox, A. M. Bass, J. J. Comeford, and D. E. Mann, *J. Chem. Phys.* **42**, 3187 (1965b). "Matrix-Isolation Study of the Reaction of F Atoms with CO. Infrared and Ultraviolet Spectra of the Free Radical FCO."

Milligan, D. E., M. E. Jacox, J. J. Comeford, and D. E. Mann, *J. Chem. Phys.* **43**, 756 (1965c). "Infrared Spectrum of the Free Radical NCN."

Milligan, D. E., M. E. Jacox, and A. M. Bass, *J. Chem. Phys.* **43**, 3149 (1965d). "Matrix Isolation Study of the Photolysis of Cyanogen Azide. The Infrared and Ultraviolet Spectra of the Free Radical NCN."

Milligan, D. E., and M. E. Jacox, *J. Chem. Phys.* **43**, 4487 (1965e). "Matrix-Isolation Infrared Spectrum of the Free Radical NH_2."

Milligan, D. E., and M. E. Jacox, *J. Chem. Phys.* **44**, 2850 (1966a). "Matrix-Isolation Study of the Infrared and Ultraviolet Spectra of the Free Radical CNN."

Milligan, D. E., M. E. Jacox, and J. J. Comeford, *J. Chem. Phys.* **44**, 4058 (1966b). "Infrared Spectrum of the Free Radical CF$_3$ Isolated in Inert Matrices."

Milligan, D. E., and M. E. Jacox, *J. Chem. Phys.* **45**, 1387 (1966c). "Matrix-Isolation Study of the Photolysis of Cyanogen Azide. II. The Symmetric Stretching Fundamental of the Free Radical NCN."

Milligan, D. E., M. E. Jacox, and L. Abouaf-Marguin, *J. Chem. Phys.* **46**, 4562 (1967a). "Vacuum-Ultraviolet Photolysis of Acetylene in Inert Matrices. Spectroscopic Study of the Species C$_2$."

Milligan, D. E., and M. E. Jacox, *J. Chem. Phys.* **47**, 278 (1967b). "Spectroscopic Study of the Vacuum-Ultraviolet Photolysis of Matrix-Isolated HCN and Halogen Cyanides. Infrared Spectra of the Species CN and XNC."

Milligan, D. E., and M. E. Jacox, *J. Chem. Phys.* **47**, 703 (1967c). "Matrix-Isolation Study of the Reaction of Carbon Atoms with Chlorine."

Milligan, D. E., and M. E. Jacox, *J. Chem. Phys.* **47**, 5146 (1967d). "Infrared and Ultraviolet Spectroscopic Study of the Products of the Vacuum-Ultraviolet Photolysis of Methane in Ar and N$_2$ Matrices. The Infrared Spectrum of the Free Radical CH$_3$."

Milligan, D. E., and M. E. Jacox, *J. Chem. Phys.* **47**, 5157 (1967e). "Matrix-Isolation Study of the Infrared and Ultraviolet Spectra of the Isocyanate Free Radical."

Milligan, D. E., and M. E. Jacox, *J. Chem. Phys.* **48**, 2265 (1968a). "Matrix-Isolation Study of the Reaction of Atomic and Molecular Fluorine with Carbon Atoms. The Infrared Spectra of Normal and ^{13}C-Substituted CF$_2$ and CF$_3$."

Milligan, D. E., and M. E. Jacox, *J. Chem. Phys.* **48**, 4811 (1968b). "Matrix-Isolation Study of the Reaction of F$_2$ and of F Atoms with NCN. The Infrared Spectra of the Species NF$_2$CN and FNCN."

Milligan, D. E., and M. E. Jacox, *J. Chem. Phys.* **49**, 1938 (1968c). "Matrix-Isolation Study of the Vacuum-Ultraviolet Photolysis of Dichlorosilane. The Infrared Spectrum of the Free Radical SiCl$_2$."

Milligan, D. E., and M. E. Jacox, *J. Chem. Phys.* **49**, 4269 (1968d). "Matrix-Isolation Study of the Vacuum-Ultraviolet Photolysis of Difluorosilane. The Infrared and Ultraviolet Spectra of the Free Radical SiF$_2$."

Milligan, D. E., M. E. Jacox, and W. A. Guillory, *J. Chem. Phys.* **49**, 5330 (1968e). "Matrix-Isolation Study of the Vacuum-Ultraviolet Photolysis of Trifluorosilane. The Infrared Spectrum of the Free Radical SiF$_3$."

Milligan, D. E., and M. E. Jacox, *J. Chem. Phys.* **51**, 277 (1969a). "Matrix-Isolation Study of the Infrared and Ultraviolet Spectra of the Free Radical HCO. The Hydrocarbon Flame Bands."

Milligan, D. E., and M. E. Jacox, *J. Chem. Phys.* **51**, 1952 (1969b). "Studies of the Photoproduction of Electrons in Inert Solid Matrices. The Electronic Spectrum of the Species C$_2^-$."

Milligan, D. E., and M. E. Jacox, in *Physical Chemistry: An Advanced Treatise*, Vol. 4: *Molecular Properties* (H. Eyring, ed.), Chapter 4, Academic Press, New York, 1969c. "Spectra of Radicals."

Milligan, D. E., and M. E. Jacox, *J. Chem. Phys.* **52**, 2594 (1970). "Infrared and Ultraviolet Spectra of the Products of the Vacuum-Ultraviolet Photolysis of Silane Isolated in an Argon Matrix."

Minkoff, G., and F. I. Scherber, *J. Chem. Phys.* **28**, 992 (1958). "Energy Release from Discharged Monatomic Gases Trapped at 4°K."

Misra, T. N., and S. P. McGlynn, *J. Chem. Phys.* **44**, 3816 (1966a). "Delayed Luminescence of Organic Mixed Crystals."

Misra, T. N., A. R. Lacey, and L. E. Lyons, *Aust. J. Chem.* 19, 415 (1966b). "Fluorescence Spectrum of Phenanthrene Single Crystal at 4°K."

Mitsuhashi, H., *Appl. Phys. Lett.* 10, 339 (1967). "Luminescence from Plastically Bent Crystals of Cadmium Sulfide."

Moisya, E. G., *Opt. Spectrosc.* (USSR) (English Transl.) 23, 119 (1967). "The Effect of Phase Transitions of the Solvent on the Electronic Spectra of Dissolved Molecules."

Moisya, E. G., *Opt. Spectrosc.* (USSR) (English Transl.) 24, 385 (1968). "Absorption Spectra of Anthracene in Solution at 77°K."

Mokeeva, G. A., and B. Y. Sveshnikov, *Opt. Spectrosc.* (USSR) (English Transl.) 9, 317 (1960). "The Concentration Quenching of Luminescence in Organoluminors."

Mokeeva, G. A., and B. Y. Sveshnikov, *Opt. Spectrosc.* (USSR) (English Transl.) 10, 41 (1961). "On the Mechanism of the Transition of Excited Organic Molecules into the Metastable State."

Moll, H. G., and W. E. Thompson, *J. Chem. Phys.* 44, 2684 (1966). "Reactions of Carbon Atoms with N_2, H_2 and D_2 at 4.2°K."

Momigny, J., and J. C. Lorquet, *Chem. Phys. Lett.* 1, 455 (1967). "On the Position of the Electronic States of the C_6H_6 and $C_6H_5F^{\oplus}$ Ions."

Moodie, M. M., and C. Reid, *J. Chem. Phys.* 22, 252 and 1126 (1954). "Inter- and Intra-molecular Energy Transfer Processes. 3. Phosphorescence Bands of Some Carcinogenic Aromatic Hydrocarbons."

Moomaw, W. R., and M. A. El-Sayed, *J. Chem. Phys.* 45, 3890 (1966). "Phosphorescence of Crystalline Pyrazine."

Moomaw, W. R., and M. A. El-Sayed, *J. Chem. Phys.* 47, 2193 (1967). "Phonon-Induced Phosphorescence in Pyrazine Molecular Crystal."

Moomaw, W. R., and M. A. El-Sayed, *J. Chem. Phys.* 48, 2502 (1968). "Phosphorescence of Crystalline Pyrazine at 4.2°K."

Mooradian, A., and H. Y. Fan, *Phys. Rev.* 148, 873 (1966). "Recombination Emission in InSb."

Moore, C. B., and G. C. Pimentel, *J. Chem. Phys.* 38, 2816 (1963). "Infrared Spectrum and Vibrational Potential Function of Ketene and the Deuterated Ketenes."

Moore, C. B., and G. C. Pimentel, *J. Chem. Phys.* 40, 342 (1964a). "Solid Infrared Spectra, Assignment and Vibrational Potential Function of Diazomethane."

Moore, C. B., and G. C. Pimentel, *J. Chem. Phys.* 41, 3504 (1964b). "Matrix Reaction of Methylene with Nitrogen to Form Diazomethane."

Moore, C. B., and G. C. Pimentel, *J. Chem. Phys.* 43, 63 (1965). "Matrix Photolysis Products of Diazomethane: Methyleneimine and Hydrogen Cyanide."

Morantz, D. J., B. G. White, and A. J. C. Wright, *J. Chem. Phys.* 37, 2041 (1962a). "Phosphorescence and Stimulated Emission in Organic Molecules."

Morantz, D. J., B. G. White, and A. J. C. Wright, *Phys. Rev. Lett.* 8, 23 (1962b). "Stimulated Light Emission by Optical Pumping and by Energy Transfer in Organic Molecules."

Morantz, D. J., B. G. White, and A. J. C. Wright, *Proc. Chem. Soc.* 1962, 26 (1962c). "Stimulated Light Emission in Organic Molecules."

Morawetz, H., in *Formation and Trapping of Free Radicals* (A. M. Bass and H. P. Broida, eds.), Academic Press, New York, 1960.

Morehouse, R. L., J. J. Christiansen, and W. Gordy, *J. Chem. Phys.* 45, 1747 (1966a). "ESR of Free Radicals Trapped in Inert Matrices at Low Temperature: P, PH_2, and As."

Morehouse, R. L., J. J. Christiansen, and W. Gordy, *J. Chem. Phys.* **45**, 1751 (1966b). "ESR of Free Radicals Trapped in Inert Matrices at Low Temperature: CH_3, SiH_3, GeH_3 and SnH_3."

Morelle, A., Ph. D. Thesis, University of Washington, Seattle, 1970. "Spectra and Properties of Matrix Isolated Molecules."

Morgan, W. A., E. Silberman, and H. W. Morgan, *Spectrochim. Acta, Part A* **23**, 2855 (1967). "Infrared Spectra of the Nitrite Ion in Solid Solutions."

Morikawa, A., and R. J. Cvetanovic, *J. Chem. Phys.* **49**, 1214 (1968). "Quenching of the Excited Singlet State of Benzene ($^1B_{2u}$) by Mono-olefins and Diolefins."

Moross, G. G., and H. S. Story, *J. Chem. Phys.* **45**, 3370 (1966). "Temperature Dependence of the Nuclear Quadrupole Resonance Frequencies in *Para*-Dichlorobenzene."

Morton, J. R., *J. Chem. Phys.* **43**, 3418 (1965). "Electron Resonance Spectrum of S_2^- in Sulfur-Doped Potassium Bromide."

Morton, J. R., *J. Chem. Phys.* **45**, 1800 (1966). "Electron Spin Resonance Spectrum of ClO_4 Trapped in Irradiated $KClO$."

Morton, J. R., *J. Phys. Chem.* **71**, 89 (1967). "Identification of Some Sulfur-Containing Radicals Trapped in Single Crystals."

Moser, F., R. K. Ahrenkiel, and S. L. Lyu, *Phys. Rev.* **161**, 897 (1967). "Optical Absorption and Luminescent Emission of the I^- Center in AgCl."

Mosher, O. A., and R. P. Frosch, *J. Chem. Phys.* **52**, 5781 (1970). "Experimental Identification of the Ground State of BN in a Rare-Gas Matrix."

Moszynska, B., and A. Tramer, *J. Chem. Phys.* **46**, 820 (1967). "'Electron Vibration' in Crystalline Charge-Transfer Complexes."

Mukherjee, K., *Phys. Lett.* **25A**, 439 (1967). "Vacancies in Solid Argon."

Müller, R., and F. Dörr, *Z. Elektrochem.* **63**, 1150 (1959). "Absorptions- und Phosphoreszenzspektren der Mono- und Diazanaphthaline (π-π Phosphoreszenz nach n-π Absorption bei den Diazanaphthalinen)."

Mulliken, R. S., *Rev. Mod. Phys.* **4**, 1 (1932). "Interpretation of Band Spectra."

Mulliken, R. S., and W. B. Person, *Ann. Rev. Phys. Chem.* **13**, 107 (1962). "Donor-Acceptor Complexes."

Munn, R. J., *J. Chem. Phys.* **40**, 1439 (1964). "Interaction Potential of the Inert Gases. I."

Murrell, J. N., *Mol. Phys.* **3**, 319 (1960). "The Effect of Paramagnetic Molecules on the Intensity of Spin-Forbidden Absorption Bands of Aromatic Molecules."

Musatov, I. K., *Izv. Vyssh. Ucheb. Zaved. Fiz.* **4**, 46 (1960). "Low-Temperature Luminescence and After-Glow of Silica Gel."

N

Naboikin, Y. V., B. A. Zadorozhnyi, and E. N. Pavlova, *Bull. Acad. Sci. USSR, Phys. Ser.* (English Transl.) **23**, 9 (1959). "Some Peculiarities of the Luminescence of Ortho-Oxy-Substituted Aromatic Hydrocarbons."

Nag-Chaudhuri, J., L. Stoessell, and S. P. McGlynn, *J. Chem. Phys.* **38**, 2027 (1963). "External Heavy-Atom Spin-Orbital Coupling Effect. II. Comments on the Effect of Ferric Acetylacetonate on the Spectra of Polyacenes."

Nagornaya, L. L., A. P. Kilimov, L. Y. Malkes, L. V. Shubina, and A. I. Timchenko, *Instrum. Exp. Tech.* (USSR) (English Transl.) **4**, 37 (1960). "Plastic Scintillators with Admixtures of 1,2-Diaryl-Ethylenes."

Nagornaya, L. L., R. N. Nurmukhametov, L. Y. Malkes, and L. V. Shubina, *Bull. Acad.*

Sci. USSR, Phys. Ser. **27**, 747 (1963). "Luminescence of Naphthylic and Anthrylic Derivatives of Ethylene."

Nagornaya, L. L., T. R. Mnatsakanova, A. P. Grekov, and O. P. Shvaika, *Opt. Spectrosc.* (USSR) (English Transl.) **18**, 228 (1965). "Photoluminescent and Scintillation Properties of Some 1,3,4-Oxadiazoles."

Nakahara, A., M. Koyanagi, and Y. Kanda, unpublished paper (1968). "The Phosphorescence Spectrum of Crystalline Benzophenone."

Nakashima, T. L., and H. W. Offen, *J. Chem. Phys.* **48**, 4817 (1968). "Crystal Spectra of Tetracene and Rubrene under Pressure."

Nakhimovskaya, L. A., *Opt. Spectrosc.* (USSR) (English Transl.) **24**, 105 (1968). "On the Conditions for Realization of the Shpolskii Effect."

Nath, A., and S. Khorana, *J. Chem. Phys.* **46**, 2858 (1967). "Photoexcited Isotopic Exchange in the Solid State—$^{57}Co^{++}$-Doped Cobalt Chelates."

Naumann, A. W., and G. J. Safford, *J. Chem. Phys.* **47**, 867 (1967). "Low-Frequency Motions in Solid SO_2 Hydrate."

Neelakantam, K., S. Narayanan, and M. Sitaraman, *Proc. Indian Acad. Sci., Sect. A* **25**, 159 (1947). "Luminescence in the Solid State: Boric Acid Glasses. III. Azo Dyes from *o*-Hydroxy Carbonyl Compounds with Activators."

Neilson, E. F., and D. White, *J. Amer. Chem. Soc.* **79**, 5618 (1957). "The Heat Capacity, Heat of Fusion, Heat of Transition and Heat of Vaporization of Chlorodifluoromethane between 16°K and the Boiling Point."

Nelson, E. D., J. Y. Wong, and A. L. Schawlow, *Phys. Rev.* **156**, 298 (1967). "Far Infrared Spectra of $Al_2O_3 : Cr^{3+}$ and $Al_2O_3 : Ti^{3+}$."

Nelson, L. Y., and G. C. Pimentel, *J. Chem. Phys.* **47**, 3671 (1967a). "Infrared Detection of the Trichloride Radical, Cl_3."

Nelson, L. Y., and G. C. Pimentel, *Inorg. Chem.* **6**, 1758 (1967b). "Infrared Detection of Xenon Dichloride."

Nelson, L. Y., and G. C. Pimentel, *Inorg. Chem.* **7**, 1695 (1968). "Infrared Spectra of Chlorine-Bromine Polyhalogens by Matrix Isolation."

Nepochatykh, P. F., *Bull. Acad. Sci. USSR, Phys. Ser.* (English Transl.) **22**, 1407 (1958). "Characteristics of the Luminescence of Difurylpolenes."

Nesmeyanov, A. N., *Vapour Pressure of the Elements* (Transl. from Russian edition and edited by J. I. Carasso), Academic Press, New York, 1963.

Newman, E., A. M. Smith, and F. E. Steigert, *Phys. Rev.* **122**, 1520 (1961). "Fluorescent Response of Scintillation Crystals to Heavy Ions."

Nibler, J. W., and G. C. Pimentel, *Spectrochim. Acta* **21**, 877 (1965). "Infrared Spectrum and Vibrational Potential Function of Amide Ion."

Nibler, J. W., and G. C. Pimentel, *J. Chem. Phys.* **47**, 710 (1967). "Infrared Spectra of Cesium Bihalide Salts."

Nichols, E. L., and E. Merritt, *Phys. Rev.* **18**, 355 (1904). "Studies in Luminescence. I. The Phosphorescence and Fluorescence of Organic Substances at Low Temperatures."

Nichols, E. L., and E. Merritt, *Phys. Rev.* **32**, 38 (1911). "Fluorescence and Phosphorescence between 20°C and − 190°C. XV."

Nicol, M. F., *J. Chem. Phys.* **45**, 4753 (1966). "Fluorescence and Phosphorescence at High Pressure: Naphthalene Dissolved in Polymethylmethacrylate."

Nicol, M., and J. Somekh, *J. Opt. Soc. Amer.* **58**, 233 (1968). "Triplet-Triplet Absorption Spectrum (4500–3800 Å) of Perdeuteronaphthalene in Polymethylmethacrylate under Very High Pressures."

Nieman, G. C., and G. W. Robinson, *J. Chem. Phys.* **37**, 2150 (1962). "Rapid Triplet Excitation Migration in Organic Crystals."

Nieman, G. C., and G. W. Robinson, *J. Chem. Phys.* **39**, 1298 (1963). "Direct Determination of Exciton Interactions for Triplet States of Organic Crystals."

Nieman, G. C., and D. S. Tinti, *J. Chem. Phys.* **46**, 1432 (1967). "Geometry of the Lowest Triplet State of Benzene."

Nieman, G. C., *J. Chem. Phys.* **50**, 1660 (1969a). "Vibronic Intensity Distribution in the Phosphorescence of Benzene and Its Deuterated Isomers."

Nieman, G. C., *J. Chem. Phys.* **50**, 1674 (1969b). "Molecular Distortions and the Phosphorescence of Benzene."

Nikitin, A. N., M. D. Galanin, G. S. Ter-Sarkisian, and B. M. Mikhailov, *Opt. Spectrosc.* (USSR) (English Transl.) **6**, 226 (1959). "The Absorption and Luminescence Spectra of Solutions of Some Substituted Polyenes."

Nikitine, S., and G. Perny, *J. Phys. Radiat.* **17**, 1017 (1956a). "Emission and Absorption Spectra of Lead Iodide at Low Temperatures."

Nikitine, S., and R. Reiss, *J. Phys. Radiat.* **17**, 1017 (1956b). "Luminescence of Copper Iodide Thin Films at Low Temperatures."

Nikitine, S., J. Burckel, J. Biellmann, and R. Reiss, *C. R. Acad. Sci.* (Paris) **251**, 935 (1960). "The Absorption, Reflection and Photoluminescence Spectra of Single Crystals of PbI, at 4°K."

Noble, P. N., and G. C. Pimentel, *J. Chem. Phys.* **44**, 3641 (1966). "Confirmation of the Identification of Dioxygen Monofluoride."

Noble, P. N., and G. C. Pimentel, *J. Chem. Phys.* **49**, 3165 (1968). "Hydrogen Dichloride Radical: Infrared Detection through the Matrix Isolation Technique."

Noda, S., K. Fueki, and Z. Kuri, *J. Chem. Phys.* **49**, 3287 (1968). "ESR and Optical Studies of Acyl Radicals Produced from Acyl Chlorides by Dissociative Electron Attachment in γ-Irradiated Organic Glasses at 77°K."

Nonhebel, G., ed., *Gas Purification Processes*, George Newnes, Ltd., London, 1964.

Nordio, P. L., M. Rossi, and G. Giacometti, *Chem. Phys. Lett.* **1**, 101 (1967). "Vibronic Coupling and Singlet-Triplet Splitting in Aromatic Dinegative Ions."

Norman, I., and G. Porter, *Nature* **174**, 508 (1954). "Trapped Atoms and Radicals in a Glass 'Cage'."

Norman, I., and G. Porter, *Proc. Roy. Soc.* (London) Ser. *A* **230**, 399 (1955). "Trapped Atoms and Radicals in Rigid Solvents."

Novak, J. R., and M. W. Windsor, *Proc. Roy. Soc.* (London) Ser. *A* **308**, 95 (1968). "Laser Photolysis and Spectroscopy: A New Technique for the Study of Rapid Reactions in the Nanosecond Time Range."

Nudelmann, R., *Optical Properties of Solids*, Plenum Press, New York, 1969 (Proceedings Nato Conference, 1966).

Nurmukhametov, R. N., E. G. Popova, and N. S. Dokimikhin, *Opt. Spectrosc.* (USSR) (English Transl.) **9**, 313 (1960). "The Luminescence of Chrysene Solutions and Powder at 77°K."

Nurmukhametov, R. N., and G. V. Gobov, *Opt. Spectrosc.* (USSR) (English Transl.) **13**, 384 (1962). "The Luminescence Spectra of Fluorine."

Nurmukhametov, R. N., D. N. Shigorin, and Y. I. Kozlov, *Bull. Acad. Sci. USSR, Phys. Ser.* **27**, 685 (1963). "Luminescence Spectra of Solutions of Indigo and Its Derivatives at 77°K."

Nurmukhametov, R. N., and G. V. Gobov, *Opt. Spectrosc.* (USSR) (English Transl.)

18, 126 (1965). "The Effect of the Heteroatom on the Luminescence of Compounds Containing a Biphenyl Nucleus."

Nurmukhametov, R. N., L. A. Mileshina, L. Y. Malkes, and L. V. Shubina, *Opt. Spectrosc.* (USSR) (English Transl.) **20**, 17 (1966). "Electronic Spectra of 1,4-Divinylbenzene Diaryl Derivatives."

Nurmukhametov, R. N., *Russ. Chem. Rev.* **36**, 693 (1967a). "The Electronic Absorption and Luminescence Spectra of N-Heteroaromatic Compounds and Their Derivatives."

Nurmukhametov, R. N., *Opt. Spectrosc.* **22**, 209 (1967). "Electronic Spectra and the Process of Singlet-Triplet Conversion in Aromatic Aldehydes."

O

Obreimov, I. W., and H. H. de Haas, *Proc. Roy. Soc. Amsterdam* **31**, 353 (1928). "Change of Color of Crystals at Low Temperatures."

Obreimov, I. W., and A. F. Prikhot'ko, *Phys. Z. Sowjetunion* **1**, 203 (1932). "The Absorption Spectra of Some Crystalline Organic Compounds at Low Temperature."

Obreimov, I. W., and A. F. Prikhot'ko, *Phys. Z. Sowjetunion* **9**, 34 (1936a). "Absorption Spectra of Crystals at Low Temperature. II. Spectrum of Phenanthrene at 20°K."

Obreimov, I. W., and A. F. Prikhot'ko, *Phys. Z. Sowjetunion* **9**, 48 (1936b). "Absorption Spectra of Crystals at Low Temperature. III. Spectrum of Anthracene at 20°K."

Obreimov, I. W., and K. Shabaldas, *J. Phys. USSR* **7**, 167 (1943). "Fluorescence of Naphthalene Crystals."

Obreimov, I. W., and K. Shabaldas, *J. Phys. USSR* **8**, 257 (1944).

Ochial, K., *Chem. Soc. Japan* **5**, 203 (1930). "Studies on the Phosphorescence of Gelatine and Fluorescein at Low Temperatures."

Offen, H. W., and B. A. Baldwin, *J. Chem. Phys.* **44**, 3642 (1966a). "Effects of High Pressures on the Phosphorescence of Naphthalene and Quinoline."

Offen, H. W., and A. H. Kadhim, *J. Chem. Phys.* **45**, 269 (1966b). "Spectroscopy of EDA Complexes at High Pressures. II. Absorption of Several TCNE Complexes in Polymer Matrices."

Offen, H. W., *J. Appl. Phys.* **38**, 5245 (1967). "High-Pressure Apparatus for Optical Studies at 77°K."

Offen, H. W., and R. A. Beardslee, *J. Chem. Phys.* **48**, 3584 (1968a). "Perylene Crystal Spectra under Pressure."

Offen, H. W., and D. T. Phillips, *J. Chem. Phys.* **49**, 3995 (1968b). "Fluorescence Lifetimes of Aromatic Hydrocarbons under Pressure."

Offen, H. W., S. A. Balbo, and R. L. Tanquary, *Spectrochim. Acta, Part A* **25**, 1023 (1969a). "Coronene Absorption Shifts with Pressure and Temperature."

Offen, H. W., and D. E. Hein, *J. Chem. Phys.* **50**, 5274 (1969b). "Environmental Effects on Phosphorescence. VI. Matrix Site Effects for Triphenylene."

Ogden, J. S., and M. J. Ricks, *J. Chem. Phys.* **52**, 352 (1970). "Matrix Isolation Studies of Group IV Oxides. II. Infrared Spectra and Structures of GeO, Ge_2O_2, Ge_3O_3, and Ge_4O_4."

Ogilvie, J. F., *Nature* **204**, 572 (1964). "Infrared Absorption of the Hydroxyl Radical."

Olds, D. W., *J. Chem. Phys.* **35**, 2248 (1961). "Polarized Phosphorescence in Crystalline Hexachlorobenzene at 77°K."

Olness, D., and H. Sponer, *J. Chem. Phys.* **38**, 1779 (1963). "Phosphorescence Lifetime Studies in Some Organic Crystals at Low Temperatures."

Oster, G., and A. H. Adelman, *J. Amer. Chem. Soc.* **78**, 913 (1956). "Long-Lived States in Photochemical Reactions. I. Photoeduction of Eosin."

Oster, G., J. Joussot-Dubien, and B. Broyde, *J. Amer. Chem. Soc.* **81**, 1869 (1959). "Photoeduction of Dyes in Rigid Media. I. Triphenylmethane Dyes."

Oster, G. K., and H. Kallmann, *Int. Symp. Luminescence, Munich, 1965*, p. 31, Thiemig, Munich, 1966. "Energy Transfer from Higher Excited States of Solvents."

Ostertag, R., and H. C. Wolf, *Phys. Status Solidi* **31**, 139 (1969). "Phononenstruktur im Emissionsspektrum dotierter Naphthalinkristalle."

Ovander, L. N., *Opt. Spectrosc.* (USSR) (English Transl.) **11**, 129 (1961). "Temperature Dependence of Infrared Absorption Lines. I."

Ovander, L. N., *Opt. Spectrosc.* (USSR) (English Transl.) **12**, 711 (1962). "Temperature Dependence of Infrared Absorption Lines. II."

P

Padhye, M. R., S. P. McGlynn, and M. Kasha, *J. Chem. Phys.* **24**, 588 (1956). "Lowest Triplet State of Anthracene."

Pandey, G. K., and S. Chandra, *J. Chem. Phys.* **45**, 4369 (1966). "On the Matrix Spectra of the HF Molecule."

Pandey, G. K., *J. Chem. Phys.* **49**, 1555 (1968). "Effect of Localized Lattice Vibration on the Matrix Spectra of Diatomic Molecules."

Pankeeva, A. E., *Bull. Acad. Sci. USSR, Phys. Ser.* (English Transl.) **23**, 108 (1959). "Quenching of the Phosphorescence of Organic Dyes by Electric Ions."

Panov, I. N., N. A. Adrova, and M. M. Koton, *Opt. Spectrosc.* (USSR) (English Transl.) **7**, 16 (1959). "Optical Characteristics of Compounds of the Oxazole, Oxadiazole and Furan Series."

Pant, D. D., and D. P. Khandelwal, *Proc. Indian Acad. Sci., Sect. A* **51**, 60 (1960). "Fluorescence Spectra of Solutions of Uranyl Nitrate at Liquid-Air Temperature."

Papazian, H. A., *J. Chem. Phys.* **27**, 813 (1957). "Technique to Produce Free Radicals in the Solid State."

Papazian, H. A., *J. Chem. Phys.* **29**, 448 (1958). "Free Radical Formation in Solids by Ion Bombardment."

Pappalardo, R., *J. Chem. Phys.* **49**, 1545 (1968). "Absorption Spectra of Erbium Tricyclopentadienide at Liquid-Helium Temperature."

Paris, J. P., R. C. Hirt, and R. G. Schmitt, *J. Chem. Phys.* **34**, 1851 (1961). "Observed Phosphorescence and Singlet-Triplet Absorption in s-Triazine and Trimethyl-s-Triazine."

Parker, C. A., and W. T. Rees, *Analyst* **85**, 587 (1960). "Correction of Fluorescence Spectra and Measurement of Fluorescence Quantum Efficiency."

Parker, C. A., and C. G. Hatchard, *Trans. Faraday Soc.* **51**, 1894 (1961). "Triplet-Singlet Emission in Fluid Solutions: Phosphorescence of Eosin."

Parker, C. A., and C. G. Hatchard, *Proc. Roy. Soc.* (London) *Ser. A* **269**, 574 (1962a). "Delayed Fluorescence from Solutions of Anthracene and Phenanthrene."

Parker, C. A., and C. G. Hatchard, *Analyst* **87**, 664 (1962b). "The Possibilities of Phosphorescence Measurement in Chemical Analysis: Tests with a New Instrument."

Parker, C. A., and C. G. Hatchard, *J. Phys. Chem.* **66**, 2506 (1962c). "Triplet-Singlet Emission in Fluid Solution."

Parker, C. A., *Spectrochim. Acta* **19**, 989 (1963). "Delayed Fluorescence from Naphthalene Solutions."

Parker, C. A., *Advan. Photochem.* **2**, 305 (1964). "Phosphorescence and Delayed Fluorescence from Solutions."

Parker, C. A., and T. A. Joyce, *J. Chem. Soc.* **A1966**, 821 (1966). "Artifacts and Trivial Effects in the Measurement of Delayed Fluorescence."

Parker, C. A., *Photoluminescence of Solutions with Applications to Photochemistry and Analytical Chemistry*, American Elsevier, New York and Amsterdam, 1968.

Parker, M. A., and D. F. Eggers, Jr., *J. Chem. Phys.* **45**, 4354 (1966). "Infrared Spectra of Carbon Dioxide Films at Nonnormal Incidence."

Parmenter, C. S., and J. D. Rau, *J. Chem. Phys.* **51**, 2242 (1969). "Fluorescence Quenching in Aromatic Hydrocarbons by Oxygen."

Partridge, R. H., *J. Chem. Phys.* **49**, 3656 (1968). "Exciton Interpretation of the Vacuum-Ultraviolet Absorption Spectra of Saturated Organic Polymers."

Pavlopoulos, T., and M. A. El-Sayed, *J. Chem. Phys.* **41**, 1082 (1964). "Spectroscopic Investigation of the Mechanism of the Intramolecular Heavy Atom Effect on the Phosphorescence Process. I. Naphthalene Emission."

Pecile, C., and B. Lunelli, *J. Chem. Phys.* **46**, 2109 (1967). "Polarized Infrared Spectra of Single Crystals of 9,10-Anthraquinone and 9,10-Anthraquinone-d_8."

Penner, S. S., *Nat. Acad. Sci.—Nat. Res. Council Publ. No.* **1470**, 28 (1967). "Selected Problem Areas in High-Temperature Chemistry."

Person, W. B., and G. C. Pimentel, *J. Chem. Phys.* **20**, 1913 (1952a). "Infrared Studies of Mixed Crystals: Naphthalene-d_8 in Naphthalene."

Person, W. B., G. C. Pimentel, and S. Pitzer, *J. Amer. Chem. Soc.* **74**, 3437 (1952b). "The Structure of Cyclooctatetraene."

Person, W. B., G. C. Pimentel, and O. Schnepp, *J. Chem. Phys.* **23**, 230 (1955). "Infrared Studies of Naphthalene and Naphthalene-d_8."

Person, W. B., C. F. Cook, and H. B. Friedrich, *J. Chem. Phys.* **46**, 2521 (1967). "Infrared Spectra of Charge-Transfer Complexes. VII. The Solid Benzene-Bromine Complex."

Personov, R. I., *Opt. Spectrosc.* (USSR) (English Transl.) **15**, 30 (1963). "Emission and Absorption Line Spectra of Phthalocyanine in Frozen Crystalline Solutions."

Personov, R. I., and V. V. Solodunov, *Opt. Spectrosc.* (USSR) (English Transl.) **22**, 317 (1967). "Temperature Dependence of the Line-Width in the Quasiline Fluorescence Spectrum of 1,12-Benzoperylene."

Personov, R. I., and V. V. Solodunov, *Opt. Spectrosc.* (USSR) (English Transl.) **24**, 70 (1968). "Interference Measurements of Line-Widths in the Quasiline Fluorescence Spectrum of 1,12-Benzoperylene at 4°K."

Pesteil, L., *J. Chim. Phys.* **58**, 204 (1961). "Spectres Electroniques de l'Acénaphtène et du Deutéroacénaphtène à Basse Température."

Pesteil, L., and M. Rabaud, *J. Chim. Phys.* **59**, 167 (1962). "Spectres Electroniques des Phénanthrènes $C_{14}H_{10}$ et $C_{14}D_{10}$ à Basse Température."

Pesteil, P., and M. Barbaron, *J. Phys. Radium* **15**, 92 (1954a). "Fluorescence Spectra of Aromatic Crystals at Low Temperature."

Pesteil, P., and L. Pesteil, *C. R. Acad. Sci.* (Paris) **238**, 226 (1954b). "Fluorescence de Quelques Cristaux Aromatiques. Discussion des Résultats."

Pesteil, P., A. Zmerli, and M. Barbaron, *C. R. Acad. Sci.* (Paris) **239**, 255 (1954c). "Photoluminescence de Cristaux aux Basses Températures. V. Quelques Molécules Carboxylées."

Pesteil, P., *Ann. Phys.* **10**, 8 (1955a). "Etude de l'Absorption et de la Fluorescence de Quelques Molécules Organiques en Milieu Cristallin."

Pesteil, P., *Ann. Phys.* **10**, 128 (1955b). "The Absorption and Fluorescence of Several Organic Molecules in the Crystalline State."

Pesteil, P., and A. Zmerli, *Ann. Phys.* **10**, 1079 (1955c). "Structure Vibrationnelle des Spectres de Phosphorescence de Cristaux Aromatiques aux Très Basses Températures."

Pesteil, P., and A. Zmerli, *C. R. Acad. Sci.* (Paris) **242**, 1876 (1956). "Luminescence of Crystals at Low Temperatures. Naphthalene at 20°K."

Pesteil, P., and A. Ciais, *C. R. Acad. Sci.* (Paris) **250**, 494 (1960). "Spectre de Fluorescence du Naphthalène en Solution dans l'Octodeutérononaphthalène à 20°K."

Peterson, N. L., *Solid State Phys.* **22**, 409 (1968). "Diffusion in Metals."

Petropoulos, B., and L. Herman, *C. R. Acad. Sci.* (Paris) *Ser. B* **264**, 1196 (1967). "Effect of Rare-Gas Matrixes on the Spectrum of the S_2 Molecule."

Peyron, M., and H. P. Broida, *J. Chem. Phys.* **30**, 139 (1959a). "Spectra Emitted from Solid Nitrogen Condensed at Very Low Temperatures from a Gas Discharge."

Peyron, M., E. M. Hörl, H. W. Brown, and H. P. Broida, *J. Chem. Phys.* **30**, 1304 (1959b). "Spectroscopic Evidence for Triatomic Nitrogen in Solids at Very Low Temperature."

Peyron, M., and Lam Thanh My, *J. Chim. Phys.* **64**, 129 (1967). "Chimiluminescence du Radical NS."

Pfann, W. G., *Zone Melting*, Wiley, New York, 1966.

Phillips, D. M. P., *Nature* **161**, 53 (1948). "Use of Ultra-Violet Fluorescence in Paper Chromatography."

Phillips, L. F., J. J. Smith, and B. Meyer, *J. Mol. Spectrosc.* **29**, 230 (1969). "The Ultraviolet Spectra of Matrix Isolated Disulfur Monoxide and Sulfur Dioxide."

Philpott, M. R., *J. Chem. Phys.* **49**, 3736 (1968). "Radiation Damping of Frenkel Excitons in Molecular Crystals."

Philpott, M. R., *J. Chem. Phys.* **51**, 2616 (1969). "Theory of the Vibrational Structure of Molecular Excitons. Soluble One-'Phonon' Models."

Pikulik, L. G., and M. A. Solomakho, *Inzh. Fiz. Zh. Akad. Nauk Belorusko SSR* **3**, 53 (1960). "Effect of Temperature on Luminescence and Absorption Spectra of Complex Molecules in Solutions."

Pikulik, L. G., and L. F. Gladchenko, *Bull. Acad. Sci. USSR Phys. Ser.* (English Transl.) **27**, 756 (1963). "Influence of Temperature on the Luminescence of Complex Molecules in Different Media."

Pilon, A. M., *C. R. Acad. Sci.* (Paris) **249**, 1492 (1959). "The Phosphorescence of Solid Nitrogen."

Pimentel, G. C., and K. S. Pitzer, *J. Chem. Phys.* **17**, 882 (1949). "The Ultraviolet Absorption and Luminescence of Decaborane."

Pimentel, G. C., G. Jura, and L. Grotz, *J. Chem. Phys.* **19**, 513 (1951a). "The Infrared Spectra of Mesitylene Complexes."

Pimentel, G. C., *J. Chem. Phys.* **19**, 1536 (1951b). "Infrared Studies of Mixed Crystals: Naphthalene in Anthracene."

Pimentel, G. C., C. W. Garland, and G. Jura, *J. Amer. Chem. Soc.* **75**, 803 (1952a). "Infrared Spectra of Heavy Water Adsorbed on Silica Gel."

Pimentel, G. C., and A. L. McClellan, *J. Chem. Phys.* **20**, 270 (1952b). "The Infrared Spectra of Naphthalene Crystals, Vapor, and Solutions."

Pimentel, G. C., A. L. McClellan, W. B. Person, and O. Schnepp, *J. Chem. Phys.* **23**, 234 (1955a). "Interpretation of the Infrared Spectrum of a Molecular Crystal:

Naphthalene."

Pimentel, G. C., and W. A. Klemperer, *J. Chem. Phys.* **23**, 376 (1955b). "Infrared Spectrum of Solid η-Octane-1,1,1,8,8,8-d$_6$."

Pimentel, G. C., and C. H. Sederholm, *J. Chem. Phys.* **24**, 639 (1956). "Correlation of Infrared Stretching Frequencies and Hydrogen Bond Distances in Crystals."

Pimentel, G. C., *J. Amer. Chem. Soc.* **79**, 3323 (1957a). "Hydrogen Bonding and Electronic Transitions: The Role of the Franck-Condon Principle."

Pimentel, G. C., *IUPAC Conf. Hydrogen Bonding, Ljubljana, 1957*, Pergamon Press, New York, 1957b. "Low Temperature Spectral Behaviour of Hydrogen Bonded Species."

Pimentel, G. C., *Spectrochim. Acta* **12**, 94 (1958a). "The Promise and Problems of the Matrix Isolation Method for Spectroscopic Studies."

Pimentel, G. C., *J. Amer. Chem. Soc.* **80**, 62 (1958b). "Reaction Kinetics by the Matrix Isolation Method: Diffusion in Argon; *cis-trans* Isomerization of Nitrous Acid."

Pimentel, G. C., in *Formation and Trapping of Free Radicals* (A. M. Bass and H. P. Broida, eds.), Academic Press, New York, 1960. "Radical Formation and Trapping in the Solid Phase."

Pimentel, G. C., paper presented at American Petroleum Institute's Division of Refining Meeting, Houston, Texas (1961a). "Investigation of Highly Reactive Species by the Matrix Isolation Technique."

Pimentel, G. C., *J. Amer. Chem. Soc.* **83**, 2217 (1961b). "Photochemistry in the Liquid and Solid States."

Pimentel, G. C., M. O. Bulanin, and M. Van Thiel, *J. Chem. Phys.* **36**, 500 (1962a). "Infrared Spectra of Ammonia Suspended in Solid Nitrogen."

Pimentel, G. C., *Pure Appl. Chem.* **4**, 61 (1962). "Matrix Technique and Its Application in the Field of Chemical Physics."

Pimentel, G., and R. Spratley, *J. Amer. Chem. Soc.* **85**, 826 (1963a). "The Bonding in the Inert Gas-Halogen Compounds—the Likely Existence of Helium Difluoride."

Pimentel, G. C., *Science* **140**, 974 (1963b). "Krypton Fluoride: Preparation by the Matrix Isolation Technique."

Pimentel, G. C., and S. W. Charles, *Pure Appl. Chem.* **7**, 111 (1963c). "Infrared Spectral Perturbations in Matrix Experiments."

Pimentel, G. C., R. D. Spratley, and A. R. Miller, *Science* **143**, 674 (1964a). "Helium Difluoride: Possible Preparative Techniques Based on Nuclear Transmutations."

Pimentel, G. C., and K. C. Herr, *J. Chim. Phys.* **1964**, 1509 (1964b). "The Infrared Detection of Free Radicals Using Flash Photolysis Methods."

Pimentel, G. C., *Pure Appl. Chem.* **11**, 563 (1965). "Infrared Detection of Reactive Species Produced through Flash Photolysis."

Pimentel, G. C., S. W. Charles, and K. Rosengren, *J. Chem. Phys.* **44**, 3029 (1966). "Hydrogen Bonding of Hydrazoic Acid in Solid Nitrogen."

Pinnington, E. H., *J. Opt. Soc. Amer.* **57**, 1252 (1967). "Zeeman-Effect Analysis of the Spectrum of Neutral Gadolinium (Gd I)."

Pissarenko, V. F., and S. V. Voropaeva, *Phys. Status Solidi* **15**, K95 (1966). "The Luminescence of Dy^{3+} in NaCl and KCl."

Pitzer, K. S., *Advan. Chem. Phys.* **2**, 59 (1959a). "Inter- and Intramolecular Forces and Molecular Polarizability."

Pitzer, K. S., and E. Clementi, UCRL-8675, U.S. Atomic Energy Commission Contract No. W-7405-eng-48 (1959b). "Large Molecules in Carbon Vapor."

Platt, J. R., *J. Opt. Soc. Amer.* **43**, 252 (1953). "Classification and Assignment of UV Spectra of Conjugated Organic Molecules."

Pollack, G., and H. P. Broida, *J. Chem. Phys.* **38**, 968 (1963a). "Vapor Snakes in Argon Solid."

Pollack, G. L., and H. P. Broida, *J. Chem. Phys.* **38**, 2012 (1963b). "Spectroscopic Absorption of NO in Crystalline and Liquid Krypton."

Pollack, G. L., *Rev. Mod. Phys.* **36**, 748 (1964). "The Solid State of Rare Gases."

Pople, J. A., *Mol. Phys.* **3**, 16 (1960). "The Renner Effect and Spin-Orbit Coupling."

Port, H., and H. C. Wolf, in *The Triplet State* (A. B. Zahlan, ed.), p. 393, Cambridge University Press, London and New York, 1967. "Optical Investigations of the Triplet State of Naphthalene in Different Crystalline Environments."

Port, H., and H. C. Wolf, *Z. Naturforsch.* **23a**, 315 (1968). "Phosphoreszenz und verzögerte Fluoreszenz von Naphthalin in verschiedenen Mischkristallen."

Porter, G., and F. J. Wright, *Disc. Faraday Soc.* **14**, 23 (1953). "Studies of Free Radical Reactivity by the Methods of Flash Photolysis. The Photochemical Reaction between Chlorine and Oxygen."

Porter, G., and M. W. Windsor, *J. Chem. Phys.* **21**, 2088 (1954a). "Triplet States in Solution."

Porter, G., and M. W. Windsor, *Disc. Faraday Soc.* **17**, 178 (1954b). "Studies of the Triplet State in Fluid Solvents."

Porter, G., and M. R. Wright, *J. Chim. Phys.* **55**, 705 (1958a). "Energy Transfer from the Triplet State in Solution."

Porter, G., and E. Strachan, *Trans. Faraday Soc.* **54**, 1595 (1958b). "Primary Photochemical Processes in Aromatic Molecules. Part 4. Side-Chain Photolysis in Rigid Media."

Porter, G., and E. Strachan, *Spectrochim. Acta* **12**, 299 (1958c). "The Electronic Spectra of Benzyl."

Powling, J., and H. Bernstein, *J. Amer. Chem. Soc.* **73**, 1815 (1951). "Internal Rotation. VI. A Dilute Solution Method for the Spectroscopic Determination of the Energy Difference between Rotational Isomers."

Prask, H. J., and H. Boutin, *J. Chem. Phys.* **45**, 3284 (1966). "Low-Frequency Motions of H_2O Molecules in Crystals. III."

Price, W. C., W. F. Sherman, and G. R. Wilkinson, *Spectrochim. Acta* **16**, 663 (1960). "Infra-red Studies on Polyatomic Ions Isolated in Alkali-Halide Lattices."

Priestley, E. B., and A. Haug, *J. Chem. Phys.* **49**, 622 (1968). "Phosphorescence Spectrum of Pure Crystalline Naphthalene."

Prikhotko, A., *Acta Physicochem.* **16**, 125 (1942). "The Absorption Spectra of Halogen Solutions at Low Temperatures."

Prikhotko, A. F., *Izv. Akad. Nauk SSSR, Ser. Fiz.* **15**, 608 (1951). "Luminescence and Absorption of Light in Crystalline Organic Compounds."

Prikhotko, A. F., and I. Y. Fugol, *Opt. Spectrosc.* (USSR) (English Transl.) **7**, 19 (1959). "Luminescence of Stilbene Crystals at 20°K."

Prikhotko, A. F., and A. F. Skorobogatko, *Opt. Spectrosc.* (USSR) (English Transl.) **20/1**, 33 (1966). "Spectral Study of Naphthacene Single Crystals."

Pringsheim, P., and S. J. Vavilov, *Z. Phys.* **37**, 705 (1926a). "Polarisierte und unpolarisierte Phosphoreszenz fester Farbstofflösungen."

Pringsheim, P., and A. Kronenberger, *Z. Phys.* **40**, 75 (1926b). "Absorption Spectrum of Solid Benzene at − 180°C."

Pringsheim, P., *Acta Phys. Pol.* **5**, 361 (1936a). "Fluoreszenz und Phosphoreszenz adsorbierter Farbstoffe."

Pringsheim, P., *Acta Phys. Pol.* **6**, 158 (1936b). "Bemerkung über die 'Spiegelsymmetrie' der Fluoreszenz- und Absorptionsbanden in Lösungen."

Prins, R., and J. D. W. van Voorst, *Chem. Phys. Lett.* **1**, 54 (1967). "Zero-field Splitting in the Triplet Ground State of Nickelocene."

Pröpstl, A., and H. C. Wolf, *Z. Naturforsch.* **18a**, 822 (1963). "Die Temperaturabhängigkeit der sensibilisierten Fluoreszenz in Naphthalin-Kristallen zwischen 2 und 100°K."

Pullin, A. D. E., *Proc. Roy. Soc.* (London) *Ser. A* **255**, 39 (1960). "A Theory of Solvent Effects in Infra-Red Spectra."

Pyatnitskii, B. A., *Dokl. Akad. Nauk SSSR* **71**, 457 (1950). "Phosphorescence of Benzene Hydrocarbons at the Temperature of Liquid Oxygen."

Pyatnitskii, B. A., *Izv. Akad. Nauk SSSR, Ser. Fiz.* **15**, 597 (1951). "Decay of Phosphorescence and Duration of the Metastable State of Organic Molecules at Low Temperature."

Pyatnitskii, B. A., *Dokl. Akad. Nauk SSSR* **109**, 503 (1956). "Phosphorescence Spectra of Some Aromatic Acids at Liquid Air Temperature."

Pyatnitskii, B. A., *Izv. Akad. Nauk SSSR, Ser. Fiz.* **22**, 1304 (1958). "Phosphorescence Spectra of Some Aromatic Acids at Liquid-Air Temperature."

Pyatnitskii, B. A., and A. I. Vlasenko, *Bull. Acad. Sci. USSR Phys. Ser.* (English Transl.) **27**, 648 (1963). "Phosphorescence of Carbazole and Phenanthrene at Liquid Oxygen Temperature."

Q

Quiring, F. S., *J. Chem. Phys.* **49**, 2448 (1968). "Nonradiative Transfer of Excitation Energy between Rare-Earth Ions in Aqueous Solution."

R

Rabalais, J. W., H. J. Maria, and S. P. McGlynn, *Chem. Phys. Lett.* **3**, 59 (1969a). "Comments on Phosphorescence Decay Times of Benzene and Methyl-Benzene Derivatives."

Rabalais, J. W., H. J. Maria, and S. P. McGlynn, *J. Chem. Phys.* **51**, 2259 (1969b). "Phosphorescence Decay of Benzene and Methylbenzene Derivatives."

Rahn, R. O., T. Yamane, J. Eisinger, J. W. Longworth, and R. G. Shulman, *J. Chem. Phys.* **45**, 2947 (1966a). "Luminescence and Electron Spin Resonance Studies of Adenine in Various Polynucleotides."

Rahn, R. O., R. G. Shulman, and J. W. Longworth, *J. Chem. Phys.* **45**, 2955 (1966b). "Phosphorescence and Electron Spin Resonance Studies of the uv-Excited Triplet State of DNA."

Rajnak, K., and W. F. Krupke, *J. Chem. Phys.* **46**, 3532 (1967). "Energy Levels of Ho^{3+} in $LaCl_3$."

Rammensee, H., and V. Zanker, *Z. Angew. Phys.* **12**, 237 (1960). "Beitrag zum Zusammenhang zwischen Lichtabsorption, Abklingzeit und absoluter Fluoreszenzquantenausbeute bei organischen Farbstoffmolekülen."

Ramsey, B., M. A. El-Bayoumi, and M. Kasha, *J. Chem. Phys.* **35**, 1502 (1961). "Intramolecular Charge-Transfer Bands Observed in the Spectra of Some Aryl Boron Compounds."

Ramsay, D. A., *J. Chem. Phys.* **21**, 960 (1953). "Absorption Spectrum of Free HCO

Radicals."

Ramsay, D. A., *Nature* **178**, 374 (1956). "Absorption Spectra of Free PH_2 and PD_2 Radicals."

Ramsay, D. A., *Mem. Soc. Roy. Sci. Liege* **18**, 471 (1957). "The Analysis of the α-Bands of Ammonia."

Ramsay, D. A., *Advan. Spectrosc.* **1**, 1 (1959). "The Spectra of Polyatomic Free Radicals."

Ramsay, D. A., in *Determination of Organic Structures by Physical Methods* (F. C. Nachod and W. D. Phillips, eds.), Vol. 2, Academic Press, New York, 1961. "Electronic Spectra of Polyatomic Molecules and the Configuration of Molecules in Excited Electronic States."

Ranayne, M. R., J. P. Guarino, and W. H. Hornible, *J. Amer. Chem. Soc.* **84**, 4230 (1962). "Electron Attachment and Solvation in Gamma Irradiated Organic Glasses at $-196°$."

Randazzo, D. J., *J. Chem. Phys.* **49**, 1808 (1968). "Zeeman Studies on Er^{3+} in $GdCl_3$."

Rapoport, E., *J. Chem. Phys.* **45**, 2721 (1966). "Phase Diagrams of Sodium Nitrite and Potassium Nitrite to 40 kbar."

Rast, H. E., J. L. Fry, and H. H. Caspers, *J. Chem. Phys.* **46**, 1460 (1967a). "Energy Levels of Sm^{3+} in LaF_3."

Rast, H. E., H. H. Caspers, and S. A. Miller, *J. Chem. Phys.* **47**, 3874 (1967b). "Fluorescence and Energy Transfer between Nd^{3+} and Yb^{3+} in LaF_3."

Rathmann, G. B., *Nat. Acad. Sci.—Nat. Res. Council*, Publ. No. **1740**, 76 (1967). "Problems in High-Temperature Chemistry."

Rautian, S. G., and I. I. Sobel'man, *Opt. Spectrosc.* (USSR) (English Transl.) **10**, 65 (1961). "Remarks on Negative Absorption."

Rawlings, I. R., *Brit. J. Appl. Phys.* [2] **1**, 733 (1968). "Optical Absorption in Silicon Monoxide."

Raynes, W. T., *J. Chem. Phys.* **44**, 2755 (1966). "Rotational Analysis of Some Bands of the Triplet-Singlet Transition in Formaldehyde."

Raz, B., and J. Jortner, *J. Chem. Phys.* **49**, 3318 (1968). "Trapped Exciton States in Liquid Argon."

Razi Naqvi, K., *Chem. Phys. Lett.* **1**, 497 (1967). "P-type Delayed Fluorescence from Rigid Solutions."

Reband, K. K., and O. I. Sild, *Opt. Spectrosc.* (USSR) (English Transl.) **22**, 222 (1967). "The Theory of Isotopic Composition Effect in the Spectra of Impurity Crystals."

Rebbert, R. E., and P. Ausloos, *J. Chem. Phys.* **46**, 4333 (1967). "Vacuum-Ultraviolet Photolysis of Solid Propane at 20° and 77°K."

Rebbert, R. E., and P. Ausloos, *J. Chem. Phys.* **48**, 306 (1968). "Photolysis of Methyl Iodide in Matrices of Organic Compounds at 20° and 77°K. Reactions of Hot Methyl Radicals."

Redington, R. L., and D. E. Milligan, *J. Chem. Phys.* **37**, 2162 (1962). "Infrared Spectroscopic Evidence for the Rotation of the Water Molecule in Solid Argon."

Redington, R. L., and D. E. Milligan, *J. Chem. Phys.* **39**, 1276 (1963). "Molecular Rotation and Ortho-Para Nuclear Spin Conversion of Water Suspended in Solid Ar, Kr, and Xe."

Reid, C., *J. Chem. Phys.* **20**, 1212 (1952a). "Inter- and Intra-Molecular Energy Transfer Processes. I. Nitro-compounds and Hydrocarbons."

Reid, C., *J. Chem. Phys.* **20**, 1214 (1952b). "The Lowest Triplet Levels of Aromatic Hydrocarbons."

Reid, C., *J. Chem. Phys.* **21**, 1906 (1953). "*n − π* Emission Spectra."

Reid, C., *J. Amer. Chem. Soc.* **76**, 3264 (1954). "The Aromatic Carbonium Ions."

Reid, C., *Quart. Rev.* (London) **12**, 205 (1958). "The Triplet State."

Reilly, M. H., *Phys. Chem. Solids* **28**, 2067 (1967). "Band Structure, Deformation Potentials, and Exciton States in Solid Xenon."

Rentzepis, P., D. White, and P. N. Walsh, *J. Phys. Chem.* **64**, 784 (1960). "The Reaction between $B_2O_3(1)$ and $C(s)$: Heat of Formation of $B_2O_2(g)$."

Rentzepis, P. M., *Chem. Phys. Lett.* **2**, 117 (1968). "Direct Measurements of Radiationless Transitions in Liquids."

Rhodes, W., B. R. Henry, and M. Kasha, *Proc. Nat. Acad. Sci. U.S.* **63**, 29 (1969a). "A Stationary State Approach to Radiationless Transitions. Radiation Bandwidth Effect on Excitation Processes in Polyatomic Molecules."

Rhodes, W., *J. Chem. Phys.* **50**, 2885 (1969b). "Radiationless Transitions in Isolated Molecules. The Effect of Molecular Size and Radiation Bandwidth."

Rice, F. O., and M. Freamo, *J. Amer. Chem. Soc.* **73**, 5529 (1951). "The Imine Radical."

Rice, F. O., and M. Freamo, *J. Amer. Chem. Soc.* **75**, 548 (1953a). "The Formation of the Imine Radical in the Electrical Discharge."

Rice, F. O., and C. Grelecki, *J. Phys. Chem.* **61**, 824 (1953b). "An Active Species Formed in the Electrical Decomposition of Dimethylamine."

Rice, F. O., and C. Sparrow, *J. Amer. Chem. Soc.* **75**, 848 (1953c). "Purple Sulfur, a New Allotropic Form."

Rice, F. O., and J. Ditter, *J. Amer. Chem. Soc.* **75**, 6066 (1953d). "Green Sulfur, a New Allotropic Form."

Rice, F. O., and F. Scherber, *J. Amer. Chem. Soc.* **77**, 291 (1955). "The Hydroazino Radical and Tetrazene."

Rice, F. O., and C. Grelecki, *J. Amer. Chem. Soc.* **79**, 1880 (1957). "The Imine Radical."

Rice, F. O., and R. B. Ingalls, *J. Amer. Chem. Soc.* **81**, 1856 (1959). "Absorption Spectra of Some Active Species."

Rice, O. K., *J. Chem. Phys.* **5**, 492 (1937). "On Transitions in Condensed Systems."

Riehl, N., H. Kallmann, and H. Vogel, *Proc. Int. Symp. Luminescence, Munich, 1965*. Thiemig, Munich, 1966. "The Physics and Chemistry of Scintillators."

Rinck, V. B., *Z. Naturforsch.* **3a**, 406 (1948). "Übergangswahrscheinlichkeiten für strahlende und strahlungslose Prozesse."

Ripoche, J., *Bull. Soc. Sci. Bretagne, Sci. Mat. Phys. Nat.* (France) **40**, 129 (1965). "Contribution to the Techniques of Formation, and to the Spectroscopic Study of Free Radicals Trapped in Crystal Lattices at Low Temperature."

Ripoche, J., *C. R. Acad. Sci.* (Paris) **263**, 912 (1966). "Spectre de Fluorescence du Radical Benzyle Piégé à la Température de l'Hélium Liquide dans le Cyclopentane et le Méthyl-Cyclopentane."

Ripoche, J., *J. Phys.* (Paris) **28**, C 3–153 (1967). "Spectre de Fluorescence du Radical Benzyle Piégé à la Température de l'Hélium Liquide dans Quelques Matrices Cristallines: Methylcyclohexane, Cyclopentane et Methylcyclopentane."

Robertson, W. W., and R. E. Reynolds, *J. Chem. Phys.* **29**, 138 (1958). "Effects of Hydrostatic Pressure on the Intensity of the Singlet-Triplet Transition of α-Chloronaphthalene in Ethyl Iodide."

Robinson, C. C., *J. Opt. Soc. Amer.* **57**, 4 (1967). "Excited-State Absorption in Fluorescent Uranium, Erbium, and Copper-Tin Glasses."

Robinson, G. W., and C. D. Cornwell, *J. Chem. Phys.* **21**, 1436 (1953). "The Interaction with Molecular Rotation of the Nuclear Electric Quadrupole Moments of Two Nuclei Having Spins 3/2."

Robinson, G. W., *J. Chem. Phys.* **22**, 1384 (1954). "Techniques in the Study of Emission Spectra of Polyatomic Molecules—the Spectra of Benzaldehyde and Acetophenone."

Robinson, G. W., M. McCarty, Jr., and M. C. Keelty, *J. Chem. Phys.* **27**, 972 (1957a). "Electronic Spectrum of Monomeric Nitrogen Dioxide at Liquid Helium Temperature."

Robinson, G. W., *J. Chem. Phys.* **27**, 1227 (1957b). "On Asymmetric Rotors."

Robinson, G. W., and M. McCarty, Jr., *J. Chem. Phys.* **28**, 349 (1958a). "Electronic Spectra of Free Radicals at $4°K-NH_2$."

Robinson, G. W., and M. McCarty, Jr., *Can. J. Phys.* **36**, 1590 (1958b). "Radical Spectra at Liquid Helium Temperatures."

Robinson, G. W., and M. McCarty, Jr., Informal Discussions Faraday Soc., unpublished preprints, Sheffield (September, 1958c). "Some Diatomic and Triatomic Free Radicals Trapped at 4.2°K."

Robinson, G. W., and M. McCarty, Jr., *J. Chem. Phys.* **29**, 883 (1958d). "Electronic Spectra of Free Radicals at $4°K-HNO$, NH and OH."

Robinson, G. W., and M. McCarty, Jr., *J. Chem. Phys.* **30**, 999 (1959). "Trapped HN_2 Radicals at 4.2°K."

Robinson, G. W., *Mol. Phys.* **3**, 301 (1960a). "Discrete Sites in Liquids."

Robinson, G. W., and M. McCarty, Jr., *J. Amer. Chem. Soc.* **82**, 1859 (1960b). "The Production and Subsequent Photolysis of Transient Products from the Photodecomposition of Diazomethane at 4.2°K."

Robinson, G. W., and L. Keyser, *J. Amer. Chem. Soc.* **82**, 5245 (1960c). "Frozen NH and NH_2 Radicals from the Photodecomposition of Hydrazoic Acid."

Robinson, G. W., in *Light and Life* (W. D. McElroy and B. Glass, eds.), The Johns Hopkins Press, Baltimore, Maryland, 1961a. "Electronic Excited States of Simple Molecules."

Robinson, G. W., *J. Mol. Spectrosc.* **6**, 58 (1961b). "Spectra and Energy Transfer Phenomena in Crystalline Rare Gas Solvents."

Robinson, G. W., in *Methods of Experimental Physics*, Vol. 3: *Molecular Physics* (D. Williams, ed.), p. 155, Academic Press, New York, 1961c. "Electronic Spectra."

Robinson, G. W., and R. P. Frosch, *J. Chem. Phys.* **37**, 1962 (1962a). "Theory of Electronic Energy Relaxation in the Solid Phase."

Robinson, G. W., *Advan. Chem. Ser.* **36**, 10 (1962b). "Production of Free Radicals and Their Physical Properties in the Liquid and Solid State."

Robinson, G. W., *Proc. Nat. Acad. Sci. U.S.* **49**, 521 (1963a). "Dynamic Role of the Triplet States in Photosynthesis."

Robinson, G. W., and R. P. Frosch, *J. Chem. Phys.* **38**, 1187 (1963b). "Electronic Excitation Transfer and Relaxation."

Robinson, G. W., *Ann. Rev. Phys. Chem.* **15**, 311 (1964). "Quantum Processes in Photosynthesis."

Robinson, G. W., *Brookhaven Symp. Biol.* **19**, 16 (1966). "Excitation Transfer and Trapping in Photosynthesis."

Robinson, G. W., *J. Chem. Phys.* **46**, 572 (1967a). "Intensity Enhancement of Forbidden Electronic Transitions by Weak Intermolecular Interactions."

Robinson, G. W., *J. Chem. Phys.* **47**, 1967 (1967b). "Intersystem Crossing in Gaseous Molecules."

Robinson, G. W., in *The Triplet State, Proc. Int. Symp. Amer. Univ., Beirut* (A. B.

Zahlan, ed.), p. 213, Cambridge University Press, London and New York, 1967c. "Radiationless Transitions in Gaseous Benzene."

Robinson, G. W., private communication, 1969. "Heavy Atom Effect of Electronic Transitions of Azulene."

Rochkind, M. M., and G. C. Pimentel, *J. Chem. Phys.* **42**, 1361 (1965). "Infrared Spectrum and Vibrational Assignment for Chlorine Monoxide, Cl_2O."

Rochkind, M. M., *Environ. Sci. Technol.* **1**, 434 (1967a). "Infrared Analysis of Gases: A New Method."

Rochkind, M. M., and G. C. Pimentel, *J. Chem. Phys.* **46**, 4481 (1967b). "Photolysis of Matrix-Isolated Dichlorine Monoxide: Infrared Spectra of ClClO and $(ClO)_2$."

Rochkind, M. M., *Appl. Spectrosc.* **22**, 313 (1968a). "Cryogenic System for Optical Spectroscopy."

Rochkind, M. M., and G. C. Pimentel, *J. Chem. Phys.* **42**, 1361 (1968b). "Infrared Spectrum and Vibrational Assignment for Chlorine Monoxide, Cl_2O."

Rochkind, M. M., *Science* **160**, 196 (1968c). "Infrared Pseudo Matrix Isolation Spectroscopy: Analysis of Gas Mixtures."

Rochkind, M., Applied Spectroscopy Conference, San Francisco (November, 1968d). "Matrix Isolation Spectroscopy and Infrared Spectro-chemical Analysis."

Rochkind, M., Applied Spectroscopy Conference, San Francisco (November, 1968e). "Matrix Isolation Studies of Molecular Bromine: Infrared Evidence for a Double Molecule in the Gas."

Roebber, J. L., G. K. Rollefson, and G. C. Pimentel, *J. Amer. Chem. Soc.* **80**, 255 (1958). "High Intensity Photolysis of Acetone."

Roebber, J. L., *J. Chem. Phys.* **37** (9), 1974 (1962). "Photolysis of the Phenoxy Radical in a Nitrogen Matrix."

Rolfe, J., F. R. Lipsett, and W. J. King, *Phys. Rev.* **123**, 447 (1961). "Optical Absorption and Fluorescence of Oxygen in Alkali Halide Crystals."

Rolfe, J., *J. Chem. Phys.* **49**, 4193 (1968). "Emission Spectra of S_2^-, Se_2^-, and SeS^- Ions in KI Crystals."

Romand, J., and J. Granier-Mayence, *C. R. Acad. Sci.* (Paris) **235**, 1023 (1952). "Spectre d'Absorption de l'Oxyde Azoteux Solide dans la Région de Schumann."

Ron, A., and O. Schnepp, *J. Chem. Phys.* **46**, 3991 (1967). "Lattice Vibrations of the Solids N_2, CO_2, and CO."

Roncin, J.-Y., and N. Damany-Astoin, *C. R. Acad. Sci.* (Paris) **253**, 835 (1961a). "Spectre d'Absorption entre 1650 et 2600 Å, du Mercure Piégé dans des Matrices d'Isopentane et d'Argon à 20°K."

Roncin, J.-Y., S. Y. Ch'en, J. Granier, et N. Damany-Astoin, *Spectrochim. Acta* **18**, 835 (1961b). "Spectres d'Absorption de Quelques Corps Organiques Purs ou en Matrices, dans l'Ultraviolet Lointain."

Roncin, J.-Y., V. Chandrasekharan, N. Damany, and B. Vodar, *J. Chim. Phys.* **60**, 1212 (1963). "Spectre d'Absorption entre 1150 et 1550 Å du Xénon Piégé dans des Matrices d'Argon et de Krypton à Basse Température."

Roncin, J.-Y., V. Chandrasekharan, and N. Damany, *C. R. Acad. Sci.* (Paris) **258**, 2513 (1964). "Spectres d'Absorption entre 1070 et 1400 Å du Xénon et du Krypton Solides, Purs ou en Matrices à Basse Température."

Roncin, J.-Y., N. Damany, and B. Vodar, *C. R. Acad. Sci.* (Paris) **260**, 96 (1965a). "Perturbation de la Raie d'Absorption Lyman α de l'Hydrogene Atomique Piege dans une Matrice Solids."

Roncin, J.-Y., and N. Damany, *C. R. Acad. Sci.* (Paris) **260**, 6069 (1965b). "Spectres d'Absorption dans l'Ultraviolet Lointain, de l'Oxyde de Carbone et de l'Azote Solides a Basse Température."

Roncin, J.-Y., and N. Damany, *C. R. Acad. Sci.* (Paris) **261**, 4697 (1965c). "Spectre d'Absorption, dans l'Ultraviolet Lointain de l'Oxyde Azotique en Matrice, à Basse Température."

Roncin, J.-Y., and N. Damany, *C. R. Acad. Sci.* (Paris) **262**, 1436 (1966). "Spectre d'Absorption dans l'Ultraviolet Lointain de l'Oxyde de Carbone et de l'Oxyde Azotique en Matrice de Néon à 1,5°K."

Roncin, J.-Y., *J. Phys.* (Paris) **28**, C3–159 (1967a). "Etats Electroniques Excités de NO piégé en Matrice à Basse Température."

Roncin, J.-Y., N. Damany, and J. Romand, *J. Mol. Spectrosc.* **22**, 154 (1967b). "Far Ultraviolet Absorption Spectra of Atoms and Molecules Trapped in Rare Gas Matrices at Low Temperature."

Roncin, J.-Y., and K. Moorjani, *Phys. Status Solidi* **23**, K1 (1967c). "On the Absorption Spectrum of Gaseous and Solid Xenon."

Roncin, J.-Y., *J. Mol. Spectrosc.* **26**, 105 (1968). "Electronic Transitions of CO, N_2 and NO Molecules Trapped in Solid Rare Gas Matrices: Qualitative Discussion."

Roncin, J.-Y., N. Damany, and B. Vodar, *Chem. Phys. Lett.* **3**, 197 (1969a). "Electronic Transitions of CS_2 and OCS Trapped in Solid Matrices and Rydberg Series in Dense Media."

Roncin, J.-Y., *Chem. Phys. Lett.* **3**, 408 (1969b). "Intermolecular Potential Parameters of Some Electronically Excited Species."

Rosahl, D., *Ann. Phys.* **12**, 35 (1953). "Fluorescence Spectra and Quantum Yields of Some Organic Materials Excited with Ultraviolet Light."

Rosen, B., *Nature* **157**, 692 (1946). "Electronic Spectra of Some Bent Triatomic Molecules."

Rosenbaum, R. L., *Rev. Sci. Instrum.* **39**, 890 (1968). "Some Properties of Gold-Iron Thermocouple Wire."

Rosengren, K. J., *Acta Chem. Scand.* **16**, 1401 (1962a). "A Systematic Study of the Photolysis of Some Dialkyl Disulfides in a Rigid Glass at 77°K."

Rosengren, K. J., *Acta Chem. Scand.* **16**, 1418 (1962b). "The Photolysis of Alkanethiols in a Rigid Glass at 77°K with the Possible Formation of Thiyl Radicals."

Rosengren, K. J., *Acta Chem. Scand.* **16**, 1421 (1962c). "A Study on Contraction, Relative Viscosity and Melting Curves of Some Glass-Forming Hydrocarbon Mixtures."

Rosengren, K., and G. C. Pimentel, *J. Chem. Phys.* **43**, 507 (1965). "Infrared Detection of Diimide, N_2H_2, and Imidogen, NH, by the Matrix Isolation Method."

Roshchupkin, E. I., and Y. A. Vladimirov, *J. Appl. Spectrosc.* **3**, 184 (1965). "A Study of the Primary Photochemical Processes Occurring in Proteins. III. The Luminescence and Kinetics Involved in the Formation of the Photoproducts of Aromatic Amino Acids at Low Temperatures."

Ross, S., and J. P. Olivier, *On Physical Adsorption*, Interscience (Wiley), New York, 1964.

Rothman, W., A. Case, and D. R. Kearns, *J. Chem. Phys.* **43**, 1067 (1965). "Determination of Singlet→Triplet Absorption Spectra from Phosphorescence Excitation Spectra: α-Bromonaphthalene."

Rousset, A., R. Lochet, and J. Darrine, *C. R. Acad. Sci.* (Paris) **237**, 37 (1953). "Phosphorescence de la Cellulose."

Roy, J. K., *Indian J. Phys.* **34**, 331 (1960). "Singlet-Triplet Absorption in Halogen

Substituted Toluenes."

Roy, J. K., *Indian J. Phys.* **36**, 507 (1962). "Luminescence Spectra of 2,4-Dichloro-and 3,4-Dichlorotoluene in the Solid State at − 180°C."

Roy, J. K., and M. A. El-Sayed, *J. Chem. Phys.* **40**, 3442 (1964). "Donor-Acceptor Relative Orientation for Maximum Triplet-Triplet Energy Transfer."

Roy, N. K., *Indian J. Phys.* **28**, 365 (1954). "On the Raman Spectra of Styrene and Polystyrene at − 180°C."

Rozman, I. M., and S. F. Kilin, *Sov. Phys.-Usp.* (English Transl.) **2**, 856 (1959). "Luminescence of Plastic Scintillators."

Runciman, W. A., *Rep. Progr. Phys.* **21**, 30 (1958). "Absorption and Fluorescence Spectra of Ions in Crystals."

Rush, J. J., *J. Chem. Phys.* **45**, 1312 (1966). "Motions of Water Molecules in Potassium Ferrocyanide Trihydrate, Water, and Ice: A Neutron Scattering Study."

Rush, J. J., *J. Chem. Phys.* **46**, 2285 (1967). "Cold-Neutron Study of Hindered Rotations in Solid and Liquid Methylchloroform, Neopentane, and Ethane."

Ruzevich, Z. S., *Opt. Spectrosc.* (USSR) (English Transl.) **15**, 191 (1963). "Fluorescence and Absorption Spectra of Azulene in Frozen Crystalline Solutions."

Ryazanova, E. F., *Bull. Acad. Sci. USSR, Phys. Ser.* (English Transl.) **23**, 136 (1959). "Luminescence of Two Dicarbonyl Acids at Different Temperatures."

Rylkov, V. V., V. E. Kholmogorov, and A. N. Terenin, *Opt. Spectrosc.* (USSR) (English Transl.) **22**, 129 (1967). "Triplet-Triplet Energy Transfer in Two-Photon Processes of Molecular Breakdown."

S

Sackmann, E., *J. Amer. Chem. Soc.* **90**, 3569 (1968). "On the Polarization of Optical Transitions of Dye Molecules Oriented in an Ordered Glass Matrix."

Sadlej, A. J., *Chem. Phys. Lett.* **2**, 451 (1968). "Temperature Dependence of the Fluorescence Spectra of Weakly Coupled Dimeric Systems."

Salis, G. A. von, and H. Labhart, *J. Phys. Chem.* **72**, 752 (1968). "On the Temperature Dependence of the Viscosity of Organic Glasses."

Samelson, H., and A. Lempicki, *J. Chem. Phys.* **39**, 110 (1963). "Fluorescence and Lifetimes of Eu Chelates."

Sancier, K. M., W. H. Fredericks, H. Wise, and W. J. Silva, *U.S. Dept. Comm., Office Tech. Serv., P.B. Rep.* **143**, 35 (1959). "Luminescence of Solids Produced by Surface Recombination of Atoms."

Santiago, G., and M. Kasha, *J. Amer. Chem. Soc.* **91**, 757 (1969). "Intraconfigurational Spin-Forbidden Transitions in Cr (III), Mn (II), and Ni (II) Complexes in Aqueous Glass Solutions at 77°K."

Sato, M., T. Azumi, and H. Azumi, *Bull. Chem. Soc. Jap.* **40**, 1031 (1967). "Delayed Thermal Excimer Fluorescence of Acriflavine in a Stretched PVA Sheet."

Sauter, H., and A. C. Albrecht, *Chem. Phys. Lett.* **2**, 8 (1968). "Electric-Field Broadening of an Electronic Transition in Azulene."

Sayre, E. V., D. G. Miller, and S. Freed, *J. Chem. Phys.* **26**, 109 (1957). "Symmetries of Electric Fields about Ions in Solutions. Absorption and Fluorescence Spectra of Europic Chloride in Water, Methanol, and Ethanol."

Sazonova, S. A., and B. S. Skorobogatov, *Opt. Spectrosc.* (USSR) (English Transl.) **22**, 87 (1967). "Sensitized Luminescence of Rare Earth Ions in NaCl : TR^{3+}-Se^{2-} Crystals."

Schadt, M., and D. F. Williams, *J. Chem. Phys.* **50**, 4364 (1969). "Low Temperature Hole Injection and Hole Trap Distribution in Anthracene."

Schawlow, A. L., D. L. Wood, and A. M. Clogston, *Phys. Rev. Lett.* **3**, 271 (1959). "Electronic Spectra of Exchange-Coupled Ion Pairs in Crystals."

Schawlow, A. L., in *Advances in Quantum Electronics* (J. R. Singer, ed.), Vol. 2, p. 50, Columbia University Press, New York, 1961a. "Fine Structure and Properties of Chromium Fluorescence in Aluminum and Magnesium Oxide."

Schawlow, A. L., A. H. Piksis, and S. Sugano, *Phys. Rev.* **122**, 1469 (1961b). "Strain-Induced Effects on the Degenerate Spectral Line of Chromium in MgO Crystals."

Schawlow, A. L., in *Advances in Quantum Electronics* (P. Grivel and N. Bloemberger, eds.), Vol. 3, p. 645, Columbia University Press, New York, 1964. "Width and Positions of Sharp Optical Lines."

Schawlow, A. W., ARPA Order No. 206-64, Tech. Summary Rep. No. 14, M.L. Report No. 1065, December, 1967. "Research in Laser Physics."

Scheibe, G. F., F. Dörr, and H. Detzer, *Abhandl. Bayer. Akad. Wiss. Math.-Naturw. Kl.* (1954).

Schenck, G. O., and E. Koch, *Z. Electrochem.* **64**, 170 (1960). "Zwischenreaktionen bei photosensibilisierten Prozessen in Lösungen."

Schildknecht, H., *Zonenschmelzen*, Verlag Chemie, Weinheim, 1964.

Schmid, D., and V. Zimmermann, *Phys. Lett.* **27A**, 459 (1968). "The Influence of Light on the ESR of F Centers."

Schmidt, J., I. A. M. Hesselmann, M. S. De Groot, and J. H. van der Waals, *Chem. Phys. Lett.* **1**, 434 (1967). "Optical Detection of Electron Resonance Transitions in Phosphorescent Quinoxaline."

Schmillen, A., *Z. Phys.* **150**, 123 (1958). "Zur Frage der Energieübertragung in festen Polyacenlösungen."

Schmillen, A., *Z. Naturforsch.* **16a**, 5 (1961). "Fluorescence of Pyrene in Solid Hydrocarbons."

Schmillen, A., and R. Legler, *Z. Naturforsch.* **18a**, 1 (1963). "Über die Fluoreszenz von binären Systemen kristalliner aromatischer Kohlenwasserstoffe."

Schneider, T., and H. Labhart, *Helv. Phys. Acta* **38**, 606 (1965). "Transfer and Conversion of Optical Excitation in Molecular Crystals."

Schnepp, O., and D. S. McClure, *J. Chem. Phys.* **26**, 83 (1957). "Near Ultraviolet Spectrum of Crystalline Hexamethyl Benzene and the Structure of the Hexamethyl Benzene Molecule."

Schnepp, O., *J. Chem. Phys.* **29**, 56 (1958). "Changes in the Near Ultraviolet Spectrum of Crystalline Hexamethylbenzene Accompanying a Low Temperature Phase Transition."

Schnepp, O., *J. Chem. Phys.* **30**, 48 (1959a). "Low-Temperature Phase Transition of Crystalline Hexamethylbenzene. II."

Schnepp, O., *J. Chem. Phys.* **30**, 863 (1959b). "Near Ultraviolet Absorption Spectrum of Crystalline 1,3,5-Trichlorobenzene."

Schnepp, O., *J. Chem. Phys.* **30**, 868 (1959c). "Near Ultraviolet Spectrum of Crystalline Hexachlorobenzene."

Schnepp, O., and D. S. McClure, *J. Chem. Phys.* **30**, 874 (1959d). "Near Ultraviolet Spectrum of Crystalline Durene."

Schnepp, O., *4th Int. Symp. Free Radical Stabilization*, Washington, D.C. (1959e). "Interactions between Trapped Species and the Matrix. I. Nuclear Degrees of

Freedom."

Schnepp, O., and K. Dressler, *J. Chem. Phys.* **32**, 1682 (1960a). "Photolysis of Ammonia in a Solid Matrix at Low Temperature."

Schnepp, O., and K. Dressler, *J. Chem. Phys.* **33**, 49 (1960b). "Absorption Spectra of Solid Xenon, Krypton, and Argon in the Vacuum Ultraviolet."

Schnepp, O., *J. Phys. Chem. Solids* **17**, 188 (1961). "The Absorption Spectra of Magnesium and Manganese Atoms in Solid Rare Gas Matrices."

Schnepp, O., and M. Levy, *J. Amer. Chem. Soc.* **84**, 172 (1962). "Intramolecular Energy Transfer in a Naphthalene-Anthracene System."

Schnepp, O., *Ann. Rev. Phys. Chem.* **14**, 35 (1963). "Electronic Spectra of Molecular Crystals."

Schnepp, O., and K. Dressler, *J. Chem. Phys.* **42**, 2482 (1965). "Schumann-Runge Bands of O_2 in Solid Phases: Spectroscopic Measurement of Intermolecular Potentials."

Schnepp, O., *J. Chem. Phys.* **46**, 3983 (1967). "Theory for the Infrared Absorption Intensities of the Lattice Vibrations of Molecular Solids."

Schoen, L. J., L. E. Kuentzel, and H. P. Broida, *Rev. Sci. Instrum.* **29**, 633 (1958). "Glass Dewars for Optical Studies at Low Temperatures."

Schoen, L. J., and H. P. Broida, *J. Mol. Spectrosc.* **5**, 416 (1960a). "Effect of Structure on the Spectra Emitted by Solid Nitrogen during Electron Bombardment."

Schoen, L. J., and H. P. Broida, *J. Chem. Phys.* **32**, 1184 (1960b). "Spectra Emitted from Rare Gas-Oxygen Solids during Electron Bombardment."

Schoen, L. J., and H. P. Broida, *Rev. Sci. Instrum.* **33**, 470 (1962a). "Glass Dewars for Optical and Other Studies at Low Temperatures."

Schoen, L. J., D. E. Mann, C. Knobler, and D. White, *J. Chem. Phys.* **37**, 1146 (1962b). "Rotation-Vibration Spectrum of Matrix-Isolated Hydrogen Chloride."

Schoen, L. J., *J. Chem. Phys.* **45**, 2773 (1966). "Flash Photolysis of Matrix Isolated Cyanogen Azide in Solid Nitrogen."

Schoen, L. J., *Rev. Sci. Instrum.* **38**, 1531 (1967). "Sapphire Window Mountings for Low Temperature Spectroscopy."

Schumacher, E., and B. Meyer, *Nature* **186**, 801 (1960). "Colored Sulfur Allotropes."

Schumacher, E., *Chimia* **15**, 471 (1961). "Untersuchungen an eingefrorenen, reaktionsfähigen Substanzen."

Schutt, H. U., and H. Zimmermann, *Z. Elektrochem.* **67**, 54 (1963). "Polarisation der Elektronenbanden von Aromaten; 5. Mitt.: Indol, Indazol, Benzimidazol, Benztriazol, Carbazol."

Schwager, I., and A. Arkell, *J. Amer. Chem. Soc.* **89**, 6006 (1967). "Matrix Infrared Spectra of HOBr and HOCl."

Schweig, A., *Mol. Phys.* **15**, 1 (1968). "Solvent Effects on the Electronic Spectra of Polar Conjugated Systems. 4-Dimethylamino-prop-2-en-1-al, A Simple Merocyanine."

Schwoerer, M., and H. C. Wolf, *Int. Conf. Magnetic Resonance and Relaxation, Ljubljana,* 1966. "Excitation Exchange and Optical Spin Polarization in the Triplet State of Naphthalene as Studied by ESR."

Schwoerer, M., and H. C. Wolf, in *The Triplet State* (A. B. Zahlan, ed.), p. 133, Cambridge University Press, London and New York, 1967a. "ESR Investigations of Naphthalene-d_8 : Naphthalene-h_8 Mixed Crystals."

Schwoerer, M., and H. C. Wolf, in *Molecular Crystals*, Vol. 3, p. 177, Gordon and Breach, 1967b. "ESR-Untersuchungen an Naphthalin-d_8 : Naphthalin-h_8-Mischkristallen in deren Triplett-Zustand."

Schwoerer, M., Ph. D. Thesis, Technische Hochschule Stuttgart, 1968a. "ESR-Untersuchungen an Naphthalin-d_8 : Naphthalin-h_8-Mischkristallen in deren Triplett-Zustand."

Schwoerer, M., and H. Sixl, *Chem. Phys. Lett.* **2**, 14 (1968b). "Optical Spin Polarisation in the Triplet State of Naphthalene."

Scott, D. R., and O. Maltenieks, *J. Phys. Chem.* **72**, 3354 (1968). "Experimental Method for Determining the Intersystem Crossing Rate Constant from Lowest Excited Singlet to Lowest Excited Triplet."

Scott, R. B., *Technology and Uses of Liquid Hydrogen*, Pergamon Press, New York, 1969.

Scott, R. E., *Cryogenic Engineering*. Academic Press, New York, 1959.

Sears, D. R., and H. P. Klug, *J. Chem. Phys.* **37**, 3002 (1962). "Density and Expansivity of Solid Xenon."

Sell, D. D., R. L. Greene, W. M. Yen, A. L. Schawlow, and R. M. White, *J. Appl. Phys.* **37**, 1229 (1966). "Magnetic Effects in the Optical Spectrum of MnF_2."

Sell, D. D., R. L. Greene, and R. M. White, *Phys. Rev.* **158**, 489 (1967). "Optical Exciton-Magnon Absorption in MnF_2."

Serafini, T. T., and J. L. Keenig, *Cryogenic Properties of Polymers*, Dekker, New York, 1968.

Serway, R. A., and S. A. Marshall, *J. Chem. Phys.* **45**, 4098 (1966). "ESR Absorption Spectra of Two Phosphorous Defect Centers in Irradiated Single-Crystal Calcite."

Seshadri, K. S., D. White, and D. E. Mann, *J. Chem. Phys.* **45**, 4697 (1966). "Low-Frequency Region of the Infrared Spectrum of Matrix Isolated Vapors from Li_2O (s)."

Sevchenko, A. N., K. N. Solov'ev, S. F. Shkirman, and M. V. Sarzhevskaya, *Dokl. Akad. Nauk SSSR* **153**, 1391 (1963). "Electronic Vibrational Quasiline Spectra of Porphin and Dihydroporphin."

Sevchenko, A. N., K. N. Solovev, V. A. Mashenkov, and S. F. Shkirman, *Sov. Phys. Dokl.* **10**, 778 (1966). "Low Temperature Polarization Spectra of Porphine Derivatives."

Seybold, P., and M. Gouterman, *Chem. Rev.* **65**, 199 (1965). "Radiationless Transitions in Gases and Liquids."

Shablya, A. V., and A. N. Terenin, *Opt. Spectrosc.* (USSR) (English Transl.) **10**, 324 (1961). "The Phototransfer of a Proton in Acridine Derivatives at Low Temperatures as Observed in the Luminescence Spectrum."

Shalimova, K. V., V. N. Khirin, and O. I. Korolev, *Opt. Spectrosc.* (USSR) (English Transl.) **20**, 587 (1966a). "Spectral Distribution of the Relative Quantum Yield of Photoluminescence of Polycrystalline Cadmium Sulfide Films at 77°K."

Shalimova, K. V., V. N. Khirin, and O. I. Korolev, *Opt. Spectrosc.* (USSR) (English Transl.) **21**, 256 (1966b). "Temperature Dependence of the Absorption, Reflection, Emission, and Excitation Spectra and of the Luminescence Quantum Yield of Polycrystalline Sulfide Films."

Shamovskii, L. M., and M. G. Larionov, *Opt. Spectrosc.* (USSR) (English Transl.) **22**, 319 (1967). "Study of the Recombination Luminescence Mechanism in Alkali-Halide Phosphors Activated by Thallium and Indium."

Sharma, J., *J. Chem. Phys.* **24**, 39 (1956). "Thermoluminescence of Some Aromatic Hydrocarbons."

Sharma, R. D., *Phys. Rev. Lett.* **18**, 1139 (1967). "Autoionization in Anthracene Crystal."

Sharn, C. F., *J. Chem. Phys.* **34**, 240 (1961). "High-Energy Radiation Damage to Fluorescent Organic Solids."

Sharp, J. H., and M. Lardon, *J. Phys. Chem.* **72**, 3230 (1968). "Spectroscopic Characterization of a New Polymorph of Metal-free Phthalocyanine."

Sheppard, N., and G. B. B. M. Sutherland, *Nature* **159**, 739 (1947). "Infrared Spectrum of C_nD_{2n+2} and the 'Long Chain Frequency' in Paraffins."

Sherman, W. F., *J. Sci. Instrum.* **43**, 462 (1966). "A High-Pressure Absorption Cell for Obtaining Well-Resolved Infra-red Spectra of Samples under 50 kb Pressures at 90°K."

Shigorin, D. N., N. A. Shcheglova, R. N. Nurmukhametov, and N. S. Dokunikhin, *Sov. Phys. Dokl.* (English Transl.) **3**, 628 (1958). "Influence of the Position and Nature of the Substituent on the Fluorescence Spectra of Anthraquinone Derivatives in Frozen Solutions."

Shigorin, D. N., N. A. Shcheglova, and R. N. Nurmukhametov, *Bull. Acad. Sci. USSR, Phys. Ser.* (English Transl.) **23**, 39 (1959). "Effect of the Position and Nature of the Substituent on the Fluorescence Spectra of Anthraquinone Derivatives in Frozen Solutions."

Shigorin, D. N., N. A. Shcheglova, and N. S. Dokunikhin, *Bull. Acad. Sci. USSR, Phys. Ser.* (English Transl.) **24**, 781 (1960). "Luminescence Spectra of Halogen Derivatives of Anthraquinone in Frozen Solutions."

Shimada, R., *Spectrochim. Acta* **17**, 30 (1961). "The Lowest Multiplicity-Forbidden Transitions in Diazines. II. The Phosphorescence Spectrum of Pyrimidine at 90°K."

Shirk, J. S., and A. M. Bass, *J. Chem. Phys.* **49**, 5156 (1968). "Matrix Isolation Spectra of Discharge 'Sputtered' Metals."

Shiron, M., and J. E. Willard, *J. Phys. Chem.* **72**, 1702 (1968). "Radical Production by γ Irradiation of 3-Methylpentane, Methyltetrahydrofuran, and Methylcyclohexane Glasses at 77°K with and without Alkyl Halide Solutes."

Shockey, D. A., and G. W. Groves, *J. Amer. Ceram. Soc.* **51**, 299 (1968). "Effect of Water on Toughness of MgO Crystals."

Shpak, M. T., and E. F. Sheka, *Opt. Spectrosc.* (USSR) (English Transl.) **8**, 32 (1960a). "On the Intrinsic Luminescence of Crystalline Naphthalene."

Shpak, M. T., and E. F. Sheka, *Opt. Spectrosc.* (USSR) (English Transl.) **9**, 29 (1960b). "The Influence of Impurities on the Luminescence of Crystalline Naphthalene."

Shpak, M. T., *Bull. Acad. Sci. USSR, Phys. Ser.* **25**, 13 (1961). "Role of Impurities in the Luminescence of Molecular Crystals at Low Temperatures."

Shpol'skii, E. V., and A. A. Il'ina, *Zh. Eksp. Teor. Fiz.* **21**, 142 (1951). "Fluorescence of 3,4-Benzopyrene in Frozen Solutions."

Shpol'skii, E. V., A. A. Il'ina, and L. A. Klimova, *Dokl. Akad. Nauk SSSR* **87**, 935 (1952). "Fluorescence Spectrum of Coronene in Frozen Solutions."

Shpol'skii, E. V., and L. A. Klimova, *Sov. Phys. Dokl.* (English Transl.) **1**, 732 (1956a). "Emission Spectrum of Coronene in Solutions at Low Temperatures."

Shpol'skii, E.V., and L. A. Klimova, *Bull. Acad. Sci. USSR, Phys. Ser* (English Transl.) **20**, 428 (1956b). "Influence of the Solvent on the Luminescence Spectrum of Aromatic Hydrocarbons at Low Temperatures."

Shpol'skii, E. V., E. A. Girdzhiyauskaite, and L. A. Klimova, *Fiz. Sb.* **1**, 24 (1957). "Emission Spectra of Aromatic Hydrocarbons at Low Temperatures."

Shpol'skii, E. V., and E. A. Girdzhiyauskaite, *Opt. Spectrosc.* (USSR) (English Transl.) **4**, 620 (1958). "Luminescence and Absorption of Pyrene and 3,4-Benzopyrene in Frozen Solutions of Normal Paraffins."

Shpol'skii, E. V., *Sov. Phys.-Usp.* (English Transl.) **2**, 378 (1959a). "Emission Spectroscopic Analysis of Organic Compounds."

Shpol'skii, E. V., and L. A. Klimova, *Bull. Acad. Sci. USSR, Phys. Ser.* (English Transl.) **23**, 22 (1959b). "Vibrational Analysis of the Phosphorescence of Coronene."

Shpol'skii, E. V., *Sov. Phys.-Usp.* (English Transl.) **2**, 958 (1960a). "A Century of Spectrum Analysis."

Shpol'skii, E. V., and R. I. Personov, *Opt. Spectrosc.* (USSR) (English Transl.) **8**, 172 (1960b). "Emission and Absorption Spectra of Perylene in Solid Solutions at 77°K."

Shpol'skii, E. V., *Sov. Phys.-Usp.* (English Transl.) **3**, 372 (1960c). "Line Fluorescence Spectra of Organic Compounds and Their Applications."

Shpol'skii, E. V., and L. A. Klimova, *Opt. Spectrosc.* (USSR) (English Transl.) **13**, 97 (1962a). "Line Spectra of Aromatic Hydrocarbons in Frozen Crystalline Solutions."

Shpol'skii, E. V., *Sov. Phys.-Usp.* (English Transl.) **5**, 522 (1962). "Problems of the Origin and Structure of the Quasilinear Spectra of Organic Compounds at Low Temperatures."

Shpol'skii, E. V., and R. I. Personov, *Ind. Lab.* (USSR) (English Transl.) **28**, 451 (1962c). "The Spectral Analysis of Organic Compounds by Emission Using the Low Temperature Line Spectrum."

Shpol'skii, E. V., *Sov. Phys.-Usp.* **5**, 612 (1963a). "New Results on the Radiation Properties of Optical Masers (Lasers)."

Shpol'skii, E. V., *Sov. Phys.-Usp.* (English Transl.) **6**, 411 (1963b). "New Data on the Nature of the Quasilinear Spectra of Organic Compounds."

Shpol'skii, E. V., *Opt. Spectrosc.* (USSR) (English Transl.) **23**, 357 (1967). "The Development of Soviet Optics and Spectroscopy during the Past Fifty Years."

Shutte, C. J. H., and A. M. Heyns, *Chem. Phys. Lett.* **1**, 487 (1967). Low Temperature Infrared Studies. I. Preliminary Communication on the Infrared Spectrum of Ammonium Dichromiate $(NH_4)_2 Cr_2O_7$."

Sibleyras, M., J.-Y. Roncin, and N. Damany, *C. R. Acad. Sci.* (Paris) *Ser. B* **266**, 175 (1968). "Spectre Electronique du Protoxyde d'Azote Solide, Pur et en Matrice, à Basse Température."

Sidman, J. W., and D. S. McClure, *J. Amer. Chem. Soc.* **77**, 6461 (1955). "Electronic and Vibrational States of Biacetyl and Biacetyl-d_6. I. Electronic States."

Sidman, J. W., and D. S. McClure, *J. Chem. Phys.* **24**, 757 (1956a). "Electronic and Vibrational States of Azulene."

Sidman, J. W., *J. Chem. Phys.* **25**, 115 (1956b). "Electronic and Vibrational States of Anthracene."

Sidman, J. W., *J. Chem. Phys.* **25**, 122 (1956c). "Electronic and Vibrational States of Tetracene (Naphthacene)."

Sidman, J. W., *J. Chem. Phys.* **25**, 229 (1956d). "Phosphorescence Spectra of the β-Halonaphthalenes."

Sidman, J. W., *J. Amer. Chem. Soc.* **78**, 4217 (1956e). "Electronic and Vibrational States of the Pleiadienes."

Sidman, J. W., *Phys. Rev.* **102**, 96 (1956f). "Polarized Absorption and Fluorescence Spectra of Crystalline Anthracene at 4°K: Spectral Evidence for Trapped Excitons."

Sidman, J. W., *J. Amer. Chem. Soc.* **79**, 305 (1957). "Concentration Dependence of the Absorption and Fluorescence Spectra of Mixed Crystals of Anthracene with Phenanthrene at 77°K."

Sidman, J. W., *Chem. Rev.* **58**, 689 (1958). "Electronic Transitions Due to Nonbonding Electrons in Carbonyl, Aza-Aromatic, and Other Compounds."

Siebrand, W., *J. Chem. Phys.* **44**, 4055 (1966). "Mechanism of Radiationless Triplet

Decay in Aromatic Hydrocarbons and the Magnitude of the Franck-Condon Factors."

Siebrand, W., and D. F. Williams, *J. Chem. Phys.* **46**, 405 (1967a). "Isotope Rule for Radiationless Transitions with an Application to Triplet Decay in Aromatic Hydrocarbons."

Siebrand, W., *J. Chem. Phys.* **46**, 440 (1967b). "Radiationless Transitions in Polyatomic Molecules. I. Calculation of Franck-Condon Factors."

Siebrand, W., in *The Triplet State* (A. B. Zahlan, ed.), p. 31, Cambridge University Press, London and New York, 1967c. "Triplet Decay and Intersystem Crossing in Aromatic Hydrocarbons."

Siebrand, W., and D. F. Williams, *J. Chem. Phys.* **49**, 1860 (1968). "Radiationless Transitions in Polyatomic Molecules. III. Anharmonicity, Isotope Effects, and Singlet-to-Ground-State Transitions in Aromatic Hydrocarbons."

Siebrand, W., *J. Chem. Phys.* **50**, 1040 (1969). "Temperature Dependence of Radiationless Transitions."

Siegel, S., and L. Golstein, *J. Chem. Phys.* **45**, 1860 (1966). "Erratum: Study of Triplet-Triplet Transfer by the Method of Magnetophotoselection. II. Concentration Depolarization."

Siegel, S., and H. S. Judeikis, *J. Chem. Phys.* **48**, 1613 (1968). "Relative Interaction Radii for Quenching of Triplet-State Molecules."

Signeur, A. V., *Guide to Gas Chromatography Literature*, Vols. I and II, Plenum Press, New York, 1964 and 1967.

Sihvonen, Y. T., *J. Appl. Phys.* **38**, 4431 (1967). "Photoluminescence, Photocurrent, and Phase-Transition Correlations in $SrTiO_2$."

Silbey, R., *J. Chem. Phys.* **46**, 4029 (1967). "Radiation Damping of Exciton States in Molecular Crystals."

Simpson, J. D., H. W. Offen, and J. G. Burr, *Chem. Phys. Lett.* **2**, 383 (1968). "Effect of Partial Deuteration on Biphenyl Phosphorescence."

Simpson, W. T., *Radiat. Res.* **20**, 87 (1963). "Theory of the Interaction of Localized Electronic Excitations."

Sirkar, S. C., and D. C. Biswas, *Indian J. Phys.* **28**, 423 (1954). "The Fluorescence of *p*-Chlorotoluene in the Solid State at Low Temperatures."

Sirkar, S. C., and D. C. Biswas, *J. Chem. Phys.* **24**, 470 (1956). "On the Fluorescence of *p*-Chlorotoluene in the Solid State at Low Temperatures."

Skell, P. S., and L. D. Wescott, *J. Am. Chem. Soc.* **85**, 1023 (1963). "Chemical Properties of C_3, a Dicarbene."

Skettrup, T., and L. R. Lidholt, *Solid State Commun.* **6**, 589 (1968). "Decay Times of the Ultraviolet and Green Emission Lines in ZnO."

Smith, B. E., and M. Gouterman, *Chem. Phys. Lett.* **2**, 517 (1968). "Quartet Luminescence from Copper Porphyrins."

Smith, B. L., and C. J. Pings, *J. Chem. Phys.* **38**, 825 (1963). "Optical Determination of the Compressibility of Solid Argon."

Smith, B. L., and C. J. Pings, *J. Chem. Phys.* **48**, 2387 (1968). "Polarizability of an Argon Atom in Solid Argon."

Smith, D. Y., *Phys. Rev.* **133**, A1087 (1964). "Calculation of the g Factor of Hydrogen and the Alkali Atoms Trapped in Rare-Gas Solids."

Smith, D. Y., *Phys. Rev.* **166** (1968). "Possibility of Rare-Gas Color Centers in Ionic Crystals."

Smith, F. J., J. K. Smith, and S. P. McGlynn, *Rev. Sci. Instrum.* **33**, 1367 (1962).

"Low Temperature Double Path Absorption Cell."

Smith, F. J., and S. P. McGlynn, *J. Chem. Phys.* **4**, 4308 (1964). "Delayed Excimer Fluorescence of Pyrene."

Smith, G. C., and R. C. Hughes, *Phys. Rev. Lett.* **20**, 1358 (1968). "Magnetic Field Effects on Triplet-Exciton Interaction in Anthracene."

Smith, J. J., and B. Meyer, *J. Mol. Spectrosc.* **27**, 304 (1968a). "The Absorption and Fluorescence Spectrum of SnS and SnO: Matrix-Induced Intersystem Crossing."

Smith, J. J., and B. Meyer, *J. Chem. Phys.* **48**, 5436 (1968b). "Absorption and Phosphorescence Spectrum of Matrix-Isolated Ferrocene."

Smith, J. J., and B. Meyer, UCRL-18060 (July, 1968c), University of California, Berkeley. "The Photolysis of Matrix Isolated Disulfur Dichloride."

Smith, J. J., and B. Meyer, *J. Chem. Phys.* **50**, 456 (1969). "Fluorescence and Induced Phosphorescence of Formaldehyde in Solid-Low-Temperature Solutions."

Smith, M. S., Jr., and P. A. P. de Maine, *J. Nat. Acad. Sci. U.S.* **12**, 109 (1966). "Infrared Studies of Complex Formation in Inert Solvents. II. Hydrogen Bonds in Nitro Compound–Alcohol–Carbon Tetrachloride Systems."

Smith, W. H., and G. E. Leroi, *J. Chem. Phys.* **45**, 1767 (1966). "Infrared and Raman Spectra of Carbon Suboxide in Condensed Phases."

Snelson, A., and K. S. Pitzer, *J. Phys. Chem.* **67**, 882 (1963). "Infrared Spectra by Matrix Isolation of Lithium Fluoride, Lithium Chloride, and Sodium Fluoride."

Snelson, A., *J. Phys. Chem.* **70**, 3208 (1966). "Infrared Spectra of Some Alkaline Earth Halides by the Matrix Isolation Technique."

Snelson, A., *J. Phys. Chem.* **71**, 3202 (1967a). "Infrared Spectrum of AlF_3, Al_2F_6, and AlF by Matrix Isolation."

Snelson, A., *J. Chem. Phys.* **46**, 3652 (1967b). "Infrared Spectrum of LiF, Li_2F_2, and Li_3F_3 by Matrix Isolation."

Snelson, A., *J. Phys. Chem.* **72**, 250 (1968). "Infrared Spectra of the Beryllium Halides."

Snowden, R. G., and N. Davidson, *J. Amer. Chem. Soc.* **78**, 1291 (1958). "Photochemical Studies with Hydrocarbon Solvents at Low Temperature."

Sobolev, V. V., *Opt. Spectrosc.* (USSR) (English Transl.) **22**, 504 (1967). "Photoluminescence of Mixed CdSe-CdS Crystals at T = 4.2°K."

Solov'ev, A. V., *Ukr. Fiz. Zh.* **4**, 615 (1959). "Influence of Secondary Impurities on Absorption and Luminescence of Primary Impurities in Crystals."

Solov'ev, A. V., *Ukr. Fiz. Zh.* **6**, 56 (1961). "Absorption and Luminescence of Impurities in Crystals of Organic Compounds at 20°K. IV. Spectra of Anthracene in Crystals of Certain Polyphenyls."

Sommer, A., P. N. Walsh, D. White, *J. Chem. Phys.* **33**, 296 (1960). "Mass Spectrometric and Infrared Emission Investigation of the Vapor Species in the B-S System at Elevated Temperatures."

Sommer, A., D. White, M. J. Linevsky, and D. E. Mann, *J. Chem. Phys.* **38**, 87 (1963). "Infrared Absorption Spectra of B_2O_3, B_2O_2, and BO_2 in Solid Argon Matrices."

Sommer, B., and J. Jortner, *J. Chem. Phys.* **50**, 187 (1969a). "Electronic States of Mixed Molecular Crystals: Singlet Excited States of Isotopic Impurities in Crystalline Benzene and Naphthalene."

Sommer, B., and J. Jortner, *J. Chem. Phys.* **50**, 839 (1969b). "Triplet States in Mixed Molecular Crystals."

Soos, Z. G., *J. Chem. Phys.* **46**, 4284 (1967). "Frenkel and Wannier Spin-Excitons in Organic Free-Radical Crystals."

Soos, Z. G., *J. Chem. Phys.* **51**, 2107 (1969). "Zeeman Populations of Optically Produced Triplet Excitons in Anthracene."

Spangler, J. D., and H. Sponer, *Spectrochim. Acta* **19**, 169 (1963). "Environmental Effects on the Near Ultraviolet Absorption and Emission Spectra of Benzene on a Crystalline Matrix of Cyclohexane."

Spangler, J. D., and N. G. Kilmer, *J. Chem. Phys.* **48**, 698 (1968). "Electronic Spectra of Benzene in Cyclohexane at 77°K."

Sponer, H., Y. Kanda, and L. A. Blackwell, *J. Chem. Phys.* **29**, 721 (1958). "Delayed Fluorescence in Naphthalene Crystals at 4°K."

Sponer, H., Y. Kanda, and L. A. Blackwell, *Spectrochim. Acta* **16**, 1135 (1960). "Triplet-Singlet Emission Spectra of Benzene in a Crystalline Matrix of Cyclohexane at 4.2°K and 77°K."

Sponer, H., *Int. Conf., New York Univ., 1962*, p. 143. "Luminescence of Organic and Inorganic Materials." *Chem. Abstr.* **58**, 1060c (1962).

Sponer, H., and Y. Kanda, *J. Chem. Phys.* **40**, 778 (1964). "Triplet-Singlet Luminescence from Methylated Benzenes in the Crystalline State and in Rigid Glass Solutions."

Spratley, R. D., J. J. Turner, and G. C. Pimentel, *J. Chem. Phys.* **44**, 2063 (1966). "Dioxygen Monofluoride: Infrared Spectrum, Vibrational Potential Function, and Bonding."

Spurny, Z., and J. Novotny, *J. Phys. Chem. Solids* **26**, 1107 (1965). "Effect of Ionizing Radiation on Glasses: The Relation between Optical Absorption and Thermoluminescence of Borate Glasses."

Srinivasan, B. N., M. Kinoshita, and S. P. McGlynn, *J. Chem. Phys.* **47**, 5090 (1967). "Delayed Luminescence of Organic Mixed Crystals. VI. Delayed Excimer Fluorescence of Pyrene in Biphenyl."

Srinivasan, B. N., M. Kinoshita, J. W. Rabalais, and S. P. McGlynn, *J. Chem. Phys.* **48**, 1924 (1968a). "Growth and Decay of Delayed Luminescence."

Srinivasan, B. N., M. Kinoshita, J. W. Rabalais, and S. P. McGlynn, *J. Chem. Phys.* **49**, 2881 (1968b). "Erratum: the Growth and Decay of Delayed Luminescence."

Steele, R. H., and A. Szent-Györgyi, *Proc. Nat. Acad. Sci. U.S.* **43**, 477 (1957). "On Excitation of Biological Substances."

Steele, R. H., and A. Szent-Györgyi, *Proc. Nat. Acad. Sci. U.S.* **44**, 540 (1958). "Studies on the Excited States of Proteins."

Steen, H. B., *Photochem. Photobiol.* **8**, 47 (1968). "Luminescence of *L*-Tryptophan in the Dry State and in Aqueous Solution Induced by X-Rays and UV Light at 77°K."

Steinberg, I. Z., and E. Katchalski, *J. Chem. Phys.* **48**, 2404 (1968a). "Theoretical Analysis of the Role of Diffusion in Chemical Reactions, Fluorescence Quenching, and Nonradiative Energy Transfer."

Steinberg, I. Z., *J. Chem. Phys.* **48**, 2411 (1968b). "Nonradiative Energy Transfer in Systems in Which Rotatory Brownian Motion is Frozen."

Steinberger, I. T., and O. Schnepp, *Solid State Commun.* **5**, 417 (1967). "Wannier Excitons in Solid Xenon."

Stern, A., and M. Dezelic, *Z. Phys. Chem.* (Leipzig) **A180**, 131 (1937). "Über die Lichtabsorption der Porphyrine. XII. Metallkomplexe."

Sternlicht, H., and H. M. McConnell, *J. Chem. Phys.* **35**, 1793 (1961). "Paramagnetic Excitons in Molecular Crystals."

Sternlicht, H., G. C. Nieman, and G. W. Robinson, *J. Chem. Phys.* **39**, 1610 (1963).

"Errata: Triplet-Triplet Annihilation and Delayed Fluorescence in Molecular Aggregates; and Comments Concerning Ruby-Laser-Induced Fluorescence in Anthracene Crystals."

Stevens, B., and M. S. Walker, *Chem. Commun.* **1965**, 8 (1965). "A Photoionization Mechanism for the Delayed Fluorescence of Perylene in a Rigid Glass."

Stevens, B., and B. E. Algar, *Chem. Phys. Lett.* **1**, 219 (1967). "Intersystem Crossing Yields in Anthanthrene and Perylene from Photosensitized Peroxidation."

Stevens, B., and M. F. Thomaz, *Chem. Phys. Lett.* **1**, 535 (1968a). "Double Intersystem Crossing in 3-Bromopyrene."

Stevens, B., and M. F. Thomaz, *Chem. Phys. Lett.* **1**, 551 (1968b). "Double Intersystem Crossing in Naphthalene and 1-Chloronaphthalene."

Stevenson, R., *J. Chem. Phys.* **27**, 673 (1957). "Compressions and Solid Phases of CO_2, CS_2, COS, O_2, and CO."

Stewart, J. W., *J. Phys. Chem. Solids* **29**, 641 (1968). "The Compression of Solid Neon, Argon, and Krypton to 20 Kbar."

Stokowski, S. E., and A. L. Schawlow, *Phys. Rev. Lett.* **21**, 965 (1968). "Electric Field Effects on the Spectrum of Chromium in Strontium Titanate."

Stone, J. A., *Can. J. Chem.* **46**, 1267 (1968). "Radiolysis of Cyclohexane in a Xenon Matrix at 77°K."

Streng, L. V., and A. G. Streng, *Inorg. Chem.* **5**, 328 (1966). "Photochemical Formation of Krypton Difluoride from Krypton and Fluorine or Oxygen Difluoride."

Strickler, S. J., and M. Kasha, *J. Chem. Phys.* **34**, 1077 (1961). "Solvent Effects on the Spectra of Halide Ions."

Strickler, S. J., and R. A. Berg, *J. Chem. Phys.* **37**, 814 (1962). "Relationship between Absorption Intensity and Fluorescence Lifetime of Molecules."

Strickler, S. J., and M. Kasha, *J. Amer. Chem. Soc.* **85**, 2899 (1963). "Solvent Effects on the Electronic Absorption Spectrum of Nitrite Ion."

Stryer, L., *J. Mol. Biol.* **13**, 482 (1965). "The Interaction of a Naphthalene Dye with Apomyoglobin and Apohemoglobin. A Fluorescent Probe of Non-polar Binding Sites."

Stryer, L., *J. Am. Chem. Soc.* **88**, 5708 (1966). "Excited-State Proton-Transfer Reactions. A Deuterium Isotope Effect on Fluorescence."

Stryer, L., *Proc. Nat. Acad. Sci. U.S.* **58**, 719 (1967). "Biological Rulers."

Sturge, M. D., and M. H. Crozier, *J. Chem. Phys.* **46**, 4551 (1967). "Is there a Dynamic Jahn-Teller Effect in the ^{2}D-E State of Ce^{3+} in CaF_2?"

Sugano, S., A. L. Schawlow, and F. Varsanyi, *Phys. Rev.* **120**, 2045 (1960). "Zeeman Effect of the Purely Cubic Field Fluorescence Line of MgO : Cr^{3+} Crystals."

Sveshnikov, B. Y., and V. I. Shirokov, *Opt. Spectrosc.* (USSR) (English Transl.) **12**, 320 (1962). "Variation of the Mean Lifetime and Yield of Luminescence in the Process of Quenching as a Function of the Law of Molecular Interaction."

Svishchev, G. M., *Bull. Acad. Sci. USSR, Phys. Ser.* (English Transl.) **27**, 695 (1963). "Concerning the Nature of the Fine Structure of the Quasiline Spectra of Aromatic Hydrocarbons in Frozen Paraffin Solutions."

Swenberg, C. E., and W. T. Stacy, *Chem. Phys. Lett.* **2**, 327 (1968). "Bimolecular Radiationless Transitions in Crystalline Tetracene."

Swenberg, C. E., *J. Chem. Phys.* **51**, 1753 (1969). "Theory of Triplet Exciton Annihilation in Polyacene Crystals."

Swenson, C. A., W. B. Person, D. A. Dows, and R. M. Hexter, *J. Chem. Phys.* **31**, 1324

(1959). "Infrared Studies of Crystal Benzene. I. The Resolution and Assignment of v_{20}, and the Relative Magnitudes of Crystal Fields in Benzene."

Syme, R. W. G., W. J. Haas, F. H. Spedding, and R. H. Good, Jr., *J. Chem. Phys.* **48**, 2772 (1968). "Theory of Zeeman Effect for Rare-Earth Ions in Crystal Field with C_{3h} Symmetry. III."

Symons, M. C. R., and M. Townsend, *J. Chem. Phys.* **25**, 1299 (1956). "Electronic Spectrum of Trapped Ethanol Radicals."

T

Takeno, S., *J. Chem. Phys.* **46**, 2481 (1967). "Vibrational Properties of Excitons in Molecular Crystals."

Takezawa, S., F. R. Innes, and Y. Tanaka, *J. Chem. Phys.* **46**, 4555 (1967). "Selective Enhancement in Hydrogenlike Molecules with the Rare Gases. II. HD and D_2 with Ar and Kr."

Tan, L. Y., and G. C. Pimentel, *J. Chem. Phys.* **48**, 5202 (1968). "Methyl Alkali Halides: A New Molecular Type; Infrared Spectra by the Matrix Isolation Technique."

Tanaka, M., and J. Tanaka, *Mol. Phys.* **16**, 1 (1969). "Theory of Exciton States of Molecular Crystals."

Tarina, V., *J. Chem. Phys.* **46**, 3273 (1967). "On the Low-Frequency Motions in Solid Benzene by Inelastic Scattering of Cold Neutrons."

Taylor, C. A., M. A. El-Bayoumi, and M. Kasha, *Proc. Nat. Acad. Sci. U.S.* **63**, 252 (1969). "Excited-State Two-Proton Tautomerism in Hydrogen-Bonded N-Heterocyclic Base Pairs."

Ten Seldam, C. A., and S. R. De Groot, *Physica* **18**, 891 (1952). "On the Ground State of a Model for Compressed Helium."

Teplyakov, P. A., *Opt. Spectrosc.* (USSR) (English Transl.) **1**, 896 (1956a). "Effect of Solvents on the Phosphorescence of Aromatic Compounds at Low Temperature."

Teplyakov, P. A., and B. A. Piatnitski, *Bull. Acad. Sci. USSR, Phys. Ser.* (English Transl.) **20**, 476 (1956b). "Influence of Concentration and the Solvent on the Phosphorescence of Aromatic Compounds at Low Temperatures."

Teplyakov, P. A., *Opt. Spectrosc.* (USSR) (English Transl.) **2**, 269 (1957). "Influence of Concentration on Phosphorescence of Solutions of Aromatic Compounds at Low Temperature."

Teplyakov, P. A., *Opt. Spectrosc.* (USSR) (English Transl.) **15**, 350 (1963). "Quasi-Linear Phosphorescence Spectra of Phenanthrene Solutions."

Teplyakov, P. A., V. V. Trusov, V. I. Mikhailenko, and V. M. Martynchenko, *Bull. Acad. Sci. USSR, Phys. Ser.* (English Transl.) **29**, 1430 (1965). "Influence of the Solvent on the Luminescence Spectra of Diphenylene Oxide and Diphenylacetylene."

Terenin, A., *Acta Physicochim.* URSS **14**, 566 (1941). "A Correction to the Paper: Spectral Investigation of Chemical Processes in Organic Compounds at Low Temperatures. II."

Terenin, A., *Acta Physicochim.* URSS **18**, 210 (1943). "Photochemical Processes in Aromatic Compounds."

Terenin, A., and V. Ermolaev, *Trans. Faraday Soc.* **52**, 1042 (1956). "Sensitized Phosphorescence in Organic Solutions at Low Temperature. Energy Transfer between Triplet States."

Terenin, A., E. Putzeiko, and I. Akimov, *Disc. Faraday Soc.* **27**, 83 (1959). "Energy

Transfer in Systems of Connected Organic Molecules."

Terenin, A., *Recent Progress in Photobiology* (E. J. Bowen, ed.), p. 3, Academic Press, New York, 1965. "Basic Photochemistry in Relation to Photobiology."

Terry, C., *Rev. Sci. Instrum.* **39**, 925 (1968). "Self-Supporting Carbon Resistance Thermometers for Use at Low Temperatures."

Terskoi, Y. A., B. G. Brudz, and O. N. Korolkova, *Izv. Akad. Nauk. SSSR, Ser. Fiz.* **29**, 1425 (1965). "Energy Transfer of Electronic Excitation in Rigid Solutions of Organic Luminophors."

Thomas, A., in *Oxidation Combustion Rev.* **2**, 257 (1968). "Trapped Radicals and Combustion."

Thomas, J. K., *J. Chem. Phys.* **51**, 770 (1969). "Formation of Excited Singlet State in the Nanosecond Pulse Radiolysis and Nanosecond Flash Photolysis of Aromatic Molecules in Liquid and Solid Solutions."

Thompson, C. E., *J. Opt. Soc. Amer.* **55**, 1184 (1965). "Phosphorescence Lifetimes of Benzene and Naphthalene in Rare-Gas Matrices."

Thompson, K. R., and K. D. Carlson, *J. Chem. Phys.* **49**, 4379 (1968). "Bending Frequencies and New Dimer Modes in the Far Infrared Spectra of Transition Metal Dihalides."

Thompson, W. E., and G. C. Pimentel, *Z. Elektrochem.* **64** (5), 748 (1960). "The First Overtone of the Hydrogen Bending Mode of Chloroform: Enhancement by Hydrogen Bonding."

Thomson, C., *Quart. Rev.* (London) **22**, 45 (1968). "Electron Spin Resonance Studies of the Triplet State."

Tichy, M., and R. Zahradnik, *J. Phys. Chem.* **73**, 534 (1969). "Physical Properties and Chemical Reactivity of Alternant Hydrocarbons and Related Compounds. XVII. Electronic Spectra of Amino and Hydroxy Derivatives of Benzenoid Hydrocarbons."

Tiede, E., *Ber. Deut. Chem. Ges.* **53**, 2214 (1920). "Phosphoreszenz der Borsäure. III. Mitt. zur Kenntnis anorganischer Lumineszenz-Erscheinungen."

Tiede, E., *Phys. Z.* **23**, 563 (1921). "Borsäurehydrate als Grundlage hochphosphoreszenzfähiger Systeme."

Tiede, E., and P. Wulff, *Ber. Deut. Chem. Ges.* **55**, 588 (1922). "Bortrioxyd-Hydrate als Bestandteil hochphosphoreszenzfähiger, organische Verbindungen enthaltender Systeme."

Tiede, E., and A. Ragob, *Ber. Deut. Chem. Ges.* **56**, 655 (1923). "Die Borsäure-Phosphore."

Tilford, S. G., *J. Chem. Phys.* **50**, 3126 (1969). "Evidence for the Reclassification of the Upper State of the 3A Bands in the Spectrum of CO: the $c^3\Pi \leftarrow X'\Sigma'^+$ Transition."

Timm, P., *Amer. Chem. Soc. Meeting, Minneapolis, April 1969*, unpublished. "Reactions of Te, Si, Cu and Ag Atoms with Benzene, B_2F_4, PF_3 and BCl_3."

Tinti, D. S., *J. Chem. Phys.* **48**, 1459 (1968a). "Absorption and Emission Spectra of OH and OD in Solid Ne. Evidence for Rotation."

Tinti, D. S., and G. W. Robinson, *J. Chem. Phys.* **49**, 3229 (1968b). "Spectroscopic Evidence for Slow Vibrational and Electronic Relaxation in Solids. The Vegard-Kaplan and Second Positive Systems of N_2 in Solid Rare Gases."

Tinti, D. S., W. R. Moomaw, and M. A. El-Sayed, *J. Chem. Phys.* **50**, 1035 (1969). "Fine Structure of the Pyrazine Crystal Phosphorescence at 4.2°K."

Tolstoi, N. A., and A. P. Abramov, *Opt. Spectrosc.* (USSR) (English Transl.) **20**, 187 (1966). "Nonlinear Quenching of the Luminescence of Ruby Under Intense Excitation."

Tomaschek, R., *Ann. Phys.* **67**, 612 (1922). "Zur Kenntnis der Borsäurephosphore."

Tomlinson, B. L., Ph. D. Thesis, University of California, Berkeley, 1968, UCRL-18444. "Optical Properties of Nucleic Acids."

Tomura, M., T. Kitada, and S. Honda, *J. Phys. Soc. Jap.* **23**, 1179 (1967). "Luminescence of F_A Centers in KCl : Na."

Torres, J. K., and C. P. Holder, *Rev. Soc. Quim. Mex.* **11**, 73 (1967) (in Spanish). "Theory and Properties of Solid Argon."

TRACES (Technology in Retrospect and Critical Events in Science). Report prepared for the National Science Foundation by Illinois Institute of Technology Research Institute, Contract No. NSF-C535; Dec. 15, 1968. Foreword by C. E. Falk.

Travnicek, M., *Ann. Phys.* **5**, 17 (1933). "Über neue Phosphore aus Sulfathydraten des Aluminiums und anderer Metalle mit organischen Leuchtstoffen."

Trommsdorff, H. P., *Chem. Phys. Lett.* **1**, 214 (1967). "Zeeman Effect and Singlet-Triplet Absorption Spectrum of *p*-Benzoquinone Single Crystals."

Trusov, V. V., and P. A. Teplyakov, *Opt. Spectrosc.* (USSR) (English Transl.) **16**, 27 (1964). "Phosphorescence Spectra of Diphenyl Fluorene, Acenaphthene, and Carbazole."

Tsai, S. C., and G. W. Robinson, *J. Chem. Phys.* **51**, 3559 (1969). "Why Is Condensed Oxygen Blue ?"

Tschampa, A., *Z. Naturforsch.* **22a**, 112 (1967). "Lumineszenzuntersuchungen am kristallinen Phenanthren."

Tsubomura, H., and R. S. Mulliken, *J. Amer. Chem. Soc.* **82**, 5966 (1960). "Molecular Complexes and Their Spectra. XII. Ultraviolet Absorption Spectra Caused by Interaction of Oxygen with Organic Molecules."

Tsubomura, H., N. Yamamoto, and S. Tanaka, *Chem. Phys. Lett.* **1**, 309 (1967). "Transient Absorption Spectra of Benzophenone Studied by the Flash Excitation."

Turner, J. J., and G. C. Pimentel, *Science* **140**, 974 (1963a). "Krypton Fluoride: Preparation by the Matrix Isolation Technique."

Turner, J. J., and G. C. Pimentel, in *Noble-Gas Compounds* (H. H. Hyman, ed.), p. 101, University of Chicago Press, Chicago, 1963b. "Preparation of Inert-Gas Compounds by Matrix Isolation: Krypton Difluoride."

Turro, N. J. *Molecular Photochemistry*, W. A. Benjamin, New York, 1965.

U

Ubbelohde, A. R., *J. Phys. Chem. Solids* **18**, 90 (1961). "Some Concluding Remarks on Systematic Studies of Barriers to Rotation in Crystals."

Udagawa, Y., T. Azumi, M. Ito, and S. Nagakura, *J. Chem. Phys.* **49**, 3764 (1968). "Phosphorescence and Triplet ← Singlet Absorption Spectra of Benzophenone Crystal at 4.2°K."

Udenfriend, S., *Fluorescence Assay in Biology and Medicine*, 3rd printing, Academic Press, New York, 1965.

Uehara, Y., *J. Chem. Phys.* **50**, 961 (1969). "Electronic Structure of Luminescence Centers of ZnS Phosphors Activated with Impurity Ions of s^2 Configuration (I) Zns : Bi Phosphors."

Urvas, A. O., D. L. Losee, and R. O. Simmons, *J. Phys. Chem. Solids* **28**, 2269 (1967). "The Compressibility of Krypton, Argon and Other Noble Gas Solids."

Utkina, L. F., *Bull. Acad. Sci. USSR, Phys. Ser.* (English Transl.) **29**, 1420 (1965). "Effect of Conjugation of the C=C Bonds in Some Complex Derivatives of Anthracene on the Character of the Quasiline Fluorescence and Absorption Spectra."

V

Vacher, M., and Y. Lortie, *J. Chim. Phys.* **56**, 732 (1959). "Spectres d'Absorption Ultraviolette et de Fluorescence des Radicaux Produits par la Décharge Haute Fréquence dans des Vapeurs de Toluène et de Toluène Octa-Deutéré et Piégés à Basse Température."

Val'dman, M. M., and G. D. Sheremet'ev, *Bull. Acad. Sci. USSR, Phys. Ser.* (English Transl.) **27**, 692 (1963). "Luminescence Spectra of Perylene and Diisobutyl Ester of 3,9-Perylenedicarboxylic Acid at 20.4°K."

van der Waals, J. H., S. M. D. Berghuis, and M. S. De Groot, *Mol. Phys.* **13**, 301 (1967a). "Vibronic Interaction in the Lower Electronic States of Benzene. I. Review of the Static Problem and Solutions of the Pseudo-Cylindrical Vibronic Equations."

van der Waals, J. H., and M. S. De Groot, in *The Triplet State* (A. B. Zahlan, ed.), p. 101, Cambridge University Press, London and New York, 1967b. "Magnetic Interactions Related to Phosphorescence."

Van Heuvelen, A., *J. Chem. Phys.* **46**, 4903 (1967). "Relativistic Crystal-Field Splitting of Mn^{2+}."

Van Kranendonk, J., *Physica* **25**, 1080 (1959). "Rotational and Vibrational Energy Bands in Solid Hydrogen."

Van Kranendonk, J., and G. Karl, *Rev. Mod. Phys.* **40**, 531 (1968). "Theory of the Rotational and Vibrational Excitations in Solid Parahydrogen and Frequency Analysis of the Infrared and Raman Spectra."

Van Loben Sels, J. W., and J. T. Dubois, *J. Chem. Phys.* **45**, 1522 (1966). "Triplet States of Liquid Benzene and Toluene."

Vanselov, R., and A. B. E. Duncan, *J. Amer. Chem. Soc.* **75**, 829 (1953). "The Ultraviolet Absorption and Fluorescence Spectra of Acetophenone."

Van Thiel, M., E. D. Becker, and G. C. Pimentel, *J. Chem. Phys.* **27**, 95 (1957a). "Infrared Studies of Hydrogen Bonding of Methanol by the Matrix Isolation Technique."

Van Thiel, M., E. D. Becker, and G. C. Pimentel, *J. Chem. Phys.* **27**, 486 (1957b). "Infrared Studies of Hydrogen Bonding of Water by the Matrix Isolation Technique."

Van Thiel, M., and G. C. Pimentel, *J. Chem. Phys.* **32**, 133 (1960). "Matrix Isolation Studies: Infrared Spectra of Intermediate Species in the Photolysis of Hydrazoic Acid. II."

Van Uitert, L. G., E. F. Dearborn, and J. J. Rubin, *J. Chem. Phys.* **45**, 1578 (1966). "Mechanisms of Energy Transfer Involving Trivalent Tb and Sm."

Vatul'ev, V. N., *Ukr. Fiz. Zh.* **5**, 40 (1960). "Absorption and Luminescence of Anthracene Impurities in 9,10-Dihydroanthracene Crystals at 20°K."

Vatul'ev, V. N., N. I. Sheremet, and M. T. Shpak, *Opt. Spectrosc.* (USSR) (English Transl.) **16**, 315 (1964). "Luminescence of Benzene at Low Temperatures."

Vavilov, S. I., and W. L. Lewschin, *Z. Phys.* **16**, 135 (1923). "Beiträge zur Frage über polarisiertes Fluoreszenzlicht von Farbstofflösungen. II."

Vavilov, S. I., *Z. Phys.* **22**, 266 (1924). "Die Fluoreszenzausbeute von Farbstofflösungen."

Vavilov, S. I., and W. L. Lewschin, *Z. Phys.* **35**, 920 (1926). "Die Beziehungen zwischen Fluoreszenz und Phosphoreszenz in festen und flüssigen Medien."

Vavilov, S. I., and W. L. Lewschin, *Z. Phys.* **44**, 539 (1927). "Berichtigung zu unserer Arbeit ['erratum', ed.]: Die Beziehungen zwischen Fluoreszenz und Phosphoreszenz in festen und flüssigen Medien."

Vegard, L., *Nature* **113**, 716 (1924a). "The Auroral Spectrum and the Upper Atmosphere."

Vegard, L., *Nature* **114**, 357 (1924b). "The Light Emitted from Solidified Gases and Its Relation to Cosmic Phenomena."

Vegard, L., H. Kamerlingh Onnes, and W. H. Keesom, *C. R. Acad. Sci.* (Paris) **180**, 1084 (1925a). "Emission of Light by Solidified Gases at the Temperature of Liquid Helium and the Origin of the Auroral Spectrum."

Vegard, L., *Leiden Commun.* No. 175 (1925b). "The Luminescence from Solidified Gases down to the Temperature of Liquid Hydrogen and Its Application to Cosmic Phenomena."

Vegard, L., *C. R. Acad. Sci.* (Paris) **182**, 211 (1926). "Sur l'interprétation des Spectres Emis par de l'Azote Solide et des Mélanges Solidifiés d'Azote et de Gaz Inertes."

Vegard, L., and W. H. Keesom, *Verslag Akad. Wetenschap.* (Amsterdam) **36**, 364 (1927). "On the Luminescence Produced by Bombarding Solidified Gases with Electric Rays at the Temperature of Liquid Helium."

Vegard, L., *Ann. Phys.* **6**, 487 (1930a). "Die Spektren verfestigter Gase und ihre atom-theoretische Deutung."

Vegard, L., and W. H. Keesom, *Commun. Phys. Lab. Univ. Leiden* **205b**, 1949 (1930b). "Luminescence from Solidified Gases at the Temperature of Liquid Helium."

Vegard, L., *Commun. Phys. Lab. Univ. Leiden* **205a**, 3 (1930c). "Continued Investigations on the Luminescence from Solidified Gases at the Temperature of Liquid Hydrogen. II. Luminescence Produced by Canal Rays."

Vegard, L., *Nature* **162**, 967 (1948). "The Green Auroral Line as an Initiator of Phosphorescence in Condensed Systems."

Velasco, R., *Can. J. Phys.* **35**, 1204 (1957). "Ultraviolet Spectra of LiH and LiD."

Verderame, F. D., and E. R. Nixon, *J. Chem. Phys.* **44**, 43 (1966). "Infrared Spectra of Crystalline and Matrix-Isolated Carbonyl Sulfide."

Verstegen, J. M. P. J., H. Goldring, S. Kimel, and B. Katz, *J. Chem. Phys.* **44** (9), 3216 (1966). "Infrared Spectra of HCl in Pure and Impure Noble-Gas Matrices, Absolute Intensities."

Viktorova, E. N., I. A. Zhmyreva, V. P. Kolobkov, and A. A. Sagamenko, *Opt. Spektrosk.* **9**, 349 (1960a). "Duration of Phosphorescence of Solutions of Organic Compounds at $-196°$."

Viktorova, E. N., I. A. Zhmyreva, V. P. Kolobkov, and A. A. Sagamenko, *Opt. Spectrosc.* (USSR) (English Transl.) **9**, 181 (1960b). "Study of the Phosphorescence Lifetimes of Solutions of Organic Compounds at $-196°$."

Viktorova, E. N., *Opt. Spectrosc.* (USSR) (English Transl.) **10**, 141 (1961). "Certain Regularities in the Nature of Yield versus Fluorescence Band Position Functions for a Number of Organic Compounds."

Viktorova, E. N., *Opt. Spectrosc.* (USSR) (English Transl.) **22**, 206 (1967). "Spectral Dependences of the Absolute Fluorescence Quantum Yields of Organic Compounds in Mixed Solvents."

Vincent, J. S., and A. H. Makai, *J. Chem. Phys.* **39**, 3088 (1963). "Paramagnetic Resonance Measurements of the Phosphorescent State of Quinoxalline."

Viswanath, G., and M. Kasha, *J. Chem. Phys.* **24**, 574 (1956). "Confirmation of the Anomalous Fluorescence of Azulene."

Viswanathan, C. R., K. Radisavljevis, and E. Y. Wong, *J. Chem. Phys.* **46**, 4231 (1967). "Absorption Spectra of Pr^{3+} and Nd^{3+} Doped in Lanthanum Sulfate."

Vladimirov, Y. A., and F. F. Litvin, *Biophysics* (USSR) (English Transl.) **5**, 151 (1960a). "Long-Lived Phosphorescence of Aromatic Amino-Acids and Proteins at Low Temperatures."

Vladimirov, Y. A., and E. A. Burshtein, *Biophysics* (USSR) (English Transl.) **5**, 445 (1960b). "Luminescence Spectra of Aromatic Amino Acids and Proteins."

Vladimirov, Y. A., *Sov. Phys. Dokl.* (English Transl.) **6**, 167 (1961). "Fluorescence of Amino Acids in the Protein Molecule."

Vladimirov, Y. A., and D. I. Roshchupkin, *Biophysics* (USSR) (English Transl.) **9**, 305 (1964a). "Study of Primary Photochemical Processes in Proteins. I. Two Photochemical Reactions in Aromatic Amino Acids."

Vladimirov, Y. A., and O. F. L'vova, *Biophysics* (USSR) (English Transl.) **9**, 548 (1964b). "Superweak Luminescence and Oxidative Phosphorylation in Mitochondria."

Vladimirov, Y. A., and G. M. Zimina, *Biochem.* **30**, 951 (1965a). "Luminescence of Certain Proteins and Tryptophan during Monochromatic Excitation in Solutions with Various pH."

Vladimirov, Y. A., *Photochem. Photobiol.* **4**, 369 (1965b). "Primary Steps of Photochemical Reactions in Proteins and Aromatic Amino-Acids: A Review."

Voigt, E. M., and B. Meyer, *J. Chem. Phys.* **49**, 852 (1968). "Charge-Transfer Spectra of Iodine with Hydrogen Sulfide and Benzene in Low-Temperature Matrices."

Voigt, E. M., L. Bajema, J. J. Smith, and B. Meyer, unpublished, 1969. "Solvent Effect on Line Width of Electronic Transitions of Aromatic Molecules."

Voigt, E. M., B. Meyer, A. Morelle, and J. J. Smith, *J. Mol. Spectrosc.* **34**, 179 (1970). "Matrix Isolated SeO_2."

Vol'kenshtein, M. V., *Issled. Eksp. Teor. Fiz., Akad. Nauk SSSR, Fiz. Inst. P. N. Lebedeva* **1959**, 80 (1959). "Optical Properties of Substances in a Glassy State."

Volodko, L. V., A. N. Sevchenko, and D. S. Umreiko, *Opt. Spectrosc.* (USSR) (English Transl.) **22**, 46 (1967). "Manifestation of Intramolecular Vibrations in Luminescence Spectra of Uranyl Compounds."

Voltz, R., J. L. Da Silva, G. Laustriat, and A. Coche, *J. Chem. Phys.* **45**, 3306 (1966). "Influence of the Nature of Ionizing Particles on the Specific Luminescence of Organic Scintillators."

Vorob'ev, V. P., A. V. Solov'ev, and M. T. Shpak, *Bull. Acad. Sci. USSR, Phys. Ser.* (English Transl.) **29**, 1312 (1965). "Luminescence of the Products of Photolysis of Crystalline Triphenylmethane at 20°K."

Vu, H., M. R. Atwood, and E. Staude, *C. R. Acad. Sci.* (Paris) **257**, 1771 (1963). "Bande Fondamentale Induite de la Molécule H_2 en Solution dans l'Argon Gazeux, Liquide et Solide."

W

Waggener, W. C., A. J. Weinberger, and R. W. Stoughton, *J. Phys. Chem.* **71**, 4320 (1967). "Effects of Temperature on the Near-Infrared Absorption Spectra of Molecules in the Condensed States. I. Carbon Dioxide."

Wagner, E. L., and D. F. Hornig, *J. Chem. Phys.* **18**, 296 (1950). "The Vibrational Spectra of Molecules and Complex Ions in Crystals. III. Ammonium Chloride and Deutero-Ammonium Chloride."

Walsh, A. D., *J. Chem. Soc.* **1953**, 2266 (1953a). "The Electronic Orbitals, Shapes, and Spectra of Polyatomic Molecules. Part II. Non-hydride AB_2 and BAC Molecules."

Walsh, A. D., *J. Chem. Soc.* **1953**, 2288 (1953b). "The Electronic Orbitals, Shapes, and Spectra of Polyatomic Molecules. Part III. HAB and HAAH Molecules."

Wang, J. L., Ph. D. Thesis, University of California, Berkeley, 1969. "Spectroscopic Investigation of Some High Temperature Species Trapped in Low Temperature Matrices."

Wannier, G. H., *Phys. Rev.* **52**, 191 (1937). "The Structure of Electronic Excitation Levels in Insulating Crystals."

Ward, D. E., in *Purification of Cryogenic Gases* (G. Norkebel, ed.), Chapter 10, George Newnes Ltd., London, 1964.

Ware, W. R., *J. Amer. Chem. Soc.* **83**, 4374 (1961). "An Experimental Study of Energy Transfer between Unlike Molecules in Solution."

Ware, W. R., and B. A. Baldwin, *J. Chem. Phys.* **43**, 1194 (1965). "Effect of Temperature on Fluorescence Quantum Yields in Solution."

Ware, W. R., and P. J. Sullivan, *J. Chem. Phys.* **49**, 1445 (1968). "Fluorescence Lifetime of Diphenyl Methylene."

Wasserman, E., L. Barash, and W. G. Yager, *J. Amer. Chem. Soc.* **87**, 2075 (1965). "The Electron Paramagnetic Resonance of Triplet CNN, NCN, and NCCCN."

Watanabe, K., and A. S. Jursa, *J. Chem. Phys.* **41**, 1650 (1964). "Absorption and Photo-ionization Cross Sections of H_2O and H_2S."

Watts, R. J., and S. J. Strickler, *J. Chem. Phys.* **49**, 3867 (1968). "Deuterium Isotope Effects on the Lifetime of the Phosphorescent Triplet State of Naphthalene."

Weber, G., and F. W. J. Teale, *Trans. Faraday Soc.* **53**, 646 (1957). "Determination of the Absolute Quantum Yield of Fluorescent Solutions."

Weber, G., *Biochem. J.* **75**, 345 (1960). "Fluorescence-Polarization Spectrum and Electronic-Energy Transfer in Tyrosine, Tryptophan, and Related Compounds."

Wehrli, E. M., and E. Miescher, *Helv. Phys. Acta* **7**, 298 and 332 (1949). "Spektroskopische Untersuchung dampfförmiger Indiumhalogenide" and "Spektroskopische Untersuchung dampfförmiger Galliumhalogenide."

Weigl, J. W., *J. Mol. Spectrosc.* **1**, 133 (1957). "The Polarization of the Fluorescence of Tetraphenylporphine."

Weiss, J., *Trans. Faraday Soc.* **42**, 133 (1946). "Electron Transfer Processes in Photochemical Oxidations and Reductions."

Weissman, S. I., and D. Lipkin, *J. Amer. Chem. Soc.* **64**, 916 (1942). "The Electromagnetic Mechanism of the Beta Phosphorescence of Fluorescein in Acid Solution."

Weissman, S. I., *J. Chem. Phys.* **37**, 1886 (1962). "Relation between Absorption and Fluorescence Spectra of Triphenylmethyl."

Weller, A., *Naturwissenschaften* **42**, 175 (1955). "Fluorescence of Salicylic Acid and Related Compounds."

Weltner, W., Jr., *J. Chem. Phys.* **31**, 264 (1959). "Polytypism and the Origin of the Potential Barrier Hindering Internal Rotation in Molecules."

Weltner, W., Jr. and J. R. W. Warn, *J. Chem. Phys.* **37**, 292 (1962a). "Matrix Isolation of High-Temperature Vapors: Boric Oxide."

Weltner, W., Jr., *J. Chem. Phys.* **37**, 1153 (1962b). "Spectroscopy of Carbon Vapor Condensed in Inert Matrices at 4° and 20°K."

Weltner, W., Jr., P. N. Walsh, and C. L. Angell, *J. Chem. Phys.* **40**, 1299 (1964a). "Spectroscopy of Carbon Vapor Condensed in Rare-Gas Matrices at 4°K and 20°K. I."

Weltner, W., Jr. and D. McLeod, Jr., *J. Chem. Phys.* **40**, 1305 (1964b). "Spectroscopy of Carbon Vapor Condensed in Rare-Gas Matrices at 4°K and 20°K. II."

Weltner, W., Jr., and D. McLeod, Jr., *J. Chem. Phys.* **41**, 235 (1964c). "Spectroscopy of Silicon Carbide and Silicon Vapors Trapped in Neon and Argon Matrices at 4° and 20°K."

Weltner, W., Jr., *Nature* **206**, 87 (1965a). "Ground State of Zirconium Monoxide from Neon Matrix Investigations at 4°K."

Weltner, W., Jr., NASA Accession No. N65-31322, Rep. No. AD **467028** (1965b), p. 115. "On C_3 and Transition-Metal Oxide Molecules."

Weltner, W., Jr., and D. McLeod, Jr., *J. Chem. Phys.* **42**, 882 (1965c). "Spectroscopy of TaO and TaO_2 in Neon and Argon Matrices at 4° and 20°K."

Weltner, W., Jr., and D. McLeod, Jr., *J. Phys. Chem.* **69**, 3488 (1965d). "Spectroscopy of Titanium, Zirconium, and Hafnium Oxides in Neon and Argon Matrices at 4 and 20°K."

Weltner, W., Jr., and D. McLeod, Jr., *J. Mol. Spectrosc.* **17**, 276 (1965e). "Spectroscopy of Tungsten Oxide Molecules in Neon and Argon Matrices at 4° and 20°K."

Weltner, W., Jr., and D. McLeod, Jr., *J. Chem. Phys.* **45**, 3096 (1966). "Spectroscopy of Carbon Vapor Condensed in Rare-Gas Matrices at 4°K. III."

Weltner, W., Jr., D. McLeod, Jr., and P. H. Kasai, *J. Chem. Phys.* **46**, 3172 (1967a). "ESR and Optical Spectroscopy of ScO, YO, and LaO in Neon and Argon Matrices; Establishment of Their Ground Electronic States."

Weltner, W., Jr., *Science* **155**, 3759 (1967b). "Stellar and Other High-Temperature Molecules."

Werder, R. D., R. A. Frey, and H. H. Gunthard, *J. Chem. Phys.* **47**, 4159 (1967). "Far-Infrared Matrix and Solution Spectra and Solid-State Vibrational Spectra of Niobium-pentachloride."

Wesley, R. D., and C. W. DeKock, *Amer. Chem. Soc. 24th Northwest Regional Meeting, Salt Lake City, 1969.* "The Infrared Spectrum of $PrCl_3$(g) Isolated in an Argon Matrix."

West, W., in *Chemical Applications of Spectroscopy* (W. West, ed.), p. 707, Interscience (Wiley), New York, 1956a. "Fluorescence and Phosphorescence."

West, W., in *Technique of Organic Chemistry* (W. West, ed.), Vol. 9, Chapter 1, Interscience (Wiley), New York, 1956b. "Introductory Survey of Molecular Spectra."

West, W., in *Technique of Organic Chemistry* (W. West, ed.), Vol. 9, Chapter 6, Interscience (Wiley), New York, 1956c. "Fluorescence and Phosphorescence."

West, W., in *Scientific Photography* (H. Souvenier, ed.), p. 557, Pergamon Press, New York, 1962. "An Experimental Study of the Significance to the Triplet State of Sensitizing Dyes in Optical Sensitization."

Wettack, F. S., *J. Phys. Chem.* **73**, 1167 (1969). "Fluorescence of 2-Pentanone."

Weyhmann, W., and F. M. Pipkin, *Phys. Rev.* **137**, A490 (1965). "Optical Absorption Spectra of Alkali Atoms in Rare-Gas Matrices."

Whan, R. E., and G. A. Crosby, *U.S. At. Energy Comm.* SCTM 234-60 (51), 1 (1960). "Intersystem Crossing from Higher Excited States in Complex Molecules."

Whan, R. E., and G. A. Crosby, *J. Mol. Spectrosc.* **8**, 315 (1962). "Luminescence Studies of Rare Earth Complexes: Benzoylacetonate and Dibenzoyl Methide Chelates."

Whelan, D. J., *Chem. Rev.* **69**, 179 (1969). "Intermediates in Radiation Chemistry at Low Temperatures."

White, D., P. N. Walsh, and D. E. Mann, *J. Chem. Phys.* **28**, 508 (1958). "Infrared Emission Spectra of B_2O_3 (g) and B_2O_2 (g)."

White, D., J.-H. Hu, and H. L. Johnston, *J. Phys. Chem.* **63**, 1181 (1959a). "The Heats of Vaporization of Para-Hydrogen and Ortho-Deuterium from Their Boiling Points to Their Critical Temperatures."

White, D., and W. J. Haubach, *J. Chem. Phys.* **30**, 1368 (1959b). "Separation of the Hydrogen Isotopes by Preferential Adsorption at 20.4°K."

White, D., D. E. Mann, P. N. Walsh, and A. Sommer, *J. Chem. Phys.* **32**, 488 (1960).

"Infrared Emission Spectrum of Gaseous HBO_2."

White, D., W. J. Haubach, and E. N. Lassettre, *Pure Appl. Chem.* **2**, 323 (1961a). "Ortho-Para and Isotope Separations by Preferential Adsorption at Low Temperatures."

White, D., P. N. Walsh, H. W. Goldstein, and D. F. Dever, *J. Phys. Chem.* **65**, 1404 (1961b). "Rare Earths. II. A Mass Spectrometric Determination of the Heats of Sublimation (or Vaporization) of Neodymium, Praseodymium, Gadolinium, Terbium, Dysprosium, Holmium, Erbium and Lutetium."

White, D., and D. E. Mann, *Rev. Sci. Instrum.* **34**, 1370 (1963a). "Miniature Cryostats: Design and Application to Matrix-Isolation Studies."

White, D., K. S. Seshadri, D. F. Dever, D. E. Mann, and M. J. Linevsky, *J. Chem. Phys.* **39**, 2463 (1963b). "Infrared Spectra and the Structures and Thermodynamics of Gaseous LiO, Li_2O, and Li_2O_2."

White, D., and C. M. Knobler, *Ann. Rev. Phys. Chem.* **14**, 251 (1963c). "Thermodynamics of Solutions at Low Temperatures."

White, D., T. Rubin, P. Camky, and H. L. Johnston, *J. Phys. Chem.* **64**, 1607 (1964). "The Virial Coefficients of Helium from 20 to 300°K."

White, D., and J. R. Gaines, *J. Chem. Phys.* **42**, 4152 (1965). "Liquid-Solid Phase Equilibria in the Hydrogen-Deuterium System."

White, G. K., and S. B. Woods, *Nature* **177**, 851 (1956). "Thermal Conductivity of Solid Argon at Low Temperatures."

White, G. K., *Cryogenics* **4**, 2 (1964). "Thermal Expansion of Silica at Low Temperatures."

Whittle, E., D. A. Dows, and G. C. Pimentel, *J. Chem. Phys.* **22**, 1943 (1954). "Matrix Isolation Method for the Experimental Study of Unstable Species."

Whyte, T. E., Jr., *Diss. Abstr.* **26**, 5071 (1966). "Infrared Spectra of Matrix-Isolated Hydrogen Chloride in Sulfur Hexafluoride and Hydrogen Iodide."

Wiedemann, E., *Ann. Phys.* **34**, 446 (1888). "II. Ueber Fluorescenz und Phosphorescenz. I. Abhandlung."

Wiedemann, E., and G. C. Schmidt, *Ann. Phys.* **232**, 18 (1895a). "2. Ueber Lichtemission organischer Substanzen im gasförmigen, flüssigen und festen Zustand."

Wiedemann, E., and G. C. Schmidt, *Ann. Phys.* **232**, 255 (1895b). "3. Ueber Luminescenz von festen Körpern und festen Lösungen."

Wiese, W. L., *Methods Exp. Phys.* **7A**, 117 (1969). "Transition Probabilities for Allowed and Forbidden Lines."

Wilcox, W. R., R. Friedenberg, and N. Black, *Chem. Rev.* **64**, 187 (1964). "Zone Melting of Organic Compounds."

Wilkinson, F., *Advan. Photochem.* **3**, 241 (1964). "Electronic Energy Transfer between Organic Molecules in Solution."

Williams, D. F., J. Adolph, and W. G. Schneider, *J. Chem. Phys.* **45**, 575 (1966a). "Diffusion of Triplet Excitons in Anthracene Crystals."

Williams, D. F., and W. G. Schneider, *J. Chem. Phys.* **45**, 4756 (1966b). "Phosphorescence Emission from Anthracene Single Crystals."

Williams, D. F., and J. Adolph, *J. Chem. Phys.* **46**, 4252 (1967). "Diffusion Length of Triplet Excitons in Anthracene Crystals."

Williams, F. E., *J. Opt. Soc. Amer.* **39**, 648 (1949). "Review of the Interpretations of Luminescence Phenomena."

Williams, M. W., and E. T. Arakawa, *J. Appl. Phys.* **38**, 5272 (1967). "Optical Properties of Single-Crystal Magnesium Oxide."

Williams, R., and J. Dresner, *J. Chem. Phys.* **46**, 2133 (1967). "Photoemission of Holes from Metals into Anthracene."

Williamson, L. J., and B. Meyer, *Spectrochim. Acta* **26A**, 331 (1970). "The spectrum of Matrix Isolated Thiazole."

Wilt, S. J., and M. A. El-Sayed, *J. Amer. Chem. Soc.* **88**, 2911 (1966). "The Vibrational Spectra and Structure of 1,4,7-Cyclononatriene and Related Derivatives."

Windsor, M. W., in *Physics and Chemistry of the Solid State* (D. Fox, *et al.*, eds.), Vol. II, 343, 1965. "Luminescence and Energy Transfer."

Windsor, M. W., and W. R. Dawson, *Mol. Cryst.* **4**, 253 (1967); and in *Organic Scintillators* (D. L. Horrocks, ed.), Gordon and Breach, New York, 1968. "Quantum Efficiencies of Triplet Formation in Aromatic Molecules."

Winnewisser, G., M. Winnewisser, and W. Gordy, *J. Chem. Phys.* **49**, 3465 (1968). "Millimeter-Wave Rotational Spectrum of HSSH and DSSD. I. Q Branches."

Winston, H., O. J. Marsh, C. K. Suzuki, and C. L. Telk, *J. Chem. Phys.* **39**, 267 (1963). "Fluorescence of Europium Thenoyltrifluoroacetonate. I. Evaluation of Laser Threshold Parameters."

Wiseall, B., and J. E. Willard, *J. Chem. Phys.* **46**, 4387 (1967). "Electrical Conductivity of γ-Irradiated 3-MP Glass and of Photoionized 3-MP-TMPD during Warming from $4°K$ and $77°K$."

Witzmann, H., H. Anderson, and G. Grieser, *Z. Phys. Chem.* **226**, 333 (1964). "Beitrag zur Phosphoreszenz sauerstoffdominierender Luminophore." (2. Mitteilung.)

Woessner, D. E., and B. S. Snowden, Jr., *J. Phys. Chem.* **72**, 1139 (1968). "The Effect of Impurities on the Spin-Lattice Relaxation of Ammonium Chloride."

Wolf, H. C., *Z. Naturforsch.* **10a**, 270 (1955). "Zum spektroskopischen Verhalten der Methyl-Derivate des Naphthalins und zur Frage der spektroskopischen Analysierbarkeit stellungsisomerer Derivate aromatischer Kohlenwasserstoffe."

Wolf, H. C., *Z. Naturforsch.* **13a**, 420 (1958). "Der erste elektronische Anregungszustand des Phenanthren-Kristalls."

Wolf, H. C., *Solid State Phys.* **9**, 1 (1959). "The Electronic Spectra of Aromatic Molecular Crystals."

Wolf, H. C., *Naturwissenschaften* **48**, 43 (1961). "Die Eigenfluoreszenz des Naphthalinkristalls bei $4.2°K$."

Wolf, H. C., *Advan. At. Mol. Phys.* **2**, 119 (1967). "Energy Transfer in Organic Molecular Crystals: A Survey of Experiments."

Wood, D. L., and J. P. Remeika, *J. Chem. Phys.* **46**, 3595 (1967). "Optical Absorption of Tetrahedral Co^{3+} and Co^{2+} in Garnets."

Wright, M. R., R. P. Frosch, and G. W. Robinson, *J. Chem. Phys.* **33**, 934 (1960). "Phosphorescence Lifetime of Benzene. An Intermolecular Heavy-Atom Effect, a Deuterium Effect, and a Temperature Effect."

Wrzesinska, A., *Acta Phys. Pol.* **4**, 475 (1935). "Absorption und Lumineszenz-Spektren organischer Farbstoffe."

Wyckoff, R. W. G., *Crystal Structures*, Interscience (Wiley), New York, 1963.

Y

Yamamoto, M., *J. Phys. Soc. Jap.* **21**, 2415 (1966a). "Mechanical Luminescence in Europium Chelate."

Yamamoto, M., T. Kikuchi, C. Obayashi, and T. Nakano, *J. Phys. Soc. Jap.* **21**, 2417 (1966b). "Anomalous Behavior of Fluorescence Lifetime for Europium Chelate."

Yang, N. C., S. L. Murov, and Tsu-Chia Shieh, *Chem. Phys. Lett.* **3**, 6 (1969). "Radiationless Decay Processes in 2-Naphthaldehyde."

Yastrebov, V. A., *Tr. Fiz. Inst., Akad. Nauk SSSR, Fiz. Inst. P. N. Lebedeva* **3**, 121 (English summary, p. 190) (1946). "Temperature Stability of Luminescence Bands."

Yastrebov, V. A., *Zh. Eksp. Teor. Fiz.* **21**, 164 (1951). "Nonexponential Decay of the Luminescence of Solid Aromatic Hydrocarbons."

Yastrebov, V. A., *Dokl. Akad. Nauk SSSR* **90**, 1015 (1953). "On the Law of Damping of the Luminescence of Solid Organic Substances."

Yen, W. M., W. C. Scott, and A. L. Schawlow, *Phys. Rev.* **136**, A271 (1964). "Phonon-Induced Relaxation in Excited Optical States of Trivalent Praseodymium in LaF_3."

Yen, W. M., R. L. Greene, W. C. Scott, and D. L. Huber, *Phys. Rev.* **140**, A1188 (1965). "Optical Linewidth and Lineshape Studies of Energy Transfer Mechanisms between Rare-Earth Impurity Ions."

Yuster, P., and S. I. Weissman, *J. Chem. Phys.* **17**, 1182 (1949). "Effects of Perturbations on Phosphorescence: Luminescence of Metal Organic Complexes."

Z

Zahlan, A. B., ed., *The Triplet State* (*Proc. Int. Symp., Amer. Univ., Beirut*), Cambridge University Press, London and New York, 1967.

Zanker, V., and E. Miethke, *Z. Naturforsch.* **12a**, 385 (1957). "Die spektroskopisch nachweisbaren Elektronenzustände der stabilen und metastabilen Molekülform einiger Acridinfarbstoffe und des Fluoreszeinkations."

Zanker, V., M. Held, and M. H. Rammensee, *Z. Naturforsch.* **14b**, 789 (1959). "Absorptions-Fluoreszenz-Polarisations-Messungen am Acridinorange-Kation. Beitrag zur Metachromasie — Problem dieses Vitalfarbstoffes."

Zanker, V., and H. Rammensee, *Z. Phys. Chem.* (*Frankfurt*) **26**, 168 (1960). "Absolute Fluoreszenz- und Phosphoreszenzquantenausbeuten bei verschiedenen Acridin- und Fluoreszeinfarbstoffen."

Zanker, V., and W. Korber, *Z. Angew. Phys.* **14**, 43 (1962). "Fluoreszenz- und Phosphoreszenz-Ausbeute sowie Lebensdauermessungen an dihalogenierten Acridinen und Fluoreszeinen."

Zelinskii, V. V., and V. P. Kolobkov, *Dokl. Akad. Nauk SSSR* **101**, 241 (1955). "Ratio of Quantum Yields of Phosphorescence and Fluorescence of Substituted Phthalimides."

Zener, C., *Proc. Roy. Soc.* (London) *Ser. A* **137**, 696 (1932). "Non-adiabatic Crossing of Energy Levels."

Zener, C., *Proc. Roy. Soc.* (London) *Ser. A* **140**, 660 (1933). "Dissociation of Excited Diatomic Molecules by External Perturbations."

Zhitnikov, R. A., and N. I. Melnikov, *Opt. Spectrosc.* (USSR) (English Transl.) **24**, 53 (1965). "The Absorption Spectra of Silver Atoms Trapped in Frozen Solutions of Its Salts."

Zhmyreva, I. A., and I. I. Reznikova, *Opt. Spectrosc.* (USSR) (English Transl.) **10**, 142 (1961). "The Influence of the Molecular Volume of a Solute on the Susceptibility of Its Electronic Spectra to Solvent Effects."

Zhmyreva, I. A., I. V. Kovaleva, V. P. Kolobkov, P. I. Kudryashov, G. A. Mokeeva, G. T. Petrovskii, and G. A. Tsurikova, *Opt. Spectrosc.* (USSR) (English Transl.) **22**, 278 (1967). "The Absorption and Luminescence of Trivalent Rare-Earth Ions in Beryllium Fluoride Glass."

Zimbrick, J., F. Hoecker, and L. Kevan, *J. Phys. Chem.* **72**, 3277 (1968). "Spatial Distribution of Trapped Radicals in γ-Irradiated Ethylene Glycol Dimethacrylate Polymers."

Zimmermann, H., and N. Joop, *Z. Elektrochem.* **65**, 61 (1961a). "Polarisation der Elektronenbanden von Aromaten. 3. Mitt.: Chinolin, Isochinolin, Indol."

Zimmermann, H., and N. Joop, *Z. Elektrochem.* **65**, 66 (1961b). "Polarisation der Elektronenbanden von Aromaten. 4. Mitt.: Phenanthren, Chrysen, Tetraphen."

Zimmermann, H., and N. Joop, *Z. Elektrochem.* **65**, 138 (1961c). "Polarisation der Elektronenbanden von Aromaten. 5. Mitt.: Benzol, Coronen, Triphenylen, Pyren, Perylen."

Zimmermann, R., and G. C. Pimentel, *Proc. 4th Int. Meeting Mol. Spectrosc., Bologna, 1959* (A. Mangini, ed.), Vol. 2, p. 721, Macmillan, New York, 1962. "The Infrared Spectrum of Ice. Temperature Dependence of the Hydrogen Bond Potential Function."

Zinov'eva, O. G., *Dokl. Akad. Nauk SSSR* **68**, 265 (1949). "Effect of the Solvent on the Phosphorescence of Benzene and of Some Aromatic Acids at the Temperature of Liquid Oxygen."

Zinov'eva, O. G., *Zh. Eksp. Teor. Fiz.* **20**, 132 (1950). "Decay of the Phosphorescence of Alcoholic Solutions of Some Simple Aromatic Compounds at the Temperature of Liquid Oxygen."

Zmerli, A., *J. Chim. Phys.* **56**, 405 (1959a). "Spectres de Luminescence T-S des Cristaux Aromatiques à 20°K: Benzène, Hexadeutérobenzène, Naphthalène, Octodeutéronaphthalène."

Zmerli, A., *Colloq. Int. Centre Nat. Rech. Sci.* **77**, 345 (1959b). "Absorption and Luminescence of C_6H_6 and C_6D_6 at 20°K."

Zmerli, A., *J. Chim. Phys.* **56**, 387 (1959c). "Spectres d'Absorption et de Luminescence S-S des Cristaux Aromatiques à 20°K: Benzène, Hexadeuterobenzène, Naphthalène, Octodeutéronaphthalène."

Zmerli, A., and H. Poulet, *J. Chem. Phys.* **33**, 1177 (1960). "Polarized Absorption and Fluorescence Spectra of 2,6-Dimethylnaphthalene at Different Temperature."

Zmerli, A., *J. Chem. Phys.* **34**, 2130 (1961). "Phosphorescence Spectra of Acenaphthene at Low Temperatures."

Zverev, G. M., G. Y. Kolodnyi, and A. I. Smirnov, *Opt. Spectrosc.* (USSR) (English Transl.) **22**, 325 (1967). "Optical Spectra of Nd^{3+} in Single Crystals of Scandium and Yttrium Oxides."

Zweig, A., D. L. Maricle, J. S. Brinen, and A. H. Maurer, *J. Amer. Chem. Soc.* **89**, 473 (1967). "Electrochemical Generation of the Phenanthrene Triplet."

Author Index

This index not only refers to the text of Chapters 1–9 and the tables of Chapter 10, but also serves as a guide to literature references, which are compiled alphabetically by first author in the bibliography, pages 495–595. A name followed by a year in parentheses indicates that a full reference to a publication is listed in the bibliography under the quoted name and year. If a name is not followed by a year, the author is co-author of a paper quoted under the name of the cross-referenced first author.

Lipsky, S., *see* Lawson(1969)
Lisovskaya, I. A.(1967)
Little, W. A., *see* Birks(1953)
Litvin, F. F.(1961), 473, 474, 477, *see also* Vladimirov(1960a)
Livingston, R., *see* Jones(1964)
Lo, G. Y., *see* Evans(1969)
Lochet, R., *see* Coupron(1960), Rousset (1953)
Loewenschuss, A.(1968, 1969), 307, 350, 351, 357, 366, 367
Loewenthal, E.(1968a,b)
Lofgren, D., *see* Brewer(1944)
Lombardi, E., *see* Jansen(1967)
Lombardi, J. R.(1966)
Lombos, B. A.(1967a,b)
Longin, P.(1959, 1960), 384, 409
Longuet-Higgins, H. C.(1957), 40, 45, *see also* Beer(1955)
Longworth, J. W.(1966), 385, 386, 387, 388, 397, 410, 418, 419, 420, 421, *see also* Rahn(1966a,b)
Lopez-Campillo, A., *see* Leach(1966a, 1967c)
Lopez-Delgado, R., *see* Leach(1961a, 1962a, 1963a,b, 1964b, 1966a,b, 1967 a,c,e)
Lord, R. C.(1952)
Lorquet, J. C., *see* Momigny(1967)
Lortie, Y., *see* Vacher(1959)
Losee, D. L., *see* Urvas(1967)
Low, W.(1960)
Lower, S. K.(1961, 1966), 75, *see also* Hochstrasser(1964b, 1965a)
Luder, W., *see* Lippert(1961)
Lunelli, B., *see* Pecile(1967)
Lüscher, E., 231, *see* Hingsammer(1968)
Lushchik, C. B.(1965)
Lutes, O. S., *see* Broida(1956)
Lutzenberger, W., *see* Chomse(1938)
L'vova, O. F., *see* Vladimirov(1964b)
Lyalin, G. N.(1963), 473, 474
Lym, R. I., *see* Forster(1960)
Lyons, H., *see* Bhaumik(1963)
Lyons, L. E., *see* Alexander(1961), Misra (1966b)
Lysenko, G. M., *see* Kisliak(1966)
Lyu, S. L., *see* Moser(1967)

McAlpine, R. D., *see* Hunter(1969)
McAvoy, N., *see* Björklund(1968)
McCarty, M., Jr.(1959a,b,c, 1970), 37, 39, 45, 49, 72, 249, 250, 257, 260, 261, 277,
288, 294, 295, 300, 323, 329, 335, 336, 355, 356, 359, 362, *see also* Robinson (1957a, 1958a,b,c,d, 1959, 1960b)
McCarville, M., *see* McGlynn(1968)
McClain, W. M.(1965), 489, *see also* Johnson(1965)
McClellan, A. L.(1955), 315, *see also* Pimentel(1952b, 1955a)
McClure, D. S.(1949, 1951, 1954, 1955a,b, 1956a,b, 1959, 1960, 1961a,b, 1962, 1966), 6, 18, 52, 62, 97, 99, 308, 314, 386, 388, 389, 390, 395, 396, 398, 400, 402, 403, 410, 411, 412, 414, 415, 417, 423, 424, 428, 435, 436, 442, 448, 451, 453, 454, 459, 464, 467, 468, *see also* Blake(1952, 1958), Coffman(1958), Dyck (1962), Gilmore(1952, 1955), McConnell (1953), Schnepp(1957, 1959d), Sidman (1955, 1956a)
McConnell, H.(1953), 424, 431
McConnell, H. M., *see* Cole(1958), Sternlicht(1961)
McCoy, E. F., *see* Byrne(1965), Hunt (1962), McGlynn(1966)
McCumber, D. E., *see* Imbusch(1964)
MacDonald, R. E., *see* Allin(1955)
McDonald, R. S., *see* Lord(1952)
McDowell, C. A., *see* Charles(1967), Farmer(1961), Fischer(1967)
Macfarlane, R. M.(1967, 1968)
McGlynn, S. P.(1958, 1960a,b, 1962a,b, c,d, 1963, 1964a,b, 1965a,b,c, 1966, 1968, 1969), 41, 62, 63, 64, 75, 77, 99, 308, 314, 413, 442, *see also* Azarraga (1965), Azumi(1962, 1963a,b,c), Kasha (1956), Kinoshita(1966, 1967, 1968), Misra(1966a), Padhye(1956), Rabalais (1969a,b), Smith(1962, 1964), Srinivasan(1967, 1968a,b)
McIntosh, J. S. E.(1968)
McKean, D. C.(1967)
McKinley, J. D., *see* Milligan(1965a)
McLennan, J. C.(1924, 1928, 1929), 18, 243
McLeod, D., Jr.(1966), 262, 302, 303, 338, 363, *see also* Angell(1967), Kasai(1969), Weltner(1964b,c, 1965c,d,e, 1966, 1967a)
Macleod, H. A.(1969), 189
McMahon, D. H.(1967)
McMurry, H. L.(1941)
McNamee, R. W.(1962), 280, 291, 307, 350, 357, 366, 367
Macnab, R. M.(1970)

Wright, M. R.(1960), 62, 391, see also Porter(1958a)

Wrzesinska, A.(1935), 445

Wulff, P., see Tiede(1922)

Wyckoff, R. W. G.(1963)

Wyeth, N. C., see Kellogg(1966)

Wyncke, B., see Hadni(1969)

Yager, W. G., see Wasserman(1965)

Yakel, H. L., see Brynestad(1966)

Yakuba, V. V., see Blagoi(1967)

Yamamoto, M.(1966a,b)

Yamamoto, N., see Mataga(1968), Tsubomura(1967)

Yamane, T., see Rahn(1966a)

Yang, N. C.(1969)

Yaroslavskii, N. G., see Aleksandrov, A. N.(1967)

Yashiro, T., see Goto(1964)

Yastrebov, V. A.(1946, 1951, 1953)

Yatsenko, A. F., see Kulyupin(1965)

Yee, K. K., see Basco(1961, 1967)

Yen, W. M.(1964, 1965), see also Imbusch (1964), Johnson(1967), Sell(1966)

Yoshida, H., see Irie(1968)

Young, M. Y., see Lim(1965)

Ypenburg, J. W., see Gerding(1967)

Yuster, P.(1949)

Zadorozhnyi, B. A., see Naboikin(1959)

Zahlan, A. B.(1967), 104, 311, see also

Kazzaz(1968), Maria(1963, 1967)

Zahradnik, R., see Tichy(1969)

Zakharova, M. D., see Lisovskaya(1967)

Zakrevskyi, S. V., see Brodin(1965a)

Zander, M., see Clar(1956)

Zanker, V.(1957, 1959, 1960, 1962), 433, 434, 435, 437, 445, 459, 460, 466, see also Körber(1964),   Miethke(1958), Rammensee(1960)

Zelinskii, V. V.(1955), 407, 408, 417, 424, 425, 431, 438, 450, 464, see also Borgman (1960)

Zener, C.(1932, 1933), 79, 80

Zhevandrov, N. D., see Gorshkov(1967), Gribkov(1963)

Zhitnikov, R. A.(1965), 234, 320

Zhmyreva, I. A.(1961, 1967), see also Borgman(1960), Viktorova(1960a,b)

Zimbrick, J.(1968)

Zimina, G. M., see Vladimirov(1965a)

Zimmermann, H.(1961a,b,c), 407, 443, 448, 451, 452, 461, see also Schutt(1963)

Zimmermann, R.(1962)

Zimmermann, V., see Schmid(1968)

Zinov'eva, O. G.(1949, 1950)

Zmerli, A.(1959a,b,c, 1960, 1961), 33, 248, 309, 391, 413, 414, 431, see also Pesteil (1954c, 1955c, 1956)

Zverev, G. M.(1967)

Zwarich, R., see Bree(1968a,b)

Zweig, A.(1967)

Subject Index

For spectra of individual species see Formula Index, pg. 645–653.
Chemical formulae are in alphabetical order, in the sequence N, N_2, NaCl, N_2Br_2, NCl. Greek letters are listed according to the English spelling. Page numbers in italics indicate figures.
Names followed by a year indicate references in the bibliography.

AAG, acrylamide gel, 205
Absorption filters, 181–184
Absorption spectra, history, 17–20
Absorptivity, 135–137
Acenaphtene, $C_{12}H_{10}$, 429
  perdeutero, $C_{12}D_{10}$, 433
Acepleiadylene, $C_{16}H_{10}$, 448
Acetaldehyde, C_2H_4O, 384
Acetanilide, C_8H_9NO, 405
Acetic acid, hydrogen bonding, Huggins
  (1956a)
Acetone, C_3H_6O, 384
  hexafluoro, energy transfer, McIntosh
    (1968)
  photolysis, Roebber(1958)
Acetophenone, C_8H_8O, 405
Acetylene, photolysis, Milligan(1967a)
Acetylpropionyl, $C_5H_8O_2$, 388
Acids
  aromatics, phosphorescence, Pyatnitskii
    (1958)
Acridine, $C_{13}H_9N$, 84, 434
  amino, $C_{13}H_{10}N_2$, 435, 436
  diamino, $C_{13}H_{11}N_3$, 437
  dihydro, $C_{13}H_{11}N$, 437
  dyes, photoionization, Lim(1963b)
    see individual species
  orange, *33*
  N-propyl, $C_{20}H_{26}N_3Cl$, 463
  yellow, $C_{16}H_{18}N_3Cl$, 450
Acridinium chloride, N-methyl,
  $C_{14}H_{12}NCl$, 445
Acridone, $C_{13}H_9NO$, 435
Acriflavine, delayed fluorescence, Lim
  (1962), Sato(1967)

Actinometers, 185
Activated fluorescence, 9
Acyl radicals, Noda(1968)
Adenine, $C_5H_5N_5$, 387
  methyl, $C_6H_7N_4$, 396
Adenosine, $C_{10}H_{13}N_5O_4$, 418
  deoxy, $C_{10}H_{13}N_5O_3$, 418
  diphosphate, $C_{10}H_{15}N_5O_{10}P_2$, 421
  monophosphate, $C_{10}H_{14}N_5O_7P$, 420
    deoxy, $C_{10}H_{14}N_5O_6P$, 419
  triphosphate, $C_{10}H_{16}N_5O_{13}P_3$, 422
Adenylate poly, sodium,
  $(C_{10}H_{10}N_5O_5PNa)_n$, 417
Adenylic acid, $C_{10}H_{14}N_5O_7P$, 420
Ag, silver,
  absorption, 37, 42, *50*, 234–235, 320
  reactions, Timm(1969)
Aggregates, energy transfer, Kasha
  (1963b)
  formation, *see* dimers, diffusion
  optical properties, DeVos(1964)
  triplet-triplet annihilation, Sternlicht
    (1963)
$AgNO_3$, spin polarization, Maria(1969)
Air, composition, 145
  liquid, 145–147
Air gap discharge, 172
Alanine, phenyl, $C_9H_{11}NO_2$, 409
Alcohols, properties, 194
Aldehydes, Longin(1960), McMurry(1941),
  Nurmukhametov(1967b)
AlF_3, 370
Al_2F_6, 370
Alkali atoms, *see individual species*
Alkali halides, physical properties, 195

Formula Index

Page numbers refer to spectral data.
Italics indicate figures.
Formulae are organized according to the first listed element.
In this Index, the sequence is N, NCl, N_2, N_2Br_2, NaCl.
Organic molecules are listed separately.
Entries for Organic Molecules start on page 648.

Atoms, Diatomics, and Polyatomics

Ag, silver, 37, 42, *50*, 234–235, 320
$AgNO_3$, Maria(1969)
AlF_3, 370
Al_2F_6, 370
Al_2O, 269, 346
Ar, argon, 202
As, arsenic, Morehouse(1966a)
Au, gold, 40, *50*, 235, 320
BCl_3, 21
BN, 328
BO_2, 269, 346
B_2F_4, 21
B_2F_6, *see* $(BF_3)_2$, 370
$B_2H_6^-$, Kasai(1969)
B_2O_2, *see* $(BO)_2$, 370
B_2O_3, 370
Ba, barium, 235, 320
BaF_2, 270, 346
$BeBr_2$, 270, 346
$BeCl_2$, 270, 347
BeF_2, 271, 347
BeI_2, 271, 347
BrHO, *see* HOBr, 291, 356
C, carbon, Milligan(1967)
C_2, 38, 42, 111, 247–249, 328
C_2^-, 39, 72, 249–250, 328
C_3, 39, 40, 42, 56, 271–274, 347
CBrCl, 347
CBr_2, 347
CBr_3, 371
CBr_3Li, 375
CCl_2, 275, 348

CCl_3, 371
CCl_3Li, 371
CCl_4, 62–63
CF, Jacox(1969a)
CFH, *see* HCF, 287, 354
CFN, *see* FCN, 285
CF_2, 276, 348
CF_2N, *see* F_2CN, 376
CF_2O, *see* F_2CO, 376
CF_3, 371
CH, 72, 250, 329
CHCl, *see* HCCl, 287, 354
$CHCl_3$, 372
CHN, *see* HNC, 288, 355
CHNO, *see* HNCO, 377
CHO, *see* HCO, 288, 355
CH_2, 277, 349
$CH_2(CN)_2$, 372
CH_2CO, 372
CH_2F, 373
CH_2N, *see* H_2CN, 377
CH_2N_2, 373
CH_3, 371
CH_3Cl, 372
CH_3F, 373
CH_3I, 373
CH_3LiBr, 373
$(CH_3)_3N$, 374
CH_3OH, methanol, 374
$CH_3(SiH_3)_2N$, 374
$(CH_3)_2SiH_3N$, 375
CH_4, methane, 371

645

Organic Molecules